INSTRUCTOR'S
SOLUTIONS MANUAL

HOSSEIN HAMEDANI
Marquette University

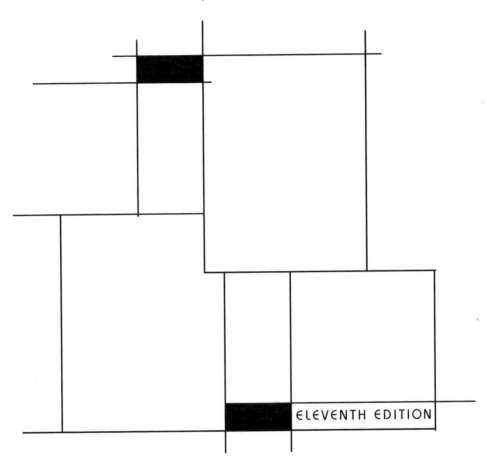

ELEVENTH EDITION

FINITE MATHEMATICS
For Business, Economics, Life Sciences, and Social Sciences

RAYMOND A. BARNETT
MICHAEL R. ZIEGLER
KARL E. BYLEEN

PEARSON
Prentice
Hall

Upper Saddle River, NJ 07458

Vice President and Editorial Director, Mathematics: Christine Hoag
Acquisitions Editor: Chuck Synovec
Print Supplement Editor: Joanne Wendelken
Senior Managing Editor: Linda Mihatov Behrens
Associate Managing Editor: Bayani Mendoza de Leon
Production Project Manager: Barbara Mack
Supplement Cover Manager: Paul Gourhan
Supplement Cover Designer: Victoria Colotta
Operations Specialist: Ilene Kahn
Senior Operations Supervisor: Diane Peirano

© 2008 Pearson Education, Inc.
Pearson Prentice Hall
Pearson Education, Inc.
Upper Saddle River, NJ 07458

Printed in the United States of America

10 9 8 7 6 5 4 3 2 1

ISBN 13: 978-0-13-225571-4

ISBN 10:   0-13-225571-5

Pearson Education Ltd., *London*
Pearson Education Australia Pty. Ltd., *Sydney*
Pearson Education Singapore, Pte. Ltd.
Pearson Education North Asia Ltd., *Hong Kong*
Pearson Education Canada, Inc., *Toronto*
Pearson Educación de Mexico, S.A. de C.V.
Pearson Education—Japan, *Tokyo*
Pearson Education Malaysia, Pte. Ltd.

CONTENTS

CHAPTER 1   LINEAR EQUATIONS AND GRAPHS

2.
$$3y - 4 = 6y - 19$$
$$3y - 4 + 4 = 6y - 19 + 4$$
$$3y = 6y - 15$$
$$3y - 6y = -15$$
$$-3y = -15$$
$$y = \frac{-15}{-3} = 5$$

4. $5x + 2 > 1$
$$5x > -1$$
$$x > -\frac{1}{5}$$

6. $-4x \leq 8$
$$\frac{-4x}{-4} \geq \frac{8}{-4} \qquad \text{(Dividing by a negative number)}$$
$$x \geq -2$$

8.
$$-2x + 8 < 4$$
$$-2x + 8 - 8 < 4 - 8$$
$$-2x < -4$$
$$\frac{-2x}{-2} > \frac{-4}{-2} \qquad \text{(Dividing by a negative number)}$$
$$x > 2 \quad \text{or} \quad (2, \infty) \xrightarrow{\qquad \overset{(}{2} \qquad} x$$

10. $-4 < 2y - 3 < 9$
$$-1 < 2y < 12$$
$$-\frac{1}{2} < y < 6 \qquad \xrightarrow{\qquad \overset{(}{-1/2} \qquad \overset{)}{6} \qquad} y$$

12. $\dfrac{m}{5} - 2 = \dfrac{3}{5}$
Multiply both sides of the equation by 5 to obtain:
$$m - 10 = 3$$
$$m = 13$$

14. $\dfrac{y}{-2} \leq -1$
Multiply both sides by (-2) which will result in changing the direction of the inequality as well.
$$y \geq 2$$

16. $\dfrac{x}{4} = 9 - \dfrac{x}{2}$
Multiply both sides of the equation by 4 to obtain:
$$x = 36 - 2x$$
$$3x = 36, \quad x = 12$$

18.
$$-3(4 - x) = 5 - (x + 1)$$
$$-12 + 3x = 5 - x - 1$$
$$-12 + 3x = 4 - x$$
$$12 - 12 + 3x = 12 + 4 - x$$
$$3x = 16 - x$$
$$4x = 16$$
$$x = 4$$

20.
$$x - 2 \geq 2(x - 5)$$
$$x - 2 \geq 2x - 10$$
$$x - 2 + 2 \geq 2x - 10 + 2$$
$$x \geq 2x - 8$$
$$x \leq 8$$

22. $\dfrac{y}{4} - \dfrac{y}{3} = \dfrac{1}{2}$

Multiply both sides by 12:
$$3y - 4y = 6$$
$$-y = 6$$
$$y = -6$$

24. $\dfrac{u}{2} - \dfrac{2}{3} < \dfrac{u}{3} + 2$
$$\dfrac{u}{2} - \dfrac{u}{3} < 2 + \dfrac{2}{3}$$
$$\dfrac{u}{6} < \dfrac{8}{3}$$
$$u < 16$$

26. $0.03(2x + 1) - 0.05x = 12$
$$0.06x + 0.03 - 0.05x = 12$$
$$0.01x = 12 - 0.03 = 11.97$$
$$x = \dfrac{11.97}{0.01} = 1{,}197$$

28.
$$-4 \leq 5x + 6 < 21$$
$$-6 - 4 \leq 5x < 21 - 6$$
$$-10 \leq 5x < 15$$
$$-2 \leq x < 3 \quad \text{or} \quad [-2, 3)$$

30. $-1 \leq \dfrac{2}{3}t + 5 \leq 11$
$$-5 - 1 \leq \dfrac{2}{3}t \leq 11 - 5$$
$$-6 \leq \dfrac{2}{3}t \leq 6$$
$$-18 \leq 2t \leq 18$$
$$-9 \leq t \leq 9$$

32. $y = -\dfrac{2}{3}x + 8$
$$y - 8 = -\dfrac{2}{3}x + 8 - 8$$
$$-\dfrac{2}{3}x = y - 8$$
$$-2x = 3y - 24$$
$$x = \dfrac{3y - 24}{-2} = -\dfrac{3}{2}y + 12$$

34. $y = mx + b$
$$y - b = mx + b - b$$
$$mx = y - b$$
$$m = \dfrac{y - b}{x}$$

36. $C = \dfrac{5}{9}(F - 32)$
$$\dfrac{9}{5}C = F - 32$$
$$32 + \dfrac{9}{5}C = F$$
$$F = \dfrac{9}{5}C + 32$$

38. $U = 3C - 2CD$
$$U = C(3 - 2D)$$
$$C = \dfrac{U}{3 - 2D}$$

40. $-10 \leq 8 - 3u \leq -6$
$$-18 \leq -3u \leq -14$$
$$18 \geq 3u \geq 14$$
$$6 \geq u \geq \dfrac{14}{3}$$

42. (A) Two must be negative and one positive or all three must be positive.

(B) Two must be positive and one negative or all three must be negative.

(C) Two must be negative and one positive or all three must be positive.

(D) $a \neq 0$ and b and c must have opposite signs.

44. $c + d < c - d$ for all real c and $d < 0$.

46. If a and b are negative and $\dfrac{b}{a} > 1$, then multiplying both sides by the negative number a we obtain $b < a$ and hence $a - b > 0$.

48. False. Consider the two closed intervals $[1, 2]$ and $[2, 3]$. Their intersection is $\{2\}$ which is not an interval.

50. False. Consider the two closed intervals $[-1, 0]$ and $[1, 2]$. Their union is $[-1, 0] \cup [1, 2]$ which is not an interval.

52. True. Let $A = [a, b]$, $B = [c, d]$, where $a < c < b < d$, so that $A \cap B \neq \varnothing$. Then $A \cap B = [c, b]$ which is a closed interval.

54. Let x = number of quarters in the meter. Then
$100 - x$ = number of dimes in the meter.
Now, $0.25x + 0.10(100 - x) = 14.50$ or
$$0.25x + 10 - 0.10x = 14.50$$
$$0.15x = 4.50$$
$$x = \frac{4.50}{0.15} = 30$$
Thus, there will be 30 quarters and 70 dimes.

56. Let x be the amount invested in "Fund A" and $(500,000 - x)$ the amount invested in "Fund B". Then $0.052x + 0.077(500,000 - x) = 30,000$.
Solving for x:
$$(0.077)(500,000) - 30,000 = (0.077 - 0.052)x$$
$$8,500 = 0.025x$$
$$x = \frac{8,500}{0.025} = \$340,000$$
So, \$340,000 should be invested in Fund A and \$160,000 in Fund B.

58. Let x be the price of the house in 1960. Then
$$\frac{29.6}{172.2} = \frac{x}{200,000} \quad \text{(refer to Table 2, Example 9)}$$
$$x = 200,000 \cdot \frac{29.6}{172.2} \approx \$34,379$$

To the nearest dollar, the house would be valued \$34,379 in 1960.

60. (A) It is $60 - 0.15(60) = \$51$

(B) Let x be the retail price. Then
$$68 = x - 0.15x = 0.85x$$
So, $\quad x = \dfrac{68}{0.85} = \$80.$

62. Let x be the number of times you must clean the living room carpet to make buying cheaper than renting. Then
$$(20 + 2(16))x = 300 + 3(3)x$$
Solving for x
$$52x = 300 + 27x$$
$$25x = 300$$
$$x = \dfrac{300}{25} = 12$$

64. Let x be the amount of the second employee's sales during the month. Then

(A) $3,000 + 0.05x = 4,000$
$$\text{or} \quad x = \dfrac{4,000 - 3,000}{0.05} = \$20,000$$

(B) In view of Problem 63 we have:
$$2,000 + 0.08(x - 7,000) = 3,000 + 0.05x$$
Solving for x:
$$2,000 - (0.08)7,000 - 3,000 = 0.05x - 0.08x$$
$$-1,560 = -0.03x$$
$$x = \dfrac{1,560}{0.03} = \$52,000$$

(C) Clearly (A) which gives the same earning with much less sale.

66. Let x = number of books produced. Then

Costs: $C = 2.10x + 92,000$
Revenue: $R = 15x$

To find the break-even point, set $R = C$:
$$15x = 2.10x + 92,000$$
$$12.9x = 92,000$$
$$x = \dfrac{92,000}{12.9} \approx 7,132$$

Thus, 7,132 books will have to be sold for the publisher to break even.

68. Let x = number of books produced.
Costs: $C(x) = 92,000 + 2.70x$
Revenue: $R(x) = 15x$

(A) The obvious strategy is to raise the price of the book.
(B) To find the break-even point, set $R(x) = C(x)$:
$$15x = 92,000 + 2.70x$$
$$12.30x = 92,000$$
$$x = 7,480$$
The company must sell more than 7,480 books to make a profit.

(C) From Problem 66, the production level at the break-even point is: 7,132 books. At this production level, the costs are

$$C(7,132) = 92,000 + 2.70(7,132) = \$111,256.40$$

If p is the new price of the book, then we need

$$7,132p = 111,256.40$$

and $\quad p \approx \$15.60$

The company should increase the price at least $0.60 (60 cents).

70. $-49 \le F \le 14$

$$-49 \le \frac{9}{5}C + 32 \le 14$$

$$-32 - 49 \le \frac{9}{5}C \le 14 - 32$$

$$-81 \le \frac{9}{5}C \le -18$$

$$(-81) \cdot 5 \le 9C \le (-18) \cdot 5$$

$$\frac{(-81) \cdot 5}{9} \le C \le \frac{(-18) \cdot 5}{9}$$

$$-45 \le C \le -10$$

72. Note that $IQ = \dfrac{MA}{CA} \times 100$
(see problem 71). Thus

$$80 < IQ < 140$$

$$80 < \frac{MA}{12} \times 100 < 140$$

or $\quad \dfrac{(80)(12)}{100} < MA < \dfrac{(140)(12)}{100}$

or $\quad 9.6 < MA < 16.8$

74. Note that $C = \dfrac{B}{L} \times 100$ (see problem 73). Thus

$$\frac{15}{17.4} \times 100 < C < \frac{20}{17.4} \times 100$$

or $\quad 86.2 < C < 114.9$

EXERCISE 1-2

2. (a)

4. (b); slope is not defined for a vertical line

6. $y = \dfrac{x}{2} + 1$

x	y
0	1
2	2
4	3

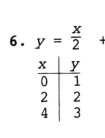
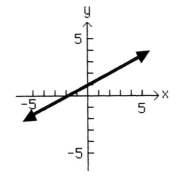

8. $8x - 3y = 24$

x	y
0	-8
3	0
6	8

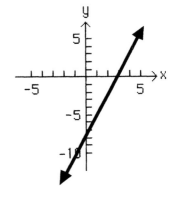

10. Slope $m = \dfrac{1}{5}$

y intercept $b = -2$

12. Slope $m = 0.7$

y intercept $b = 5$

14. $m = \dfrac{3}{4}$

$b = -5$

Using $\underline{6}$, $y = \dfrac{3}{4}x - 5$.

16. $m = -5$

$b = 9$

Using $\underline{6}$, $y = -5x + 9$.

18. x intercept: 1; y intercept: 3; $y = -3x + 3$.

20. x intercept: 2; y intercept: -1; $y = \dfrac{x}{2} - 1$.

22. $y = -\dfrac{3}{2}x + 1$

$m = -\dfrac{3}{2}$, $b = 1$

x	y
0	1
2	-1
-2	4

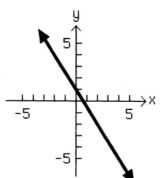

24. $5x - 6y = 15$

x	y
0	-2.5
3	0
-3	-5

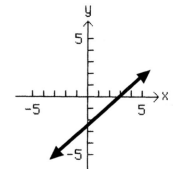

26.

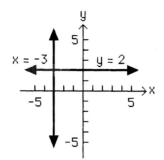

28. $5x - y = -2$

$-y = -5x - 2$

Multiply both sides by (-1);

$y = 5x + 2$

$m = 5$ (using $\underline{6}$)

30. $2x - 3y = 18$

$-3y = -2x + 18$

Divide both sides by (-3);

$y = \dfrac{2}{3}x - 6$

$m = \dfrac{2}{3}$ (using $\underline{6}$)

32.

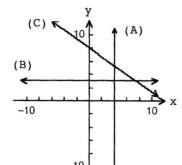

(A) $x = 4$
(B) $y = 3$
(C) $y = -\dfrac{2}{3}x + 8$

34. $g(x) = 40x + 160,\ x \geq 0$

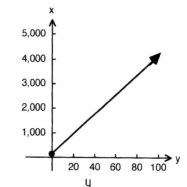

36. (A) Set $f(x) = 0$, $-0.8x + 5.2 = 0$, $x = 6.5$.
    Set $x = 0$, $y = 5.2$.

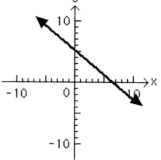

(B) *x* intercept: 6.5;
     y intercept: 5.2

(C)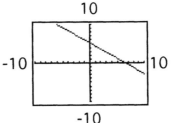

(D) *x* intercept: 6.5; *y* intercept: 5.2

38. Using $\underline{3}$ with $a = -5$ for the vertical line and $b = 6$ for the horizontal line, we find that the equation of the vertical line is $x = -5$ and the equation of the horizontal line is $y = 6$.

40. Using $\underline{3}$ with $a = 2.6$ for the vertical line and $b = 3.8$ for the horizontal line, we find that the equation of the vertical line is $x = 2.6$ and the equation of the horizontal line is $y = 3.8$.

42. $m = -6$
For the point $(-4, 1)$, $x_1 = -4$
and $y_1 = 1$. Using $\underline{7}$, we get:
$$y - 1 = -6[x - (-4)]$$
$$y - 1 = -6x - 24$$
$$y = -6x - 23$$

44. $m = \dfrac{4}{3}$
For the point $(-6, 2)$, $x_1 = -6$
and $y_1 = 2$. Using $\underline{7}$, we get:
$$y - 2 = \frac{4}{3}[x - (-6)]$$
$$y - 2 = \frac{4}{3}x + 8$$
$$y = \frac{4}{3}x + 10$$

46. $y - (-2.7) = 0[x - 3.1]$
$y + 2.7 = 0$ or $y = -2.7$

48. (A) $m = \dfrac{5 - 2}{3 - 1} = \dfrac{3}{2}$

(B) Using $y - y_1 = m(x - x_1)$, where $m = \dfrac{3}{2}$ and $(x_1, y_1) = (1, 2)$
or $(3, 5)$, we get:
$$y - 2 = \frac{3}{2}(x - 1) \quad \text{or} \quad y - 5 = \frac{3}{2}(x - 3)$$
Those two equations are equivalent. After simplifying either one of these, we obtain:
$$y - 2 = \frac{3}{2}(x - 1) \quad \text{or} \quad 3x - 2y = -1.$$

(C) Linear function

50. (A) $m = \dfrac{7 - 3}{-3 - 2} = -\dfrac{4}{5}$

(B) Using $y - y_1 = m(x - x_1)$, where $m = -\dfrac{4}{5}$ and (x_1, y_1) is either
of these points, we obtain:
$$y - 7 = -\frac{4}{5}(x + 3) \quad \text{or} \quad 4x + 5y = 23.$$

(C) Linear function

52. (A) $m = \dfrac{4 - 4}{0 - 1} = \dfrac{0}{-1} = 0$

(B) The line through (1, 4) and (0, 4) is horizontal; $y = 4$.

(C) Constant function

54. (A) $m = \dfrac{-3 - 0}{2 - 2} = \dfrac{-3}{0}$ which is not defined.

(B) The line through (2, 0) and (2, -3) is vertical; $x = 2$.

(C) Neither

56. The graphs are parallel lines with slope -0.5.

58. We are given $A = 75t + 1,000 = t \geq 0$

(A) At $t = 5$,
we have $A = 75(5) + 1,000 = \$1,375$

At $t = 20$,
we have $A = 75(20) + 1,000 = \$2,500$

(B)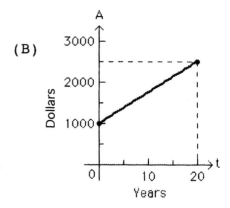

(C) The equation $A = 75t + 1,000$ is in slope-intercept form. Thus, the slope is 75. The amount in the account is growing at the rate of $75 per year.

60. Let C be the total daily cost of producing x picnic tables. Then
$C = 1,200 + 45x$
For $C = \$4,800$, we have
$1,200 + 45x = 4,800$
Solving for x we obtain
$x = \dfrac{4,800 - 1,200}{45} = 80$

62. Let y be daily cost of producing x tennis rackets. Then we have two points for (x, y):
(50, 3,855) and (60, 4,245).

(A) Since x and y are linearly related, then the two points (50, 3,855) and (60, 4,245) will lie on the line expressing the linear relationship between x and y. Therefore
$y - 3,855 = \dfrac{(4,245 - 3,855)}{(60 - 50)}(x - 50)$
or $\qquad y = 39x + 1,905$

(B)

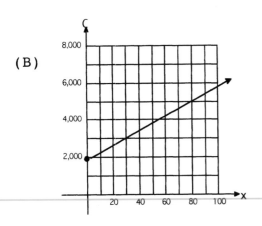

(C) The y intercept, $1,905, is the fixed cost and the slope, $39, is the cost per club.

64. Let R and C be retail price and cost respectively. Then two points for (C, R) are $(20, 33)$ and $(60, 93)$.

(A) If C and R are linearly related, then the line expressing their relationship passes through the points $(20, 33)$ and $(60, 93)$. Therefore,
$$R - 33 = \frac{(93 - 33)}{(60 - 20)}(C - 20)$$
or $\quad R = 1.5C + 3$

(B) For $R = \$240$ we have
$$240 = 1.5x + 3$$
or $\quad x = \frac{240 - 3}{1.5} = \$158$

66. We observe that for (t, V) two points are given:
$(0, 224,000)$ and $(16, 115,200)$

(A) A linear model will be a line passing through the two points $(0, 224,0000)$ and $(16, 115,200)$. The equation of this line is:
$$V - 115,200 = \frac{(224,000 - 115,200)}{(0 - 16)}(t - 16)$$
or $\quad\quad\quad V = -6,800t + 224,000$

(B) For $t = 10$
$$V = -6,800(10) + 224,000 = \$156,000$$

(C) For $V = \$100,000$
$$100,000 = -6,800t + 224,000$$
or $\quad\quad t = \frac{(224,000 - 100,000)}{6,800} = 18.24$

So, during the 19th year, the depreciated value falls below $100,000.

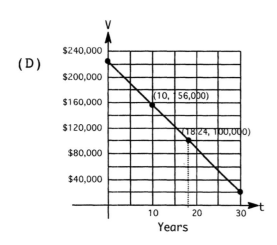

(D)

68. We have two representations for (x, T) namely:
    (29.9, 212°) and (28.4, 191°).
    (A) The line of the form $T = mx + b$ passes through the above two
        points. The slope of this line is
        $$m = \frac{(212° - 191°)}{(29.2 - 28.4)} = 14$$
        Using any of the above two points, say (29.2, 212°) will give us
        the value for b:
        $$212 = 14(29.9) + b$$
        or $b = -206.6$
        Thus, $T = 14x - 206.6$.

    (B) For $x = 31$, we have
        $$T = 14(31) - 206.6 = 227.4°F$$

    (C) For $T = 199°F$, we have
        $$199 = 14x - 206.6$$
        or $x = \frac{199 + 206.6}{14} = .97$ mHg

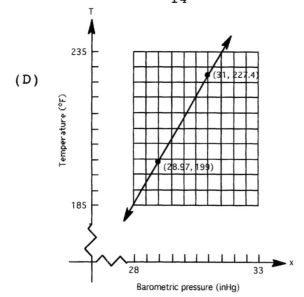

(D)

70. Let T be the true airspeed at the altitude A (thousands of feet), then we have two representations of (A, T): $(0, 200)$ and $(10,000, 360)$.

(A) A linear relationship between A and T has slope
$$m = \frac{(360 - 200)}{(10,000 - 0)} = 0.016.$$ Now using the point $(0, 200)$ we obtain the equation of the line:
$$T - 200 = (0.016)(A(1,000 - 0))$$
or $\qquad T = 16A + 200$

(B) For $A = 6.5$ (6,500 feet)
$$T = 16(6.5) + 200 = 304 \text{ mph}$$

72. For (t, I) we have two representations: $(0, 34,000)$ and $(25, 45,000)$.

(A) The linear equation will be:
$$I - 34,000 = \frac{(45,000 - 34,000)}{(25 - 0)}(t - 0)$$
or $\qquad I = 440t + 34,000$

(B) For $t = 50$, we have $I = 440(50) + 34,000 = \$56,000$.

74. We have two representations of (t, m): $(0, 25.7)$ and $(4, 23.4)$.

(A) The equation of the line relating m to t is:
$$m - 25.7 = \frac{(23.4 - 25.7)}{(4 - 0)}(t - 0)$$
or $\qquad m = -0.575t + 25.7$

(B) For $m = 20\%$, we have
$$20 = -0.575t + 25.7$$
or $\quad t = \frac{25.7 - 20}{0.575} = 9.9$
So, the year will be 2009.

(C)

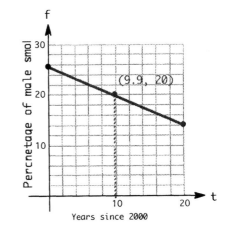

76. For (x, p) we have two representations: $(9,800, 1.94)$ and $(9,400, 1.82)$.

(A) The slope is
$$m = \frac{(1.94 - 1.82)}{(9,800 - 9,400)} = 0.0003$$
Using one of the points, say $(9,800, 1.94)$, we find b:
$$1.94 = (0.0003)(9,800) + b$$
or $\quad b = -1$
So, the desired equation is: $p = 0.0003x - 1$.

(B) Here the two representations of (x, p) are: $(9,300, 1.94)$ and $(9,500, 1.82)$. The slope is
$$m = \frac{(1.94 - 1.82)}{(9,300 - 9,500)} = -0.0006$$
Using one of the points, say $(9,300, 1.94)$ we find b:
$$1.94 = -0.0006(9,300) + b$$
or $\quad b = 7.52$

So, the desired equation is: $p = -0.0006x + 7.52$.

(C) To find the equilibrium point, we need to solve $0.0003x - 1 = -0.0006x + 7.52$ for x. Observe that
$$0.0009x = 8.52$$
or $\quad x = \dfrac{8.52}{0.0009} = 9,467$

Substituting $x = 9,467$ in either of equations in (A) or (B) we obtain
$$p = 0.0003(9,467) - 1 = 1.84$$
So, the desired point is $(9,467, 1.84)$.

(D)

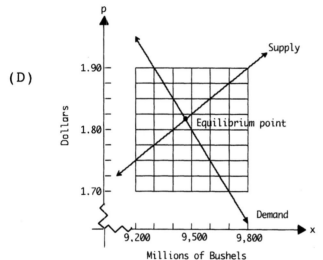

78. We have two representations of (w, d): $(3, 18)$ and $(5, 10)$.

(A) The line through these two points has a slope $\dfrac{(18 - 10)}{(3 - 5)} = -4$.

So, the equation of the line is
$$d - 10 = -4(w - 5)$$
or $\quad d = -4w + 30$

(B) For $w = 0$, $d = 30$ in.

(C) For $d = 0$,
$$-4w + 30 = 0$$
or $\quad w = \dfrac{30}{4} = 7.5$ lbs.

80. (A) This line has the following equation:
$$y - 35 = \frac{(17 - 35)}{(40 - 0)}(x - 0)$$
or $\quad y = -0.45x + 35$

(B) This line has the following equation:
$$y - 35 = \frac{(32 - 35)}{(10 - 0)}(x - 0)$$
or $\quad y = -0.3x + 35$

(C)

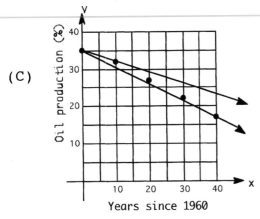

(D) $y = -0.45x + 35$:
$$y = -0.45(60) + 35 = 8\%$$

$y = -0.3x + 35$:
$$y = -0.3(60) + 35 = 17\%$$

EXERCISE 1-3

2. (A) $w = 52 + 1.9h$

(B) The rate of change of weight with respect to height is 1.9 inches per kilogram.

(C) 5'8" is 8 inches over 5 feet and the model predicts the weight to be
$$w = 52 + 1.9(8) = 67.2 \text{ kg.}$$

(D) For $w = 70$, we have
$$70 = 52 + 1.9h$$
or $\quad h = \frac{70 - 52}{1.9} \approx 9.5$

So, the height of this man is predicted to be 5'9.5".

4. We have two representations of (d, P): $(0, 14.7)$ and $(34, 29.4)$.

(A) A line relating P to d passes through the above two points. Its equation is:
$$P - 14.7 = \frac{(29.4 - 14.7)}{(34 - 0)}(d - 0)$$
or $\quad P = 0.4\overline{3}d + 14.7$

(B) The rate of change of pressure with respect to depth is $0.4\overline{3}$ lbs/in^2 per foot.

(C) For $d = 50$,
$$P = 0.4\overline{3}(50) + 14.7 \approx 36.3 \text{ lbs/in}^2$$

(D) For $P = 4$ atmospheres, we have $P = 2(29.4) = 58.8 \text{ lbs/in}^2$ and hence
$$58.8 = 0.4\overline{3}d + 14.7$$
or
$$d = \frac{58.8 - 14.7}{0.4\overline{3}} \approx 102 \text{ ft}$$

6. We have two representations of (t, a): $(0, 2{,}880)$ and $(180, 0)$.

(A) The linear model relating altitude a to the time in air t has the following equation:
$$a - 2{,}880 = \frac{(0 - 2{,}880)}{(180 - 0)}(t - 0)$$
or
$$a = -16t + 2{,}880$$

(B) The rate of descent for an ATPS system parachute is the slope of the line -16 ft/sec.

(C) It is 16 ft/sec.

8. We have two representations of (t, s): $(0, 1{,}449)$ and $(20, 1{,}521)$. So, the line passing through these points has the following equation:
$$s - 1{,}449 = \frac{(1{,}521 - 1{,}449)}{(20 - 0)}(t - 0)$$
or
$$s = 3.6t + 1{,}449$$
The slope of this line (model) is the rate of change of the speed of sound with respect to temperature; 3.6 m/s per °C.

10. (A)

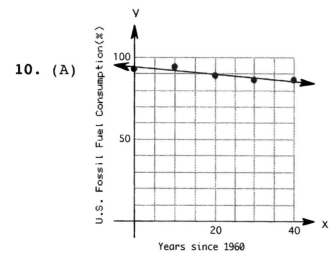

(B) The rate of change of the percentage of oil imports with respect to time is -0.22% per year.

(C) For $x = 50$ (2010 is 50 years from 1960), we have
$$y = -0.22(50) + 94 = 83,$$
i.e. 83% of total production.

(D) For $y = 80$, we have:
$$80 = -0.22x + 94$$
or
$$x = \frac{94 - 80}{0.22} \approx 64$$
So, it would be approximately 64 years after 1960, which will be 2024.

12. (A)

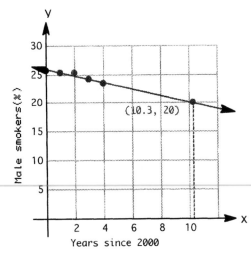

(B) For $m = 15$, we have
$$15 = -0.57t + 25.86$$
or $t = \dfrac{25.86 - 15}{0.57} \approx 19.05$

So, during 2020 the percentage of male smokers fall below 15%.

14. (A)

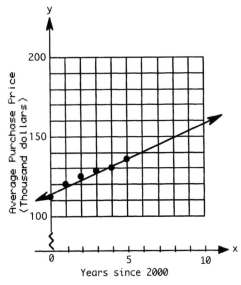

(B) For 2010, $x = 10$ and $y = 4.4(10) + 114 = 158$, so the median price in 2010 is predicted to be $158,000.

(C) The rate of change of median price with respect to time is $4,400 per year.

16. (A)

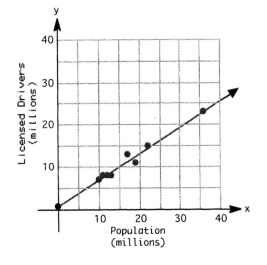

(B) For $x = 5$, we have
$$y = 0.62(5) + 0.78 = 3.88$$
So the model estimates 3,880,000 licensed drivers in Minnesota in 2004.

(C) For $y = 3.9$, we have
$$3.9 = 0.62x + 0.78$$
or $x = \dfrac{3.9 - 0.78}{0.62} \approx 5.032$.

So, the model estimates the population of Wisconsin in 2004 to be 5,032,000.

18. (A)

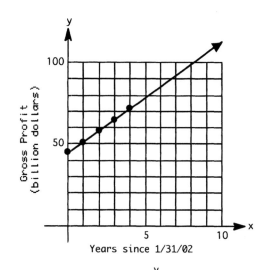

Years since 1/31/02

(B) For period ending 1/31/10, $t = 8$ and from the model
$$R = 6.8(8) + 44.6 = 99.$$
So, the predicted annual gross profit will be $99 billion.

20. (A)

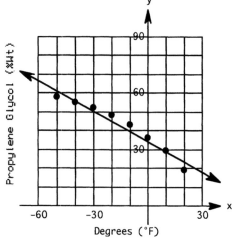

Degrees (°F)

(B) For $P = 30$, we have:
$$30 = -0.54T + 34$$
or $T = \dfrac{34 - 30}{0.54} \approx 7°F$

(C) For $T = 15$, we have:
$$P = -0.54(15) + 34 = 29.5,$$
i.e., the estimated percentage of propylene glycol is 29.5%.

22. (A) The rate of change of height with respect to Dbh is 1.66 ft/in.

(B) One inch increase in Dbh produces a height increase of approximately 1.66 ft.

(C) For $x = 12$, we have:
$$y = 1.66(12) - 5.14 \approx 15 \text{ ft.}$$

(D) For $y = 25$, we have:
$$25 = 1.66x - 5.14$$
or $x = \dfrac{25 + 5.14}{1.66} \approx 18 \text{ in.}$

24. (A) The rate of change of annual total revenue is $2.94 billion per year.

(B) For 2015, $x = 25$ and $y = 2.94(25) + 13.17 \approx 87$.
So, the predicted annual revenue is $87 billion.

26. (A) Male enrollment is increasing at the rate of 5,000 students per year; female enrollment is increasing at the rate of 20,000 students per year.

(B) For 2010, $x = 40$ and for male enrollment we have:
$$y = 0.005(40) + 0.64 = 0.84 \text{ million}$$
For female enrollment,
$$y = 0.02(40) + 0.4 = 1.2 \text{ million}$$

(C) The point of intersection of the two lines is obtained by solving
$$0.02x + 0.4 = 0.005x + 0.64$$
or $\quad x = \dfrac{(0.64 - 0.4)}{(0.02 - 0.005)} = 16$, or year 1986.

28. Men: $y = -0.289x + 125.362$;
Women: $y = -0.399x + 139.485$

The graphs of these linear regression models indicate that women will catch up to men in the year 2096. To see this mathematically, we find the intersection point of these lines by solving the following equation for x:

$$-0.289x + 125.362 = -0.399x + 139.485$$
or $\quad x = \dfrac{(139.485 - 125.362)}{(0.399 - 0.289)} \approx 128$

or the year $1968 + 128 = 2096$.

30. Supply: $y = 1.53x + 2.85$;
Demand: $y = -2.21x + 10.66$

To find equilibrium price we solve the following equation for x and then use that to find y:

$$1.53x + 2.85 = -2.21x + 10.66$$
or $\quad x = \dfrac{(10.66 - 2.85)}{(1.53 + 2.21)} \approx 2.09$,

and $\quad y = 1.53(2.09) + 2.85 \approx \$6.05$.

EXERCISE 2-1

2.

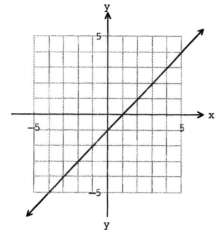

4.

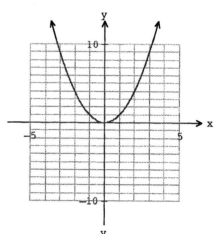

6.

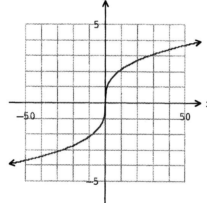

8.

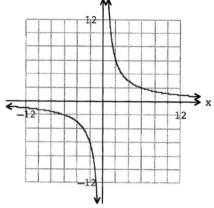

10. The table specifies a function, since for each domain value there corresponds one and only one range value.

12. The table does not specify a function, since more than one range value corresponds to a given domain value.
(Range values 1, 2 correspond to domain value 9.)

14. This is a function.

16. The graph specifies a function; each vertical line in the plane intersects the graph in at most one point.

18. The graph does not specify a function. There are vertical lines which intersect the graph in more than one point. For example, the y-axis intersects the graph in two points.

20. The graph does not specify a function.

22. $y = \pi$ is a constant function.

24. $y = 5x - \dfrac{1}{2}(4 - x)$

$\quad = 5x - 2 + \dfrac{1}{2}x$

$\quad = 5.5x - 2$ which is a linear function.

26. $y = 3x + \dfrac{1}{2}(5 - 6x)$

$\quad = 3x + \dfrac{5}{2} - 3x$

$\quad = \dfrac{5}{2}$ which is a constant function.

28. $y = \dfrac{1}{2x + 3}$. It is neither constant nor linear.

30. $y = x^2 - 9$. It is neither constant nor linear.

34.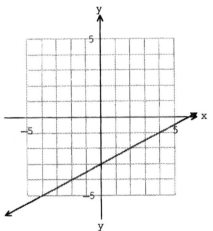

36.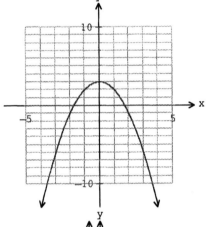

38.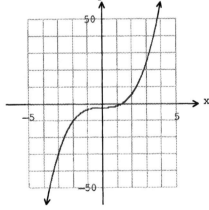

40.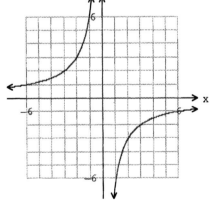

42. $f(x) = \dfrac{3x^2}{x^2 + 2}$. Since the denominator is bigger than 1, we note that the values of f are between 0 and 3. Furthermore, the function f has the property that $f(-x) = f(x)$. So, adding points $x = 3$, $x = 4$, $x = 5$, we have:

x	−5	−4	−3	−2	−1	0	1	2	3	4	5
$f(x)$	2.78	2.67	2.45	2	1	0	1	2	2.45	2.67	2.78

The sketch is:

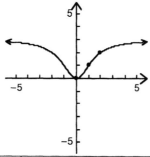

44. (A)

x	0	5	10	15	20
$f(x)$	0	750	1,000	750	0
$g(x)$	200	450	700	950	1,200
$f(x) - g(x)$	-200	300	300	-200	-1,200

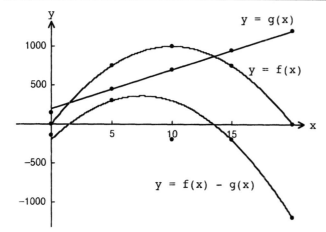

46. $y = f(4) = 0$

48. $y = f(-2) = 3$

50. $f(x) = 3$, $x < 0$ at $x = -4$, -2

52. $f(x) = 4$ at $x = 5$

54. $f(x) = 2x - 3$
$f(1) = 2(1) - 3 = -1$

56. $g(x) = x^2 + 2x$
$g(1) = (1)^2 + 2(1) = 3$

58. $g(-2) = (-2)^2 + 2(-2) = 0$

60. $f(3) - g(3) = [2(3) - 3] - [(3)^2 + 2(3)] = -12$

62. $g(0) \cdot f(-2) = [(0)^2 - 2(0)] \cdot [2(-2) - 3] = 0$

64. $\dfrac{g(-3)}{f(2)} = \dfrac{(-3)^2 + 2(-3)}{2(2) - 3} = \dfrac{3}{1} = 3$

66. domain: all real numbers or $(-\infty, \infty)$

68. domain: all real numbers except 2

72. f is not defined at the values of x where $x^2 - 9 = 0$, that is, at 3 and -3; f is defined at $x = -2$, $f(-2) = \dfrac{0}{-5} = 0$.

74. $f(x) = -3x + 4$

76. $F(x) = -8x^3 + 3\sqrt{3}$

78. Function g multiplies the domain element by -2 and adds 7 to the result.

80. Function G multiplies the square root of the domain element by 4 and subtracts the square of the domain element from the result.

82. Given $3y - 7x = 15$. Solving for y, we have:
$$3y = 7x + 15$$
$$y = \frac{7}{3}x + 5$$
Since each input value x determines a unique output value y, the equation specifies a function. The domain is R, the set of real numbers.

84. Given $x - y^2 = 1$. Solving for y, we have:
$$y^2 = x - 1$$
$$y = \pm\sqrt{x - 1}$$
This equation does not specify a function, since each value of x, $x > 1$, determines two values of y. For example, corresponding to $x = 5$, we have $y = 2$ and $y = -2$; corresponding to $x = 10$, we have $y = 3$ and $y = -3$.

86. Given $x^2 + y = 10$. Solving for y, we have:
$$y = 10 - x^2$$
This equation specifies a function. The domain is R.

88. Given $xy + y - x = 5$. Solving for y, we have:
$$(x + 1)y = x + 5 \quad \text{or} \quad y = \frac{x + 5}{x + 1}$$
This equation specifies a function. The domain is all real numbers except $x = -1$.

90. Given $x^2 - y^2 = 16$. Solving for y, we have:
$$y^2 = x^2 - 16 \quad \text{or} \quad y = \pm\sqrt{x^2 - 16}$$
Thus, the equation does not specify a function since, for $x = 5$, we have $y = \pm 3$, when $x = 6$, $y = \pm 2\sqrt{5}$, and so on.

92. Given $G(r) = 3 - 5r$. Then:
$$\frac{G(2 + h) - G(2)}{h} = \frac{3 - 5(2 + h) - (3 - 5 \cdot 2)}{h}$$
$$= \frac{-7 - 5h + 7}{h} = \frac{-5h}{h} = -5$$

94. Given $P(x) = 2x^2 - 3x - 7$. Then:

$$\frac{P(3 + h) - P(3)}{h} = \frac{2(3 + h)^2 - 3(3 + h) - 7 - (2 \cdot 3^2 - 3 \cdot 3 - 7)}{h}$$

$$= \frac{2(9 + 6h + h^2) - 9 - 3h - 7 - (2)}{h}$$

$$= \frac{2h^2 + 9h}{h} = 2h + 9$$

96. $f(x) = x^2 - 1$
$f(-3) = (-3)^2 - 1 = 9 - 1 = 8$

98. $f(x) = x^2 - 1$
$f(3 - 6) = f(-3) = (-3)^2 - 1 = 9 - 1 = 8$

100. $f(x) = x^2 - 1$
$f(3) - f(6) = [(3)^2 - 1] - [(6)^2 - 1] = 9 - 1 - 36 + 1 = -27$

102. $f(x) = x^2 - 1$
$f(f(-2)) = f((-2)^2 - 1) = f(4 - 1) = f(3) = (3)^2 - 1 = 9 - 1 = 8$

104. $f(x) = x^2 - 1$
$f(-3x) = (-3x)^2 - 1 = 9x^2 - 1$

106. $f(x) = x^2 - 1$
$f(1 - x) = (1 - x)^2 - 1 = 1 - 2x + x^2 - 1 = -2x + x^2 = x(x - 2)$

108. (A) $f(x) = -3x + 9$ (B) $f(x + h) = -3x - 3h + 9$
(C) $f(x + h) - f(x) = -3h$ (D) $\dfrac{f(x + h) - f(x)}{h} = -3$

110. (A) $f(x) = 3x^2 + 5x - 8$ (B) $f(x + h) = 3x^2 + 6xh + 3h^2 + 5x + 5h - 8$
(C) $f(x + h) - f(x) = 6xh + 3h^2 + 5h$
(D) $\dfrac{f(x + h) - f(x)}{h} = 6x + 3h + 5$

112. (A) $f(x) = x(x + 40) = x^2 + 40x$
(B) $f(x + h) = x^2 + 2xh + h^2 + 40x + 40h$
(C) $f(x + h) - f(x) = 2xh + h^2 + 40h$ (D) $\dfrac{f(x + h) - f(x)}{h} = 2x + h + 40$

114. Given $A = \ell w = 81$.

Thus, $w = \dfrac{81}{\ell}$. Now $P = 2\ell + 2w = 2\ell + 2\left(\dfrac{81}{\ell}\right) = 2\ell + \dfrac{162}{\ell}$.
The domain is $\ell > 0$.

116. Given $P = 2\ell + 2w = 160$ or $\ell + w = 80$ and $\ell = 80 - w$.

Now $A = \ell w = (80 - w)w$ and $A = 80w - w^2$.
The domain is $0 \leq w \leq 80$. [<u>Note</u>: $w \leq 80$ since $w > 80$ implies $\ell < 0$.]

118.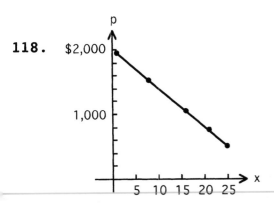

$p(11) = 1,340$ dollars per computer
$p(18) = 920$ dollars per computer

120. (A) $R(x) = xp(x)$
$= x(2,000 - 60x)$ thousands of dollars

Domain: $1 \leq x \leq 25$

(B) Table 11 Revenue

x(thousands)	R(x)(thousands)
1	$1,940
5	8,500
10	14,000
15	16,500
20	16,000
25	12,500

(C)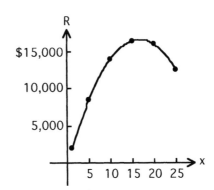

122. (A) $P(x) = R(x) - C(x)$
$= x(2,000 - 60x) - (4,000 + 500x)$ thousand dollars
$= 1,500x - 60x^2 - 4,000$

Domain: $1 \leq x \leq 25$

(B) Table 13 Profit

x(thousands)	P(x)(thousands)
1	-$2,560
5	2,000
10	5,000
15	5,000
20	2,000
25	-4,000

(C)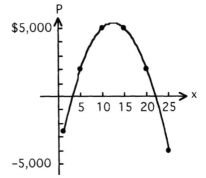

124. (A) 1.2 inches

(B) Evaluate the volume function for $x = 1.21$, 1.22, …, and choose the value of x whose volume is closest to 65.

(C) $x = 1.23$ to two decimal places

X	Y₁	
1.2	64.512	
1.21	64.682	
1.22	64.847	
1.23	65.007	
1.24	65.162	
1.25	65.313	
1.26	65.458	

X=1.23

126. (A) $V(x) = x^2(108 - 4x)$

(B) $0 \le x \le 27$

(C) Table 15 Volume

x	$V(x)$
5	2,200
10	6,800
15	10,800
20	11,200
25	5,000

(D)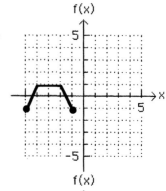

128. (A) Given $5v - 2s = 1.4$. Solving for v, we have:
$v = 0.4s + 0.28$.
If $s = 0.51$, then $v = 0.4(0.51) + 0.28 = 0.484$ or 48.4%.

(B) Solving the equation for s, we have:
$s = 2.5v - 0.7$.
If $v = 0.51$, then $s = 2.5(0.51) - 0.7 = 0.575$ or 57.5%.

EXERCISE 2-2

2. $g(x) = -0.3x$
Domain: all real numbers; range: all real numbers

4. $k(x) = 4\sqrt{x}$
Domain: $[0, \infty)$; range: $[0, \infty)$

6. $n(x) = -0.1x^2$
Domain: all real numbers; range: $(-\infty, 0]$

8. $S(x) = 5\sqrt[3]{x}$
Domain: all real numbers; range: all real numbers

10.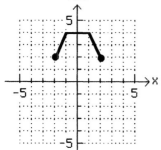

12.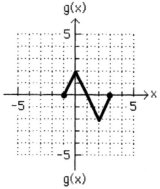

14.

16.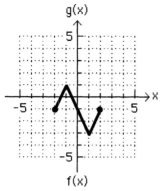

18.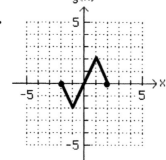

20.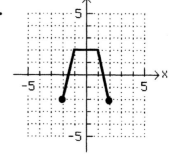

22. The graph of $h(x) = -|x - 5|$ is the graph of $y = |x|$ reflected in the x axis and shifted 5 units to the right.

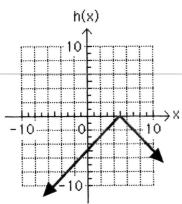

24. The graph of $m(x) = (x + 3)^2 + 4$ is the graph of $y = x^2$ shifted 3 units to the left and 4 units up.

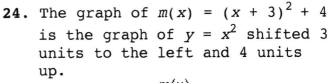
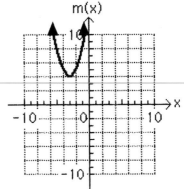

26. The graph of $g(x) = -6 + \sqrt[3]{x}$ is the graph of $y = \sqrt[3]{x}$ shifted 6 units down.

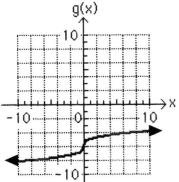

28. The graph of $m(x) = -0.4x^2$ is the same as the graph of $y = x^2$ reflected in the x axis and vertically contracted by a factor of 0.4.

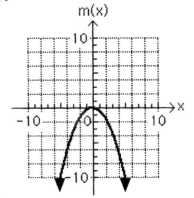

30. The graph of the basic function $y = |x|$ is shifted 3 units to the right and 2 units up. $y = |x - 3| + 2$

32. The graph of the basic function $y = |x|$ is reflected in the x axis, shifted 2 units to the left and 3 units up. Equation: $y = 3 - |x + 2|$

34. The graph of the basic function $\sqrt[3]{x}$ is reflected in the x axis and shifted up 2 units. Equation: $y = 2 - \sqrt[3]{x}$

36. The graph of the basic function $y = x^3$ is reflected in the x axis, shifted to the right 3 units and up 1 unit. Equation: $y = 1 - (x - 3)^3$

38. $g(x) = \sqrt[3]{x + 3} + 2$ **40.** $g(x) = -|x - 1|$ **42.** $g(x) = 4 - (x + 2)^2$

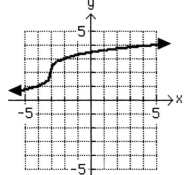   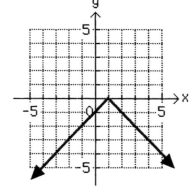   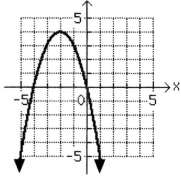

44. $g(x) = \begin{cases} x + 1 & \text{if } x < -1 \\ 2 + 2x & \text{if } x \geq -1 \end{cases}$ **46.** $h(x) = \begin{cases} 10 + 2x & \text{if } 0 \leq x \leq 20 \\ 40 + 0.5x & \text{if } x > 20 \end{cases}$

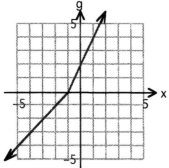

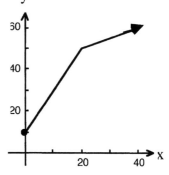

48. $h(x) = \begin{cases} 4x + 20 & \text{if } 0 \leq x \leq 20 \\ 2x + 60 & \text{if } 20 < x \leq 100 \\ -x + 360 & \text{if } x > 100 \end{cases}$

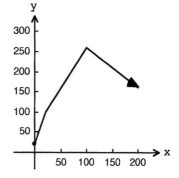

50. The graph of the basic function $y = x$ is reflected in the x axis and vertically expanded by a factor of 2. Equation: $y = -2x$

52. The graph of the basic function $y = |x|$ is vertically expanded by a factor of 4. Equation: $y = 4|x|$

54. The graph of the basic function $y = x^3$ is vertically contracted by a factor of 0.25. Equation: $y = 0.25x^3$.

56. Vertical shift, reflection in y axis.
Reversing the order does not change the result. Consider a point (a, b) in the plane. A vertical shift of k units followed by a reflection in y axis moves (a, b) to $(a, b + k)$ and then to $(-a, b + k)$. In the reverse order, a reflection in y axis followed by a vertical shift of k units moves (a, b) to $(-a, b)$ and then to $(-a, b + k)$. The results are the same.

58. Vertical shift, vertical expansion.
Reversing the order can change the result. For example, let (a, b) be a point in the plane. A vertical shift of k units followed by a vertical expansion of h ($h > 1$) moves (a, b) to $(a, b + k)$ and then to $(a, bh + kh)$. In the reverse order, a vertical expansion of h followed by a vertical shift of k units moves (a, b) to (a, bh) and then to $(a, bh + k)$; $(a, bh + kh) \neq (a, bh + k)$.

60. Horizontal shift, vertical contraction.
Reversing the order does not change the result. Consider a point (a, b) in the plane. A horizontal shift of k units followed by a vertical contraction of h ($0 < h < 1$) moves (a, b) to $(a + k, b)$ and then to $(a + k, bh)$. In the reverse order, a vertical contraction of h followed by a horizontal shift of k units moves (a, b) to (a, bh) and then to $(a + k, bh)$. The results are the same.

62. (A) The graph of the basic function $y = \sqrt{x}$ is vertically expanded by a factor of 4.

64. (A) The graph of the basic function $y = x^2$ is reflected in the x axis, vertically contracted by a factor of 0.013, and shifted 10 units to the right and 190 units up.

(B)

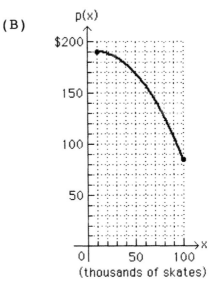

66. (A) Let x = number of kwh used in a winter month. For $0 \leq x \leq 700$, the charge is $8.5 + .065x$. At $x = 700$, the charge is $54. For $x > 700$, the charge is $54 + .053(x - 700) = 16.9 + 0.053x$. Thus,
$$W(x) = \begin{cases} 8.5 + .065x & \text{if } 0 \leq x \leq 700 \\ 16.9 + 0.053x & \text{if } x > 700 \end{cases}$$

(B)

68. (A) Let x = taxable income.
If $0 \leq x \leq 15{,}000$, the tax due is
$\$.035x$. At $x = 15{,}000$, the tax due
is $\$525$. For $15{,}000 < x \leq 30{,}00$, the
tax due is $525 + .0625(x - 15{,}000)$
$= .0625x - 412.5$. For $x > 30{,}000$,
the tax due is
$1{,}462.5 + .0645(x - 30{,}000)$
$= .0645x - 472.5$.

(B)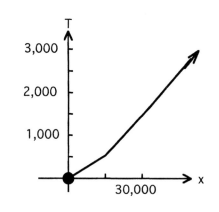

Thus,
$$T(x) = \begin{cases} 0.035x & \text{if } 0 \leq x \leq 15{,}000 \\ 0.0625x - 412.5 & \text{if } 15{,}000 < x \leq 30{,}000 \\ 0.0645x - 472.5 & \text{if } x > 30{,}000 \end{cases}$$

(C) $T(20{,}000) = \$837.50$
$T(35{,}000) = \$1{,}785$

70. (A) The graph of the basic
function $y = x^3$ is vertically
expanded by a factor of 463.

72. (A) The graph of the basic
function $y = \sqrt[3]{x}$ is reflected in
the x axis and shifted up 10
units.

(B)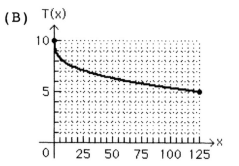

(B)

w(x) graph

EXERCISE 2-3

2. $x^2 - 2x - 5 = x^2 - 2x + 1 - 6$
    $= (x - 1)^2 - 6$

4. $-x^2 + 8x - 9 = -(x^2 - 8x + 9)$
    $= -(x^2 - 8x + 16 - 7)$
    $= -(x - 4)^2 + 7$

6. The graph of $g(x)$ is the graph of $y = x^2$ shifted right 1 unit and down
6 units.

8. The graph of $n(x)$ is the graph of $y = x^2$ reflected in the x axis, then
shifted right 4 units and up 7 units.

10. (A) g (B) m (C) n (D) f

12. (A) x intercepts: -5, -1; y intercept: -5 (B) Vertex: $(-3, 4)$

    (C) Maximum: 4   (D) Range: $y \leq 4$ or $(-\infty, 4]$

    (E) Increasing interval: $x \leq -3$ or $(-\infty, -3]$

    (F) Decreasing interval: $x \geq -3$ or $[-3, \infty)$

14. (A) x intercepts: 1, 5; y intercept: 5   (B) Vertex: $(3, -4)$

    (C) Minimum: -4 (D) Range: $y \geq 4$ or $[-4, \infty)$

    (E) Increasing interval: $x \geq 3$ or $[3, \infty)$

    (F) Decreasing interval: $x \leq 3$ or $(-\infty, 3]$

16. $g(x) = -(x + 2)^2 + 3$

    (A) x intercepts: $-(x + 2)^2 + 3 = 0$

$$(x + 2)^2 = 3$$
$$x + 2 = \pm\sqrt{3}$$
$$x = -2 - \sqrt{3}, \ -2 + \sqrt{3}$$

      y intercept: -1

    (B) Vertex: $(-2, 3)$ (C) Maximum: 3   (D) Range: $y \leq 3$ or $(-\infty, 3]$

18. $n(x) = (x - 4)^2 - 3$

    (A) x intercepts: $(x - 4)^2 - 3 = 0$

$$(x - 4)^2 = 3$$
$$x - 4 = \pm\sqrt{3}$$
$$x = 4 - \sqrt{3}, \ 4 + \sqrt{3}$$

      y intercept: 13

    (B) Vertex: $(4, -3)$ (C) Minimum: -3 (D) Range: $y \geq -3$ or $[-3, \infty)$

20. $y = -(x - 4)^2 + 2$

22. $y = [x - (-3)]^2 + 1$ or $y = (x + 3)^2 + 1$

24. $g(x) = x^2 - 6x + 5 = x^2 - 6x + 9 - 4 = (x - 3)^2 - 4$

    (A) x intercepts: $(x - 3)^2 - 4 = 0$

$$(x - 3)^2 = 4$$
$$x - 3 = \pm 2$$
$$x = 1, \ 5$$

      y intercept: 5

    (B) Vertex: $(3, -4)$ (C) Minimum: -4 (D) Range: $y \geq -4$ or $[-4, \infty)$

26. $S(x) = -4x^2 - 8x - 3 = -4\left[x^2 + 2x + \dfrac{3}{4}\right] = -4\left[x^2 + 2x + 1 - \dfrac{1}{4}\right]$

$$= -4\left[(x + 1)^2 - \dfrac{1}{4}\right] = -4(x + 1)^2 + 1$$

(A) x intercepts: $-4(x + 1)^2 + 1 = 0$

$$4(x + 1)^2 = 1$$
$$(x + 1)^2 = \dfrac{1}{4}$$
$$x + 1 = \pm\dfrac{1}{2}$$
$$x = -\dfrac{3}{2}, \ -\dfrac{1}{2}$$

y intercept: -3

(B) Vertex: $(-1, 1)$ (C) Maximum: 1 (D) Range: $y \le 1$ or $(-\infty, 1]$

28. $V(x) = .5x^2 + 4x + 10 = .5[x^2 + 8x + 20] = .5[x^2 + 8x + 16 + 4]$

$$= .5[(x + 4)^2 + 4]$$
$$= .5(x + 4)^2 + 2$$

(A) x intercepts: none
  y intercept: 10

(B) Vertex: $(-4, 2)$ (C) Minimum: 2 (D) Range: $y \ge 2$ or $[2, \infty)$

30. $g(x) = -0.6x^2 + 3x + 4$ (B) $g(x) = 5$: $-0.6x^2 + 3x + 4 = 5$

(A) $g(x) = -2$: $-0.6x^2 + 3x + 4 = -2$ $-0.6x^2 + 3x - 1 = 0$

$$0.6x^2 - 3x - 6 = 0 \qquad\qquad\qquad 0.6x^2 - 3x + 1 = 0$$

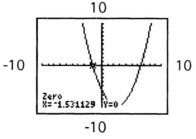

$x = -1.53, \ 6.53$ 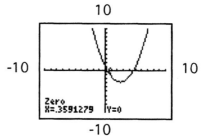 $x = 0.36, \ 4.64$

(C) $g(x) = 8$: $-0.6x^2 + 3x + 4 = 8$

$$-0.6x^2 + 3x - 4 = 0$$
$$0.6x^2 - 3x + 4 = 0$$

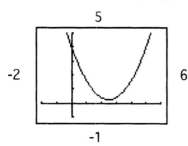

No solution

32. Using a graphing utility with $y = 100x - 7x^2 - 10$ and the calculus option with maximum command, we obtain 347.1429 as the maximum value.

34. The graph is entirely above or below the x axis.

36. $m(x) = 0.20x^2 - 1.6x - 1 = 0.20(x^2 - 8x - 5)$
$$= 0.20[(x - 4)^2 - 21]$$
$$= 0.20(x - 4)^2 - 4.2$$

(A) x intercepts: $0.20(x - 4)^2 - 4.2 = 0$
$$(x - 4)^2 = 21$$
$$x - 4 = \pm\sqrt{21}$$
$$x = 4 - \sqrt{21} = -0.6,\ 4 + \sqrt{21} = 8.6;$$

y intercept: -1

(B) Vertex: $(4, -4.2)$ (C) Minimum: -4.2
(D) Range: $y \geq -4.2$ or $[-4.2, \infty)$

38. $n(x) = -0.15x^2 - 0.90x + 3.3$
$$= -0.15(x^2 + 6x - 22)$$
$$= -0.15[(x + 3)^2 - 31]$$
$$= -0.15(x + 3)^2 + 4.65$$

(A) x intercepts: $-0.15(x + 3)^2 + 4.65 = 0$
$$(x + 3)^2 = 31$$
$$x + 3 = \pm\sqrt{31}$$
$$x = -3 - \sqrt{31} = -8.6,\ -3 + \sqrt{31}$$
$$= 2.6;$$

y intercept: 3.30

(B) Vertex: $(-3, 4.65)$ (C) Maximum: 3.30
(D) Range: $x \leq 4.65$ or $(-\infty, 4.65]$

40.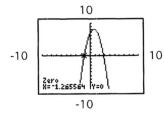
$x = -1.27, 2.77$

42.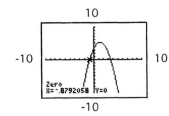
$-0.88 \leq x \leq 3.52$

44.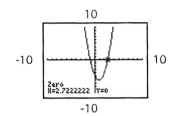
$x < -1$ or $x > 2.72$

46. f is a quadratic function and max $f(x) = f(-3) = -5$
Axis: $x = -3$
Vertex: $(-3, -5)$
Range: $y \leq -5$ or $(-\infty, -5]$
x intercepts: None

48. (A)

(B) $f(x) = g(x)$: $-0.7x(x - 7) = 0.5x + 3.5$

$$-0.7x^2 + 4.4x - 3.5 = 0$$

$$x = \frac{-4.4 \pm \sqrt{(4.4)^2 - (0.7)(3.5)}}{-1.4} = 0.93, \ 5.35$$

(C) $f(x) > g(x)$ for $0.93 < x < 5.35$

(D) $f(x) < g(x)$ for $0 \le x < 0.93$ or $5.35 < x \le 7$

50. (A)

(B) $f(x) = g(x)$: $-0.7x^2 + 6.3x = 1.1x + 4.8$

$$-0.7x^2 - 5.2x - 4.8 = 0$$

$$0.7x^2 + 5.2x + 4.8 = 0$$

$$x = \frac{-5.2 \pm \sqrt{(5.2)^2 - (0.7)(4.8)}}{1.4} = 1.08, \ 6.35$$

(C) $f(x) > g(x)$ for $1.08 < x < 6.35$

(D) $f(x) < g(x)$ for $0 \le x < 1.08$ or $6.35 < x \le 9$

52. $f(x) = x^2$ and $g(x) = -(x - 4)^2$ are two examples. The vertex of the graph is on the x axis.

54. $f(x) = -0.0206x^2 + 0.548x + 16.9$

(A)

x	0	5	10	15	20	25
Market share	17.2	18.8	20.0	20.7	20.2	17.4
$f(x)$	16.9	19.1	20.3	20.5	19.6	17.7

(B)

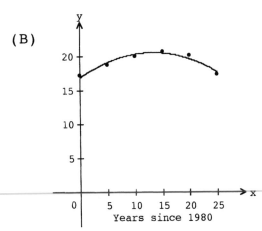

(C) For 2010, $x = 30$ and
$$f(30) = -0.0206(30)^2 + 0.548(30) + 16.9 = 14.8\%$$

For 2015, $x = 35$ and
$$f(35) = -0.0206(35)^2 + 0.548(30) + 16.9 = 10.8\%$$

58. (A)

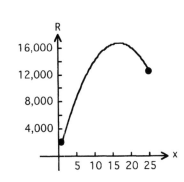

(B) $R(x) = 2,000x - 60x^2$

$$= -60\left(x^2 - \frac{100}{3}x\right)$$

$$= -60\left[x^2 - \frac{100}{3}x + \frac{2500}{9} - \frac{2500}{9}\right]$$

$$= -60\left[\left(x - \frac{50}{3}\right)^2 - \frac{2500}{9}\right]$$

$$= -60\left(x - \frac{50}{3}\right) + \frac{50,000}{3}$$

16.667 thousand computers(16,667 computers);
16,666.667 thousand dollars ($16,666,667)

(C) $p\left(\dfrac{50}{3}\right) = 2,000 - 60\left(\dfrac{50}{3}\right) = \$1,000$

60. (A)

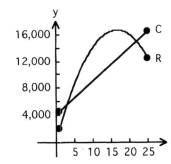

(B) $R(x) = C(x)$
$$x(2,000 - 60x) = 4,000 + 500x$$
$$2,000x - 60x^2 = 4,000 + 500x$$
$$60x^2 - 1,500x + 4,000 = 0$$
$$6x^2 - 150x + 400 = 0$$
$$x = 3.035,\ 21.965$$

Break-even at 3.035 thousands (3,035)
and 21.965 thousand (21,965)

(C) Loss: $1 \le x < 3.035$ or $21.965 < x \le 25$;
Profit: $3.035 < x < 21.965$

62. (A) $P(x) = R(x) - C(x)$

$= 1{,}500x - 60x^2 - 4{,}000$

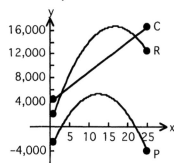

(C) Intercepts and break-even points: 3,035 computers and 21,965 computers

(E) Maximum profit is $5,375,000 when 12,500 computers are produced. This is much smaller than the maximum revenue of $16,666,667.

64. (A) Solve: $f(x) = 1{,}000(0.04 - x^2) = 30$

$$40 - 1000x^2 = 30$$
$$1000x^2 = 10$$
$$x^2 = 0.01$$
$$x = 0.10 \text{ cm}$$

(B)

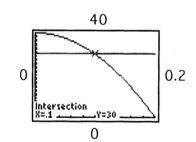

66.

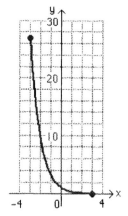

For $x = 2{,}300$, the estimated fuel consumption is $y = a(2{,}300)^2 + b(2{,}300) + c = 5.6$ mpg.

EXERCISE 2-4

2. (A) g (B) f (C) h (D) k

4. $y = 3^x$, $-3 \le x \le 3$

x	y
-3	$\frac{1}{27}$
-1	$\frac{1}{3}$
0	1
1	3
3	27

6. $y = \left(\frac{1}{3}\right)^x = 3^{-x}$, $-3 \le x \le 3$

x	y
-3	27
-1	3
0	1
1	$\frac{1}{3}$
3	$\frac{1}{9}$

8. $g(x) = -3^{-x}$, $-3 \le x \le 3$

x	y
-3	-27
-1	-3
0	-1
1	$-\frac{1}{2}$
3	$-\frac{1}{27}$

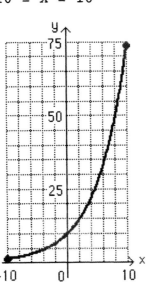

10. $y = -e^x$, $-3 \le x \le 3$

x	y
-3	≈ -0.05
-1	≈ -0.4
0	≈ -1
1	≈ -2.7
3	≈ -20

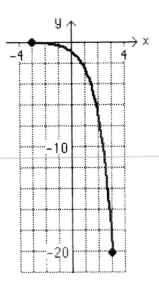

12. $y = 10e^{0.2x}$, $-10 \le x \le 10$

x	y
-10	≈ 1.4
-8	≈ 2.0
-6	≈ 3.0
0	10.0
6	≈ 33.2
8	≈ 49.5
10	≈ 73.9

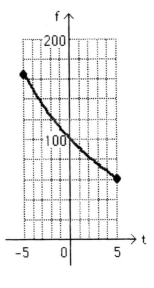

14. $f(t) = 100e^{-0.1t}$, $-5 \le t \le 5$

x	y
-5	≈ 165
-3	≈ 135
-1	≈ 111
0	100
1	≈ 90
3	≈ 74
5	≈ 60

16. $10^{2x + 3}$

18. $\dfrac{e^x}{e^{1-x}} = e^{x-(1-x)} = e^{2x - 1}$

20. $(3e^{-1.4x})^2 = 9e^{-2.8x}$

22. $g(x) = f(x - 2)$; the graph of g is the graph of f shifted 2 units to the right.

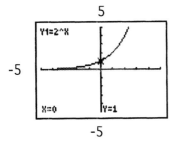

$f(x) = 2^x$

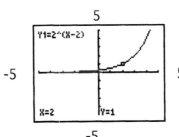

$g(x) = 2^{x-2}$

24. $g(x) = -f(x)$; the graph of g is the graph of f reflected in the x axis.

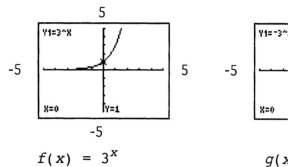
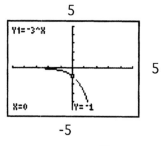

$$f(x) = 3^x \qquad\qquad g(x) = -3^x$$

26. $g(x) = f(x) - 2$; the graph of g is the graph of f shifted two units down.

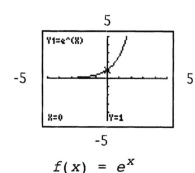
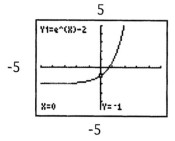

$$f(x) = e^x \qquad\qquad g(x) = e^x - 2$$

28. $g(x) = 0.5f(x - 1)$; the graph of g is the graph of f vertically contracted by a factor of 0.5 and shifted to the right 1 unit.

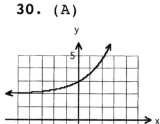
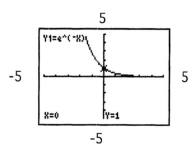

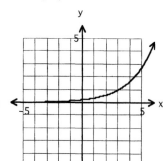
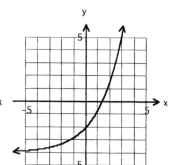
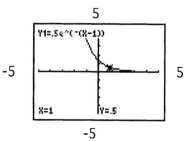
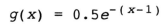

$$f(x) = e^{-x} \qquad\qquad g(x) = 0.5e^{-(x-1)}$$

30. (A)   (B)   (C)   (D)

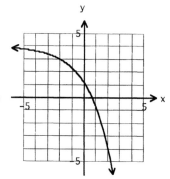

32. $G(t) = 3^{t/100}$, $-200 \leq t \leq 200$

x	y
-200	$\frac{1}{9}$
-100	$\frac{1}{3}$
0	1
100	3
200	9

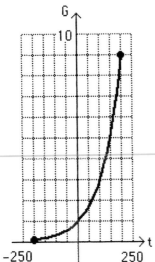

34. $y = 2 + e^{x-2}$, $-1 \leq x \leq 5$

x	y
-1	≈ 2.0
0	≈ 2.1
1	≈ 2.4
3	≈ 4.7
5	≈ 22.0

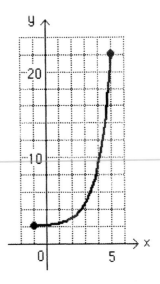

36. $y = e^{-|x|}$, $-3 \leq x \leq 3$

x	y
-3	≈ 0
-1	≈ 0.4
0	1
1	≈ 0.4
3	≈ 0

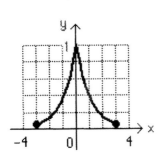

38. $M(x) = e^{x/2} + e^{-x/2}$, $-5 \leq x \leq 5$

x	y
-5	≈ 12.2
-3	≈ 4.7
-1	≈ 2.3
0	2
1	≈ 2.3
3	≈ 4.7
5	≈ 12.2

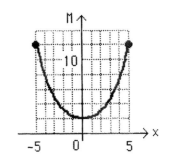

40. $y = 2^{-x^2}$, $-3 \leq x \leq 3$

x	$h(x)$
-3	$\frac{1}{512}$
-1	$\frac{1}{2}$
0	1
1	$\frac{1}{2}$
3	$\frac{1}{512}$

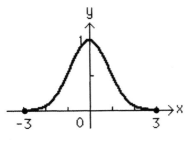

42. $a = 2$, $b = -2$ for example. The exponential function property: For $x \neq 0$, $a^x = b^x$ if and only if $a = b$ assumes $a > 0$, $b > 0$.

44. $5^{3x} = 5^{4x-2}$ implies $3x = 4x - 2$ or $x = 2$

46. $7^{x^2} = 7^{2x + 3}$ implies $x^2 = 2x + 3$
$$x^2 - 2x - 3 = 0$$
$$(x - 3)(x + 1) = 0 \text{ or } x = -1, 3$$

48. $(1 - x)^5 = (2x - 1)^5$ implies $1 - x = 2x - 1$ if $x < 1$ and $x > \frac{1}{2}$.

So $3x = 2$ or $x = \frac{2}{3}$ is a solution since $\frac{1}{2} < x - \frac{2}{3} < 1$.

50. $2xe^{-x} = 0$

$\quad\quad 2x = 0$ (since $e^{-x} \neq 0$)

$\quad\quad\quad x = 0$

52. $x^2 e^x - 5xe^x = 0$

$\quad\quad x(x - 5)e^x = 0$

$\quad\quad\quad x(x - 5) = 0$ (since $e^x \neq 0$)

$\quad\quad\quad\quad\quad x = 0, 5$

54. $m(x) = x(3^{-x})$, $0 \leq x \leq 3$

x	$m(x)$
0	0
1	$\frac{1}{3}$
2	$\frac{2}{9}$
3	$\frac{1}{9}$

56. $N(t) = \dfrac{200}{1 + 3e^{-t}}$, $0 \leq t \leq 5$

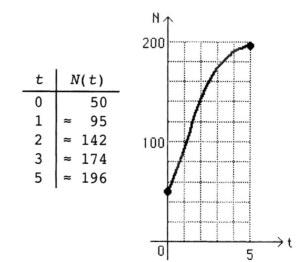

t	$N(t)$
0	50
1	$\approx$ 95
2	$\approx$ 142
3	$\approx$ 174
5	$\approx$ 196

58. $f(x) = 5 - 3^{-x}$

Solve $5 - 3^{-x} = 0$

$\quad\quad\quad\quad x = -1.46$

60. $f(x) = 7 - 2x^2 + 2^{-x}$

Solve $7 - 2x^2 + 2^{-x} = 0$

$\quad\quad\quad\quad x = -6.05, -2.53, 1.91$

62. $A = P\left(1 + \dfrac{r}{m}\right)^{mt}$, we have:

(A) $P = 4,000$, $r = 0.07$, $m = 52$, $t = \dfrac{1}{2}$

$\quad A = 4,000\left(1 + \dfrac{0.07}{52}\right)^{(52)(1/2)} = 4,142.38$

Thus, $A = \$4,142.38$.

(B) $A = 4,000\left(1 + \dfrac{0.07}{52}\right)^{(52)(10)} = 8,051.22$

Thus, $A = \$8,051.22$.

64. $A = Pe^{rt}$ with $P = 5,250$, $r = 0.0745$, we have:

(A) $A = 5,250e^{(0.0745)(6.25)} = 8,363.30$.

Thus, there will be \$8,363.30 in the account after 6.25 years.

(B) $A = 5,250e^{(0.0745)(17)} = 18,629.16$

Thus, there will be \$18,629.16 in the account after 17 years.

66. (A) $A = P\left(1 + \dfrac{r}{m}\right)^{mt}$.

Here $P = \$10,000$, $r = 0.055$, $m = 4$, $t = 5$ years.

Thus, $A = 10,000\left(1 + \dfrac{0.055}{4}\right)^{20} = \$13,140.67$.

(B) $A = P\left(1 + \dfrac{r}{m}\right)^{mt}$, where P and t are as in (A) and $r = 0.0512$,

$m = 12$. Thus, $A = 10,000\left(1 + \dfrac{0.0512}{12}\right)^{60} = \$12,910.49$.

(C) $A = P\left(1 + \dfrac{r}{m}\right)^{mt}$, where P and t are as before and $r = 0.0486$,

$m = 365$. Thus, $A = 10,000\left(1 + \dfrac{0.0486}{365}\right)^{5(365)} = \$12,750.48$.

68. Given $N = 40(1 - e^{-0.12t})$, $0 \le t \le 30$

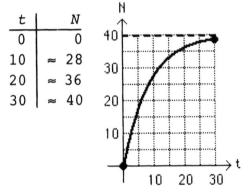

t	N
0	0
10	≈ 28
20	≈ 36
30	≈ 40

Maximum number of boards an average employee can be expected to produce in 1 day is 40.

70. (A)

(B) The model gives an average salary of \$2,039,000 in 1997. Inclusion of the data for 1997 gives an average of 20,400,000 in 2015.

72. Given $I = I_0 e^{-0.00942d}$

(A) $I = I_0 e^{-0.00942(50)} = I_0 e^{-0.471} \approx I_0(0.62)$

Thus, about 62% of the surface light will reach a depth of 50 ft.

(B) $I = I_0 e^{-0.00942(100)} = I_0 e^{-0.942} \approx I_0(0.39)$

Thus, about 39% of the surface light will reach a depth of 100 ft.

74. (A) $N = N_0e^{rt}$, where $N_0 = 25$, $r = 0.01$. Thus
$$N = 25e^{0.01t}$$

(B) Since 2006 is year 0, for 2002 we need to take $t = -4$. Thus
$$N = 25e^{(0.01)(-4)} \approx 24,000,000$$
For 2014, $t = 8$ and
$$N = 25e^{0.01(8)} \approx 27,000,000$$

(C)

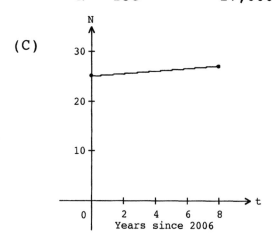

76. (A) $P = 75e^{0.023t}$

(B) For 2015, $t = 9$ (since 2006 is year 0) we have:
$$P = 75e^{0.023(9)} \approx 92 \text{ million.}$$
For 2030, $t = 24$ and
$$P = 75e^{0.023(24)} \approx 130 \text{ million.}$$

(C)

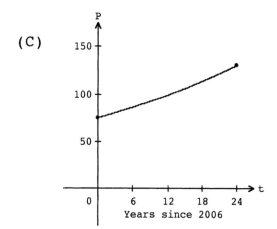

78.

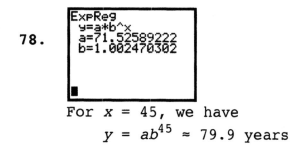

For $x = 45$, we have
$$y = ab^{45} \approx 79.9 \text{ years}$$

2. $32 = 2^5$ **4.** $e^0 = 1$ **6.** $27 = 9^{3/2}$

8. $\log_6 36 = 2$ **10.** $\log_{27} 9 = \frac{2}{3}$ **12.** $\log_b M = x$

14. $\log_e 1 = y$ is equivalent to $e^y = 1$; $y = 0$.

16. $\log_{10} 10 = y$ is equivalent to $10^y = 10$; $y = 1$.

18. $\log_{13} 13 = y$ is equivalent to $13^y = 13$; $y = 1$.

20. $\log_{10} 10^{-5} = -5$ **22.** $\log_3 3^5 = 5$ **24.** $\log_6 36 = \log_6 6^2 = 2$

26. $\log_b FG = \log_b F + \log_b G$ **28.** $\log_b w^{15} = 15 \log_b w$

30. $\text{Log}_3 P = (\text{Log}_R P)(\text{Log}_3 R)$ (change of base formula)

     or $\text{Log}_R P = \dfrac{\text{Log}_3 P}{\text{Log}_3 R}$

32. $\log_2 x = 2$ **34.** $\log_3 27 = y$

       $x = 2^2$ $\log_3 27 = \log_3 3^3 = 3 \log_3 3 = 3$

       $x = 4$ Thus, $y = 3$

36. $\log_b e^{-2} = -2$ **38.** $\log_{25} x = \frac{1}{2}$ **40.** $\log_{49}\left(\frac{1}{7}\right) = y$

   $-2 \log_b e = -2$ or $\log_b e = 1$ $x = 25^{1/2}$ $\frac{1}{7} = 49^y$

   Thus, $b = e$ $x = 5$ $y = -\frac{1}{2}$

42. $\log_b 4 = \frac{2}{3}$

       $4 = b^{2/3}$ Taking square root from both sides, we have

   $b^{1/3} = 2$ Cubing both sides yields

       $b = 8$

44. False. Take $f(x) = x^3 - x$, then $f(-1) = f(0) = f(1) = 0$.

46. True. Indeed the graph of every function (not necessarily one-to-one) intersects each vertical line exactly once.

48. False. $x = -1$ is in the domain of f, but cannot be in the range of g.

50. True. $y = \log_b x$ implies that $x = b^y$. If $b > 1$, then as y increases so does b^y. Therefore, the inverse of $x = b^y$ which is $y = \log_b x$ must be increasing as well.

52. True. Since g is the inverse of f, then (a, b) is on the graph of f if and only if (b, a) is on the graph of g. Therefore, f is also the inverse of g.

54. $\log_b x = \dfrac{2}{3}\log_b 27 + 2\log_b 2 - \log_b 3$

$\qquad = \dfrac{2}{3}\log_b 3^3 + 2\log_b 2 - \log_b 3$

$\qquad = 2\log_b 3 + 2\log_b 2 - \log_b 3 = \log_b 3 + 2\log_b 2$

$\qquad\qquad\qquad\qquad\qquad\qquad\qquad\quad = \log_b 12$

Thus, $x = 12$.

56. $\log_b x = 3\log_b 2 + \dfrac{1}{2}\log_b 25 - \log_b 20$

$\qquad = \log_b 8 + \log_b 5 - \log_b 20$

$\qquad = \log_b 40 - \log_b 20 = \log_b \dfrac{40}{20} = \log 2$

Thus, $x = 2$.

58. $\log_b(x + 2) + \log_b x = \log_b 24$

$\qquad\quad \log_b x(x + 2) = \log_b 24$

$\qquad\qquad\quad x(x + 2) = 24 \quad\text{or}\quad x^2 + 2x - 24 = 0 \quad\text{or}\quad (x - 4)(x + 6) = 4$

Thus, $x = 4$. [Note: $x = -6$ is not a solution since $\log_b(-6)$ is not defined.]

60. $\log_{10}(x + 6) - \log_{10}(x - 3) = 1$

$\log_{10}\dfrac{x + 6}{x - 3} = 1$ implies that $\dfrac{x + 6}{x - 3} = 10$ or

$x + 6 = 10x - 30$ or $9x = 36$ or $x = 4$.

62. $y = \log_3(x + 2)$

$x + 2 = 3^y$

$x = 3^y - 2$

x	y
$-\dfrac{53}{27}$	-3
$-\dfrac{17}{9}$	-2
$-\dfrac{5}{3}$	-1
-1	0
1	1
7	2
25	3

64. The graph of $y = \log_3(x + 2)$ is the graph of $y = \log_3 x$ shifted to the left 2 units.

66. Since logarithmic functions are defined only for positive "inputs", we must have $x - 1 > 0$ or $x > 1$; domain: $(1, \infty)$. The range of $y = \log(x - 1) - 1$ is the set of all real numbers.

68. (A) 1.86096

(B) -1.48095

(C) 10.60304

(D) -5.12836

70. (A) $\log x = 2.0832$

$x = 121.1156$

(B) $\log x = -1.1577$

$x = 0.0696$

(C) $\ln x = 3.1336$

$x = 22.9565$

(D) $\ln x = -4.3281$

$x = 0.0132$

---

72. $10^x = 153$ (Take common logarithms of both sides)

$\log 10^x = \log 153 = 2.1847$

$x = 2.1847$ ($\log 10^x = x \log 10 = x$; $\log 10 = 1$)

74. $e^x = 0.3059$ (Take natural logarithms of both sides)

$\ln e^x = \ln 0.3059 = -1.1845$

$x = -1.1845$ ($\ln e^x = x \ln e = x$; $\ln e = 1$)

76. $1.075^x = 1.837$ (Take either common or natural logarithms of both sides.)

We use natural logarithms.

$\ln 1.075^x = \ln 1.837$

$x = \dfrac{\ln 1.837}{\ln 1.075} = 8.4089$

78. $1.02^{4t} = 2$ (Take either common or natural logarithms of both sides.)

Here we'll use common logarithms.

$\log 1.02^{4t} = \log 2$

$t = \dfrac{\log 2}{4 \log 1.02} = 8.7507$

80. $y = -\ln x,\ x > 0$

x	y
0.5	≈ 0.69
1	0
2	≈ -0.69
4	≈ -1.39
5	≈ -1.61

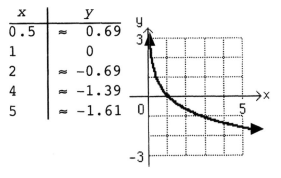

decreasing $(0, \infty)$

82. $y = \ln|x|$

x	y
-5	≈ 1.61
-2	0.69
1	0
2	≈ 0.69
5	≈ 1.61

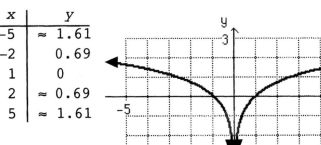

decreasing $(-\infty, 0)$

increasing $(0, \infty)$

84. $y = 2 \ln x + 2$

x	y
0.5	≈ 0.62
1	2
2	≈ 3.38
4	≈ 4.78
5	≈ 5.52

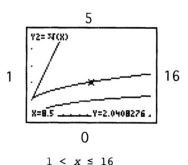

increasing $(0, \infty)$

86. $y = 4 \ln(x - 3)$

x	y
4	0
6	≈ 2.77
8	≈ 6.44
10	≈ 7.78
12	≈ 8.79

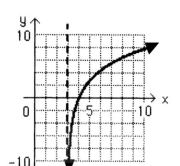

increasing $(3, \infty)$

88. It is not possible to find a power of 1 that is an arbitrarily selected real number, because 1 raised to any power is 1.

90. $\log_e x - \log_e 25 = 0.2t$

$\log_e \dfrac{x}{25} = 0.2t$

Therefore, $\dfrac{x}{25} = e^{0.2t}$, and $x = 25e^{0.2t}$

92.

```
          5
┌─────────────────┐
│ Y2=³√(X)        │
│ .               │
│ .             ✶ │
1 │ .               │ 16
│ .               │
│ X=8.5    Y=2.0408276. │
└─────────────────┘
          0
```

$1 < x \le 16$

A function f is "larger than" a function g on an interval $[a, b]$ if $f(x) > g(x)$ for $a \le x \le b$. $r(x) > q(x) > p(x)$ for $1 < x \le 16$, that is $x > \sqrt[3]{x} > \log x$.

94. From the compound interest formula $A = P(1 + r)^t$, we have:

$2P = P(1 + 0.0958)^t$ or $(1.0958)^t = 2$

Take the natural log of both sides of this equation:

$\ln(1.0958)^t = \ln 2$ [Note: The common log could have been used instead of the natural log.]

$t \ln(1.0958) = \ln 2$

$$t = \frac{\ln 2}{\ln(1.0958)} \approx \frac{0.69315}{0.09148} \approx 8 \text{ years}$$

96. $A = P\left(1 + \dfrac{r}{m}\right)^{mt}$.

For $P = \$5,000$, $A = \$7,500$, $r = 0.08$, $m = 2$, we have:

$$7,500 = 5,000\left(1 + \frac{0.08}{2}\right)^{2t}$$

$$(1 + 0.04)^{2t} = \frac{7,500}{5,000} = 1.5$$

$$2t\,\ln(1.04) = \ln(1.5)$$

$$t = \frac{\ln(1.5)}{2\,\ln(1.04)} \approx 5.17 \text{ years}$$

If compounded monthly, then $m = 12$ and

$$7,500 = 5,000\left(1 + \frac{0.08}{2}\right)^{12t}$$

$$\left(1 + \frac{0.08}{2}\right)^{12t} = 1.5$$

$$12t\,\ln\left(1 + \frac{0.08}{2}\right) = \ln(1.5)$$

$$t = \frac{\ln(1.5)}{12\,\ln\left(1 + \frac{0.08}{12}\right)} \approx 5.09 \text{ years}$$

98. 6,145 screwdrivers at $46.77 each.

100. (A) $N = 10\,\log \dfrac{I}{I_0} = 10\,\log \dfrac{10^{-13}}{10^{-16}} = 10\,\log 10^3 = 30$

(B) $N = 10\,\log \dfrac{3.16 \times 10^{-10}}{10^{-16}} = 10\,\log 3.16 \times 10^6 \approx 65$

(C) $N = 10\,\log \dfrac{10^{-8}}{10^{-16}} = 10\,\log 10^8 = 80$

(D) $N = 10\,\log \dfrac{10^{-1}}{10^{-16}} = 10\,\log 10^{15} = 150$

102.

```
LnReg
y=a+blnx
a=-39370.20369
b=10572.08468
```

For 2015, $x = 115$ and

$y = -39,370.20369 + 10,572.08468(115) \approx 10,794$ million bushels.

2. 6.15% = 0.0615 in decimal form

8 months = $\dfrac{2}{3}$ of a year $\left(\dfrac{8}{12} = \dfrac{2}{3}\right)$

4. 0.035 = 3.5%

48 weeks = $\dfrac{12}{13}$ of a year $\left(\dfrac{48}{52} = \dfrac{12}{13}\right)$

6. 0.87% = 0.087 in decimal form

3 quarters = $\dfrac{3}{4}$ of a year

8. 2.09 = 209%

60 days = $\dfrac{1}{6}$ of a year $\left(\dfrac{60}{360} = \dfrac{1}{6}\right)$

10. $I = Prt$

For $P = \$950$, $r = 0.09$ and $t = 1$, we have:

$\qquad I = 950(0.09)(1) = \$85.50$

12. $I = Prt$

For $I = \$15$, $r = 0.08$ and $t = \dfrac{3}{4}$, we have:

$$P = \frac{I}{rt} = \frac{15}{(0.08)\left(\dfrac{3}{4}\right)} = \$250$$

14. $I = Prt$

For $I = \$28$, $P = \$700$ and $t = \dfrac{13}{52}$, we have:

$$r = \frac{I}{Pt} = \frac{28}{700\left(\dfrac{13}{52}\right)} = 0.16 \text{ or } 16\%$$

16. $I = Prt$

For $I = \$96$, $P = \$3,200$ and $r = 0.04$, we have:

$$t = \frac{I}{Pr} = \frac{96}{(3200)(0.04)} = \frac{3}{4} \text{ year}$$

18. $A = P(1 + rt)$

For $P = \$3,000$, $r = 0.045$ and $t = \dfrac{30}{360} = \dfrac{1}{12}$, we have:

$$A = 3,000\left(1 + (0.045)\left(\dfrac{1}{12}\right)\right) = \$3,011.25$$

20. $A = P(1 + rt)$

For $A = \$6,608$, $r = 0.24$ and $t = \dfrac{3}{4}$, we have:

$$P = \frac{A}{1 + rt} = \frac{6,608}{1 + (0.24)\left(\dfrac{3}{4}\right)} = \$5,600$$

22. $A = P(1 + rt)$

For $A = \$22,135$, $P = \$19,000$ and $t = \dfrac{39}{52} = \dfrac{3}{4}$, we have:

$$r = \frac{A - P}{Pt} = \frac{22,135 - 19,000}{19,000\left(\dfrac{3}{4}\right)} = 0.22 \text{ or } 22\%$$

24. $A = P(1 + rt)$

For $A = \$410$, $P = \$400$ and $r = 0.10$, we have:

$$t = \frac{A - P}{Pr} = \frac{410 - 400}{400(0.10)} = \frac{1}{4} \text{ year}$$

26. $I = Prt$

Divide both sides by rt.

$$\frac{I}{rt} = \frac{Prt}{rt} = P \text{ or } P = \frac{I}{rt}$$

28. $A = P + Prt$

Subtract P from both sides.

$$A - P = Prt$$

Divide both sides by Pt.

$$r = \frac{A - P}{Pt}$$

30. $I = Prt$. Divide both sides by Pr to obtain

$$t = \frac{I}{Pr}$$

32. Each of the graphs is a straight line; the y intercepts are 400, 800, and 1200, and their slopes are 30, 60, and 90, respectively.

34. $P = \$5,000$, $r = 6.2\% = 0.062$, $t = 9$ months $= \dfrac{3}{4}$ year

$$I = Prt = 5,000(0.062)\left(\frac{3}{4}\right) = \$232.50$$

36. $P = \$835$, $r = 18\% = 0.18$, $t = 2$ months $= \dfrac{1}{6}$ year

$$I = Prt = 835(0.18)\left(\frac{1}{6}\right) = \$25.05$$

38. $P = \$10,000$, $r = 6.5\% = 0.065$, $t = 6$ months $= \dfrac{1}{2}$ year

$$A = 10,000\left[1 + 0.065\left(\frac{1}{2}\right)\right] = \$10,325.00$$

40. $P = \$3,000$, $A = \$3,097.50$, $t = 5$ months $= \dfrac{5}{12}$ year

The interest on the loan is $A - P = \$3,097.50 - 3,000 = \$97.50$.

$$r = \frac{I}{Pt} = \frac{97.50}{(3,000)\left(\dfrac{5}{12}\right)} = 0.078 \text{ or } 7.8\%.$$

42. $P = \$2,000$, $I = \$120$, $t = 90$ days $= \dfrac{90}{360} = \dfrac{1}{4}$ year

$$r = \frac{I}{Pt} = \frac{120}{2000\left(\dfrac{1}{4}\right)} = \frac{120}{500} = 2.4 \text{ or } 24\%.$$

44. $P = \$3,000$. The amount of interest paid is $I = (0.59)(3)(60) = \$106.20$. Thus, the total amount repaid is $\$3,000 + \$106.20 = \$3,106.20$. To find the annual interest rate, we let $t = 60$ days $= \dfrac{60}{360} = \dfrac{1}{6}$ year. Then

$$r = \frac{I}{Pt} = \frac{106.20}{3,000\left(\dfrac{1}{6}\right)} = 0.2124 \text{ or } 21.24\%.$$

46. $A = \$1,000$, $P = \$996.16$, $t = 33$ days $= \dfrac{33}{360}$ year

$$r = \frac{A - P}{Pt} = \frac{1,000 - 996.16}{(996.16)\left(\dfrac{33}{360}\right)} = 0.04205 \text{ or } 4.205\%.$$

48. $A = \$1,000$, $r = 4.903\% = 0.04903$, $t = 26$ weeks $= \dfrac{1}{2}$ year

From Problem 28, $P = \dfrac{A}{1 + rt} = \dfrac{1,000}{1 + (0.04903)\left(\dfrac{1}{2}\right)} = \$976.07.$

50. Principal plus interest on the original note:

$$A = P(1 + rt) = \$10,000\left[1 + 0.07\left(\frac{180}{360}\right)\right] = \$10,350$$

The third party pays $\$10,124$ and will receive $\$10,350$ after 120 days. We want to find r given that $A = 10,350$, $P = 10,124$ and $t = \dfrac{120}{180} = \dfrac{1}{3}$ year.

$$r = \frac{A - P}{Pt} = \frac{10,350 - 10,124}{(10,124)\left(\dfrac{1}{3}\right)} = 0.06697 \text{ or } 6.697\%$$

52. The principal P is the cost of the stock plus the broker's commission. The cost of the stock is $450(21.40) = \$9,630$ and the commission on this is $37 + 0.014(9,630) = \$171.82$. Thus, $P = \$9,801.82$.

The investor sells the stock for $450(24.60) = \$11,070$, and the commission on this amount is $107 + 0.007(11,070) = \$184.49$. Thus, the investor has $11,070 - 184.49 = \$10,885.51$ after selling the stock. We can now conclude that the investor has earned $10,885.5 - 9,801.82 = \$1,083.69$.

Now, $P = \$9,801.82$, $I = \$1,083.69$, $t = 26$ weeks $= \dfrac{1}{2}$ year. Therefore,

$$r = \frac{I}{Pt} = \frac{1,083.69}{(9,801.82)\left(\dfrac{1}{2}\right)} = 0.22112 \quad \text{or} \quad 22.112\%.$$

54. The principal P is the cost of the stock plus the broker's commission. The cost of the stock is: $75(37.90) = \$2,842.50$, and the commission on this amount is: $32 + 0.018(2,842.50) = \$83.165$. Thus $P = \$2,925.665$. The investor sells this stock for $75(41.20) = \$3,090$, and the commission on this amount is: $56 + 0.01(3,090) = \$86.90$. Thus, the investor has $3,090 - 86.90 = \$3,003.10$ after selling the stock. We can now conclude that the investor has earned $3,003.10 - 2,925.665 = \$77.435$.

Now, $P = \$2,925.665$, $I = \$77.435$, $t = 150$ days $= \dfrac{150}{360} = \dfrac{5}{12}$ year.

Therefore, $r = \dfrac{I}{Pt} = \dfrac{77.435}{(2,925.665)\left(\dfrac{5}{12}\right)} = 0.06352$ or 6.352%.

56. $P = \$1,100$, $A = \$1,100 + \$49.00 = \$1,149.00$, and $t = \dfrac{30}{360} = \dfrac{1}{12}$ year.

Thus $r = \dfrac{A - P}{Pt} = \dfrac{49.00}{1,100\left(\dfrac{1}{12}\right)} = 0.53454$ or 53.454%.

58. $P = \$3,000$, $A = \$3,000 + \$89.00 = \$3,089.00$, and $t = \dfrac{25}{360} = \dfrac{5}{72}$ year.

Thus $r = \dfrac{A - P}{Pt} = \dfrac{89.00}{3,000\left(\dfrac{5}{72}\right)} = 0.4272$ or 42.72%.

60. $C = \begin{cases} 32 + 0.018p & \text{if} & 0 \le p < 3,000 \\ 56 + 0.01p & \text{if} & 3,000 \le p < 10,000 \\ 106 + 0.005p & \text{if} & 10,000 \le p \end{cases}$

2. $P = \$1,000$, $i = 0.015$, $n = 20$
Using $\underline{1}$,
$$A = P(1 + i)^n = 1000(1 + 0.015)^{20}$$
$$= 1000(1.015)^{20}$$
$$= \$1,346.86$$

4. $P = \$10,000$, $i = 0.08$, $n = 30$
Using $\underline{1}$,
$$A = P(1 + i)^n = 10,000(1 + 0.08)^{30}$$
$$= 10,000(1.08)^{30}$$
$$= \$100,626.57$$

6. $A = \$1,000$, $i = 0.015$, $n = 60$
Using $\underline{1}$,
$$A = P(1 + i)^n$$
$$P = \frac{A}{(1 + i)^n} = \frac{1,000}{(1 + 0.015)^{60}}$$
$$= \frac{1,000}{(1.015)^{60}} = \$409.30$$

8. $A = \$50,000$, $i = 0.005$, $n = 70$
Refer to Problem 6:
$$P = \frac{A}{(1 + i)^n} = \frac{50,000}{(1 + 0.005)^{70}}$$
$$= \frac{50,000}{(1.005)^{70}} = \$35,265.15$$

10. $A = Pe^{rt}$
For $P = \$995$, $r = 0.22$ and $t = 2$, we have:
$$A = 995e^{(0.22)(2)} = \$1,544.94$$

12. $A = Pe^{rt}$
For $A = \$19,000$, $r = 0.0769$ and $t = 5$, we have:
$$P = \frac{A}{e^{rt}} = \frac{19,000}{e^{0.0769(5)}} = \$12,935.03$$

14. $A = Pe^{rt}$
For $A = \$32,982$, $P = \$27,200$ and $r = 0.0593$, we have:
$$32,982 = 27,200e^{0.0593t}$$
$$e^{0.0593t} = \frac{32,982}{27,200}$$
$$0.0593t = \ln\left(\frac{32,982}{27,200}\right)$$
$$t = \frac{1}{0.0593}\ln\left(\frac{32,982}{27,200}\right) = 3.25 \text{ years}$$

16. $A = Pe^{rt}$
For $A = \$23,600$, $P = \$19,150$ and $t = \frac{60}{12} = 5$, we have:
$$23,600 = 19,150e^{5r}$$
$$e^{5r} = \frac{23,600}{19,150}$$
$$5r = \ln\left(\frac{23,600}{19,150}\right)$$
$$r = \frac{1}{5}\ln\left(\frac{23,600}{19,150}\right) \approx 0.04179 \text{ or } 4.179\%$$

18. $i = \dfrac{r}{m}$

For $r = 0.07$ and $m = 2$ we have:

$i = \dfrac{0.07}{2} = 0.035$ or 3.5% per half-year

20. $i = \dfrac{r}{m}$

For $r = 0.1095$ and $m = 360$, we have:

$i = \dfrac{0.1095}{360} = 0.0003$ or 0.03% per day

22. $i = \dfrac{r}{m}$

For $r = 0.21$ and $m = 12$, we have:

$i = \dfrac{0.21}{12} = 0.0175$ or 1.75% per month

24. $i = \dfrac{r}{m}$

For $r = 0.05$ and $m = 4$, we have:

$i = \dfrac{0.05}{12} = 0.0125$ or 1.25% per quarter

26. $r = im$

For $i = 0.014$ and $m = 12$, we have

$r = (0.014)(12) = 0.168$ or 16.8% per year

28. $r = im$ (Note: $r = i$ since $m = 1$)

For $i = 0.0675$ and $m = 1$, we have:

$r = (0.0675)(1) = 0.0675$ or 6.75% per year

30. $r = im$

For $i = 0.0965$ and $m = 2$, we have:

$r = (0.0965)(2) = 0.193$ or 19.3% per year

32. $r = im$

For $i = 0.0325$ and $m = 4$, we have:

$r = (0.0325)(4) = 0.13$ or 13% per year

34. $P = \$2,000$, $r = 7\%$

(A) $m = 1$, $i = 0.07$, $n = 5$

$A = (1 + i)^n$

$= 2,000(1 + 0.07)^5$

$= 2,000(1.07)^5 = \$2,805.10$

Int. $= 2,805.10 - 2,000 = \$805.10$

(B) $m = 4$, $i = \dfrac{0.07}{4} = 0.0175$

$n = 4(5) = 20$

$A = 2,000(1 + 0.0175)^{20}$

$= 2,000(1.0175)^{20} = \$2,829.56$

Int. $= 2,829.56 - 2,000 = \$829.56$

(C) $m = 12$, $i = \dfrac{0.07}{12} = 0.0058\overline{3}$, $n = 5(12) = 60$

$A = 2,000(1 + 0.0058\overline{3})^{60}$

$\quad = 2,000(1.0058\overline{3})^{60} = \$2,835.25$

Interest $= 2,835.25 - 2,000 = \$835.25$

36. $P = \$20,000$, $r = 4\%$, $m = 12$

(A) $n = 5(12) = 60$

$\quad i = \dfrac{0.04}{12}$

$\quad A = 20,000\left(1 + \dfrac{0.04}{12}\right)^{60}$

$\qquad = \$24,419.93$

(B) $n = 8(12) = 96$

$\quad i = \dfrac{0.04}{12}$

$\quad A = 20,000\left(1 + \dfrac{0.04}{12}\right)^{96}$

$\qquad = \$27,527.90$

38. $A = Pe^{rt}$

For $P = \$23,000$, $r = 0.135$ and $t = 15$, we have:

$\quad A = 23,000e^{(0.135)(15)} = \$17,425.55$

40. Each of the graphs is increasing, curves upward. The y intercepts are 4,000, 8,000, and 12,000 respectively (or are always in the ratio 1:2:3). The amounts owed at the end of 8 years are: \$7,274.88, \$14,549.76, and \$21,824.64.

42. $P = \$2,000$, $r = 8.25\% = 0.0825 = i$ since the interest is compounded annually.

1st year: $A = P(1 + i)^{n} = 2000(1 + 0.0825)^{1} = \$2,165.00$

$\qquad\qquad$ Interest: $2,165.00 - 2,000 = \$165.00$

2nd year: $A = 2000(1 + 0.0825)^{2} = \$2,343.61$

$\qquad\qquad$ Interest: $2,343.61 - 2,165.00 = \$178.61$

3rd year: $A = 2000(1 + 0.0825)^{3} = \$2,536.96$

$\qquad\qquad$ Interest: $2,536.96 - 2,343.61 = \$193.35$

and so on. The results are:

Period	Interest	Amount
0		$2,000.00
1	$165.00	$2,165.00
2	$178.61	$2,343.61
3	$193.35	$2,536.96
4	$209.30	$2,746.26
5	$226.57	$2,972.83

44. $A = \$6,000$, $r = 8\% = 0.08$, $i = \dfrac{0.08}{4} = 0.02$

(A) $n = 4(3) = 12$

$$A = P(1 + i)^n$$
$$6,000 = P(1 + 0.02)^{12}$$
$$= P(1.02)^{12}$$
$$P = \frac{6,000}{(1.02)^{12}} = \$4,730.96$$

(B) $n = 4(6) = 24$

$$P = \frac{A}{(1 + i)^n} = \frac{6,000}{(1 + 0.02)^{24}}$$
$$= \frac{6,000}{(1.02)^{24}}$$
$$= \$3,730.33$$

46. $A = Pe^{rt}$

(A) For $A = \$4,800$, $r = 0.12$ and $t = \dfrac{48}{12} = 4$, we have:

$$4,800 = Pe^{0.12(4)}$$
$$P = \frac{4,800}{e^{0.48}} = \$2,970.16$$

(B) For $t = 7$, we have:
$$4,800 = Pe^{0.12(7)}$$
$$P = \frac{4,800}{e^{0.84}} = \$2,072.21$$

48. $\text{APY} = \left(1 + \dfrac{r}{m}\right)^m - 1$

(A) For $r = 0.062$ and $m = 2$, we have:

$$\text{APY} = \left(1 + \frac{0.062}{2}\right)^2 - 1 = 0.06296 \text{ or } 6.296\%$$

(B) For $r = 0.071$ and $m = 12$, we have:

$$\text{APY} = \left(1 + \frac{0.071}{12}\right)^{12} - 1 = 0.07336 \text{ or } 7.336\%$$

50. (A) $\text{APY} = \left(1 + \dfrac{r}{m}\right)^m - 1$

For $r = 0.1875$ and $m = 360$, we have:

$$\text{APY} = \left(1 + \frac{0.1875}{360}\right)^{360} - 1 = 0.20617 \text{ or } 20.617\%$$

(B) $\text{APY} = e^r - 1$

For $r = 0.1525$, we have:

$$\text{APY} = e^{0.1525} - 1 = 0.16474 \text{ or } 16.474\%$$

52. We have $P = \$5{,}000$, $A = \$7{,}000$, $r = 6\% = 0.06$, $m = 4$, and

$i = \dfrac{0.06}{4} = 0.015$. Since $A = P(1 + i)^n$, we have:

$7{,}000 = 5{,}000(1 + 0.015)^n$ or $(1.015)^n = 1.4$

Use logarithms and a calculator:

$\ln(1.015)^n = \ln 1.4$

$n \ln 1.015 = \ln 1.4$

$$n = \frac{\ln 1.4}{\ln 1.015} \approx 23$$

Thus, $n = 23$ quarters or 5 years and 9 months, or $5\frac{3}{4}$ years.

54. $A = Pe^{rt}$

For $A = \$60{,}276$, $P = \$42{,}000$ and $r = 0.0425$, we have:

$60{,}276 = 42{,}000e^{0.0425t}$

$e^{0.0425t} = \dfrac{60{,}276}{42{,}000}$

$0.0425t = \ln\left(\dfrac{60{,}276}{42{,}000}\right)$

$t = \dfrac{1}{0.0425} \ln\left(\dfrac{60{,}276}{42{,}000}\right) = 8.5$ years

56. $A = 2P$, $i = 0.05$

$A = P(1 + i)^n$

$2P = P(1 + 0.05)^n$

$(1.05)^n = 2$

$\ln(1.05)^n = \ln 2$

$n \ln 1.05 = \ln 2$

$$n = \frac{\ln 2}{\ln 1.05} \approx 14.21 \approx 15$$

58. We have $A = P(1 + i)^n$. To find the doubling time, set $A = 2P$. This yields:

$2P = P(1 + i)^n$ or $(1 + i)^n = 2$

Taking the natural logarithm of both sides, we obtain:

$\ln(1 + i)^n = \ln 2$

$n \ln(1 + i) = \ln 2$

$$n = \frac{\ln 2}{\ln(1 + i)}$$

(A) $r = 8\% = 0.08$, $m = 2$. Thus,

$i = \dfrac{0.08}{2} = 0.04$ and $n = \dfrac{\ln 2}{\ln(1.04)} \approx 17.67$ half-years

or $n = 8\frac{5}{7}$ yrs.

(B) $r = 7\% = 0.07$, $m = 2$. Thus,

$$i = \frac{0.07}{2} = 0.035 \text{ and } n = \frac{\ln 2}{\ln(1.035)} \approx 20.15 \text{ half-years}$$

or $n = 10\frac{3}{40}$ yrs.

60. (A) $A = Pe^{rt}$
For $A = 2P$ and $r = 0.21$,
we have:

$$2P = Pe^{0.21t}$$
$$e^{0.21t} = 2$$
$$0.21t = \ln 2$$
$$t = \frac{\ln 2}{0.21} = 3.3 \text{ years}$$

(B) For $r = 0.33$, we have:
$$e^{0.33t} = 2$$
$$0.33t = \ln 2$$
$$t = \frac{\ln 2}{0.33} = 2.1 \text{ years}$$

62. $A = P\left(1 + \dfrac{r}{m}\right)^{mt}$

For $P = \$14,000$, $r = 0.065$, $m = 2$ and $t = 3$, we have:

$$A = 14,000\left(1 + \frac{0.065}{2}\right)^{2(3)} = \$16,961.66$$

64. $A = P\left(1 + \dfrac{r}{m}\right)^{mt}$

For $P = \$17,000$, $r = 0.04$, $m = 1$ and $t = 5$, we have:

$$A = 17,000\left(1 + \frac{0.04}{1}\right)^{1(5)} = \$20,683.10$$

66. $A = P\left(1 + \dfrac{r}{m}\right)^{mt}$

For $A = \$260,000$, $r = 0.052$, $m = 1$ and $t = 8$, we have:

$$260,000 = P\left(1 + \frac{0.052}{1}\right)^{1(8)}$$
$$P = \frac{260,000}{(1.052)^8} = \$173,319.50$$

68. $N = N_0 e^{rt}$

For $N = 10$, $N_0 = 6.5$ and $r = 0.0114$, we have:

$$10 = 6.5e^{0.0114t}$$
$$e^{0.0114t} = \frac{10}{6.5}$$
$$0.0114t = \ln\left(\frac{10}{6.5}\right) \quad \text{or} \quad t = \frac{1}{0.0114}\ln\left(\frac{10}{6.5}\right) \approx 38 \text{ years}$$

70. The effective rate, APY, of $r = 8\% = 0.08$ compounded quarterly is:

$$APY = \left(1 + \frac{0.08}{4}\right)^4 - 1 = 0.0824 \text{ or } 8.24\%$$

The effective rate of 8.3% compounded annually is 8.3% which is higher than 8.24%. Thus, 8.3% compounded annually is better.

74. $A = Pe^{rt}$

For $A = \$12,500$, $P = \$10,000$ and $t = 4$, we have:

$$12,500 = 10,000e^{4r}$$

$$e^{4r} = \frac{12,500}{10,000} = 1.25$$

$$4r = \ln(1.25)$$

$$r = \frac{1}{4}\ln(1.25) = 0.05579 \text{ or } 5.579\%$$

76. $A = \$20,000$, $P = \$15,000$, $r = 7\% = 0.07$, $m = 4$, $i = \dfrac{0.07}{4} = 0.0175$

Since $A = P(1 + i)^n$, we have:

$$20,000 = 15,000(1 + 0.0175)^n \text{ or } (1.0175)^n = \frac{4}{3}$$

Therefore, $\ln(1.0175)^n = \ln\left(\dfrac{4}{3}\right)$

$$n \ln(1.0175) = \ln\left(\frac{4}{3}\right)$$

$$n = \frac{\ln\left(\dfrac{4}{3}\right)}{\ln(1.0175)} \approx 17 \text{ quarters or } n = 4\frac{1}{4} \text{ years}$$

78. $A = P\left(1 + \dfrac{r}{m}\right)^{mt}$

For $P = \$1$, $r = 0.02$, $m = 1$ and $t = 950$, we have:

$$A = 1\left(1 + \frac{0.02}{1}\right)^{1(950)} = \$147,966,422.56$$

Simple Interest: $A = Prt = (1)(0.02)(950) = \$19$

80. Compounded daily: $A = P\left(1 + \dfrac{r}{m}\right)^{mt}$: For $A = 3P$, $m = 365$ and $r = 0.05$, we have:

$$3P = P\left(1 + \frac{0.05}{365}\right)^{365t}$$

$$\left(1 + \frac{0.05}{365}\right)^{365t} = 3$$

$$365t \ln\left(1 + \frac{0.05}{365}\right) = \ln 3$$

$$t = \frac{1}{365} \cdot \frac{\ln 3}{\ln\left(1 + \dfrac{0.05}{365}\right)} = 21.97375068 \text{ yrs or } 8,021 \text{ days.}$$

Compounded continuously: $A = Pe^{rt}$: For $A = 3P$ and $r = 0.06$, we have:

$$3P = Pe^{0.06t}$$
$$e^{0.06t} = 3$$
$$0.06t = \ln 3$$
$$t = \frac{\ln 3}{0.06} \approx 18.310 \text{ years}$$

82.

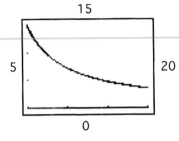

84. \$4,800 at 8% compounded monthly:

Value after n months: $A_1 = 4,800\left(1 + \dfrac{0.08}{12}\right)^n$.

\$5,000 at 5% compounded monthly:

Value after n months: $A_2 = 5,000\left(1 + \dfrac{0.05}{12}\right)^n$. Graph A_1 and A_2:

The graphs intersect at $n = 16.42$.
$A_2(n) > A_1(n)$ for $n < 16.42$,
$A_1(n) > A_2(n)$ for $n > 16.42$.

Thus it will take 17 months for the \$4,800 investment to be worth more than the \$5,000 investment.

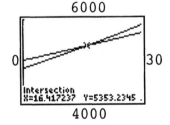

86. The value of P dollars at 9% simple interest after t years is given by
$$A_s = P(1 + 0.09t)$$
The value of P dollars at 6% interest compounded monthly after t years is given by
$$A_c = P\left(1 + \frac{0.06}{12}\right)^{12t}$$

Let $P = \$1$ and graph $A_s = 1 + 0.09t$, $A_c = (1.005)^{12t}$.
The graphs intersect at the point where $t = 12.8\overline{3}$ years or 154 months.
For the investment of less than 154 months, simple interest at 9% is better; for investments of more than 154 months, interest compounded monthly at 6% is better.

88. The relationship between the annual percentage yield rate and the annual nominal rate is:

$$\text{APY} = \left(1 + \frac{r}{m}\right)^m - 1$$

In this case, APY = 0.059 and $m = 12$. Thus, we must solve

$$0.059 = \left(1 + \frac{r}{12}\right)^{12} - 1 \text{ for } r$$

$$\left(1 + \frac{r}{12}\right)^{12} = 1.059$$

$$\left(1 + \frac{r}{12}\right) = (1.059)^{1/12}$$

$$r = 12[(1.059)^{1/12} - 1] = 0.0575 \text{ or } r = 5.75\%$$

90. $\left(1 + \dfrac{r_1}{m}\right)^m = e^{r_2}$

For $r_1 = 0.06$ and $m = 12$, we have:

$$\left(1 + \frac{0.06}{12}\right)^{12} = e^{r_2}$$

$$r_2 = \ln\left(\left(1 + \frac{0.06}{12}\right)^{12}\right) = 0.05985 \text{ or } 5.985\%$$

92. $A = \$20{,}000$, $m = 1$, $t = 10$ years, $r = 0.04194$.
Then we must solve $20{,}000 = P(1 + 0.04194)^{10}$ for P.

$$P = \frac{20{,}000}{(1 + 0.04194)^{10}} = \$13{,}261.81$$

94. $A = \$40{,}000$, $P = \$32{,}000$, $m = 1$, $t = 5$.
Then we must solve $40{,}000 = 32{,}000(1 + r)^5$ for r.

$$r = \left(\frac{40{,}000}{32{,}000}\right)^{1/5} - 1 = \left(\frac{5}{4}\right)^{1/5} - 1 = 0.04564 \text{ or } 4.564\%$$

96. (A) $\left(1 + \dfrac{r}{m}\right)^m - 1 = \left(1 + \dfrac{0.045}{4}\right)^4 - 1 = 0.04577 \text{ or } 4.577\%$

(B) $\left(1 + \dfrac{r}{m}\right)^m - 1 = \left(1 + \dfrac{0.046}{12}\right)^{12} - 1 = 0.04698 \text{ or } 4.698\%$

(C) $e^r - 1 = e^{0.046} - 1 = 0.04707 \text{ or } 4.707\%$

98. P = cost of the stock plus the broker's commission =
$28,500 + $97 + (0.002)(28,500) = $28,654. The investor sells the
stock for 300(156) = $46,800 and the commission on this amount is
97 + (0.002)(46,800) = $190.60. Thus, the investor has
$46,800 - 190.60 = $46,609.40 after selling the stock.
Now we must solve $46,609.40 = 28,654(1 + r)^3$ for r.

$$r = \left(\frac{46,609.40}{28,654}\right)^{1/3} - 1 = 0.17605 \text{ or } 17.61\%.$$

100. P = cost of the stock plus the broker's commission =
$19,200 + 75 + (0.003)(19,200) = $19,332.60. The investor sells the
stock for 400(147) = $58,800 and the commission on this amount is
147 + (.001)(58,800) = $205.80. Thus, the investor has
$58,800 - 205.80 = $58,594.20 after selling the stock.
Now we must solve $58,594.20 = 19,332.60(1 + r)^6$ for r.

$$r = \left(\frac{58,594.20}{19,332.60}\right)^{1/6} - 1 = 0.2030 \text{ or } 20.30\%$$

EXERCISE 3-3

2. $i = \dfrac{r}{m}$

For $r = 0.06$ and $m = 12$, we have:

$i = \dfrac{0.06}{12} = 0.005$

For $m = 12$ and $t = 6$, we have:

$n = mt = (12)(6) = 72$ periods

4. $i = \dfrac{r}{m} = r = 0.0625$ since $m = 1$.

$n = mt = (1)(15) = 15$ periods

6. $i = \dfrac{r}{m}$

For $r = 0.085$ and $m = 2$, we have:

$i = \dfrac{0.085}{2} = 0.0425$

For $m = 2$ and $t = 7$, we have:

$n = mt = (2)(7) = 14$ periods

8. $i = \dfrac{r}{m}$

For $r = 0.076$ and $m = 4$, we have:

$i = \dfrac{0.076}{4} = 0.019$

For $m = 4$ and $t = 18$, we have:

$n = mt = (4)(18) = 72$ periods

10. $n = 25$, $i = 0.04$, $PMT = \$100$

$$FV = PMT\frac{(1 + i)^n - 1}{i}$$

$$= 100\frac{(1 + 0.04)^{25} - 1}{0.04}$$

$$= \$4,164.59$$

12. $n = 30$, $i = 0.01$, $PMT = \$50$

$$FV = PMT\frac{(1 + i)^n - 1}{i}$$

$$= 50\frac{(1 + 0.01)^{30} - 1}{0.01}$$

$$= \$1,739.24$$

14. $FV = \$8,000$, $n = 30$, $i = 0.03$

$$PMT = FV\frac{i}{(1 + i)^n - 1}$$

$$= 8,000\frac{0.03}{(1 + 0.03)^{30} - 1}$$

$$= \$168.15$$

16. $FV = \$2,500$, $n = 10$, $i = 0.08$

$$PMT = FV\frac{i}{(1 + i)^n - 1}$$

$$= 2,500\frac{0.08}{(1 + 0.08)^{10} - 1}$$

$$= \$172.57$$

18. $FV = \$8,000$, $i = 0.04$, $PMT = 500$

$$FV = PMT\frac{(1 + i)^n - 1}{i}$$

$$8,000 = 500\frac{(1 + 0.04)^n - 1}{0.04}$$

$$(1.04)^n = \frac{(8,000)(0.04)}{500} + 1 = 1.64$$

$$n \ln(1.04) = \ln(1.64)$$

$$n = \frac{\ln 1.64}{\ln 1.04} \approx 13 \text{ periods}$$

20. $FV = \$4,100$; $PMT = \$100$; $n = 20$

$$FV = PMT\frac{(1 + i)^n - 1}{i}$$

$$4,100 = 100\frac{(1 + i)^{20} - 1}{i}$$

and $\dfrac{(1 + i)^{20} - 1}{i} = 41$

Graph $Y_1 = \dfrac{(1 + x)^{20} - 1}{x}$,

$Y_2 = 41$.

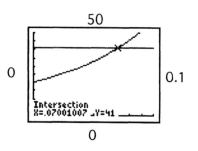

The graphs intersect at the point where $x = 0.07$. Thus, $i = 0.07$.

22. $PMT = \$1,000$, $n = 15(12) = 180$, $i = \dfrac{r}{12} = \dfrac{0.0725}{12}$

$$FV = 1,000\frac{\left(1 + \frac{0.0725}{12}\right)^{180} - 1}{\frac{0.0725}{12}} = \$323,943.07$$

Total deposits $= 1,000(180) = \$180,000$.
Interest $= FV - 180,000 = \$143,943.07$.

24. $PMT = \$7,500$, $n = 20(1) = 20$, $i = r = 0.08$

$$FV = 7,500\frac{(1 + 0.08)^{20} - 1}{0.08} = \$343,214.73.$$

26. $FV = \$100,000$, $n = 10(12) = 120$, $r = 0.055$, $i = \dfrac{0.055}{12}$

$$PMT = FV\frac{i}{(1 + i)^n - 1}$$

$$= 100,000\frac{\dfrac{0.055}{12}}{\left(1 + \dfrac{0.055}{12}\right)^{120} - 1} = \$626.93$$

28. $FV = \$120,000$, $n = 15(2) = 30$, $r = 6.8\% = 0.068$, $i = \dfrac{0.068}{2} = 0.034$

$$PMT = FV\frac{i}{(1 + i)^n - 1}$$

$$= 120,000\frac{0.034}{(1 + 0.034)^{30} - 1} = \$2,363.07$$

30. $PMT = \$2,000$, $i = \dfrac{0.079}{4} = 0.01975$, $n = 2(4) = 8$

$$FV = PMT\frac{(1 + i)^n - 1}{i} = 2,000\frac{(1.01975)^n - 1}{0.01975}$$

$n = 1$: $FV = \$2,000$
$n = 2$: $FV = \$4,039.50$
   Interest: $4,039.50 - 4,000 = \$39.50$
$n = 3$: $FV = \$6,119.28$
   Interest: $6,119.28 - 4,039.50 = \$79.78$ and so on.

Balance Sheet

Period	Amount	Interest	Balance
1	$2,000.00	$0.00	$2,000.00
2	$2,000.00	$39.50	$4,039.50
3	$2,000.00	$79.78	$6,119.28
4	$2,000.00	$120.86	$8,240.14
5	$2,000.00	$162.74	$10,402.88
6	$2,000.00	$205.46	$12,608.34
7	$2,000.00	$249.01	$14,857.35
8	$2,000.00	$293.43	$17,150.78

32. $FV = PMT\dfrac{(1 + i)^n - 1}{i} = 500\dfrac{\left(1 + \dfrac{0.08}{4}\right)^4 - 1}{\dfrac{0.08}{4}}$ (after one year)

$$= 500\frac{(1 + 0.02)^4 - 1}{0.02} \approx \$2,060.80$$

Total deposits in one year = $4(500) = \$2,000$.

Interest earned in first year $= FV - 2,000 = 2,060.80 - 2,000 = \$60.80.$

At the end of the second year:

$$FV = 500\frac{(1 + 0.02)^8 - 1}{0.02} = \$4,291.48$$

Total deposits plus interest in the second year =
$4,291.48 - 2,060.80 = \$2,230.68$
Interest earned in the second year $= 2,230.68 - 2,000 = \$230.68.$
At the end of the third year,

$$FV = 500\frac{(1.02)^{12} - 1}{0.02} = \$6,706.04$$

Total deposits plus interest in the third year =
$6,706.04 - 4,291.48 = \$2,414.56$

Interest earned in the third year $= 2,414.56 - 2,000 = \$414.56.$

34. $PMT = \$1,000,$ $r = 6.4\% = 0.064,$ $m = 1,$ $n = 30,$

$$FV = 1,000\frac{(1 + .064)^{30} - 1}{0.064} = \$84,852.51$$

36. Bob: $PMT = \$1,000,$ $r = 6.4\% = 0.064,$ $m = 1,$ $n = 42,$

$$FV = 1,000\frac{(1 + .064)^{42} - 1}{0.064} = \$195,903.26.$$

John: $FV = 195,903.26,$ $r = 6.4\% = 0.064,$ $m = 1,$ $n = 30,$

$$PMT = 195,903.26\frac{.064}{(1 + .064)^{30} - 1} = \$2,308.75.$$

38. (A) $APY = \left(1 + \dfrac{r}{12}\right)^{12} - 1 = 0.0565$ which needs to be solved for r:

$$\left(1 + \frac{r}{12}\right)^{12} = 1.0565 \quad \text{or} \quad 1 + \frac{r}{12} = (1.0565)^{1/12},$$

$$r = 12[(1.0565)^{1/12} - 1] = 0.05508 \approx 0.0551 \text{ or } 5.51\%$$

(B) $FV = \$1,000,000.00,$ $r = 0.0551,$ $m = 12,$ $n = 96$

$$PMT = 1,000,000\frac{\dfrac{.0551}{12}}{\left(1 + \dfrac{.0551}{12}\right)^{96} - 1} = \$8,312.47$$

40. $PMT = \$2,000$, $r = 6.6\% = 0.066$, $m = 12$, $i = \dfrac{.066}{12}$,

$FV = \$100,000$.

$$FV = PMT\frac{(1 + i)^n - 1}{i}$$

$$100,000 = 2,000\frac{\left(1 + \dfrac{.066}{12}\right)^n - 1}{\dfrac{.066}{12}}$$

$$\left(1 + \frac{.066}{12}\right)^n = \frac{100,000(.066)}{24,000} + 1$$

$$n \ln\left(1 + \frac{.066}{12}\right) = \ln(1.275)$$

$$n = \frac{\ln(1.275)}{\ln(1.0055)} = 45 \text{ months}$$

42. $PMT = \$2,000$, $FV = \$14,000$, $n = 6$, $m = 1$, $r = i$

$$FV = PMT\frac{(1 + i)^n - 1}{i}$$

$$14,000 = 2,000\frac{(1 + r)^6 - 1}{r}$$

$$\frac{(1 + r)^6 - 1}{r} = 7$$

Graph $Y_1 = \dfrac{(1 + x)^6 - 1}{6}$

$Y_2 = 7$

These graphs intersect at the point $x = 0.0614$.
Thus, $r = 0.0614$ or 6.14%.

44. $FV = \$2,100$, $PMT = \$80$, $m = 12$, $n = (12)(2) = 24$, $i = \dfrac{r}{12}$

$$FV = PMT\frac{\left(1 + \dfrac{r}{12}\right)^n - 1}{\dfrac{r}{12}}$$

$$2,100 = 80\frac{\left(1 + \dfrac{r}{12}\right)^{24} - 1}{\dfrac{r}{12}}$$

$$\frac{\left(1 + \dfrac{r}{12}\right)^{24} - 1}{\dfrac{r}{12}} = \frac{210}{8} = 26.25$$

Graph $Y_1 = \dfrac{(1 + x)^{24} - 1}{x}$

$Y_2 = 26.25$

These graphs intersect at the point $x = 0.0077$.

Thus, $\dfrac{r}{12} = 0.0077$ or $r = 0.0924$ or 9.24%.

46. Annuity: $PMT = \$200$, $i = \dfrac{0.05}{12}$, $n = 12x$

$$Y_1 = 200 \dfrac{\left(1 + \dfrac{0.05}{12}\right)^{12x} - 1}{\dfrac{0.05}{12}}$$

Compound interest: $P = \$10,000$, $r = 7.5\% = 0.075$, $m = 12$, $i = \dfrac{0.075}{12}$,

$n = 12x$

$$Y_2 = 10,000\left(1 + \dfrac{0.075}{12}\right)^{12x}$$

Graph Y_1 and Y_2.

The point of intersection is $x = 5.5$ years.

$Y_1(x) > Y_2(x)$ for $x > 5.5$. Thus, after 66 months the annuity will be more than the compound interest.

EXERCISE 3-4

2. $i = \dfrac{r}{m}$

For $r = 0.099$ and $m = 2$, we have:

$i = \dfrac{0.099}{2} = 0.0495$

For $m = 2$ and $t = 12$, we have:

$n = mt = (2)(12) = 24$ periods

4. $i = \dfrac{r}{m}$ (since $m = 1$, $i = r$ and $n = t$)

For $r = 0.0475$ and $m = 1$, we have:

$i = r = 0.0475$

For $m = 1$ and $t = 5$, we have:

$n = mt = (1)(5) = 5$ periods

6. $i = \dfrac{r}{m}$

For $r = 0.0824$ and $m = 4$, we have:

$i = \dfrac{0.0824}{4} = 0.0206$

For $m = 4$ and $t = 6$, we have:

$n = mt = (4)(6) = 24$ periods

8. $i = \dfrac{r}{m}$

For $r = 0.108$ and $m = 12$, we have:

$i = \dfrac{0.108}{12} = 0.009$

For $m = 12$ and $t = 3$, we have:

$n = mt = (12)(3) = 36$ periods

10. $PV = 400\ \dfrac{1 - (1 + 0.01)^{-40}}{0.01}$

$= \$13,133.87$

12. $PV = 500\ \dfrac{1 - (1 + 0.0075)^{-60}}{0.0075}$

$= \$24,086.69$

14. $PMT = 1,200\ \dfrac{0.025}{1 - (1 + 0.025)^{-40}}$

$= \$47.80$

16. $PMT = 14,000\ \dfrac{0.005}{1 - (1 + 0.005)^{-72}}$

$= \$232.02$

18. $PV = \$20,000$, $i = 0.0175$, $PMT = \$500$

We have, $PV = PMT\ \dfrac{1 - (1 + i)^{-n}}{i}$

$20,000 = 500\ \dfrac{1 - (1 + 0.0175)^{-n}}{0.0175}$

$(1 + 0.0175)^{-n} = 1 - \dfrac{20,000(0.0175)}{500} = 0.3$

$-n\ \ln(1.0175) = \ln(0.3)$

$n = -\dfrac{\ln(0.3)}{\ln(1.0175)} = 69.4$ or $n \approx 70$

20. $PV = \$12,000$, $PMT = \$400$, $n = 40$

$PV = PMT\ \dfrac{1 - (1 + i)^{-n}}{i}$

Substituting the given values into this formula gives

$12,000 = 400\ \dfrac{1 - (1 + i)^{-40}}{i}$

$30i = 1 - (1 + i)^{-40}$

$(1 + i)^{-40} + 30i = 1$

Graph $Y_1 = 30x + \dfrac{1}{(1 + x)^{40}}$, $Y_2 = 1$.

The curves intersect at $x = 0$ and $x = 0.015$. Thus $i = 0.015$.

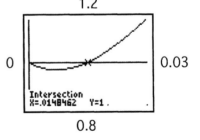

22. $PMT = \$10,000$, $n = 7$, $r = 6.35\% = 0.0635$, $i = 0.0635$

$PV = $ Present value

$= PMT\ \dfrac{1 - (1 + i)^{-n}}{i}$

$= 10,000\ \dfrac{1 - (1 + 0.0635)^{-7}}{0.0635}$

$= \$55,135.98$

24. $PMT = \$350$, $r = 9.84\% = 0.0984$, $m = 12$, $i = \dfrac{.0984}{12}$, $n = 36$.

$$PV = 350\,\frac{1 - \left(1 + \dfrac{.0984}{12}\right)^{-36}}{\dfrac{.0984}{12}} = \$10{,}872.23$$

Total Interest $= nPMT - PV = 36(350) - 10{,}872.23 = \$1{,}727.77$

26. $PV = \$3{,}500$, $i = 0.0175$, $n = 60$.

$$PMT = PV\,\frac{i}{1 - (1 + i)^{-n}} = 3{,}500\,\frac{.0175}{1 - (1 + .0175)^{-60}} = \$94.69$$

Total Interest $= nPMT - PV = 60(94.69) - 3{,}500 = \$2{,}181.40$

28. For 0% financing, the monthly payments should be $\dfrac{12{,}640}{72} = \$176.25$, not $222. If a loan of $12,690 is amortized in 72 payments of $222, the rate can be calculated from the following equation:

$$(72)(222) = 12{,}690\left(1 + \frac{r}{12}\right)^{72}$$

or $r = 12\left[\left(\dfrac{15{,}984}{12{,}690}\right)^{1/72} - 1\right] = 0.0385$ or 3.85% compounded monthly.

30. For 0% financing, the monthly payments should be $\dfrac{28{,}500}{60} = \$475$. If you choose $6,000 rebate and borrow $28,500 - $6,000 = $22,500 at 6.2% compounded monthly for 60 months, the monthly payments will be

$$PMT = PV\,\frac{i}{1 - (1 + i)^{-n}} = 22{,}500\,\frac{1}{1 - \left(1 + \dfrac{0.062}{12}\right)^{-60}} = \$437.08$$

You should choose the $6,000 rebate. You will save $475 - 437.08 = \$37.92$ monthly or $60(37.92) = \$2{,}275.20$ over the life of the loan.

32. Amortized amount $= 80{,}000 - (80{,}000)(0.10) = \$72{,}000$.

Thus, $PV = \$72{,}000$, $n = 12(7) = 84$, $r = 9.25\% = 0.0925$, $i = \dfrac{.0925}{12}$.

$$PMT = 72{,}000\,\frac{\dfrac{.0925}{12}}{1 - \left(1 + \dfrac{.0925}{12}\right)^{-84}} = \$1{,}167.57$$

Total Interest $= nPMT - PV = 84(1{,}167.57) - 72{,}000 = \$26{,}075.88$

34. First, we compute the required quarterly payment for $PV = \$10,000$, $i = 0.026$, and $n = 6$, as follows:

$$PMT = PV \frac{i}{1 - (1 + i)^{-n}} = 10,000 \frac{0.026}{1 - (1 + 0.026)^{-6}}$$
$$= \$1,821.58 \text{ per quarter}$$

The amortization schedule is as follows:

Payment number	Payment	Interest	Unpaid balance reduction	Unpaid balance
0				$10,000.00
1	$1,821.58	$260.00	$1,561.58	8,438.42
2	1,821.58	219.40	1,602.18	6,836.24
3	1,821.58	177.74	1,643.84	5,192.40
4	1,821.58	135.00	1,686.58	3,505.82
5	1,821.58	91.15	1,730.43	1,775.39
6	1,821.55	46.16	1,775.39	0.00
Totals	$10,929.45	$929.45	$10,000.00	

36. First, we compute the required PMT for $PV = \$50,000$,
$i = \dfrac{0.072}{12} = 0.006$, $n = 5(12) = 60$.

$$PMT = 50,000 \frac{0.006}{1 - (1 + 0.006)^{-60}} = \$994.78 \text{ per month}$$

The amount, D, in the account at the end of first year is the present value of a 4 year annuity:

$$D = 994.78 \frac{1 - (1 + 0.006)^{-48}}{0.006} = \$41,381.67$$

Total amount withdrawn in the first year $= (994.78)(12) = \$11,937.36$
Interest $= 11,937.36 - (50,000 - 41,381.67) = \$3,319.03$.

38. Amortized amount $= 120,000 - (120,000)(0.20) = \$96,000$.
Thus $PV = \$96,000$, $n = 12(30) = 360$, $r = 7.5\% = 0.075$,
$i = \dfrac{0.075}{12} = 0.00625$.

$$PMT = 96,000 \frac{0.00625}{1 - (1 + 0.00625)^{-360}} = \$671.25 \text{ (per month)}.$$

Total payment over 30 years $= (671.25)(360) = \$241,650$.
Interest $= 241,650 - 96,000 = \$145,650$.

40. First, compute FV for $PMT = \$7,500$, $r = 9\% = 0.09$, $n = 20$:

$$FV = 7,500 \frac{(1 + 0.09)^{20} - 1}{0.09} = \$383,700.90$$

Now using $\$383,700.90$ as PV with $r = 9\%$ and $n = 20$, we compute PMT per year:

$$PMT = 383,700.90 \frac{0.09}{1 - (1 + 0.09)^{-20}} = \$42,033.08$$

42. $PV = \$50,000$, $r = 7.2\% = 0.072$, $i = \dfrac{0.072}{12} = 0.006$ (per year);
$n = 240$.

Thus $PMT = 50,000 \dfrac{0.006}{1 - (1 + 0.006)^{-240}} = \$393.67$ (per month)

(A) Now to compute the balance after 5 years (with balance of the loan to be paid in 15 years), use $PMT = \$393.67$, $i = 0.006$, and $n = 15(12) = 180$.

$$\text{Balance after 5 years} = PMT \frac{1 - (1 + i)^{-n}}{i}$$

$$= 393.67 \frac{1 - (1 + 0.006)^{-180}}{0.006} = \$43,258.22$$

(B) Balance after 10 years:
Use $PMT = \$393.67$, $i = 0.006$ and $n = 10(12) = 120$.

$$\text{Balance after 10 years} = 393.67 \frac{1 - (1 + 0.006)^{-120}}{0.006} = \$33,606.26$$

(C) Balance after 15 years:
Use $PMT = \$393.67$, $i = 0.006$ and $n = 5(12) = 60$.

$$\text{Balance after 15 years} = 393.67 \frac{1 - (1 + 0.006)^{-60}}{0.006} = \$19,786.69$$

44. (A) $PV = \$200,000$, $r = 8.4\% = 0.084$, $m = 12$, $i = \dfrac{0.084}{12} = 0.007$, $n = 10(12) = 120$

$$PMT = 200,000 \frac{0.007}{1 - (1 + 0.007)^{-120}} = \$2,469.03 \text{ (per month)}$$

(B) $PMT = \$3,000$, $r = 8.4\% = 0.084$, $i = 0.007$, $PV = \$200,000$

$$\text{Thus, } 200,000 = 3,000 \frac{1 - (1 + 0.007)^{-n}}{0.007}$$

$$1 - (1.007)^{-n} = \frac{1.4}{3}$$

$$(1.007)^{-n} = 1 - \frac{1.4}{3} = 0.5\bar{3}$$

$$-n \ln(1.007) = \ln(0.5\bar{3})$$

$$n = -\frac{\ln(0.5\bar{3})}{\ln(1.007)} \approx 90 \text{ withdrawals}$$

46. (A) $\$522,241.29$ (B) $\$569,216.34$ (C) $\$668,430.68$

48. (A) First, calculate the present value of the ordinary annuity:
$PMT = \$1,500$, $i = \dfrac{0.0648}{12} = 0.0054$, $n = 20(12) = 240$

$$PV = 1,500 \frac{1 - (1.0054)^{-240}}{0.0054} = \$201,505.61$$

Next, using $\$201,505.61$ as the future value of an annuity, we calculate the monthly deposit:

$$FV = \$201,505.61, \quad i = 0.0054, \quad n = 15(12) = 180$$

$$PMT = 201,505.61 \frac{0.0054}{(1 + 0.0054)^{180} - 1} = \$664.99$$

Total deposits: $(664.99)(180) = \$119,698.20$.
Total withdrawals: $(1,500)(240) = \$360,000$
Total interest: $360,000 - 119,698.20 = \$240,301.80$

(B) First, calculate the FV with $PMT = \$1,000$, $i = 0.0054$, $n = 15(12) = 180$

$$FV = 1,000 \frac{(1.0054)^{180} - 1}{0.0054} = \$303,022.71$$

Next use this as PV and compute PMT with $n = 240$:

$$PMT = 303,022.71 \frac{0.0054}{1 - (1.0054)^{-240}} = \$2,255.69 \text{ (monthly withdrawal).}$$

50. Amortized amount $= \$100,000 - (100,000)(0.20) = \$80,000$.
Thus, $PV = \$80,000$, $i = 0.008$, $n = 360$.

$$PMT = 80,000 \frac{0.008}{1 - (1.008)^{-360}} = \$678.53$$

Balance after 10 years:
$PMT = \$678.53$, $i = 0.008$, $n = 20(12) = 240$,

So the balance after 10 years $= 678.53 \frac{1 - (1.008)^{-240}}{0.008} = \$72,286.24$.

New loan amount is $(136,000)(0.80) = \$108,800$, so the cash the owner will receive will be $108,800 - 72,286.24 = \$36,514$.

52. $PV = \$200,000 - (0.20)(200,000) = \$160,000$

$$r = 13.2\% = 0.132, \quad i = \frac{0.132}{12} = 0.011, \quad n = 360.$$

$$PMT = 160,000 \frac{0.011}{1 - (1 + 0.011)^{-360}} = \$1,794.97$$

Unpaid balance after 20 years is

$$D = 1,794.97 \frac{1 - (1 + 0.011)^{-120}}{.011} = \$119,272.89$$

Interest paid in the first 20 years
$= 240(1,794.97) - (160,000 - 119,272.89) = \$390,065.69$

Now refinancing $D = \$119,227.89$ at the rate $r = 8.2\%$ over 10 year period, the monthly payment will be

$$PMT = 119,272.89 \frac{\frac{0.082}{12}}{1 - \left(1 + \frac{0.082}{12}\right)^{-120}} = \$1,459.74$$

Interest paid in the last 10 year mortgage
$= 120(1,459.74) - 119,272.89 = \$55,895.91$

Total interest paid $= 390,065.69 + 55,895.91 = \$445,961.60$

Interest saved by refinancing
$= [360(1,794.97) - 160,000] - 445,961.60 = \$40,227.60$

54. All three graphs are decreasing, curve downward, and have the same x and y intercepts; the greater the interest rate, the greater the unpaid balance. The monthly payments and total interest in each case are:

$\underline{r = 7\%}$: $PV = \$60,000$, $i = \dfrac{0.07}{12}$, $n = 360$

$$PMT = 60,000 \frac{\dfrac{0.07}{12}}{1 - \left(1 + \dfrac{0.07}{12}\right)^{-360}} = \$399.18$$

Total interest $= (399.18)(360) - 60,000 = \$83,704.80$

$\underline{r = 10\%}$: $PV = \$60,000$, $i = \dfrac{0.10}{12}$, $n = 360$

$$PMT = 60,000 \frac{\dfrac{0.10}{12}}{1 - \left(1 + \dfrac{0.10}{12}\right)^{-360}} = \$526.54$$

Total interest $= (526.54)(360) - 60,000 = \$129,554.40$

$\underline{r = 13\%}$: $PV = \$60,000$, $i = \dfrac{0.13}{12}$, $n = 360$

$$PMT = 60,000 \frac{\dfrac{0.13}{12}}{1 - \left(1 + \dfrac{0.13}{12}\right)^{-360}} = \$663.72$$

Total interest $= (663.72)(360) - 60,000 = \$178,939.20$

56. $PV = \$2,000$, $PMT = \$100$, $m = 12$, $n = 2(12) = 24$

$$2,000 = 100 \frac{1 - \left(1 + \dfrac{r}{12}\right)^{-24}}{\dfrac{r}{12}}$$

$$\frac{1 - (1 + x)^{-24}}{x} = 20$$

Graph $Y_1 = \dfrac{1 - (1 + x)^{-24}}{x}$, $Y_2 = 20$. These graphs intersect at $x = 0.015\overline{13}$. Thus, $r = 12(x) = 0.1816$ or 18.16%.

58. $PV = \$200,000$, $PMT = \$2,000$, $m = 12$, $n = 15(12) = 180$

Thus, $\quad 200{,}000 = 2{,}000 \, \dfrac{1 - \left(1 + \dfrac{r}{12}\right)^{-180}}{\dfrac{r}{12}}$, or

$$\dfrac{1 - (1 + x)^{-180}}{x} = 100$$

Graph $Y_1 = \dfrac{1 - (1 + x)^{-180}}{x}$, $Y_2 = 100$. These graphs intersect at

$x = 0.0073$. Thus, $r = 12(0.0073) = 0.0876$ or $r = 8.76\%$.

4 SYSTEMS OF LINEAR EQUATIONS; MATRICES

EXERCISE 4-1

2. (D); $x = 1$, $y = 2$

6. $3x - 2y = 12$
$7x + 2y = 8$
Point of intersection: $(2, -3)$
Solution: $x = 2$; $y = -3$

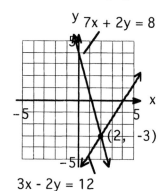

4. (C); infinite number of solutions

8. $3u + 5v = 15$
$6u + 10v = -30$
Since the graphs of the given equations are parallel lines, there is no solution.

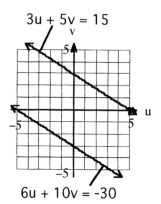

10. $y = x - 4$ (1)
$x + 3y = 12$ (2)
By substituting y from (1) into (2), we get:
$x + 3(x - 4) = 12$
$x + 3x - 12 = 12$
$4x = 24$
$x = 6$
Now, substituting $x = 6$ into (1), we have:
$y = 6 - 4 = 2$
Solution: $x = 6$
          $y = 2$

12. $3x - y = 7$ (1)
$2x + 3y = 1$ (2)
Solve (1) for y to obtain:
$y = 3x - 7$ (3)
Substitute y from (3) into (2):
$2x + 3(3x - 7) = 1$
$2x + 9x - 21 = 1$
$11x = 22$
$x = 2$
Now, substituting $x = 2$ into (3), we get:
$y = 6 - 7 = -1$
Solution: $x = 2$
          $y = -1$

14. $2x - 3y = -8$ (1)
$5x + 3y = 1$ (2)
Add (1) and (2):
$7x = -7$
$x = -1$
Substituting $x = -1$ into (2), we get:
$5(-1) + 3y = 1$
$3y = 6$
$y = 2$
Solution: $x = -1$
          $y = 2$

16. $2x + 3y = 1$ (1)
$3x - y = 7$ (2)
Multiply (2) by 3 and add to (1) to obtain:
$11x = 22$
$x = 2$
Substituting $x = 2$ into (2), we get:
$3(2) - y = 7$
$y = -1$
Solution: $x = 2$
          $y = -1$

18. $4x + 3y = 26$ (1)
$3x - 11y = -7$ (2)

Solve (1) for y to obtain:

$y = -\frac{4}{3}x + \frac{26}{3}$ (3)

and substitute into (2):

$3x - 11\left(-\frac{4}{3}x + \frac{26}{3}\right) = -7$

$3x + \frac{44}{3}x - \frac{286}{3} = -7$

$\frac{53}{3}x = \frac{265}{3}$

$x = \frac{265}{3} = 5$

Now, substitute $x = 5$ into (3):

$y = -\frac{4}{3}(5) + \frac{26}{3} = -\frac{20}{3} + \frac{26}{3} = 2$

Solution: $x = 5$, $y = 2$

22. $7m + 12n = -1$ (1)
$5m - 3n = 7$ (2)

Multiply (2) by 4 and add to (1) to get: $27m = 27$

$m = 1$

Substituting $m = 1$ into (2), we get: $5(1) - 3n = 7$

$3n = -2$

$n = -\frac{2}{3}$

Solution: $m = 1$, $n = -\frac{2}{3}$

24. $2x + 4y = -8$ (1)
$x + 2y = 4$ (2)

No solution. (1) and (2) represent two parallel lines. Slope of line (1) is $-\frac{2}{4} = -\frac{1}{2}$ and slope of line (2) is $-\frac{1}{2}$.

26. $x + y = 1$ (1)
$0.5x - 0.4y = 0$ (2)

Multiply equation (1) by 0.4 and add to (2):

$0.9x = 0.4$

$x = \frac{0.4}{0.9} = \frac{4}{9}$

Now substitute $x = \frac{4}{9}$ in (1): $\frac{4}{9} + y = 1$

$y = 1 - \frac{4}{9} = \frac{5}{9}$

Solution: $x = \frac{4}{9}$, $y = \frac{5}{9}$

20. $3x - 6y = -9$ (1)
$-2x + 4y = 12$ (2)

No solution since (1) and (2) represent two parallel lines.

Slope of line (1) is $\frac{3}{6} = \frac{1}{2}$,

and slope of line (2) is

$\frac{2}{4} = \frac{1}{2}$.

28. $0.3u - 0.6v = 0.18$ (1)
$0.5u + 0.2v = 0.54$ (2)

Multiply (2) by 3 and add to (1) to get:

$1.8u = 1.8$
   $u = 1$

Now, substitute $u = 1$ into (2):

$0.5(1) + 0.2v = 0.54$
        $0.2v = 0.04$
          $v = \dfrac{0.04}{0.2} = 0.2$

Solution: $u = 1$
           $v = 0.2$

30. $\dfrac{7}{2}x - \dfrac{5}{6}y = 10$ (1)
$\dfrac{2}{5}x + \dfrac{4}{3}y = 6$ (2)

Multiply (1) by $\dfrac{8}{5}$ and add to (2):

$$\left(\dfrac{7}{2}\right)\left(\dfrac{8}{5}\right)x + \dfrac{2}{5}x = 10\left(\dfrac{8}{5}\right) + 6$$
$$\dfrac{60}{10}x = \dfrac{110}{5}$$
$$6x = 22$$
$$x = \dfrac{22}{15} = \dfrac{11}{3}$$

Now substitute $x = \dfrac{11}{3}$ into (2), we get

$$\dfrac{2}{5}\left(\dfrac{11}{3}\right) + \dfrac{4}{3}y = 6$$
$$\dfrac{4}{3}y = 6 - \dfrac{22}{15} = \dfrac{68}{15}$$
$$y = \dfrac{68}{15} \cdot \dfrac{3}{4} = \dfrac{17}{5}$$

Solution: $x = \dfrac{11}{3}$, $y = \dfrac{17}{5}$

36. $y = -3x + 3$
$y = 5x + 8$
The graphs of the these equations are shown at the right.

Intersection: $x = -0.625$
               $y = 4.875$

38. $y = -3x + 6$
$y = -3x + 9$
These lines have the same slopes and hence are parallel and do not intersect each other. They have, therefore, no common point and hence there is no solution. When you use a calculator to find the intersection, you will see ERROR message.

40. $3x - 7y = -20$
$2x + 5y = 8$

First solve each equation for y:

$y = \dfrac{3}{7}x + \dfrac{20}{7}$

$y = -\dfrac{2}{5}x + \dfrac{8}{5}$

The graphs of these equations are:

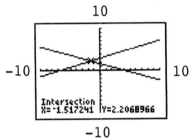

intersection: $x = -1.52$
$y = 2.21$

$(-1.52, 2.21)$

42. First solve each equation for y:

$y = -\dfrac{4.2}{5.4}x - \dfrac{12.9}{5.4}$

$y = -\dfrac{6.4}{3.7}x - \dfrac{4.5}{3.7}$

or

$y = -\dfrac{7}{9}x - \dfrac{43}{18}$

$y = -\dfrac{64}{37}x - \dfrac{45}{37}$

The graphs of the equations are:

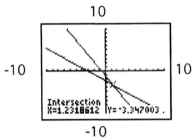

intersection: $x = 1.23$
$y = -3.35$

$(1.23, -3.35)$

44. $\quad x + y = 3 \quad (L_1)$
$\quad x + 3y = 15 \quad (L_2)$
$\quad 3x - y = 5 \quad (L_3)$

(A) L_1 and L_2 intersect:

$\quad x + y = 3 \quad (1)$
$\quad x + 3y = 15 \quad (2)$

Multiply (1) by -1 and add to (2):
$\quad 2y = 12, \; y = 6$

Substitute $y = 6$ in (1) to get
$\quad x + 6 = 3$
$\quad\quad x = -3$
Solution: $x = -3$, $y = 6$

(B) L_1 and L_3 intersect:
$\quad x + y = 3 \quad\quad (3)$
$\quad 3x - y = 5 \quad\quad (4)$
Add (3) and (4):
$\quad 4x = 8$
$\quad\quad x = 2$
Substitute $x = 2$ in (3) to get
$\quad 2 + y = 3$
$\quad\quad\quad y = 1$
Solution: $x = 2$, $y = 1$

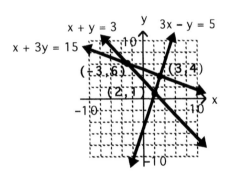

(C) L_2 and L_3 intersect:
$\quad x + 3y = 15 \quad\quad (5)$
$\quad 3x - y = 5 \quad\quad (6)$
Multiply (6) by 3 and add to (5)
$\quad 10x = 30$
$\quad\quad x = 3$
Substitute $x = 3$ in (6) to get
$\quad 3(3) - y = 5$
$\quad\quad\quad\quad y = 4$
Solution: $x = 3$, $y = 4$

46. $x - y = 6$ (L_1)

    $x - 2y = 8$ (L_2)

    $x + 4y = -4$ (L_3)

(A) L_1 and L_2 intersect

    $x - y = 6$ (1)

    $x - 2y = 8$ (2)

    Multiply (2) by -1 and add to (1):

    $y = -2$

    Substitute $y = -2$ in (1) to get

    $x - (-2) = 6$

        $x = 4$

    Solution: $x = 4$, $y = -2$

(B) L_1 and L_3 intersect:

    $x - y = 6$ (3)

    $x + 4y = -4$ (4)

    Multiply (3) by -1 and add to (4):

    $5y = -10$

    $y = -2$

    Substitute $y = -2$ in (3) to get

    $x - (-2) = 6$

        $x = 4$

    Solution: $x = 4$, $y = -2$

(C) L_2 and L_3 intersect:

    $x - 2y = 8$ (5)

    $x + 4y = -4$ (6)

    Multiply (3) by -1 and add to (6):

    $6y = -12$

    $y = -2$

    Substitute $y = -2$ into (5):

    $x - 2(-2) = 8$

        $x = 4$

    Solution: $x = 4$, $y = -2$

NOTE: As you can see, all three lines intersect at one point namely (4, -2).

48. $2x + 3y = 18$ (L_1)

    $2x - 6y = -6$ (L_2)

    $4x + 6y = -24$ (L_3)

(A) L_1 and L_2 intersect:

    $2x + 3y = 18$ (1)

    $2x - 6y = -6$ (2)

    Multiply (2) by -1 and add to (1):

    $9y = 24$

    $y = \dfrac{24}{9} = \dfrac{8}{3}$

    Substitute $y = \dfrac{8}{3}$ in (1) to get

    $2x + 3\left(\dfrac{8}{3}\right) = 18$

      $2x + 8 = 18$

         $2x = 10$

          $x = 5$

    Solution: $x = 5$, $y = \dfrac{8}{3}$

(B) L_1 and L_3 do not intersect, since they have the same slope and hence are parallel. Slope of (L_1) is $-\dfrac{2}{3}$ and slope of (L_3) is $-\dfrac{4}{6} = -\dfrac{2}{3}$.

(C) L_2 and L_3 intersect:

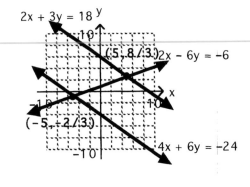

$$2x - 6y = -6 \quad (3)$$
$$4x + 6y = -24 \quad (4)$$

Add (3) and (4) to obtain:
$$6x = -30$$
$$x = -5$$

Substitute $x = -5$ in (3) to get
$$2(-5) - 6y = -6$$
$$-10y - 6y = -6$$
$$6y = -4$$
$$y = -\dfrac{2}{3}$$

Solution: $x = -5$, $y = -\dfrac{2}{3}$

50. (A)

$$6x - 5y = 10$$
$$-13x + 11y = -20$$

Multiply the top equation by 11 and the bottom equation by 5.

$$66x - 55y = 110$$
$$\underline{-65x + 55y = -100}$$
$$x = 10$$

Add the equations.

$$6(10) - 5y = 10$$
$$-5y = -50$$
$$y = 10$$

Substitute $x = 10$ in the first equation.

Solution: $(10, 10)$

(B)

$$6x - 5y = 10$$
$$\underline{-13x + 10y = -20}$$
$$-x = 0$$

Multiply the top equation by 2 and add to the bottom equation.

$$x = 0$$
$$6(0) - 5y = 10$$
$$-5y = 10$$
$$y = -2$$

Substitute $x = 0$ in the first equation.

Solution: $(0, -2)$

(C)

$$6x - 5y = 10$$
$$-12x + 10y = -20$$

Multiply the top equation by -2. The result will be $-12x + 10y = -20$ which is indeed the bottom equation. Therefore, the system has an infinite number of solutions.

52. $p = 0.4q + 3.2$ Supply equation
$p = -1.9q + 17$ Demand equation

(A) $p = \$4$
Supply: $4 = 0.4q + 3.2$
$$0.4q = 0.8$$
$$q = \frac{0.8}{0.4} = 2$$
Thus, the supply will be 200 baseball caps.
Demand: $4 = -1.9q + 17$
$$1.9q = 13$$
$$q = \frac{13}{1.9} = 6.84$$
Thus, the demand will be 684 baseball caps. At this price level, the demand exceeds the supply; the price will rise.

(B) $p = \$9$
Supply: $9 = 0.4q + 3.2$
$$0.4q = 5.8$$
$$q = \frac{5.8}{0.4} = 14.5$$
Thus, the supply will be 1,450 baseball caps.
Demand: $9 = -1.9q + 17$
$$1.9q = 8$$
$$q = \frac{8}{1.9} = 4.21$$
Thus, the demand will be 421 baseball caps. At this price level, the supply exceeds the demand; the price will fall.

(C) Solve the pair of equations to find the equilibrium price and the equilibrium quantity.
$$0.4q + 3.2 = -1.9q + 17$$
$$2.3q = 13.8$$
$$q = \frac{13.8}{2.3} = 6$$
The equilibrium quantity is 600 baseball caps. Substitute $q = 6$ in either of the two equations to find p.
$$p = 0.4(6) + 3.2 = 2.4 + 3.2$$
$$p = 5.6$$
The equilibrium price is $5.60.

(D)

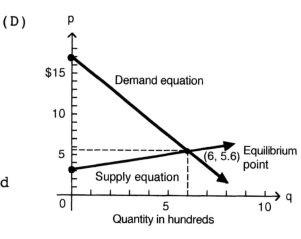

54. (A) $\dfrac{P - 2.13}{1.5 - 2.13} = \dfrac{x - 8.9}{8.2 - 8.9}$

or

$P = \dfrac{(1.5 - 2.13)}{(8.2 - 8.9)}(x - 8.9) + 2.13$

So, Supply Equation is:

$P = 1.04x - 7.05$

(B) $\dfrac{P - 2.13}{1.5 - 2.13} = \dfrac{x - 6.5}{7.4 - 6.5}$

or

$P = \dfrac{(1.5 - 2.13)}{(7.4 - 6.5)}(x - 6.5) + 2.13$

So, Demand Equation is:

$P = -0.81x + 7.50$

(C) To find the equilibrium price and quantity, we solve the following equation for x:

$\qquad 1.04x - 7.05 = -0.81x + 7.50$

or

$\qquad\qquad 1.85x = 14.55$

or

$\qquad x = \dfrac{14.55}{1.85} = 7.86$ billion bushels

To find the equilibrium price, we substitute $x = 7.86$ in $P = 1.04x - 7.05 = 1.04(7.86) - 7.05 = \$1.12$ per bushel.

(D)

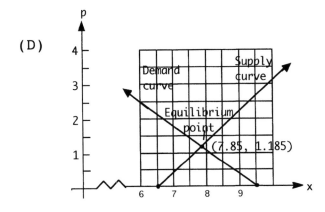

56. $y = 65,000 + 1,110x \qquad$ Cost equation
$y = 1,600x \qquad\qquad\quad$ Revenue equation

(A) To break even, we need to solve the following equation:

$\qquad 65,000 + 1,100x = 1,600x$

or $\quad x = \dfrac{65,000}{(1,600 - 1,100)} = 130$ mowers

(B)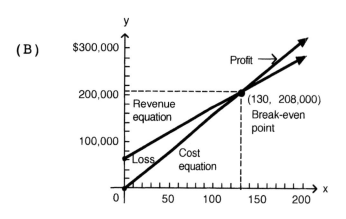

58. (A) $C = 27{,}200 + 9.15x$ Cost equation
     $R = 21.95x$ Revenue equation

(B) Break even: $27{,}200 + 9.15x = 21.95x$

or $x = \dfrac{27{,}200}{(21.95 - 9.15)} = 2{,}125$ CD's

(C)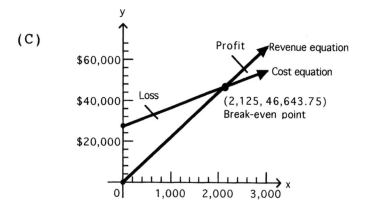

60. Let x = base price
     y = surcharge

(A) 5 pound package: $x + 4y = 29.95$ (1)
    20 pound package: $x + 19y = 59.20$ (2)

Solve the two equations (1) and (2).
Subtract equation (1) from equation (2):
   $15y = 29.25$
   $y = 1.95$

Substitute $y = 1.95$ into (1):
  $x + 4(1.95) = 29.95$
       $x = 22.15$

Thus, the base price is \$22.15; the surcharge is \$1.95 per pound.

(B) Ship packages under 10 pounds with United Express and all others with the Federated Shipping.

62. (A) Total amount of Columbian beans: $132 \times 50 = 6,600$ lbs.
Total amount of Brazilian beans: $132 \times 40 = 5,280$ lbs.

To make a pound of mild blend, we need $\dfrac{6}{16}$ pound of Columbian beans

and $\dfrac{10}{16}$ pound of Brazilian beans. Since there are 5,280 pounds of

Brazilian beans, they can produce $(5,280) \cdot \dfrac{16}{10} = 8,448$ lbs of mild

blend. The Columbian mix will then be $(8,448) \cdot \dfrac{6}{10} = 3,168$ lbs. So,

the company can produce 8,448 pounds of the mild blend by blending
3,168 pounds of Columbian beans with 5,280 pounds of Brazilian beans.
There will be $6,600 - 3,168 = 3,422$ pounds of Columbian beans that
are not used.

(B) To produce a pound of robust blend, we need $\dfrac{12}{16}$ pound of Columbian

beans and $\dfrac{4}{16}$ pound of Brazilian beans. Since there are 6,600 lbs of

Columbian beans, they can produce $(6,600) \cdot \dfrac{16}{10} = 8,800$ lbs of robust

blend. The Brazilian mix will then be $(8,800) \cdot \dfrac{4}{16} = 2,200$ lbs. So,

the company can produce 8,800 lbs of the robust blend by blending
6,600 lbs of Columbian beans with 2,200 lbs of Brazilian beans. There
will be $5,280 - 2,200 = 3,080$ lbs of Brazilian beans that are not
used.

64. Let x = number of bags of Brand A fertilizer needed, and
y = number of bags of Brand B fertilizer needed.

We want to solve the following system of equations:
$8x + 7y = 720$ (1)
$4x + 6y = 500$ (2)
Multiply (2) by -2 and add to (1):
$-5y = -280$
$y = 56$
Now substitute $y = 56$ into (2):
$4x + 6(56) = 500$
$4x = 164$
$x = 41$
Solution: 41 bags of brand A and 56 bags of brand B.

66. Let x and y be the number of production hours of Green Bay plant and Sheboygan plant. Then

$$\begin{cases} 800x + 500y = 62,250 \\ 800x + 1,000y = 76,500 \end{cases} \quad \text{or} \quad \begin{cases} 8x + 5y = 622.5 \\ 8x + 10y = 765 \end{cases}$$

To find y, we subtract the first equation from the second equation to obtain:

$$5y = 765 - 622.5 = 142.5$$

or $\quad y = \dfrac{142.5}{5} = 28.5$ hours

Substituting this value for y in $8x + 5y = 622.5$, we obtain x:

$$8x + 5(28.5) = 622.5$$

or $\quad x = \dfrac{622.5 - 5(28.5)}{8} = 60$ hours.

68. We have $s = a + bt^2$ and for $t = 1$, $s = 240$ and for $t = 2$, $s = 192$.

(A) We note that

$$\begin{cases} 240 = a + b(1)^2 = a + b \\ 192 = a + b(2)^2 = a + 4b \end{cases}$$

Subtracting the second equation from the first results in:

$$48 = -3b \quad \text{or} \quad b = -16$$

and $240 = a - 16$ or $a = 256$

(B) For $t = 0$, $s = a = 256$ ft.

(C) For $s = 0$, $t = \sqrt{-\dfrac{a}{b}} = \sqrt{-\dfrac{256}{-16}} = 4$ seconds.

70. Let t_1 and t_2 be the time recorded in water and air respectively. Then

$$\begin{cases} t_2 - t_1 = 6 \\ 1,100t_2 = 5,000t_1 \end{cases} \quad \text{or} \quad \begin{cases} t_2 - t_1 = 6 \\ t_2 = \dfrac{50}{11}t_1 \end{cases}$$

(A) Substituting t_2 from the second equation into the first equation, we obtain:

$$\frac{50}{11}t_1 - t_1 = 6 \quad \text{or} \quad \left(\frac{50}{11} - 1\right)t_1 = 6 \quad \text{or} \quad \frac{39}{11}t_1 = 6$$

or $\quad t_1 = \dfrac{66}{39} = \dfrac{22}{13}$ sec

$$t_2 = t_1 + 6 = \frac{22}{13} + 6 = \frac{100}{13} \text{ sec.}$$

(B) $5,000\left(\dfrac{22}{13}\right) \approx 8,462$ ft.

EXERCISE 4-2

2. 3×3; 2×1 **4.** D **6.** $b_{21} = -4$, $b_{13} = 0$

8. $c_{13} = 0$, $d_{21} = 8$ **10.** $2, -1$

12. (A) $F = \begin{bmatrix} 4 & -6 \\ 2 & 3 \\ -5 & 7 \end{bmatrix}$; size 3×2

(B) $E = \begin{bmatrix} 1 & -2 & 3 & 9 \\ -5 & 0 & 7 & -8 \end{bmatrix}$; size 2×4. E would have to have two more rows to be square.

(C) $e_{14} = 9$; $f_{31} = -5$

14. Multiply row 2 by $\frac{1}{2}$.

$\begin{bmatrix} 1 & -3 & | & 2 \\ 2 & -3 & | & -4 \end{bmatrix}$

16. Multiply row 1 by -2.

$\begin{bmatrix} -2 & 6 & | & -4 \\ 4 & -6 & | & -8 \end{bmatrix}$

18. Multiply row 2 by -1.

$\begin{bmatrix} 1 & -3 & | & 2 \\ -4 & 6 & | & 8 \end{bmatrix}$

20. Replace row 1 by the sum of row 1 and $-\frac{1}{2}$ times row 2.

$\begin{bmatrix} -1 & 0 & | & 6 \\ 4 & -6 & | & -8 \end{bmatrix}$

22. Replace row 2 by the sum of row 2 and -3 times row 1.

$\begin{bmatrix} 1 & -3 & | & 2 \\ 1 & 3 & | & -4 \end{bmatrix}$

24. Replace row 2 by the sum of row 2 and row 1.

$\begin{bmatrix} 1 & -3 & | & 2 \\ 5 & -9 & | & -6 \end{bmatrix}$

26. $\begin{bmatrix} -2 & 4 & | & -6 \\ 6 & -3 & | & 12 \end{bmatrix}$ $2R_1 \rightarrow R_1$

28. $\begin{bmatrix} 3 & 0 & | & 5 \\ 6 & -3 & | & 12 \end{bmatrix}$ $\frac{2}{3}R_2 + R_1 \rightarrow R_1$

30. $\begin{bmatrix} -1 & 2 & | & -3 \\ 2 & 5 & | & 0 \end{bmatrix}$ $4R_1 + R_2 \rightarrow R_2$

32. $\begin{bmatrix} -1 & 2 & | & -3 \\ 0 & 9 & | & -6 \end{bmatrix}$ $6R_1 + R_2 \rightarrow R_2$

34. $\begin{bmatrix} 3 & 0 & | & 5 \\ 6 & -3 & | & 12 \end{bmatrix}$ $\frac{2}{3}R_2 + R_1 \rightarrow R_1$

36. $\begin{bmatrix} 1 & -2 & | & 5 \\ -2 & 4 & | & -10 \end{bmatrix}$ $2R_1 + R_2 \rightarrow R_2$ $\begin{bmatrix} 1 & -2 & | & 5 \\ 0 & 0 & | & 0 \end{bmatrix}$

Thus, the system has infinitely many solutions (consistent and dependent). Let $x_2 = t$.

Then $x_1 - 2t = 5$ or $x_1 = 2t + 5$.

The set of solutions is $x_2 = t$, $x_1 = 2t + 5$ for any real number $t \approx \{(2t + 5, t) \mid t$ is any real number$\}$.

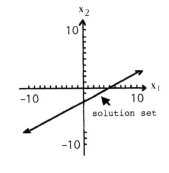

38. $\begin{bmatrix} 1 & -2 & | & 1 \\ -2 & 5 & | & 2 \end{bmatrix}$ $2R_1 + R_2 \rightarrow R_2$ $\begin{bmatrix} 1 & -2 & | & 1 \\ 0 & 1 & | & 4 \end{bmatrix}$ $2R_2 + R_1 \rightarrow R_1$ $\begin{bmatrix} 1 & 0 & | & 9 \\ 0 & 1 & | & 4 \end{bmatrix}$

Thus, $x_1 = 9$, $x_2 = 4$, and the solution set is $\{(9, 4)\}$ one single point in the two dimensional Cartesian Coordinate System.

40. System   Augmented matrix   Graphs:

$x_1 - x_2 = 2$

$x_1 + x_2 = 6$

$$\begin{bmatrix} 1 & -1 & | & 2 \\ 1 & 1 & | & 6 \end{bmatrix}$$

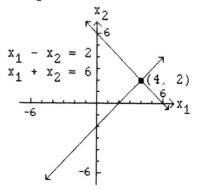

$$\begin{bmatrix} 1 & -1 & | & 2 \\ 1 & 1 & | & 6 \end{bmatrix} (-1)R_1 + R_2 \rightarrow R_2 \begin{bmatrix} 1 & -1 & | & 2 \\ 0 & 2 & | & 4 \end{bmatrix}$$

$x_1 - x_2 = 2$

$ 2x_2 = 4$

$$\begin{bmatrix} 1 & -1 & | & 2 \\ 1 & 1 & | & 6 \end{bmatrix} (-1)R_1 + R_2 \rightarrow R_2 \begin{bmatrix} 1 & -1 & | & 2 \\ 0 & 2 & | & 4 \end{bmatrix}$$

$$\frac{1}{2}R_2 \rightarrow R_2 \begin{bmatrix} 1 & -1 & | & 2 \\ 0 & 1 & | & 2 \end{bmatrix}$$

$x_1 - x_2 = 2$

$ x_2 = 2$

$$\begin{bmatrix} 1 & -1 & | & 2 \\ 1 & 1 & | & 6 \end{bmatrix} (-1)R_1 + R_2 \rightarrow R_2 \begin{bmatrix} 1 & -1 & | & 2 \\ 0 & 2 & | & 4 \end{bmatrix}$$

$$\frac{1}{2}R_2 \rightarrow R_2 \begin{bmatrix} 1 & -1 & | & 2 \\ 0 & 1 & | & 2 \end{bmatrix} R_1 + R_2 \rightarrow R_1$$

$x_1 = 4$ $\begin{bmatrix} 1 & 0 & | & 4 \\ 0 & 1 & | & 2 \end{bmatrix}$

$ x_2 = 2$

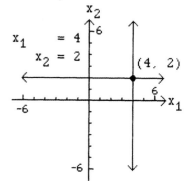

NOTE: Solution: $x_1 = 4$, $x_2 = 2$. Each pair of lines has the same intersection point.

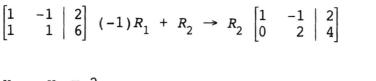

42. $\begin{bmatrix} 1 & 3 & | & 1 \\ 3 & -2 & | & 14 \end{bmatrix} \sim \begin{bmatrix} 1 & 3 & | & 1 \\ 0 & -11 & | & 11 \end{bmatrix} \sim \begin{bmatrix} 1 & 3 & | & 1 \\ 0 & 1 & | & -1 \end{bmatrix} \sim \begin{bmatrix} 1 & 0 & | & 4 \\ 0 & 1 & | & -1 \end{bmatrix}$ Thus, $x_1 = 4$ and $x_2 = -1$.

$(-3)R_1 + R_2 \rightarrow R_2 \left(-\dfrac{1}{11}\right)R_2 \rightarrow R_2 \ (-3)R_2 + R_1 \rightarrow R_1$

44. $\begin{bmatrix} 1 & -3 & | & -5 \\ -3 & -1 & | & 5 \end{bmatrix} \sim \begin{bmatrix} 1 & -3 & | & -5 \\ 0 & -10 & | & -10 \end{bmatrix} \sim \begin{bmatrix} 1 & -3 & | & -5 \\ 0 & 1 & | & 1 \end{bmatrix} \sim \begin{bmatrix} 1 & 0 & | & -2 \\ 0 & 1 & | & 1 \end{bmatrix}$ Thus, $x_1 = -2$ and $x_2 = -1$.

$\qquad 3R_1 + R_2 \to R_2 \qquad \left(-\dfrac{1}{10}\right) R_2 \to R_2 \qquad 3R_2 + R_1 \to R_1$

46. $\begin{bmatrix} 2 & 1 & | & 0 \\ 1 & -2 & | & 5 \end{bmatrix} \sim \begin{bmatrix} 1 & 3 & | & 5 \\ 1 & -2 & | & -5 \end{bmatrix} \sim \begin{bmatrix} 1 & 3 & | & 5 \\ 0 & -5 & | & -10 \end{bmatrix} \sim \begin{bmatrix} 1 & 3 & | & 5 \\ 0 & 1 & | & 2 \end{bmatrix} \sim \begin{bmatrix} 1 & 0 & | & -1 \\ 0 & 1 & | & 2 \end{bmatrix}$

$\qquad (-1)R_2 + R_1 \to R_1 \quad (-1)R_1 + R_2 \to R_2 \quad \left(-\dfrac{1}{5}\right) R_2 \to R_2 \quad (-3)R_2 + R_1 \to R_1$

Thus, $x_1 = -1$ and $x_2 = 2$.

---

48. $\begin{bmatrix} 2 & -3 & | & -2 \\ -4 & 6 & | & 7 \end{bmatrix} \sim \begin{bmatrix} 1 & -\dfrac{3}{2} & | & -1 \\ -4 & 6 & | & 7 \end{bmatrix} \sim \begin{bmatrix} 1 & -\dfrac{3}{2} & | & -1 \\ 0 & 0 & | & 3 \end{bmatrix}$

$\qquad \dfrac{1}{2} R_1 \to R_1 \qquad\qquad 4R_1 + R_2 \to R_2$

The system is inconsistent; there is no solution.

50. $\begin{bmatrix} 3 & -1 & | & -5 \\ 1 & 3 & | & 5 \end{bmatrix} \sim \begin{bmatrix} 1 & -\dfrac{1}{3} & | & -\dfrac{5}{3} \\ 1 & 3 & | & 5 \end{bmatrix} \sim \begin{bmatrix} 1 & -\dfrac{1}{3} & | & -\dfrac{5}{3} \\ 0 & \dfrac{10}{3} & | & \dfrac{20}{3} \end{bmatrix} \sim \begin{bmatrix} 1 & -\dfrac{1}{3} & | & -\dfrac{5}{3} \\ 0 & 1 & | & 2 \end{bmatrix}$

$\qquad \dfrac{1}{3} R_1 \to R_1 \qquad (-1)R_1 + R_2 \to R_2 \qquad \dfrac{3}{10} R_2 \to R_2 \qquad \dfrac{1}{3}R_2 + R_1 \to R_1$

$\sim \begin{bmatrix} 1 & 0 & | & -1 \\ 0 & 1 & | & 2 \end{bmatrix}$ Thus, $x_1 = -1$ and $x_2 = 2$

52. $\begin{bmatrix} 2 & -4 & | & -2 \\ -3 & 6 & | & 3 \end{bmatrix} \sim \begin{bmatrix} 1 & -2 & | & -1 \\ -3 & 6 & | & 3 \end{bmatrix} \sim \begin{bmatrix} 1 & -2 & | & -1 \\ 1 & -2 & | & -1 \end{bmatrix}$

$\qquad \dfrac{1}{2} R_1 \to R_1 \qquad\qquad \left(-\dfrac{1}{3}\right) R_2 \to R_2$

Thus, the system has infinitely many solutions (consistent and dependent). Let $x_2 = s$, then $x_1 - 2s = -1$ or $x_1 = 2s - 1$.
The set of solutions is $x_2 = s$, $x_1 = 2s - 1$, for any real number s.

54. $\begin{bmatrix} -6 & 2 & | & 4 \\ 3 & -1 & | & -2 \end{bmatrix} \sim \begin{bmatrix} 3 & -1 & | & -2 \\ 3 & -1 & | & -2 \end{bmatrix}$

$\qquad \left(-\dfrac{1}{2}\right) R_1 \to R_1$

Thus, the system has infinitely many solutions (consistent and dependent). Let $x_2 = s$. Then

$\qquad 3x_1 - s = -2 \quad$ or $\quad x_1 = \dfrac{1}{3} s - \dfrac{2}{3}$

The set of solutions is $x_2 = s$, $x_1 = \dfrac{1}{3} s - \dfrac{2}{3}$ for any real number s.

56. $\begin{bmatrix} 2 & -1 & | & -8 \\ 2 & 1 & | & 8 \end{bmatrix} \sim \begin{bmatrix} 1 & -\dfrac{1}{2} & | & -4 \\ 2 & 1 & | & 8 \end{bmatrix} \sim \begin{bmatrix} 1 & -\dfrac{1}{2} & | & -4 \\ 0 & 2 & | & 16 \end{bmatrix} \sim \begin{bmatrix} 1 & -\dfrac{1}{2} & | & -4 \\ 0 & 1 & | & 8 \end{bmatrix}$

$\qquad \left(\dfrac{1}{2}\right) R_1 \to R_1 \quad (-2)R_1 + R_2 \to R_2 \quad \dfrac{1}{2} R_2 \to R_2 \quad \dfrac{1}{2}R_2 + R_1 \to R_1$

$\sim \begin{bmatrix} 1 & 0 & | & 0 \\ 0 & 1 & | & 8 \end{bmatrix}$ Thus, $x_1 = 0$ and $x_2 = 8$

58. $\begin{bmatrix} 2 & -4 & | & -4 \\ -3 & 6 & | & 4 \end{bmatrix} \sim \begin{bmatrix} 1 & -2 & | & -2 \\ -3 & 6 & | & 4 \end{bmatrix} \sim \begin{bmatrix} 1 & -2 & | & -2 \\ 0 & 0 & | & -2 \end{bmatrix}$

$\quad \dfrac{1}{2}R_1 \to R_1 \qquad 3R_1 + R_2 \to R_2$

The second row of the final augmented matrix corresponds to
$0x_1 + 0x_2 = -2$

which has no solution. Thus, the system has no solution; it is inconsistent.

60. $\begin{bmatrix} -2 & 4 & | & 4 \\ 3 & -6 & | & -6 \end{bmatrix} \sim \begin{bmatrix} 1 & -2 & | & -2 \\ 3 & -6 & | & -6 \end{bmatrix} \sim \begin{bmatrix} 1 & -2 & | & -2 \\ 1 & -2 & | & -2 \end{bmatrix}$

$\quad \left(-\dfrac{1}{2}\right)R_1 \to R_1 \qquad \dfrac{1}{3}R_2 \to R_2$

The last augmented matrix implies $x_1 - 2x_2 = -2$. So there are infinitely many solutions. Let $x_2 = s$, then $x_1 = 2s - 2$. The set of solutions is $x_2 = s$, $x_1 = 2s - 2$ for any real number s.

62. $\begin{bmatrix} 2 & -3 & | & -8 \\ 5 & 3 & | & 1 \end{bmatrix} \sim \begin{bmatrix} 1 & -\frac{3}{2} & | & -4 \\ 5 & 3 & | & 1 \end{bmatrix} \sim \begin{bmatrix} 1 & -\frac{3}{2} & | & -4 \\ 0 & \frac{21}{2} & | & 21 \end{bmatrix} \sim \begin{bmatrix} 1 & -\frac{3}{2} & | & -4 \\ 0 & 1 & | & 2 \end{bmatrix} \sim \begin{bmatrix} 1 & 0 & | & -1 \\ 0 & 1 & | & 2 \end{bmatrix}$

$\quad \dfrac{1}{2}R_1 \to R_1 \qquad (-5)R_1 + R_2 \to R_1 \qquad \left(\dfrac{2}{21}\right)R_2 \to R_2 \qquad \left(\dfrac{3}{2}\right)R_2 + R_1 \to R_1$

Thus, $x_1 = -1$ and $x_2 = 2$.

64. $\begin{bmatrix} 4 & 3 & | & 26 \\ 3 & -11 & | & -7 \end{bmatrix} \sim \begin{bmatrix} 1 & \frac{3}{4} & | & \frac{13}{2} \\ 3 & -11 & | & -7 \end{bmatrix} \sim \begin{bmatrix} 1 & \frac{3}{4} & | & \frac{13}{2} \\ 0 & -\frac{53}{4} & | & -\frac{53}{2} \end{bmatrix} \sim \begin{bmatrix} 1 & \frac{3}{4} & | & \frac{13}{2} \\ 0 & 1 & | & 2 \end{bmatrix} \sim \begin{bmatrix} 1 & 0 & | & 5 \\ 0 & 1 & | & 2 \end{bmatrix}$

$\quad \dfrac{1}{4}R_1 \to R_1 \qquad (-3)R_1 + R_2 \to R_2 \qquad \left(-\dfrac{4}{53}\right)R_2 \to R_2 \qquad \left(-\dfrac{3}{4}\right)R_2 + R_1 \to R_1$

Thus, $x_1 = 5$ and $x_2 = 2$.

66. $\begin{bmatrix} 0.3 & -0.6 & | & 0.18 \\ 0.5 & -0.2 & | & 0.54 \end{bmatrix} \sim \begin{bmatrix} 1 & -2 & | & 0.6 \\ 0.5 & -0.2 & | & 0.54 \end{bmatrix} \sim \begin{bmatrix} 1 & -2 & | & 0.6 \\ 0 & 0.8 & | & 0.24 \end{bmatrix}$

$\quad \dfrac{1}{0.3}R_1 \to R_1 \qquad (-0.5)R_1 + R_2 \to R_2 \qquad \dfrac{1}{0.8}R_2 \to R_2$

$\sim \begin{bmatrix} 1 & -2 & | & 0.6 \\ 0 & 1 & | & 0.3 \end{bmatrix} \sim \begin{bmatrix} 1 & 0 & | & 1.2 \\ 0 & 1 & | & 0.3 \end{bmatrix}$ Thus, $x_1 = 1.2$ and $x_2 = 0.3$.

$\quad 2R_2 + R_1 \to R_1$

68. $\begin{bmatrix} 2.7 & -15.12 & | & 27 \\ 3.25 & -18.52 & | & 33 \end{bmatrix} \sim \begin{bmatrix} 1 & -5.6 & | & 10 \\ 3.25 & -18.52 & | & 33 \end{bmatrix} \sim \begin{bmatrix} 1 & -5.6 & | & 10 \\ 0 & -0.32 & | & 0.5 \end{bmatrix} \sim$

$\quad \left(\dfrac{1}{2.7}\right)R_1 \to R_1 \qquad (-3.25)R_1 + R_2 \to R_2 \qquad \left(-\dfrac{1}{0.32}\right)R_2 \to R_2$

$\begin{bmatrix} 1 & -5.6 & | & 10 \\ 0 & 1 & | & -1.5625 \end{bmatrix} \sim \begin{bmatrix} 1 & 0 & | & 1.25 \\ 0 & 1 & | & -1.5625 \end{bmatrix}$

$\quad 5.6R_2 + R_1 \to R_1$

Thus, $x_1 = 1.25$ and $x_2 = -1.5625$.

70. $\begin{bmatrix} 5.7 & -8.55 & | & -35.91 \\ 4.5 & 5.73 & | & 76.17 \end{bmatrix} \sim \begin{bmatrix} 1 & -1.5 & | & -6.3 \\ 4.5 & 5.73 & | & 76.17 \end{bmatrix} \sim \begin{bmatrix} 1 & -1.5 & | & -6.3 \\ 0 & 12.48 & | & 104.52 \end{bmatrix} \sim$

$\qquad \left(\dfrac{1}{5.7}\right)R_1 \rightarrow R_1 \qquad\qquad (-4.5)R_1 + R_2 \rightarrow R_2 \qquad\qquad \left(\dfrac{1}{12.48}\right)R_2 \rightarrow R_2$

$\begin{bmatrix} 1 & -1.5 & | & -6.3 \\ 0 & 1 & | & 8.375 \end{bmatrix} \sim \begin{bmatrix} 1 & 0 & | & 6.2625 \\ 0 & 1 & | & 8.375 \end{bmatrix}$

$(1.5)R_2 + R_1 \rightarrow R_1$

Thus, $x_1 = 6.2625$ and $x_2 = 8.375$.

EXERCISE 4-3

2. $\begin{bmatrix} 0 & 1 & | & 2 \\ 1 & 0 & | & -1 \end{bmatrix}$

is not in reduced form:
condition 2 is violated; the
first row should be at the
bottom.

$R_1 \leftrightarrow R_2$

4. $\begin{bmatrix} 1 & 0 & 0 & | & -2 \\ 0 & 1 & 0 & | & 0 \\ 0 & 0 & 1 & | & 1 \end{bmatrix}$

is in reduced form.

6. $\begin{bmatrix} 1 & 2 & -3 & | & 1 \\ 0 & 0 & 1 & | & 4 \\ 0 & 0 & 0 & | & 0 \end{bmatrix}$

is not in reduced form: The
column containing the left-most
1 in row 2 has a non-zero
element; condition 3 is
violated.

$3R_2 + R_1 \rightarrow R_1$

8. $\begin{bmatrix} 1 & 0 & -1 & | & 3 \\ 0 & 2 & 1 & | & 1 \\ 0 & 0 & 0 & | & 0 \end{bmatrix}$

is not in reduced form: the
first non-zero element in the
second row is not 1; condition
2 is violated.

$\dfrac{1}{2}R_2 \rightarrow R_2$

10. $\begin{bmatrix} 1 & -2 & 0 & 0 & | & 1 \\ 0 & 0 & 1 & 1 & | & 0 \end{bmatrix}$ is in reduced form.

12. $x_1 \qquad\qquad = -2$

$\qquad x_2 \qquad\quad = 0$

$\qquad\quad x_3 \qquad = 1$

$\qquad\qquad x_4 = 3$

Solution: $x_1 = -2$, $x_2 = 0$,

$x_3 = 1$, $x_4 = 3$

14. $x_1 - 2x_2 = -3 \quad (1)$

$\qquad\qquad x_3 = 5 \quad (2)$

Let $x_2 = t$. From (1), $x_1 = 2t - 3$.
Thus, the solution is

$x_1 = 2t - 3$

$x_2 = t$

$x_3 = 5$

t any real number.

16. $x_1 \quad = 5$
$\quad\quad x_2 = -3$
Solution: $x_1 = 5$, $x_2 = -3$.

18. $\begin{bmatrix} 1 & 0 & 1 & | & -4 \\ 0 & 1 & -1 & | & 6 \end{bmatrix}$ $\quad \begin{matrix} x_1 + x_3 = -4 \\ x_2 - x_3 = 6 \end{matrix}$ or $\begin{matrix} x_1 = -x_3 - 4 \\ x_2 = x_3 + 6 \end{matrix}$

If we let $x_3 = t$, then $x_1 = -t - 4$ and $x_2 = t + 6$.
Thus, $x_1 = -t - 4$
$\quad\quad\quad x_2 = t + 6$
$\quad\quad\quad x_3 = t$
t any real number.

20. $x_1 - \quad\quad 2x_3 + 3x_4 = 4 \quad (1)$
$\quad\quad x_2 - x_3 + 2x_4 = -1 \quad (2)$
Let $x_3 = s$ and $x_4 = t$. Then from (1), $x_1 = 2s - 3t + 4$, and from (2),
$x_2 = s - 2t - 1$. Thus, the solution is
$\quad\quad x_1 = 2s - 3t + 4$
$\quad\quad x_2 = s - 2t - 1$
$\quad\quad x_3 = s$
$\quad\quad x_4 = t$
s and t any real numbers.

24. $\begin{bmatrix} 1 & 3 & | & 1 \\ 0 & 2 & | & -4 \end{bmatrix} \sim \begin{bmatrix} 1 & 3 & | & 1 \\ 0 & 1 & | & -2 \end{bmatrix} \sim \begin{bmatrix} 1 & 0 & | & 7 \\ 0 & 1 & | & -2 \end{bmatrix}$

$\quad \frac{1}{2}R_2 \rightarrow R_2 \quad\quad (-3)R_2 + R_1 \rightarrow R_1$

26. $\begin{bmatrix} 1 & 1 & 1 & | & 8 \\ 3 & 5 & 7 & | & 30 \end{bmatrix} (-3)R_1 + R_2 \rightarrow R_2 \begin{bmatrix} 1 & 1 & 1 & | & 8 \\ 0 & 2 & 4 & | & 6 \end{bmatrix} \frac{1}{2}R_2 \rightarrow R_2$

$\begin{bmatrix} 1 & 1 & 1 & | & 8 \\ 0 & 1 & 2 & | & 3 \end{bmatrix} -R_2 + R_1 \rightarrow R_1 \begin{bmatrix} 1 & 0 & -1 & | & 5 \\ 0 & 1 & 2 & | & 3 \end{bmatrix}$

28. $\begin{bmatrix} 1 & 0 & 4 & | & 0 \\ 0 & 1 & -3 & | & -1 \\ 0 & 0 & -2 & | & 2 \end{bmatrix} \sim \begin{bmatrix} 1 & 0 & 4 & | & 0 \\ 0 & 1 & -3 & | & -1 \\ 0 & 0 & 1 & | & -1 \end{bmatrix} \sim \begin{bmatrix} 1 & 0 & 4 & | & 0 \\ 0 & 1 & 0 & | & -4 \\ 0 & 0 & 1 & | & -1 \end{bmatrix} \sim \begin{bmatrix} 1 & 0 & 0 & | & 4 \\ 0 & 1 & 0 & | & -4 \\ 0 & 0 & 1 & | & -1 \end{bmatrix}$

$\quad \left(-\frac{1}{2}\right)R_3 \rightarrow R_3 \quad\quad 3R_3 + R_2 \rightarrow R_2 \quad\quad (-4)R_3 + R_1 \rightarrow R_1$

30. $\begin{bmatrix} 0 & -2 & 8 & | & 1 \\ 2 & -2 & 6 & | & -4 \\ 0 & -1 & 4 & | & \frac{1}{2} \end{bmatrix} \sim \begin{bmatrix} 2 & -2 & 6 & | & -4 \\ 0 & -2 & 8 & | & 1 \\ 0 & -1 & 4 & | & \frac{1}{2} \end{bmatrix} \sim \begin{bmatrix} 1 & -1 & 3 & | & -2 \\ 0 & -2 & 8 & | & 1 \\ 0 & -1 & 4 & | & \frac{1}{2} \end{bmatrix} \sim \begin{bmatrix} 1 & -1 & 3 & | & -2 \\ 0 & 1 & -4 & | & -\frac{1}{2} \\ 0 & -1 & 4 & | & \frac{1}{2} \end{bmatrix}$

$\quad\quad R_1 \leftrightarrow R_2 \quad\quad\quad \frac{1}{2}R_1 \rightarrow R_1 \quad\quad\quad -\frac{1}{2}R_2 \rightarrow R_2 \quad\quad R_2 + R_3 \rightarrow R_3$

$\sim \begin{bmatrix} 1 & -1 & 3 & | & -2 \\ 0 & 1 & -4 & | & -\frac{1}{2} \\ 0 & 0 & 0 & | & 0 \end{bmatrix} \sim \begin{bmatrix} 1 & 0 & -1 & | & -\frac{5}{2} \\ 0 & 1 & -4 & | & -\frac{1}{2} \\ 0 & 0 & 0 & | & 0 \end{bmatrix}$

$\quad\quad R_2 + R_1 \rightarrow R_1$

32. The corresponding augmented matrix is:

$$\begin{bmatrix} 3 & 5 & -1 & | & -7 \\ 1 & 1 & 1 & | & -1 \\ 2 & 0 & 11 & | & 7 \end{bmatrix} \sim \begin{bmatrix} 1 & \frac{5}{3} & -\frac{1}{3} & | & -\frac{7}{3} \\ 1 & 1 & 1 & | & -1 \\ 0 & -2 & 9 & | & 9 \end{bmatrix} \sim \begin{bmatrix} 1 & \frac{5}{3} & -\frac{1}{3} & | & -\frac{7}{3} \\ 0 & -\frac{2}{3} & \frac{4}{3} & | & \frac{4}{3} \\ 0 & -2 & 9 & | & 9 \end{bmatrix} \sim \begin{bmatrix} 1 & \frac{5}{3} & -\frac{1}{3} & | & -\frac{7}{3} \\ 0 & 1 & -2 & | & -2 \\ 0 & -2 & 9 & | & 9 \end{bmatrix}$$

$$\left(\tfrac{1}{3}\right)R_1 \to R_1 \qquad (-1)R_1 + R_2 \to R_2 \qquad \left(-\tfrac{3}{2}\right)R_2 \to R_2 \qquad 2R_2 + R_3 \to R_3$$

$$(-2)R_2 + R_3 \to R_3$$

$$\sim \begin{bmatrix} 1 & \frac{5}{3} & -\frac{1}{3} & | & -\frac{7}{3} \\ 0 & 1 & -2 & | & -2 \\ 0 & 0 & 5 & | & 5 \end{bmatrix} \sim \begin{bmatrix} 1 & \frac{5}{3} & -\frac{1}{3} & | & -\frac{7}{3} \\ 0 & 1 & -2 & | & -2 \\ 0 & 0 & 1 & | & 1 \end{bmatrix} \sim \begin{bmatrix} 1 & \frac{5}{3} & -\frac{1}{3} & | & -\frac{7}{3} \\ 0 & 1 & 0 & | & 0 \\ 0 & 0 & 1 & | & 1 \end{bmatrix} \sim \begin{bmatrix} 1 & 0 & -\frac{1}{3} & | & -\frac{7}{3} \\ 0 & 1 & 0 & | & 0 \\ 0 & 0 & 1 & | & 1 \end{bmatrix}$$

$$\tfrac{1}{5}R_3 \to R_3 \qquad 2R_3 + R_2 \to R_2 \qquad \left(-\tfrac{5}{3}\right)R_2 + R_1 \to R_1 \qquad \tfrac{1}{3}R_3 + R_1 \to R_1$$

$$\sim \begin{bmatrix} 1 & 0 & 0 & | & -2 \\ 0 & 1 & 0 & | & 0 \\ 0 & 0 & 1 & | & 1 \end{bmatrix} \quad \text{Thus, } x_1 = -2,\ x_2 = 0,\ x_3 = 1.$$

34. The corresponding augmented matrix is:

$$\begin{bmatrix} 2 & 6 & 15 & | & -12 \\ 4 & 7 & 13 & | & -10 \\ 6 & 6 & 12 & | & -9 \end{bmatrix} \sim \begin{bmatrix} 1 & 3 & \frac{15}{2} & | & -6 \\ 4 & 7 & 13 & | & -10 \\ 3 & 6 & 12 & | & -9 \end{bmatrix} \sim \begin{bmatrix} 1 & 3 & \frac{15}{2} & | & -6 \\ 0 & -5 & -17 & | & 14 \\ 0 & -3 & -\frac{21}{2} & | & 9 \end{bmatrix} \sim \begin{bmatrix} 1 & 3 & \frac{15}{2} & | & -6 \\ 0 & 1 & \frac{17}{5} & | & -\frac{14}{5} \\ 0 & -3 & -\frac{21}{2} & | & 9 \end{bmatrix}$$

$$\tfrac{1}{2}R_1 \to R_1 \qquad (-4)R_1 + R_2 \to R_2 \qquad \left(-\tfrac{1}{5}\right)R_2 \to R_2 \qquad -3R_2 + R_1 \to R_1$$

$$(-3)R_1 + R_3 \to R_3 \qquad\qquad\qquad\qquad\qquad 3R_2 + R_3 \to R_3$$

$$\sim \begin{bmatrix} 1 & 0 & \frac{7}{10} & | & -\frac{2}{5} \\ 0 & 1 & \frac{17}{5} & | & -\frac{14}{5} \\ 0 & 0 & -\frac{3}{10} & | & \frac{3}{5} \end{bmatrix} \sim \begin{bmatrix} 1 & 0 & \frac{7}{10} & | & -\frac{2}{5} \\ 0 & 1 & \frac{17}{5} & | & -\frac{14}{5} \\ 0 & 0 & 1 & | & -2 \end{bmatrix} \sim \begin{bmatrix} 1 & 0 & 0 & | & 1 \\ 0 & 1 & 0 & | & 4 \\ 0 & 0 & 1 & | & -2 \end{bmatrix} \quad \begin{array}{l} \text{Thus, } x_1 = 1,\ x_2 = 4, \\ \qquad\quad x_3 = -2 \end{array}$$

$$\left(-\tfrac{10}{3}\right)R_3 \to R_3 \qquad \left(-\tfrac{17}{5}\right)R_3 + R_2 \to R_2$$

$$\left(-\tfrac{7}{10}\right)R_3 + R_1 \to R_1$$

36. $$\begin{bmatrix} 2 & 4 & -6 & | & 10 \\ 3 & 3 & -3 & | & 6 \end{bmatrix} \sim \begin{bmatrix} 1 & 2 & -3 & | & 5 \\ 1 & 1 & -1 & | & 2 \end{bmatrix} \sim \begin{bmatrix} 1 & 2 & -3 & | & 5 \\ 0 & -1 & 2 & | & -3 \end{bmatrix} \sim \begin{bmatrix} 1 & 2 & -3 & | & 5 \\ 0 & 1 & -2 & | & 3 \end{bmatrix}$$

$$\tfrac{1}{2}R_1 \to R_1 \qquad (-1)R_1 + R_2 \to R_2 \qquad (-1)R_2 \to R_2 \qquad (-2)R_2 + R_1 \to R_1$$

$$\tfrac{1}{3}R_3 \to R_3$$

$$\sim \begin{bmatrix} 1 & 0 & 1 & | & -1 \\ 0 & 1 & -2 & | & 3 \end{bmatrix} \quad \begin{array}{l} \text{Thus, } x_1 \ + x_3 = -1 \\ \qquad\quad x_2 - 2x_3 = \ \ 3 \end{array}$$

Let $x_3 = t$, then $x_1 = -t - 1$, $x_2 = 2t + 3$.

Solution: $x_1 = -t - 1;\ x_2 = 2t + 3;\ x_3 = t$ for any real number t.

38. $\begin{bmatrix} 2 & -1 & | & 0 \\ 3 & 2 & | & 7 \\ 1 & -1 & | & -2 \end{bmatrix} \sim \begin{bmatrix} 1 & -\frac{1}{2} & | & 0 \\ 3 & 2 & | & 7 \\ 1 & -1 & | & -2 \end{bmatrix} \sim \begin{bmatrix} 1 & -\frac{1}{2} & | & 0 \\ 3 & \frac{7}{2} & | & 7 \\ 1 & -\frac{1}{2} & | & -2 \end{bmatrix} \sim \begin{bmatrix} 1 & -\frac{1}{2} & | & 0 \\ 0 & 1 & | & 2 \\ 0 & -\frac{1}{2} & | & -2 \end{bmatrix} \sim \begin{bmatrix} 1 & 0 & | & -1 \\ 0 & 1 & | & 2 \\ 0 & 0 & | & -1 \end{bmatrix}$

$\frac{1}{2}R_1 \to R_1$ $\qquad$ $(-3)R_1 + R_2 \to R_2$ $\qquad$ $\left(\frac{2}{7}\right)R_2 \to R_2$ $\qquad$ $\frac{1}{2}R_2 + R_1 \to R_1$

$\qquad\qquad\qquad$ $(-1)R_1 + R_3 \to R_3$ $\qquad\qquad\qquad\qquad\qquad$ $\frac{1}{2}R_2 + R_3 \to R_3$

From the last row we conclude that there is no solution; the system is inconsistent.

40. $\begin{bmatrix} 3 & 7 & -1 & | & 11 \\ 1 & 2 & -1 & | & 3 \\ 2 & 4 & -2 & | & 10 \end{bmatrix} \sim \begin{bmatrix} 1 & \frac{7}{3} & -\frac{1}{3} & | & \frac{11}{3} \\ 1 & 2 & -1 & | & 3 \\ 2 & 4 & -2 & | & 10 \end{bmatrix} \sim \begin{bmatrix} 1 & \frac{7}{3} & -\frac{1}{3} & | & \frac{11}{3} \\ 0 & -\frac{1}{3} & -\frac{2}{3} & | & -\frac{2}{3} \\ 0 & -\frac{2}{3} & -\frac{4}{3} & | & \frac{8}{3} \end{bmatrix} \sim \begin{bmatrix} 1 & \frac{7}{3} & -\frac{1}{3} & | & \frac{11}{3} \\ 0 & 1 & 2 & | & 2 \\ 0 & -\frac{2}{3} & -\frac{4}{3} & | & \frac{8}{3} \end{bmatrix}$

$\frac{1}{3}R_1 \to R_1$ $\qquad$ $(-1)R_1 + R_2 \to R_2$ $\qquad$ $(-3)R_2 \to R_2$ $\qquad$ $\left(-\frac{7}{3}\right)R_2 + R_1 \to R_1$

$\qquad\qquad\qquad$ $(-2)R_1 + R_3 \to R_3$ $\qquad\qquad\qquad\qquad\qquad$ $\left(\frac{2}{3}\right)R_2 + R_3 \to R_3$

$\sim \begin{bmatrix} 1 & 0 & -5 & | & -1 \\ 0 & 1 & 2 & | & 2 \\ 0 & 0 & 0 & | & 4 \end{bmatrix}$ Thus, $0x_1 + 0x_2 + 0x_3 = 4$, which is not possible.

No solution.

42. $\begin{bmatrix} 2 & 3 & 5 & | & 21 \\ 1 & -1 & -5 & | & -2 \\ 2 & 1 & -1 & | & 11 \end{bmatrix} \sim \begin{bmatrix} 1 & 4 & 10 & | & 23 \\ 1 & -1 & -5 & | & -2 \\ 0 & 3 & 9 & | & 15 \end{bmatrix} \sim \begin{bmatrix} 1 & 4 & 10 & | & 23 \\ 0 & -5 & -15 & | & -25 \\ 0 & 3 & 9 & | & 15 \end{bmatrix}$

$-R_2 + R_1 \to R_1$ $\qquad\qquad$ $-R_1 + R_2 \to R_2$ $\qquad\qquad$ $\left(-\frac{1}{5}\right)R_2 \to R_2$
$(-2)R_2 + R_3 \to R_3$

$\sim \begin{bmatrix} 1 & 4 & 10 & | & 23 \\ 0 & 1 & 3 & | & 5 \\ 0 & 3 & 9 & | & 15 \end{bmatrix} \sim \begin{bmatrix} 1 & 0 & -2 & | & 3 \\ 0 & 1 & 3 & | & 5 \\ 0 & 0 & 0 & | & 0 \end{bmatrix}$ Thus, $x_1 - 2x_3 = 3$
$\qquad\qquad\qquad\qquad\qquad\qquad\qquad\qquad\qquad\qquad x_2 + 3x_3 = 5$

$(-4)R_2 + R_1 \to R_1$
$(-3)R_2 + R_3 \to R_3$

The system has infinitely many solutions. Let $x_3 = t$, then
$x_1 = 2t + 3$ and $x_2 = -3t + 5$.
Solution: $x_1 = 2t + 3$; $x_2 = -3t + 5$; $x_3 = t$ for t any real number.

44. $\begin{bmatrix} 3 & -9 & 12 & | & 6 \\ -2 & 6 & -8 & | & -4 \end{bmatrix} \sim \begin{bmatrix} 1 & -3 & 4 & | & 2 \\ -2 & 6 & -8 & | & -4 \end{bmatrix} \sim \begin{bmatrix} 1 & -3 & 4 & | & 2 \\ 0 & 0 & 0 & | & 0 \end{bmatrix}$

$\frac{1}{3}R_1 \to R_1$ $\qquad\qquad$ $2R_1 + R_2 \to R_2$

Thus, $x_1 - 3x_2 + 4x_3 = 2$ and the system has infinitely many solutions.
Let $x_2 = t$, $x_3 = s$, then $x_1 = 3t - 4s + 2$.
Solution: $x_1 = 3t - 4s + 2$; $x_2 = t$; $x_3 = s$ for t, s any real numbers.

46. $\begin{bmatrix} 4 & -2 & 2 & | & 5 \\ -6 & 3 & -3 & | & -2 \\ 10 & -5 & 9 & | & 4 \end{bmatrix} \sim \begin{bmatrix} 1 & -\frac{1}{2} & \frac{1}{2} & | & \frac{5}{4} \\ -6 & 3 & -3 & | & -2 \\ 10 & -5 & 9 & | & 4 \end{bmatrix} \sim \begin{bmatrix} 1 & -\frac{1}{2} & \frac{1}{2} & | & \frac{5}{4} \\ 0 & 0 & 0 & | & 13 \\ 10 & -5 & 9 & | & 4 \end{bmatrix}$

$\qquad \frac{1}{4}R_1 \to R_1 \qquad\qquad 6R_1 + R_2 \to R_2$

No solution since $0x_1 + 0x_2 + 0x_3 = 13$ is impossible.

48. $\begin{bmatrix} -4 & 8 & 10 & | & -6 \\ 6 & -12 & -15 & | & 9 \\ -8 & 14 & 19 & | & -8 \end{bmatrix} \sim \begin{bmatrix} 1 & -2 & -\frac{5}{2} & | & \frac{3}{2} \\ 6 & -12 & -15 & | & 9 \\ -8 & 14 & 19 & | & -8 \end{bmatrix} \sim \begin{bmatrix} 1 & -2 & -\frac{5}{2} & | & \frac{3}{2} \\ 0 & 0 & 0 & | & 0 \\ 0 & -2 & -1 & | & 4 \end{bmatrix}$

$\left(-\frac{1}{4}\right)R_1 \to R_1 \qquad\qquad (-6)R_1 + R_2 \to R_2$

$\qquad\qquad\qquad\qquad\qquad\quad 8R_1 + R_3 \to R_3$

Thus, $x_1 - 2x_2 - \frac{5}{2}x_3 = \frac{3}{2}$ and $-2x_2 - x_3 = 4$. Let $x_2 = t$, then

$x_3 = -2t + 4$ and $x_1 = 2t + \frac{5}{2}(-2t + 4) + \frac{3}{2} = -3t + \frac{23}{2}$.

Solution: $x_1 = -3t + \frac{23}{2}$; $x_2 = t$; $x_3 = -2t + 4$ for t any real numbers.

Note: if we let $x_3 = t$, then $x_1 = 1.5t - 2.5$; $x_2 = -0.5t - 2$.

50. $\begin{bmatrix} 4 & -2 & 3 & | & 3 \\ 3 & -1 & -2 & | & -10 \\ 2 & 4 & -1 & | & -1 \end{bmatrix} \sim \begin{bmatrix} 1 & -\frac{1}{2} & \frac{3}{4} & | & \frac{3}{4} \\ 3 & -1 & -2 & | & -10 \\ 2 & 4 & -1 & | & -1 \end{bmatrix} \sim \begin{bmatrix} 1 & -\frac{1}{2} & \frac{3}{4} & | & \frac{3}{4} \\ 0 & \frac{1}{2} & -\frac{17}{4} & | & -\frac{49}{4} \\ 0 & 5 & -\frac{5}{2} & | & -\frac{5}{2} \end{bmatrix}$

$\qquad \frac{1}{4}R_1 \to R_1 \qquad\qquad (-3)R_1 + R_2 \to R_2 \qquad\qquad 2R_2 \to R_2$

$\qquad\qquad\qquad\qquad\qquad\quad (-2)R_1 + R_3 \to R_3$

$\sim \begin{bmatrix} 1 & -\frac{1}{2} & \frac{3}{4} & | & \frac{3}{4} \\ 0 & 1 & -\frac{17}{2} & | & -\frac{49}{2} \\ 0 & 5 & -\frac{5}{2} & | & -\frac{5}{2} \end{bmatrix} \sim \begin{bmatrix} 1 & 0 & -\frac{7}{2} & | & -\frac{23}{2} \\ 0 & 1 & -\frac{17}{2} & | & -\frac{49}{2} \\ 0 & 5 & 40 & | & 120 \end{bmatrix}$

$\qquad \frac{1}{2}R_2 + R_1 \to R_1 \qquad\qquad \frac{1}{40}R_3 \to R_3$

$(-5)R_2 + R_3 \to R_3$

$\sim \begin{bmatrix} 1 & 0 & -\frac{7}{2} & | & -\frac{23}{2} \\ 0 & 1 & -\frac{17}{2} & | & -\frac{49}{2} \\ 0 & 0 & 1 & | & 3 \end{bmatrix} \sim \begin{bmatrix} 1 & 0 & 0 & | & -1 \\ 0 & 1 & 0 & | & 1 \\ 0 & 0 & 1 & | & 3 \end{bmatrix}$ Thus, $x_1 = -1$
$\qquad\qquad\qquad\qquad\qquad\qquad\qquad\qquad\qquad\qquad\qquad\qquad\qquad\qquad\quad x_2 = 1$
$\qquad\qquad\qquad\qquad\qquad\qquad\qquad\qquad\qquad\qquad\qquad\qquad\qquad\qquad\quad x_3 = 3$

$\frac{7}{2}R_3 + R_1 \to R_1$

$\frac{17}{2}R_3 + R_2 \to R_2$

52. (A) $\begin{bmatrix} 1 & 0 & m & | & a \\ 0 & 1 & n & | & b \\ 0 & 0 & 0 & | & 0 \end{bmatrix}$, $\begin{bmatrix} 1 & m & 0 & | & a \\ 0 & 1 & 1 & | & b \\ 0 & 0 & 0 & | & 0 \end{bmatrix}$, $\begin{bmatrix} 1 & m & n & | & a \\ 0 & 0 & 0 & | & 0 \\ 0 & 0 & 0 & | & 0 \end{bmatrix}$

(B) $\begin{bmatrix} 1 & 0 & m & | & 0 \\ 0 & 1 & n & | & 0 \\ 0 & 0 & 0 & | & 1 \end{bmatrix}$, $\begin{bmatrix} 1 & m & n & | & 0 \\ 0 & 0 & 0 & | & 1 \\ 0 & 0 & 0 & | & 0 \end{bmatrix}$, $\begin{bmatrix} 1 & m & 0 & | & 0 \\ 0 & 0 & 1 & | & 0 \\ 0 & 0 & 0 & | & 1 \end{bmatrix}$

54. $x_1 + 2x_2 = 4$

$-2x_1 + kx_2 = -8$

If $k = -4$, then these two equations will be identical, and hence the system has an infinite number of solutions. For $k \neq -4$, the system has a unique solution.

56. $x_1 + kx_2 = 3$

$2x_1 + 4x_2 = 8$

If $k = 2$, then $\begin{bmatrix} 1 & 2 & | & 3 \\ 2 & 4 & | & 8 \end{bmatrix} \sim \begin{bmatrix} 1 & 2 & | & 3 \\ 0 & 0 & | & 2 \end{bmatrix}$.

$$-2R_1 + R_2 \to R_2$$

Thus, $0x_1 + 0x_2 = 2$ which is impossible, so the system has no solution for $k = 2$. If $k \neq 2$, the system has a unique solution.

58. $\begin{bmatrix} 2 & 4 & 5 & 4 & | & 8 \\ 1 & 2 & 2 & 1 & | & 3 \end{bmatrix} \sim \begin{bmatrix} 1 & 2 & 3 & 3 & | & 5 \\ 1 & 2 & 2 & 1 & | & 3 \end{bmatrix} \sim \begin{bmatrix} 1 & 2 & 3 & 3 & | & 5 \\ 0 & 0 & -1 & -2 & | & -2 \end{bmatrix}$

$\quad (-1)R_2 + R_1 \to R_1 \qquad (-1)R_1 + R_2 \to R_2 \qquad\quad 3R_2 + R_1 \to R_1$

$\sim \begin{bmatrix} 1 & 2 & 0 & -3 & | & -1 \\ 0 & 0 & -1 & -2 & | & -2 \end{bmatrix} \sim \begin{bmatrix} 1 & 2 & 0 & -3 & | & -1 \\ 0 & 0 & 1 & 2 & | & 2 \end{bmatrix}$ Thus, $x_1 + 2x_2 - 3x_3 = -1$

$\qquad (-1)R_2 \to R_2$ $\hspace{4.5cm} x_3 + 2x_4 = 2$

Let $x_2 = t$, $x_4 = s$, then $x_3 = -2s + 2$ and $x_1 = -2t + 3s - 1$.
Solution: $x_1 = -2t + 3s - 1$; $x_2 = t$; $x_3 = -2s + 2$; $x_4 = s$ for t, s any real numbers.

60. $\begin{bmatrix} 1 & 1 & 4 & 1 & | & 1.3 \\ -1 & 1 & -1 & 0 & | & 1.1 \\ 2 & 0 & 1 & 3 & | & -4.4 \\ 2 & 5 & 11 & 3 & | & 5.6 \end{bmatrix} \sim \begin{bmatrix} 1 & 1 & 4 & 1 & | & 1.3 \\ 0 & 2 & 3 & 1 & | & 2.4 \\ 0 & -2 & -7 & 1 & | & -7 \\ 0 & 3 & 3 & 1 & | & 3 \end{bmatrix} \sim \begin{bmatrix} 1 & 1 & 4 & 1 & | & 1.3 \\ 0 & 1 & \frac{3}{2} & \frac{1}{2} & | & 1.2 \\ 0 & -2 & -7 & 1 & | & -7 \\ 0 & 3 & 3 & 1 & | & 3 \end{bmatrix}$

$\qquad\quad R_1 + R_2 \to R_2 \qquad\qquad\qquad \frac{1}{2}R_2 \to R_2 \qquad\qquad\qquad (-1)R_2 + R_1 \to R_1$

$\qquad (-2)R_1 + R_3 \to R_3 \hspace{7cm} 2R_2 + R_3 \to R_3$

$\qquad (-2)R_1 + R_4 \to R_4 \hspace{6.8cm} (-3)R_2 + R_4 \to R_4$

$$\sim \begin{bmatrix} 1 & 0 & \frac{5}{2} & \frac{1}{2} & \Big| & 0.1 \\ 0 & 1 & \frac{3}{2} & \frac{1}{2} & \Big| & 1.2 \\ 0 & 0 & -4 & 2 & \Big| & -4.6 \\ 0 & 0 & -\frac{3}{2} & -\frac{1}{2} & \Big| & -0.6 \end{bmatrix} \sim \begin{bmatrix} 1 & 0 & \frac{5}{2} & \frac{1}{2} & \Big| & 0.1 \\ 0 & 1 & \frac{3}{2} & \frac{1}{2} & \Big| & 1.2 \\ 0 & 0 & 1 & -\frac{1}{2} & \Big| & 1.15 \\ 0 & 0 & -\frac{3}{2} & -\frac{1}{2} & \Big| & -0.6 \end{bmatrix} \sim \begin{bmatrix} 1 & 0 & 0 & \frac{7}{4} & \Big| & -2.775 \\ 0 & 1 & 0 & \frac{5}{4} & \Big| & -0.525 \\ 0 & 0 & 1 & -\frac{1}{2} & \Big| & 1.15 \\ 0 & 0 & 0 & -\frac{5}{4} & \Big| & 1.125 \end{bmatrix}$$

$$\left(-\frac{1}{4}\right) R_3 \to R_3 \qquad\qquad \left(-\frac{5}{2}\right) R_3 + R_1 \to R_1 \qquad\qquad \left(-\frac{4}{5}\right) R_4 \to R_4$$

$$\left(-\frac{3}{2}\right) R_3 + R_2 \to R_2$$

$$\left(\frac{3}{2}\right) R_3 + R_4 \to R_4$$

$$\begin{bmatrix} 1 & 0 & 0 & \frac{9}{4} & \Big| & -2.775 \\ 0 & 1 & 0 & \frac{5}{4} & \Big| & -0.525 \\ 0 & 0 & 1 & -\frac{1}{2} & \Big| & 1.15 \\ 0 & 0 & 0 & 1 & \Big| & -0.9 \end{bmatrix} \sim \begin{bmatrix} 1 & 0 & 0 & 0 & \Big| & -1.2 \\ 0 & 1 & 0 & 0 & \Big| & 0.6 \\ 0 & 0 & 1 & 0 & \Big| & 0.7 \\ 0 & 0 & 0 & 1 & \Big| & -0.9 \end{bmatrix}$$

Thus, $x_1 = -1.2$
$x_2 = 0.6$
$x_3 = 0.7$
$x_4 = -0.9$

$$\left(-\frac{9}{4}\right) R_4 + R_1 \to R_1$$

$$\left(-\frac{5}{4}\right) R_4 + R_2 \to R_2$$

$$\left(\frac{1}{2}\right) R_4 + R_3 \to R_3$$

62. $\begin{bmatrix} 1 & -3 & 1 & 1 & 2 & \Big| & 2 \\ -1 & 5 & 2 & 2 & -2 & \Big| & 0 \\ 2 & -6 & 2 & 2 & 4 & \Big| & 4 \\ -1 & 3 & -1 & 0 & 1 & \Big| & -3 \end{bmatrix} \sim \begin{bmatrix} 1 & -3 & 1 & 1 & 2 & \Big| & 2 \\ 0 & 2 & 3 & 3 & 0 & \Big| & 2 \\ 0 & 0 & 0 & 0 & 0 & \Big| & 0 \\ 0 & 0 & 0 & 1 & 3 & \Big| & -1 \end{bmatrix}$

$$R_1 + R_2 \to R_2 \qquad\qquad \frac{1}{2} R_2 \to R_2$$
$$(-2) R_1 + R_3 \to R_3$$
$$R_1 + R_4 \to R_4$$

$$\sim \begin{bmatrix} 1 & -3 & 1 & 1 & 2 & \Big| & 2 \\ 0 & 1 & \frac{3}{2} & \frac{3}{2} & 0 & \Big| & 1 \\ 0 & 0 & 0 & 0 & 0 & \Big| & 0 \\ 0 & 0 & 0 & 1 & 1 & \Big| & -1 \end{bmatrix} \sim \begin{bmatrix} 1 & 0 & \frac{4}{2} & \frac{4}{2} & 2 & \Big| & 5 \\ 0 & 1 & \frac{3}{2} & \frac{3}{2} & 0 & \Big| & 1 \\ 0 & 0 & 0 & 0 & 0 & \Big| & 0 \\ 0 & 0 & 0 & 1 & 3 & \Big| & -1 \end{bmatrix} \sim \begin{bmatrix} 1 & 0 & \frac{11}{2} & \frac{11}{2} & 2 & \Big| & 5 \\ 0 & 1 & \frac{3}{2} & \frac{3}{2} & 0 & \Big| & 1 \\ 0 & 0 & 0 & 1 & 3 & \Big| & -1 \\ 0 & 0 & 0 & 0 & 0 & \Big| & 0 \end{bmatrix}$$

$$3R_2 + R_1 \to R_1 \qquad\qquad R_3 \leftrightarrow R_4 \qquad\qquad \left(-\frac{11}{2}\right) R_3 + R_1 \to R_1$$

$$\left(-\frac{3}{2}\right) R_3 + R_2 \to R_2$$

$$\sim \begin{bmatrix} 1 & 0 & \frac{11}{2} & 0 & -\frac{29}{2} & \Big| & \frac{21}{2} \\ 0 & 1 & \frac{3}{2} & 0 & -\frac{9}{2} & \Big| & \frac{5}{2} \\ 0 & 0 & 0 & 1 & 3 & \Big| & -1 \\ 0 & 0 & 0 & 0 & 0 & \Big| & 0 \end{bmatrix}$$

Thus, the system has an infinite number of solutions;

$$x_1 \quad\quad + 5.5x_3 \quad\quad - 14.5x_5 = 10.5$$
$$x_2 + 1.5x_3 \quad\quad - 4.5x_5 = 2.5$$
$$x_4 + 3x_5 = -1$$

Let $x_5 = t$, $x_3 = s$, then

$$x_1 = -5.5s + 14.5t + 10.5$$
$$x_2 = -1.5s + 4.5t + 2.5$$
$$x_3 = s$$
$$x_4 = -3t - 1$$
$$x_5 = t \text{ for } t \text{ and } s \text{ any real numbers.}$$

64. $y = ax^2 + bx + c$

For $(-1, -5)$: $-5 = a(-1)^2 + b(-1) + c = a - b + c$ \quad (1)

For $(2, 7)$: \quad $7 = a(2)^2 + b(2) + c = 4a + 2b + c$ \quad (2)

For $(5, 1)$: \quad $1 = a(5)^2 + b(5) + c = 25a + 5b + c$ \quad (3)

Subtract (1) from (2): $12 = 3a + 3b$ \quad or \quad $a + b = 4$

Subtract (2) from (3): $-6 = 21a + 3b$ \quad or \quad $7a + b = -2$

$$\begin{cases} a + b = 4 & (4) \\ 7a + b = -2 & (5) \end{cases}$$

Subtract (4) from (5): $6a = -6$ or $a = -1$ and then from (4) we have $-1 + b = 4$ or $b = 5$. Now from (1) we have $-5 = -1 - 5 + C$ or $C = 1$.

So the desired quadratic equation is:

$$y = -x^2 + 5x + 1$$

66. Let x_1 = Number of one-person boats

x_2 = Number of two-person boats

x_3 = Number of four-person boats

(A) The mathematical model is:

$$0.5x_1 + \quad x_2 + 1.5x_3 = 350$$
$$0.6x_1 + 0.9x_2 + 1.2x_3 = 330$$
$$0.2x_1 + 0.3x_2 + 0.5x_3 = 115$$

$$\begin{bmatrix} 0.5 & 1 & 1.5 & | & 350 \\ 0.6 & 0.9 & 1.2 & | & 330 \\ 0.2 & 0.3 & 0.5 & | & 115 \end{bmatrix} \sim \begin{bmatrix} 1 & 2 & 3 & | & 700 \\ 0.6 & 0.9 & 1.2 & | & 330 \\ 0.2 & 0.3 & 0.5 & | & 115 \end{bmatrix} \sim \begin{bmatrix} 1 & 2 & 3 & | & 700 \\ 0 & -0.3 & -0.6 & | & -90 \\ 0 & -0.1 & -0.1 & | & -25 \end{bmatrix}$$

$2R_1 \rightarrow R_1$ \qquad\qquad $(-0.6)R_1 + R_2 \rightarrow R_2$ \qquad\qquad $\left(-\dfrac{1}{0.3}\right)R_2 \rightarrow R_2$

\qquad\qquad\qquad\qquad\qquad $(-0.2)R_1 + R_3 \rightarrow R_3$

$$\sim \begin{bmatrix} 1 & 2 & 3 & | & 700 \\ 0 & 1 & 2 & | & 300 \\ 0 & -0.1 & -0.1 & | & -25 \end{bmatrix} \sim \begin{bmatrix} 1 & 0 & -1 & | & 100 \\ 0 & 1 & 2 & | & 300 \\ 0 & 0 & 0.1 & | & 5 \end{bmatrix} \sim \begin{bmatrix} 1 & 0 & -1 & | & 100 \\ 0 & 1 & 2 & | & 300 \\ 0 & 0 & 1 & | & 50 \end{bmatrix}$$

$(0.1)R_2 + R_3 \rightarrow R_3$ \qquad\qquad $10R_3 \rightarrow R_3$ \qquad\qquad $R_3 + R_1 \rightarrow R_1$

$(-2)R_2 + R_1 \rightarrow R_1$ \qquad\qquad\qquad\qquad\qquad $(-2)R_3 + R_2 \rightarrow R_2$

$$\sim \begin{bmatrix} 1 & 0 & 0 & | & 150 \\ 0 & 1 & 0 & | & 200 \\ 0 & 0 & 1 & | & 50 \end{bmatrix}$$

Thus, $x_1 = 150$ one-person boats

$x_2 = 200$ two-person boats

$x_3 = 50$ four-person boats

(B) $\quad 0.5x_1 + \quad x_2 + 1.5x_3 = 350$

$\quad 0.6x_1 + 0.9x_2 + 1.2x_3 = 330$

The corresponding augmented matrix is:

$$\begin{bmatrix} 0.5 & 1 & 1.5 & | & 350 \\ 0.6 & 0.9 & 1.2 & | & 330 \end{bmatrix} \sim \begin{bmatrix} 1 & 2 & 3 & | & 700 \\ 0.6 & 0.9 & 1.2 & | & 330 \end{bmatrix} \sim \begin{bmatrix} 1 & 2 & 3 & | & 700 \\ 0 & -0.3 & -0.6 & | & -90 \end{bmatrix}$$

$\qquad 2R_1 \rightarrow R_1 \qquad\qquad (-0.6)R_1 + R_2 \rightarrow R_2 \qquad \left(-\dfrac{1}{0.3}\right)R_2 \rightarrow R_2$

$$\sim \begin{bmatrix} 1 & 2 & 3 & | & 700 \\ 0 & 1 & 2 & | & 300 \end{bmatrix} \sim \begin{bmatrix} 1 & 0 & -1 & | & 100 \\ 0 & 1 & 2 & | & 300 \end{bmatrix}$$

Thus, $x_1 - x_3 = 100$

$x_2 + 2x_3 = 300$

$\qquad (-2)R_2 + R_1 \rightarrow R_1$

Let $x_3 = t$. Then $x_1 = t + 100$ one-person boats, $x_2 = (300 - 2t)$ two-person boats, and $x_3 = t$ four-person boats where t is an integer satisfying $0 \leq x \leq 150$.

(C) $\quad 0.5x_1 + \quad x_2 = 350$

$\quad 0.6x_1 + 0.9x_2 = 330$

$\quad 0.2x_1 + 0.3x_2 = 115$

The corresponding augmented matrix is:

$$\begin{bmatrix} 0.5 & 1 & | & 350 \\ 0.6 & 0.9 & | & 330 \\ 0.2 & 0.3 & | & 115 \end{bmatrix} \sim \begin{bmatrix} 1 & 2 & | & 700 \\ 0.6 & 0.9 & | & 330 \\ 0.2 & 0.3 & | & 115 \end{bmatrix} \sim \begin{bmatrix} 1 & 2 & | & 700 \\ 0 & -0.3 & | & -90 \\ 0 & -0.1 & | & -25 \end{bmatrix} \sim \begin{bmatrix} 1 & 2 & | & 700 \\ 0 & 1 & | & 300 \\ 0 & -0.1 & | & -25 \end{bmatrix}$$

$2R_1 \rightarrow R_1 \qquad\qquad (-0.6)R_1 + R_2 \rightarrow R_2 \qquad \left(-\dfrac{1}{0.3}\right)R_2 \rightarrow R_2 \qquad -10R_3 \rightarrow R_3$

$\qquad\qquad\qquad\qquad (-0.2)R_1 + R_3 \rightarrow R_3$

$$\sim \begin{bmatrix} 1 & 2 & | & 700 \\ 0 & 1 & | & 300 \\ 0 & 1 & | & 250 \end{bmatrix} \sim \begin{bmatrix} 1 & 0 & | & 100 \\ 0 & 1 & | & 300 \\ 0 & 0 & | & -50 \end{bmatrix}$$ Inconsistent; no solution

$(-2)R_2 + R_1 \rightarrow R_1$

$(-1)R_2 + R_3 \rightarrow R_3$

Thus, there is no production schedule that will use all the labor-hours in all departments.

68. Let x_1 = number of 10-passenger planes

x_2 = number of 15-passenger planes

x_3 = number of 20-passenger planes

Then, the mathematical model is:

$\quad x_1 + \quad x_2 + \quad x_3 = 12$

$10x_1 + 15x_2 + 20x_3 = 220$

Divide the second equation by 5 to get the following system:

$\quad x_1 + \quad x_2 + \quad x_3 = 12$

$\quad 2x_1 + 3x_2 + 4x_3 = 44$

The augmented matrix corresponding to this system is:

$$\begin{bmatrix} 1 & 1 & 1 & | & 12 \\ 2 & 3 & 4 & | & 44 \end{bmatrix} \sim \begin{bmatrix} 1 & 1 & 1 & | & 12 \\ 0 & 1 & 2 & | & 20 \end{bmatrix} \sim \begin{bmatrix} 1 & 0 & -1 & | & -8 \\ 0 & 1 & 2 & | & 20 \end{bmatrix}$$

$(-2)R_1 + R_2 \to R_2 \quad (-1)R_2 + R_1 \to R_1$

Thus, $x_1 - x_3 = -8$, $x_2 + 2x_3 = 20$

Let $x_3 = t$. Then $x_1 = t - 8$ and $x_2 = -2t + 20$.
For $t = 8$, 9, or 10, $(t - 8)$ 10-passenger planes, $(20 - 2t)$ 15-passenger planes, and t 20-passenger planes can be purchased.

70. Let $C = 8,000x_1 + 14,000x_2 + 16,000x_3$. Then
for $x_1 = 0$, $x_2 = 4$, $x_3 = 8$, $C = \$184,000$;
for $x_1 = 1$, $x_2 = 2$, $x_3 = 9$, $C = \$180,000$;
for $x_1 = 2$, $x_2 = 0$, $x_3 = 10$, $C = \$176,000$.

Thus, the minimum monthly cost is $176,000 when 2 10-passenger and 10 20-passenger planes are leased.

72. Let x_1 = Federal income tax
x_2 = State income tax
x_3 = Local income tax

Then the mathematical model is:
$$x_1 + 0.5x_2 \qquad = 3,825,000$$
$$0.2x_1 + \quad x_2 \qquad = 1,530,000$$
$$0.1x_1 + 0.1x_2 + x_3 = \quad 765,000$$

The corresponding augmented matrix is:

$$\begin{bmatrix} 1 & 0.5 & 0 & | & 3,825,000 \\ 0.2 & 1 & 0 & | & 1,530,000 \\ 0.1 & 0.1 & 1 & | & 765,000 \end{bmatrix} \sim \begin{bmatrix} 1 & 0.5 & 0 & | & 3,825,000 \\ 0 & 0.9 & 0 & | & 765,000 \\ 0 & 0.05 & 1 & | & 382,000 \end{bmatrix} \sim$$

$\quad (-0.2)R_1 + R_2 \to R_2 \qquad\qquad 20R_3 \to R_3$

$\quad (-0.1)R_1 + R_3 \to R_3$

$$\begin{bmatrix} 1 & 0.5 & 0 & | & 3,825,000 \\ 0 & 0.9 & 0 & | & 765,000 \\ 0 & 1 & 20 & | & 7,650,000 \end{bmatrix} \sim \begin{bmatrix} 1 & 0.5 & 0 & | & 3,825,000 \\ 0 & 1 & 20 & | & 7,650,000 \\ 0 & 0.9 & 0 & | & 765,000 \end{bmatrix} \sim$$

$\qquad R_2 \leftrightarrow R_3 \qquad\qquad\qquad (-0.5)R_2 + R_1 \to R_1$

$\qquad\qquad\qquad\qquad\qquad\qquad (-0.9)R_2 + R_3 \to R_3$

$$\begin{bmatrix} 1 & 0 & -10 & | & 0 \\ 0 & 1 & 20 & | & 7,650,000 \\ 0 & 0 & -18 & | & -6,120,000 \end{bmatrix} \sim \begin{bmatrix} 1 & 0 & -10 & | & 0 \\ 0 & 1 & 20 & | & 7,650,000 \\ 0 & 0 & 1 & | & 340,000 \end{bmatrix} \sim$$

$\quad \left(-\dfrac{1}{18}\right)R_3 \to R_3 \qquad\qquad 10R_3 + R_1 \to R_1$

$\qquad\qquad\qquad\qquad\qquad (-20)R_3 + R_2 \to R_2$

$$\begin{bmatrix} 1 & 0 & 0 & | & 3,400,000 \\ 0 & 1 & 0 & | & 850,000 \\ 0 & 0 & 1 & | & 340,000 \end{bmatrix}$$

Thus, $x_1 = \$3,400,000$ (Federal income tax)
$x_2 = \quad\$850,000$ (State income tax)
and $x_3 = \quad\$340,000$ (Local income tax)

The total tax liability is $x_1 + x_2 + x_3 = \$4,590,000$ which is 60% of the taxable income $\left(\dfrac{4,590,000}{7,650,000} = 0.6 \text{ or } 60\%\right)$.

74. Let x_1 = taxable income of company A
x_2 = taxable income of company B
x_3 = taxable income of company C
x_4 = taxable income of company D
The taxable income of each company is given by the system of equations:

$$x_1 - 0.08x_2 - 0.03x_3 - 0.07x_4 = 3.2$$
$$-0.12x_1 + x_2 - 0.11x_3 - 0.13x_4 = 2.6$$
$$-0.11x_1 - 0.09x_2 + x_3 - 0.08x_4 = 3.8$$
$$-0.06x_1 - 0.02x_2 - 0.14x_3 + x_4 = 4.4$$

The augmented coefficient matrix is:

$$\begin{bmatrix} 1 & -0.08 & -0.03 & -0.07 & 3.2 \\ -0.12 & 1 & -0.11 & -0.13 & 2.6 \\ -0.11 & -0.09 & 1 & -0.08 & 3.8 \\ -0.06 & -0.02 & -0.14 & 1 & 4.4 \end{bmatrix}$$

and the corresponding reduced from (from a graphing utility) is:

$$\begin{bmatrix} 1 & 0 & 0 & 0 & 4.082 \\ 0 & 1 & 0 & 0 & 4.356 \\ 0 & 0 & 1 & 0 & 5.076 \\ 0 & 0 & 0 & 1 & 5.443 \end{bmatrix}$$

Taxable incomes are $x_1 = \$4,082,000$ for company A, $x_2 = \$4,356,000$ for company B, $x_3 = \$5,076,000$ for company C, and $x_4 = \$5,443,000$ for company D.

76. Let x_1 = number of ounces of food A
x_2 = number of ounces of food B
x_3 = number of ounces of food C

(A) The mathematical model is:
$$30x_1 + 10x_2 + 20x_3 = 400$$
$$10x_1 + 10x_2 + 20x_3 = 160$$
$$10x_1 + 30x_2 + 20x_3 = 240$$

$$\begin{bmatrix} 30 & 10 & 20 & 400 \\ 10 & 10 & 20 & 160 \\ 10 & 30 & 20 & 240 \end{bmatrix} \sim \begin{bmatrix} 10 & 10 & 20 & 160 \\ 30 & 10 & 20 & 400 \\ 10 & 30 & 20 & 240 \end{bmatrix} \sim \begin{bmatrix} 1 & 1 & 2 & 16 \\ 3 & 1 & 2 & 40 \\ 1 & 3 & 2 & 24 \end{bmatrix} \sim \begin{bmatrix} 1 & 1 & 2 & 16 \\ 0 & -2 & -4 & -8 \\ 0 & 2 & 0 & 8 \end{bmatrix}$$

$$R_1 \leftrightarrow R_2 \qquad \dfrac{1}{10}R_1 \to R_1 \qquad (-3)R_1 + R_2 \to R_2 \qquad \left(-\dfrac{1}{2}\right)R_2 \to R_2$$
$$\dfrac{1}{10}R_2 \to R_2 \qquad (-1)R_1 + R_3 \to R_3$$
$$\dfrac{1}{10}R_3 \to R_3$$

$$\sim \begin{bmatrix} 1 & 1 & 2 & | & 16 \\ 0 & 1 & 2 & | & 4 \\ 0 & 2 & 0 & | & 8 \end{bmatrix} \sim \begin{bmatrix} 1 & 0 & 0 & | & 12 \\ 0 & 1 & 2 & | & 4 \\ 0 & 0 & -4 & | & 0 \end{bmatrix} \sim \begin{bmatrix} 1 & 0 & 0 & | & 12 \\ 0 & 1 & 2 & | & 4 \\ 0 & 0 & 1 & | & 0 \end{bmatrix} \sim \begin{bmatrix} 1 & 0 & 0 & | & 12 \\ 0 & 1 & 0 & | & 4 \\ 0 & 0 & 1 & | & 0 \end{bmatrix}$$

$(-1)R_2 + R_1 \rightarrow R_1$ $\left(-\dfrac{1}{4}\right)R_3 \rightarrow R_3$ $(-2)R_3 + R_2 \rightarrow R_2$

$(-2)R_2 + R_3 \rightarrow R_3$

Thus, $x_1 = 12$, $x_2 = 4$, and $x_3 = 0$.

Therefore, 12 ounces of food A, 4 ounces of food B, and 0 ounces of food C.

(B) The mathematical model is:

$$30x_1 + 10x_2 = 400$$
$$10x_1 + 10x_2 = 160$$
$$10x_1 + 30x_2 = 240$$

$$\begin{bmatrix} 30 & 10 & | & 400 \\ 10 & 10 & | & 160 \\ 10 & 30 & | & 240 \end{bmatrix} \sim \begin{bmatrix} 10 & 10 & | & 160 \\ 30 & 10 & | & 400 \\ 10 & 30 & | & 240 \end{bmatrix} \sim \begin{bmatrix} 1 & 1 & | & 16 \\ 3 & 1 & | & 40 \\ 1 & 3 & | & 24 \end{bmatrix} \sim \begin{bmatrix} 1 & 1 & | & 16 \\ 0 & -2 & | & -8 \\ 0 & 2 & | & 8 \end{bmatrix}$$

$R_1 \leftrightarrow R_2$ $\dfrac{1}{10}R_1 \rightarrow R_1$ $(-3)R_1 + R_2 \rightarrow R_2$ $\left(-\dfrac{1}{2}\right)R_2 \rightarrow R_2$

               $\dfrac{1}{10}R_2 \rightarrow R_2$ $(-1)R_1 + R_3 \rightarrow R_3$

               $\dfrac{1}{10}R_3 \rightarrow R_3$

$$\sim \begin{bmatrix} 1 & 1 & | & 16 \\ 0 & 1 & | & 4 \\ 0 & 2 & | & 8 \end{bmatrix} \sim \begin{bmatrix} 1 & 0 & | & 12 \\ 0 & 1 & | & 4 \\ 0 & 0 & | & 0 \end{bmatrix}$$

$(-1)R_2 + R_1 \rightarrow R_1$

$(-2)R_2 + R_3 \rightarrow R_3$

Thus, $x_1 = 12$, $x_2 = 4$, i.e. 12 ounces of food A and 4 ounces of food B.

(C) The mathematical model is:

$$30x_1 + 10x_2 + 20x_3 = 400$$
$$10x_1 + 10x_2 + 20x_3 = 160$$

$$\begin{bmatrix} 30 & 10 & 20 & | & 400 \\ 10 & 10 & 20 & | & 160 \end{bmatrix} \sim \begin{bmatrix} 10 & 10 & 20 & | & 160 \\ 30 & 10 & 20 & | & 400 \end{bmatrix} \sim \begin{bmatrix} 1 & 1 & 2 & | & 16 \\ 3 & 1 & 2 & | & 40 \end{bmatrix} \sim \begin{bmatrix} 1 & 1 & 2 & | & 16 \\ 0 & -2 & -4 & | & -8 \end{bmatrix}$$

$R_1 \leftrightarrow R_2$ $\dfrac{1}{10}R_1 \rightarrow R_1$ $(-3)R_1 + R_2 \rightarrow R_2$

              $\dfrac{1}{10}R_2 \rightarrow R_2$

$$\sim \begin{bmatrix} 1 & 1 & 2 & | & 16 \\ 0 & 1 & 2 & | & 4 \end{bmatrix} \sim \begin{bmatrix} 1 & 0 & 0 & | & 12 \\ 0 & 1 & 2 & | & 4 \end{bmatrix}$$

$\left(-\dfrac{1}{2}\right)R_2 \rightarrow R_2$ $(-1)R_2 + R_1 \rightarrow R_1$

Thus, $x_1 = 12$, $x_2 + 2x_3 = 4$. Letting $x_3 = t$, we have $x_1 = 12$, $x_2 = -2t + 4$, $x_3 = t$, i.e. 12 ounces of food A, $(4 - 2t)$ ounces of food B, and t ounces of food C where $0 \le t \le 2$.

78. Let x_1 = number of packets of brand A
x_2 = number of packets of brand B
x_3 = number of packets of brand C
x_4 = number of packets of brand D
The mathematical model is
$$x_1 + x_2 + x_3 + x_4 = 5$$
$$5x_1 + 10x_2 + 15x_3 + 20x_4 = 80$$
Divide each side of the second equation by 5 to obtain the following equivalent system:
$$x_1 + x_2 + x_3 + x_4 = 5$$
$$x_1 + 2x_2 + 3x_3 + 4x_4 = 16$$

$$\begin{bmatrix} 1 & 1 & 1 & 1 & | & 5 \\ 1 & 2 & 3 & 4 & | & 16 \end{bmatrix} \sim \begin{bmatrix} 1 & 1 & 1 & 1 & | & 5 \\ 0 & 1 & 2 & 3 & | & 11 \end{bmatrix} \sim \begin{bmatrix} 1 & 0 & -1 & -2 & | & -6 \\ 0 & 1 & 2 & 3 & | & 11 \end{bmatrix}$$

$(-1)R_1 + R_2 \to R_2$ $\qquad (-1)R_2 + R_1 \to R_1$

Thus,
$$x_1 \qquad - x_3 - 2x_4 = -6$$
$$x_2 + 2x_3 + 3x_4 = 11$$

Solution: $x_1 = 0$, $x_2 = 2$, $x_3 = 0$, $x_4 = 3$
$\qquad\qquad x_1 = 1$, $x_2 = 0$, $x_3 = 1$, $x_4 = 3$
$\qquad\qquad x_1 = 0$, $x_2 = 1$, $x_3 = 2$, $x_4 = 2$
$\qquad\qquad x_1 = 0$, $x_2 = 0$, $x_3 = 4$, $x_4 = 1$

80. From Problem 78 we have:
Solution: $x_1 = 0$, $x_2 = 2$, $x_3 = 0$, $x_4 = 3$ $\qquad$ cost: $\qquad 6 + 6.75 = \$12.75$
$\qquad\qquad x_1 = 1$, $x_2 = 0$, $x_3 = 1$, $x_4 = 3$ $\qquad 1.5 + 3.75 + 6.75 = \$12$
$\qquad\qquad x_1 = 0$, $x_2 = 1$, $x_3 = 2$, $x_4 = 2$ $\qquad\qquad 3 + 7.5 + 4.5 = \$15$
$\qquad\qquad x_1 = 0$, $x_2 = 0$, $x_3 = 4$, $x_4 = 1$ $\qquad\qquad\qquad 15 + 2.25 = \$17.25$

Clearly, 1 packet of brand A, 0 packets of brand B, 1 packet of brand C, and 3 packets of brand D will cost $12.75, which is the minimum amount.

82. Let $y = ax^2 + bx + c$ be the quadratic equation for which we need to find a, b, c based on the information provided.
For $(0, 24)$: $\quad 24 = a(0)^2 + b(0) + c \quad$ or $\quad c = 24$
For $(10, 30)$: $30 = a(10)^2 + b(10) + c \quad$ or $\quad 30 = 100a + 10b + c$
For $(20, 34)$: $34 = a(20)^2 + b(20) + c \quad$ or $\quad 34 = 400a + 20b + c$

Since $c = 24$, we have
$$\begin{cases} 100a + 10b = 30 - 24 = 6 \\ 400a + 20b = 34 - 24 = 10 \end{cases} \text{ or } \begin{cases} 50a + 5b = 3 \\ 40a + 2b = 1 \end{cases}$$

Multiplying the second equation by 2.5 and then subtracting from the first equation results in
$$50a - 100a = 3 - 2.5$$
or $\quad a = -\dfrac{0.5}{50} = -0.01$

and from $50(-0.01) + 5b = 3$ we have $b = 0.7$.
So, the desired quadratic equation is:
$$y = -0.01x^2 + 0.7x + 24.$$
For 2010, $x = 2010 - 1980 = 30$ and
$$y = -0.01(30)^2 + 0.7(30) + 24 = 36 \text{ million}$$

84. Let $y = ax^2 + x + c$

For $(0, 70.7)$: $\quad 70.7 = a(0)^2 + b(0) + c$ or $\quad c = 70.7$

For $(5, 71.1)$: $\quad 71.1 = a(5)^2 + b(5) + 70.7 = 25a + 5b + 70.7$

For $(10, 71.8)$: $71.8 = a(10)^2 + b(10) + 70.7 = 100a + 10b + 70.7$

or $\begin{cases} 25a + 5b = 0.4 & (1) \\ 100a + 10b = 1.1 & (2) \end{cases}$

Multiply (1) by (-2) and then add to (2):

$\quad 50a = 1.1 - 0.8 = 0.3$

$\qquad a = 0.006$

Use this to find b from (1): $25(0.006) + 5b = 0.4$

or $b = \dfrac{0.4 - 0.15}{5} = 0.05$.

Thus the desired quadratic equation is:

$\quad y = 0.006x^2 + 0.05x + 70.7$

For 1995-2000: $x = 15$ and $y = 0.006(15)^2 + 0.05(15) + 70.7 = 72.8$ yr.

For 2000-2005: $x = 20$ and $y = 0.006(20)^2 + 0.005(20) + 70.7 = 74.1$ yrs.

86.

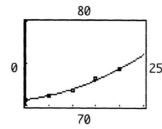

88. Let x_1 = number of hours for company A, and

$\qquad x_2$ = number of hours for company B

The mathematical model is:

$30x_1 + 20x_2 = 650$

$10x_1 + 20x_2 = 350$

$\begin{bmatrix} 30 & 20 & | & 650 \\ 10 & 20 & | & 350 \end{bmatrix} \sim \begin{bmatrix} 10 & 20 & | & 350 \\ 30 & 20 & | & 650 \end{bmatrix} \sim \begin{bmatrix} 1 & 2 & | & 35 \\ 3 & 2 & | & 65 \end{bmatrix} \sim \begin{bmatrix} 1 & 2 & | & 35 \\ 0 & -4 & | & -40 \end{bmatrix} \sim$

$\quad R_1 \leftrightarrow R_2 \qquad \dfrac{1}{10}R_1 \to R_1 \qquad (-3)R_1 + R_2 \to R_2 \qquad \left(-\dfrac{1}{4}\right)R_2 \to R_2$

$\qquad\qquad\qquad \dfrac{1}{10}R_2 \to R_2$

$\begin{bmatrix} 1 & 2 & | & 35 \\ 0 & 1 & | & 10 \end{bmatrix} \sim \begin{bmatrix} 1 & 0 & | & 15 \\ 0 & 1 & | & 10 \end{bmatrix}$ Thus, $x_1 = 15$

$(-2)R_2 + R_1 \to R_1 \qquad\qquad\qquad\qquad x_2 = 10$

Solution: company A: 15 hours; company B: 10 hour

90. (A) 6th Street and Washington Avenue: $x_1 + x_2 = 800$

6th Street and Lincoln Avenue: $x_2 + x_3 = 1,000$

5th Street and Lincoln Avenue: $x_3 + x_4 = 1,700$

(B) The augmented matrix is:

$$\begin{bmatrix} 1 & 1 & 0 & 0 & | & 800 \\ 0 & 1 & 1 & 0 & | & 1,000 \\ 0 & 0 & 1 & 1 & | & 1,700 \end{bmatrix} \sim \begin{bmatrix} 1 & 0 & -1 & 0 & | & -200 \\ 0 & 1 & 1 & 0 & | & 1,000 \\ 0 & 0 & 1 & 1 & | & 1,700 \end{bmatrix} \sim$$

$(-1)R_2 + R_1 \to R_1$ $\qquad\qquad$ $(-1)R_3 + R_2 \to R_2$

$$\begin{bmatrix} 1 & 0 & -1 & 0 & | & -200 \\ 0 & 1 & 0 & -1 & | & -700 \\ 0 & 0 & 1 & 1 & | & 1,700 \end{bmatrix} \sim \begin{bmatrix} 1 & 0 & 0 & 1 & | & 1,500 \\ 0 & 1 & 0 & -1 & | & -700 \\ 0 & 0 & 1 & 1 & | & 1,700 \end{bmatrix}$$

$R_3 + R_1 \to R_1$

Thus, $x_1 + x_4 = 1,500$, $x_2 - x_4 = -700$, $x_3 + x_4 = 1,700$.

Letting $x_4 = t$, we have: $x_1 = 1,500 - t$, $x_2 = t - 700$, $x_3 = 1,700 - t$, $x_4 = t$ where $700 \le t \le 1,500$.

(C) 1,500; 700

(D) If $x_4 = t = 1,000$, then Washington Avenue: $1,500 - 1,000 = 500$; 6th Street: $t - 700 = 300$; Lincoln Avenue: $1,700 - t = 700$.

EXERCISE 4-4

2. $\begin{bmatrix} -3 & 5 \\ 2 & 0 \\ 1 & 4 \end{bmatrix} + \begin{bmatrix} 2 & 1 \\ -6 & 3 \\ 0 & -5 \end{bmatrix} = \begin{bmatrix} -1 & 6 \\ -4 & 3 \\ 1 & -1 \end{bmatrix}$

4. Addition not defined; the matrices have different dimensions.

6. $\begin{bmatrix} 6 & 2 & -3 \\ 0 & -4 & 5 \end{bmatrix} - \begin{bmatrix} 4 & -1 & 2 \\ -5 & 1 & -2 \end{bmatrix} = \begin{bmatrix} 2 & 3 & -5 \\ 5 & -5 & 7 \end{bmatrix}$

8. $10\begin{bmatrix} 2 & -1 & 3 \\ 0 & -4 & 5 \end{bmatrix} = \begin{bmatrix} 20 & -10 & 30 \\ 0 & -40 & 50 \end{bmatrix}$ **10.** $\begin{bmatrix} -1 & 1 \\ 2 & -3 \end{bmatrix}\begin{bmatrix} 4 \\ -2 \end{bmatrix} = \begin{bmatrix} -6 \\ 14 \end{bmatrix}$

12. $\begin{bmatrix} -3 & 2 \\ 4 & -1 \end{bmatrix}\begin{bmatrix} -2 & 5 \\ -1 & 3 \end{bmatrix} = \begin{bmatrix} 4 & -9 \\ -7 & 17 \end{bmatrix}$ **14.** $\begin{bmatrix} -2 & 5 \\ -1 & 3 \end{bmatrix}\begin{bmatrix} -3 & 2 \\ 4 & -1 \end{bmatrix} = \begin{bmatrix} 26 & -9 \\ 15 & -5 \end{bmatrix}$

16. $A = \begin{bmatrix} 1 & 2 \\ 3 & 4 \end{bmatrix}$

$A + A + A = \begin{bmatrix} 1 + 1 + 1 & 2 + 2 + 2 \\ 3 + 3 + 3 & 4 + 4 + 4 \end{bmatrix} = \begin{bmatrix} 3 & 6 \\ 9 & 12 \end{bmatrix}$

$3A = \begin{bmatrix} 3(1) & 3(2) \\ 3(3) & 3(4) \end{bmatrix} = \begin{bmatrix} 3 & 6 \\ 9 & 12 \end{bmatrix}$

18. $A = \begin{bmatrix} 1 & 2 \\ 3 & 4 \end{bmatrix}$

$A + A + A + A + A = \begin{bmatrix} 1 + 1 + 1 + 1 + 1 & 2 + 2 + 2 + 2 + 2 \\ 3 + 3 + 3 + 3 + 3 & 4 + 4 + 4 + 4 + 4 \end{bmatrix} = \begin{bmatrix} 5 & 10 \\ 15 & 20 \end{bmatrix}$

$5A = \begin{bmatrix} 5(1) & 5(2) \\ 5(3) & 5(4) \end{bmatrix} = \begin{bmatrix} 5 & 10 \\ 15 & 20 \end{bmatrix}$

20. $\begin{bmatrix} -4 & 3 \end{bmatrix} \begin{bmatrix} -2 \\ 1 \end{bmatrix} = [8 + 3] = [11]$ **22.** $\begin{bmatrix} -2 \\ 1 \end{bmatrix} \begin{bmatrix} -4 & 3 \end{bmatrix} = \begin{bmatrix} 8 & -6 \\ -4 & 3 \end{bmatrix}$

24. $\begin{bmatrix} 1 & -2 & 2 \end{bmatrix} \begin{bmatrix} 2 \\ -1 \\ 1 \end{bmatrix} = [2 + 2 + 2] = [6]$

26. $\begin{bmatrix} 2 \\ -1 \\ 1 \end{bmatrix} \begin{bmatrix} 1 & -2 & 2 \end{bmatrix} = \begin{bmatrix} 2 & -4 & 4 \\ -1 & 2 & -2 \\ 1 & -2 & 2 \end{bmatrix}$

28. CA is not defined; the number of columns of C (3) does not equal the number of rows of A (2).

30. $BA = \begin{bmatrix} -3 & 1 \\ 2 & 5 \end{bmatrix} \begin{bmatrix} 2 & -1 & 3 \\ 0 & 4 & -2 \end{bmatrix} = \begin{bmatrix} -6 & 7 & -11 \\ 4 & 18 & -4 \end{bmatrix}$

32. $C^2 = CC = \begin{bmatrix} -1 & 0 & 2 \\ 4 & -3 & 1 \\ -2 & 3 & 5 \end{bmatrix} \begin{bmatrix} -1 & 0 & 2 \\ 4 & -3 & 1 \\ -2 & 3 & 5 \end{bmatrix} = \begin{bmatrix} -3 & 6 & 8 \\ -18 & 12 & 10 \\ 4 & 6 & 24 \end{bmatrix}$

34. $C + DA = \begin{bmatrix} -1 & 0 & 2 \\ 4 & -3 & 1 \\ -2 & 3 & 5 \end{bmatrix} + \begin{bmatrix} 3 & -2 \\ 0 & -1 \\ 1 & 2 \end{bmatrix} \begin{bmatrix} 2 & -1 & 3 \\ 0 & 4 & -2 \end{bmatrix}$

$= \begin{bmatrix} -1 & 0 & 2 \\ 4 & -3 & 1 \\ -2 & 3 & 5 \end{bmatrix} + \begin{bmatrix} 6 & -11 & 13 \\ 0 & -4 & 2 \\ 2 & 7 & -1 \end{bmatrix} = \begin{bmatrix} 5 & -11 & 15 \\ 4 & -7 & 3 \\ 0 & 10 & 4 \end{bmatrix}$

36. $(0.2)CD = (0.2) \begin{bmatrix} -1 & 0 & 2 \\ 4 & -3 & 1 \\ -2 & 3 & 5 \end{bmatrix} \begin{bmatrix} 3 & -2 \\ 0 & -1 \\ 1 & 2 \end{bmatrix} = (0.2) \begin{bmatrix} -1 & 6 \\ 13 & -3 \\ -1 & 11 \end{bmatrix} = \begin{bmatrix} -0.2 & 1.2 \\ 2.6 & -0.6 \\ -0.2 & 2.2 \end{bmatrix}$

38. $(2)DB + (5)CD = (2) \begin{bmatrix} 3 & -2 \\ 0 & -1 \\ 1 & 2 \end{bmatrix} \begin{bmatrix} -3 & 1 \\ 2 & 5 \end{bmatrix} + (5) \begin{bmatrix} -1 & 6 \\ 13 & -3 \\ -1 & 11 \end{bmatrix}$

$= (2) \begin{bmatrix} -13 & -7 \\ -2 & -5 \\ 1 & 11 \end{bmatrix} + (5) \begin{bmatrix} -1 & 6 \\ 13 & -3 \\ -1 & 11 \end{bmatrix}$

$= \begin{bmatrix} -26 & -14 \\ -4 & -10 \\ 2 & 22 \end{bmatrix} + \begin{bmatrix} -5 & 30 \\ 65 & -15 \\ -5 & 55 \end{bmatrix} = \begin{bmatrix} -31 & 16 \\ 61 & -25 \\ -3 & 77 \end{bmatrix}$

40. $(-1)AC + (3)DB$ is not defined; AC is 3×2 and DB is 2×3.

42. From problem 34, $DA = \begin{bmatrix} 6 & -11 & 13 \\ 0 & -4 & 2 \\ 2 & 7 & -1 \end{bmatrix}$. Thus

$$CDA = C(DA) = \begin{bmatrix} -1 & 0 & 2 \\ 4 & -3 & 1 \\ -2 & 3 & 5 \end{bmatrix}\begin{bmatrix} 6 & -11 & 13 \\ 0 & -4 & 2 \\ 2 & 7 & -1 \end{bmatrix} = \begin{bmatrix} -2 & 25 & -15 \\ 26 & -25 & 45 \\ -2 & 45 & -25 \end{bmatrix}$$

44. $BAD = B(AD) = \begin{bmatrix} -3 & 1 \\ 2 & 5 \end{bmatrix}\left(\begin{bmatrix} 2 & -1 & 3 \\ 0 & 4 & -2 \end{bmatrix}\begin{bmatrix} 3 & -2 \\ 0 & -1 \\ 1 & 2 \end{bmatrix}\right)$

$$= \begin{bmatrix} -3 & 1 \\ 2 & 5 \end{bmatrix}\begin{bmatrix} 9 & 3 \\ -2 & -8 \end{bmatrix} = \begin{bmatrix} -29 & -17 \\ 8 & -34 \end{bmatrix}$$

46. $A = \begin{bmatrix} a & b \\ -a & -b \end{bmatrix}$, $B = \begin{bmatrix} a & a \\ a & a \end{bmatrix}$

$$AB = \begin{bmatrix} a & b \\ -a & -b \end{bmatrix}\begin{bmatrix} a & a \\ a & a \end{bmatrix} = \begin{bmatrix} a^2 + ab & a^2 + ab \\ -a^2 - ab & -a^2 - ab \end{bmatrix}$$

$$BA = \begin{bmatrix} a & a \\ a & a \end{bmatrix}\begin{bmatrix} a & b \\ -a & -b \end{bmatrix} = \begin{bmatrix} a^2 - a^2 & ab - ab \\ a^2 - a^2 & ab - ab \end{bmatrix} = \begin{bmatrix} 0 & 0 \\ 0 & 0 \end{bmatrix}$$

48. $A = \begin{bmatrix} ab & b - ab^2 \\ a & 1 - ab \end{bmatrix}$

$$A^2 = \begin{bmatrix} ab & b - ab^2 \\ a & 1 - ab \end{bmatrix}\begin{bmatrix} ab & b - ab^2 \\ a & 1 - ab \end{bmatrix}$$

$$= \begin{bmatrix} a^2b^2 + ab - a^2b^2 & ab^2 - a^2b^3 + b - 2ab^2 + a^2b^3 \\ a^2b + a - a^2b & ab - a^2b^2 + 1 - 2ab + a^2b^2 \end{bmatrix} = \begin{bmatrix} ab & b - ab^2 \\ a & 1 - ab \end{bmatrix} = A$$

50. $B^n \rightarrow \begin{bmatrix} 0.75 & 0.25 \\ 0.75 & 0.25 \end{bmatrix}$, $AB^n \rightarrow \begin{bmatrix} 0.75 & 0.25 \end{bmatrix}$

52. $\begin{bmatrix} 4 & -2 \\ -3 & 0 \end{bmatrix} + \begin{bmatrix} w & x \\ y & z \end{bmatrix} = \begin{bmatrix} 4 + w & -2 + x \\ -3 + y & z \end{bmatrix} = \begin{bmatrix} 2 & -3 \\ 0 & 5 \end{bmatrix}$. Thus

$4 + w = 2, \quad w = -2$

$-2 + x = -3, \quad x = -1$

$-3 + y = 0, \quad y = 3$

$z = 5, \quad z = 5$

54. $\begin{bmatrix} 5 & 3x \\ 2x & -4 \end{bmatrix} + \begin{bmatrix} 1 & -4y \\ 7y & 4 \end{bmatrix} = \begin{bmatrix} 6 & 3x - 4y \\ 2x + 7y & 0 \end{bmatrix} = \begin{bmatrix} 6 & -7 \\ 5 & 0 \end{bmatrix}$. Thus

$3x - 4y = -7 \quad (1)$

$2x + 7y = 5 \quad (2)$

Multiply (1) by $\left(-\dfrac{2}{3}\right)$ and add to (2), to obtain

$\dfrac{29}{3}y = \dfrac{29}{3}$ or $y = 1$

Now, substituting $y = 1$ into (2), we get:

$2x + 7(1) = 5$ or $x = -1$

Thus, the solution is $x = -1$ and $y = 1$.

56. $\begin{bmatrix} 1 & 3 \\ -2 & -2 \end{bmatrix}\begin{bmatrix} x & 1 \\ 3 & 2 \end{bmatrix} = \begin{bmatrix} y & 7 \\ y & -6 \end{bmatrix}$

$\begin{bmatrix} x + 9 & 7 \\ -2x - 6 & -6 \end{bmatrix} = \begin{bmatrix} y & 7 \\ y & -6 \end{bmatrix}$

implies $x + 9 = y$

$\qquad -2x - 6 = y.$

Thus, $x + 9 = -2x - 6$

$\qquad\qquad x = -5$

and $\qquad y = x + 9 = 4$

58. $\begin{bmatrix} 1 & 3 \\ 1 & 4 \end{bmatrix}\begin{bmatrix} a & b \\ c & d \end{bmatrix} = \begin{bmatrix} 6 & -5 \\ 7 & -7 \end{bmatrix}$

$\begin{bmatrix} a + 3c & b + 3d \\ a + 4c & b + 4d \end{bmatrix} = \begin{bmatrix} 6 & -5 \\ 7 & -7 \end{bmatrix}$

implies $a + 3c = 6$ or $a + 3c = 6$ and $b + 3d = -5$

$\qquad\qquad b + 3d = -5 \qquad a + 4c = 7 \qquad\qquad b + 4d = -7$

$\qquad\qquad a + 4c = 7$

$\qquad\qquad b + 4d = -7$

The augmented matrix for the first system is

$\begin{bmatrix} 1 & 3 & | & 6 \\ 1 & 4 & | & 7 \end{bmatrix} \sim \begin{bmatrix} 1 & 3 & | & 6 \\ 0 & 1 & | & 1 \end{bmatrix} \sim \begin{bmatrix} 1 & 0 & | & 3 \\ 0 & 1 & | & 1 \end{bmatrix}$. Thus, $a = 3$ and $c = 1$.

$(-1)R_1 + R_2 \rightarrow R_2 \quad (-3)R_2 + R_1 \rightarrow R_1$

For the second system, the augmented matrix is:

$\begin{bmatrix} 1 & 3 & | & -5 \\ 1 & 4 & | & -7 \end{bmatrix} \sim \begin{bmatrix} 1 & 3 & | & -5 \\ 0 & 1 & | & -2 \end{bmatrix} \sim \begin{bmatrix} 1 & 0 & | & 1 \\ 0 & 1 & | & -2 \end{bmatrix}$. Thus, $b = 1$, $d = -2$.

$(-1)R_1 + R_2 \rightarrow R_2 \quad (-3)R_2 + R_1 \rightarrow R_1$

Solution: $a = 3$, $b = 1$, $c = 1$, $d = -2$.

60. Let $A = \begin{bmatrix} a_1 & b_1 \\ 0 & d_1 \end{bmatrix}$ and $B = \begin{bmatrix} a_2 & b_2 \\ 0 & d_2 \end{bmatrix}$

(A) Always true:

$A + B = \begin{bmatrix} a_1 + a_2 & b_1 + b_2 \\ 0 & d_1 + d_2 \end{bmatrix}$

(B) Always true:

$B + A = \begin{bmatrix} a_2 & b_2 \\ 0 & d_2 \end{bmatrix} + \begin{bmatrix} a_1 & b_1 \\ 0 & d_1 \end{bmatrix} = \begin{bmatrix} a_2 + a_1 & b_2 + b_1 \\ 0 & d_2 + d_1 \end{bmatrix} = \begin{bmatrix} a_1 + a_2 & b_1 + b_2 \\ 0 & d_1 + d_2 \end{bmatrix}$

$\qquad = A + B$ [From part (A)]

(C) Always true:

$AB = \begin{bmatrix} a_1 & b_1 \\ 0 & d_1 \end{bmatrix}\begin{bmatrix} a_2 & b_2 \\ 0 & d_2 \end{bmatrix} = \begin{bmatrix} a_1 a_2 & a_1 b_2 + b_1 d_2 \\ 0 & d_1 d_2 \end{bmatrix}$

(D) False: Let $A = \begin{bmatrix} 1 & 1 \\ 0 & 1 \end{bmatrix}$, $B = \begin{bmatrix} -1 & 1 \\ 0 & 1 \end{bmatrix}$. Then

$AB = \begin{bmatrix} -1 & 2 \\ 0 & 1 \end{bmatrix}$ and $BA = \begin{bmatrix} -1 & 0 \\ 0 & 1 \end{bmatrix}$ which are not equal.

62. $(1.2)A = \begin{bmatrix} \$56.4 & \$46.8 \\ \$45 & \$150 \end{bmatrix}$

$\dfrac{1}{2}(1.2A + B) = \dfrac{1}{2}\left(\begin{bmatrix} \$56.4 & \$46.8 \\ \$45 & \$150 \end{bmatrix} + \begin{bmatrix} \$56 & \$42 \\ \$84 & \$115 \end{bmatrix}\right)$

$\qquad\qquad\quad \overset{\text{Guitar}\quad\text{Banjo}}{= \begin{bmatrix} \$56.20 & \$44.40 \\ \$96.00 & \$132.50 \end{bmatrix}} \begin{matrix} \text{Materials} \\ \text{Labor} \end{matrix}$

64. The dealer is increasing the retail price by 15%. Thus, the new retail price matrix M' (to the nearest dollar) is given by:

$M' = M + 0.15M = 1.15M = 1.15\begin{bmatrix} \$35,075 & \$2,560 & \$1,070 & \$640 \\ \$39,045 & \$1,840 & \$770 & \$460 \\ \$45,535 & \$3,400 & \$1,415 & \$850 \end{bmatrix}$

The new dealer invoice matrix N' is given by

$N' = N + 0.20N = 1.2N = 1.2\begin{bmatrix} \$30,996 & \$2,050 & \$850 & \$510 \\ \$34,857 & \$1,585 & \$660 & \$395 \\ \$41,667 & \$2,890 & \$1,200 & \$725 \end{bmatrix}$

The new markup is:

$M' - N' = \overset{\begin{matrix}\text{Basic}\\\text{car}\end{matrix}\quad\text{Air}\;\;\begin{matrix}\text{AM/FM}\\\text{radio}\end{matrix}\;\begin{matrix}\text{Cruise}\\\text{control}\end{matrix}}{\begin{bmatrix} \$3,141 & \$484 & \$211 & \$124 \\ \$3,073 & \$214 & \$94 & \$55 \\ \$2,365 & \$442 & \$187 & \$108 \end{bmatrix}} \begin{matrix}\text{Model } A\\\text{Model } B\\\text{Model } C\end{matrix}$

66. (A) $\begin{bmatrix} 2 & 3 & 5 & 0 & 6 \end{bmatrix} \begin{bmatrix} 840 \\ 1,800 \\ 2,400 \\ 3,300 \\ 4,900 \end{bmatrix} = \$48,480$

(B) $\begin{bmatrix} 10 & 4 & 3 & 4 & 3 \end{bmatrix} \begin{bmatrix} 700 \\ 1,400 \\ 1,800 \\ 2,700 \\ 3,500 \end{bmatrix} = \$39,300$

(C) Matrix MN gives the wholesale and retail values of the inventories at each store. NM is not defined.

(D) $MN = \overset{W\qquad\quad R}{\begin{bmatrix} \$33,400 & \$42,160 \\ \$35,600 & \$48,480 \\ \$39,300 & \$50,700 \end{bmatrix}} \begin{matrix}\text{Store 1}\\\text{Store 2}\\\text{Store 3}\end{matrix}$

(E) $\begin{bmatrix} 1 & 1 & 1 \end{bmatrix} M = \overset{A\quad B\quad C\quad\;\; D\quad\;\; E}{\begin{bmatrix} 16 & 9 & 11 & 11 & 10 \end{bmatrix}}$

(F) $M\begin{bmatrix} 1 \\ 1 \\ 1 \\ 1 \\ 1 \end{bmatrix} = \begin{bmatrix} 17 \\ 16 \\ 27 \end{bmatrix} \begin{matrix}\text{Store 1}\\\text{Store 2}\\\text{Store 3}\end{matrix}$

68. $A = \begin{bmatrix} 0 & 1 & 0 & 0 & 0 \\ 0 & 0 & 1 & 0 & 1 \\ 0 & 0 & 0 & 0 & 1 \\ 0 & 1 & 0 & 0 & 0 \\ 1 & 1 & 0 & 1 & 0 \end{bmatrix}$; $A + A^2 + A^3 = \begin{bmatrix} 1 & 2 & 1 & 1 & 2 \\ 2 & 4 & 2 & 2 & 3 \\ 1 & 3 & 1 & 1 & 2 \\ 1 & 2 & 1 & 1 & 2 \\ 2 & 4 & 3 & 2 & 4 \end{bmatrix}$

It is possible to travel from any destination origin to any in three or fewer flights.

70. (A) $M + N = \begin{bmatrix} 315 & 101 \\ 108 & 32 \end{bmatrix} + \begin{bmatrix} 370 & 128 \\ 110 & 36 \end{bmatrix} = \begin{bmatrix} 685 & 229 \\ 218 & 68 \end{bmatrix} \begin{matrix} \text{Yellow} \\ \text{Green} \end{matrix}$ Round Wrinkled

(B) $\begin{bmatrix} 1 & 1 \end{bmatrix}(M + N)\begin{bmatrix} 1 \\ 1 \end{bmatrix} = \begin{bmatrix} 1 & 1 \end{bmatrix}\begin{bmatrix} 685 & 229 \\ 218 & 68 \end{bmatrix}\begin{bmatrix} 1 \\ 1 \end{bmatrix} = \begin{bmatrix} 1 & 1 \end{bmatrix}\begin{bmatrix} 914 \\ 286 \end{bmatrix}$
$$= 914 + 286 = 1200$$

(C) $\dfrac{1}{1200}(M + N) = \dfrac{1}{1200}\begin{bmatrix} 685 & 229 \\ 218 & 68 \end{bmatrix} = \begin{bmatrix} 57\% & 19\% \\ 18\% & 6\% \end{bmatrix}\begin{matrix} \text{Yellow} \\ \text{Green} \end{matrix}$ Round Wrinkled

72. (A) $M\begin{bmatrix} 0.25 \\ 0.25 \\ 0.25 \\ 0.25 \end{bmatrix} = \begin{bmatrix} 78 & 84 & 81 & 86 \\ 91 & 65 & 84 & 92 \\ 95 & 90 & 92 & 91 \\ 75 & 82 & 87 & 91 \\ 83 & 88 & 81 & 76 \end{bmatrix}\begin{bmatrix} 0.25 \\ 0.25 \\ 0.25 \\ 0.25 \end{bmatrix} = \begin{bmatrix} 82.25 \\ 83 \\ 92 \\ 83.75 \\ 82 \end{bmatrix}\begin{matrix} \text{Ann} \\ \text{Bob} \\ \text{Carol} \\ \text{Dan} \\ \text{Eric} \end{matrix}$

(B) $M\begin{bmatrix} 0.2 \\ 0.2 \\ 0.2 \\ 0.4 \end{bmatrix} = \begin{bmatrix} 83 \\ 84.8 \\ 91.8 \\ 85.2 \\ 80.8 \end{bmatrix}\begin{matrix} \text{Ann} \\ \text{Bob} \\ \text{Carol} \\ \text{Dan} \\ \text{Eric} \end{matrix}$

(C)

	Test 1	Test 2	Test 3	Test 4
			Class Average	

$\begin{bmatrix} 0.2 & 0.2 & 0.2 & 0.2 & 0.2 \end{bmatrix}M = \begin{bmatrix} 84.4 & 81.8 & 85 & 87.2 \end{bmatrix}$

74. (A)

	Anne	Bridget	Carol	Diane	Erlene
Anne	0	0	0	1	0
Bridget	1	0	1	1	0
Carol	1	0	0	0	0
Diane	0	0	1	0	1
Erlene	1	1	1	0	0

$= A$

(B) $B = A + A^2 = \begin{bmatrix} 0 & 0 & 0 & 1 & 0 \\ 1 & 0 & 1 & 1 & 0 \\ 1 & 0 & 0 & 0 & 0 \\ 0 & 0 & 1 & 0 & 1 \\ 1 & 1 & 1 & 0 & 0 \end{bmatrix} + \begin{bmatrix} 0 & 0 & 1 & 0 & 1 \\ 1 & 0 & 1 & 1 & 1 \\ 0 & 0 & 0 & 1 & 0 \\ 2 & 1 & 1 & 0 & 0 \\ 2 & 0 & 1 & 2 & 0 \end{bmatrix}$

$= \begin{bmatrix} 0 & 0 & 1 & 1 & 1 \\ 2 & 0 & 2 & 2 & 1 \\ 1 & 0 & 0 & 1 & 0 \\ 2 & 1 & 2 & 0 & 1 \\ 3 & 1 & 2 & 2 & 0 \end{bmatrix}$

(C) Let $C = \begin{bmatrix} 1 \\ 1 \\ 1 \\ 1 \\ 1 \end{bmatrix}$. Then $BC = \begin{bmatrix} 0 & 0 & 1 & 1 & 1 \\ 2 & 0 & 2 & 2 & 1 \\ 1 & 0 & 0 & 1 & 0 \\ 2 & 1 & 2 & 0 & 1 \\ 3 & 1 & 2 & 2 & 0 \end{bmatrix} \begin{bmatrix} 1 \\ 1 \\ 1 \\ 1 \\ 1 \end{bmatrix} = \begin{bmatrix} 3 \\ 7 \\ 2 \\ 6 \\ 8 \end{bmatrix}$

(D) The ranking from strongest to weakest is:
    Erlene, Bridget, Diane, Anne, Carol.

The entries in A are the first stage dominances.

The entries in A^2 are the second stage dominances. By summing the rows of $A + A^2$, we calculate the sum of the first and second stage dominances.

EXERCISE 4-5

2. $\begin{vmatrix} 1 & 0 \\ 0 & 1 \end{vmatrix}\begin{vmatrix} -1 & 6 \\ 0 & 2 \end{vmatrix} = \begin{vmatrix} (1) \cdot (-1) + (0) \cdot (0) & (1) \cdot (6) + (0) \cdot (2) \\ (0) \cdot (-1) + (1) \cdot (0) & (0) \cdot (6) + (1) \cdot (2) \end{vmatrix} = \begin{vmatrix} -1 & 6 \\ 0 & 2 \end{vmatrix}$

4. $\begin{vmatrix} -1 & 6 \\ 0 & 2 \end{vmatrix}\begin{vmatrix} 1 & 0 \\ 0 & 1 \end{vmatrix} = \begin{vmatrix} (-1) \cdot (-1) + (6) \cdot (1) & (-1) \cdot (0) + (6) \cdot (1) \\ (0) \cdot (1) + (2) \cdot (0) & (0) \cdot (0) + (2) \cdot (1) \end{vmatrix} = \begin{vmatrix} -1 & 6 \\ 0 & 2 \end{vmatrix}$

6. $\begin{vmatrix} 1 & 0 & 0 \\ 0 & 1 & 0 \\ 0 & 0 & 1 \end{vmatrix}\begin{vmatrix} 3 & -4 & 0 \\ 1 & 2 & -5 \\ 6 & -3 & -1 \end{vmatrix}$

$= \begin{bmatrix} (1) \cdot (3) + (0) \cdot (1) + (0) \cdot (6) & (1) \cdot (-4) + (0) \cdot (2) + (0) \cdot (-3) & (1) \cdot (0) + (0) \cdot (-5) + (0) \cdot (-1) \\ (0) \cdot (3) + (1) \cdot (1) + (0) \cdot (6) & (0) \cdot (-4) + (1) \cdot (2) + (0) \cdot (-3) & (0) \cdot (0) + (1) \cdot (-5) + (0) \cdot (-1) \\ (0) \cdot (3) + (0) \cdot (1) + (0) \cdot (6) & (0) \cdot (-4) + (0) \cdot (2) + (1) \cdot (-3) & (0) \cdot (0) + (0) \cdot (-5) + (1) \cdot (-1) \end{bmatrix}$

$= \begin{vmatrix} 3 & -4 & 0 \\ 1 & 2 & -5 \\ 6 & -3 & -1 \end{vmatrix}$

8. $\begin{vmatrix} 3 & -4 & 0 \\ 1 & 2 & -5 \\ 6 & -3 & -1 \end{vmatrix}\begin{vmatrix} 1 & 0 & 0 \\ 0 & 1 & 0 \\ 0 & 0 & 1 \end{vmatrix}$

$= \begin{bmatrix} (3) \cdot (1) + (-4) \cdot (0) + (0) \cdot (0) & (3) \cdot (0) + (-4) \cdot (1) + (0) \cdot (0) & (3) \cdot (0) + (-4) \cdot (0) + (0) \cdot (0) \\ (1) \cdot (1) + (2) \cdot (0) + (-5) \cdot (0) & (1) \cdot (0) + (2) \cdot (1) + (-5) \cdot (0) & (1) \cdot (0) + (2) \cdot (0) + (-5) \cdot (0) \\ (6) \cdot (1) + (-3) \cdot (0) + (-1) \cdot (0) & (6) \cdot (0) + (-3) \cdot (1) + (-1) \cdot (0) & (6) \cdot (0) + (-3) \cdot (0) + (-1) \cdot (0) \end{bmatrix}$

$= \begin{vmatrix} 3 & -4 & 0 \\ 1 & 2 & -5 \\ 6 & -3 & -1 \end{vmatrix}$

10. $\begin{bmatrix} -2 & -1 \\ -4 & 2 \end{bmatrix}\begin{bmatrix} 1 & -1 \\ 2 & -2 \end{bmatrix} = \begin{bmatrix} -4 & 4 \\ 0 & 0 \end{bmatrix} \neq \begin{bmatrix} 1 & 0 \\ 0 & 1 \end{bmatrix}$ No

12. $\begin{bmatrix} 5 & -7 \\ -2 & 3 \end{bmatrix}\begin{bmatrix} 3 & 7 \\ 2 & 5 \end{bmatrix} = \begin{bmatrix} 1 & 0 \\ 0 & 1 \end{bmatrix}$ Yes

14. $\begin{bmatrix} 7 & 4 \\ -5 & -3 \end{bmatrix}\begin{bmatrix} 3 & 4 \\ -5 & -7 \end{bmatrix} = \begin{bmatrix} 1 & 0 \\ 0 & 1 \end{bmatrix}$ Yes

16. $\begin{bmatrix} 1 & 0 & 1 \\ -3 & 1 & -2 \\ 0 & 0 & 1 \end{bmatrix} \begin{bmatrix} 1 & 0 & -1 \\ 3 & 1 & -1 \\ 0 & 0 & 1 \end{bmatrix} = \begin{bmatrix} 1 & 0 & 0 \\ 0 & 1 & 0 \\ 0 & 0 & 1 \end{bmatrix}$ Yes

18. $\begin{bmatrix} 1 & 0 & -1 \\ 3 & 1 & -1 \\ 0 & 0 & 0 \end{bmatrix} \begin{bmatrix} 1 & 0 & -1 \\ -3 & 1 & -2 \\ 0 & 0 & 1 \end{bmatrix}$

No. The first matrix has a row of zeros; it does not have an inverse.

30. $\begin{bmatrix} 1 & -5 & | & 1 & 0 \\ 0 & -1 & | & 0 & 1 \end{bmatrix} \sim \begin{bmatrix} 1 & -5 & | & 1 & 0 \\ 0 & 1 & | & 0 & -1 \end{bmatrix} \sim \begin{bmatrix} 1 & 0 & | & 1 & -5 \\ 0 & 1 & | & 0 & -1 \end{bmatrix}$

$\quad (-1)R_2 \to R_2 \qquad\qquad 5R_2 + R_1 \to R_1$

Thus, $M^{-1} = \begin{bmatrix} 1 & -5 \\ 0 & -1 \end{bmatrix}$.

Check:

$M \cdot M^{-1} = \begin{bmatrix} 1 & -5 \\ 0 & -1 \end{bmatrix}\begin{bmatrix} 1 & -5 \\ 0 & -1 \end{bmatrix}$

$\quad = \begin{bmatrix} (1) \cdot (1) + (-5) \cdot (0) & (1) \cdot (-5) + (-5) \cdot (-1) \\ (0) \cdot (1) + (-1) \cdot (0) & (0) \cdot (-5) + (-1) \cdot (-1) \end{bmatrix} = \begin{bmatrix} 1 & 0 \\ 0 & 1 \end{bmatrix}$

32. $\begin{bmatrix} 2 & 1 & | & 1 & 0 \\ 5 & 3 & | & 0 & 1 \end{bmatrix} \sim \begin{bmatrix} 1 & \frac{1}{2} & | & \frac{1}{2} & 0 \\ 5 & 3 & | & 0 & 1 \end{bmatrix} \sim \begin{bmatrix} 1 & \frac{1}{2} & | & \frac{1}{2} & 0 \\ 0 & \frac{1}{2} & | & -\frac{5}{2} & 1 \end{bmatrix} \sim \begin{bmatrix} 1 & \frac{1}{2} & | & \frac{1}{2} & 0 \\ 0 & 1 & | & -5 & 2 \end{bmatrix}$

$\quad \left(\frac{1}{2}\right)R_1 \to R_1 \qquad (-5)R_1 + R_2 \to R_2 \qquad 2R_2 \to R_2 \qquad \left(-\frac{1}{2}\right)R_2 + R_1 \to R_1$

$\sim \begin{bmatrix} 1 & 0 & | & 3 & -1 \\ 0 & 1 & | & -5 & 2 \end{bmatrix}$

Thus, $M^{-1} = \begin{bmatrix} 3 & -1 \\ -5 & 2 \end{bmatrix}$.

Check:

$M \cdot M^{-1} = \begin{bmatrix} 2 & 1 \\ 5 & 3 \end{bmatrix}\begin{bmatrix} 3 & -1 \\ -5 & 2 \end{bmatrix} = \begin{bmatrix} 2 \cdot 3 + 1 \cdot (-5) & 2 \cdot (-1) + 1 \cdot 2 \\ 5 \cdot 3 + 3 \cdot (-5) & 5 \cdot (-1) + 3 \cdot 2 \end{bmatrix} = \begin{bmatrix} 1 & 0 \\ 0 & 1 \end{bmatrix}$

34. $\begin{bmatrix} 2 & 1 & | & 1 & 0 \\ 1 & 1 & | & 0 & 1 \end{bmatrix} \sim \begin{bmatrix} 1 & 0 & | & 1 & -1 \\ 1 & 1 & | & 0 & 1 \end{bmatrix} \sim \begin{bmatrix} 1 & 0 & | & 1 & -1 \\ 0 & 1 & | & -1 & 2 \end{bmatrix}$

$\quad (-1)R_2 + R_1 \to R_1 \qquad (-1)R_1 + R_2 \to R_2$

Thus, $M^{-1} = \begin{bmatrix} 1 & -1 \\ -1 & 2 \end{bmatrix}$

Check:

$M \cdot M^{-1} = \begin{bmatrix} 2 & 1 \\ 1 & 1 \end{bmatrix}\begin{bmatrix} 1 & -1 \\ -1 & 2 \end{bmatrix} = \begin{bmatrix} 2 \cdot 1 + 1 \cdot (-1) & 2 \cdot (-1) + 1 \cdot 2 \\ 1 \cdot 1 + 1 \cdot (-1) & 1 \cdot (-1) + 1 \cdot 2 \end{bmatrix} = \begin{bmatrix} 1 & 0 \\ 0 & 1 \end{bmatrix}$

36. $\begin{bmatrix} 2 & 3 & 0 & | & 1 & 0 & 0 \\ 1 & 2 & 3 & | & 0 & 1 & 0 \\ 0 & -1 & -5 & | & 0 & 0 & 1 \end{bmatrix}$ ~ $\begin{bmatrix} 1 & 2 & 3 & | & 0 & 1 & 0 \\ 2 & 3 & 0 & | & 1 & 0 & 0 \\ 0 & -1 & -5 & | & 0 & 0 & 1 \end{bmatrix}$ ~

$\qquad\qquad R_1 \leftrightarrow R_2 \qquad\qquad\qquad\qquad (-2)R_1 + R_2 \rightarrow R_2$

$\begin{bmatrix} 1 & 2 & 3 & | & 0 & 1 & 0 \\ 0 & -1 & -6 & | & 1 & -2 & 0 \\ 0 & -1 & -5 & | & 0 & 0 & 1 \end{bmatrix}$ ~ $\begin{bmatrix} 1 & 2 & 3 & | & 0 & 1 & 0 \\ 0 & 1 & 6 & | & -1 & 2 & 0 \\ 0 & -1 & -5 & | & 0 & 0 & 1 \end{bmatrix}$ ~

$\qquad (-1)R_2 \rightarrow R_2 \qquad\qquad\qquad\qquad R_2 + R_3 \rightarrow R_3$

$\qquad\qquad\qquad\qquad\qquad\qquad\qquad (-2)R_2 + R_1 \rightarrow R_1$

$\begin{bmatrix} 1 & 0 & -9 & | & 2 & -3 & 0 \\ 0 & 1 & 6 & | & -1 & 2 & 0 \\ 0 & 0 & 1 & | & -1 & 2 & 1 \end{bmatrix}$ ~ $\begin{bmatrix} 1 & 0 & 0 & | & -7 & 15 & 9 \\ 0 & 1 & 0 & | & 5 & -10 & -6 \\ 0 & 0 & 1 & | & -1 & 2 & 1 \end{bmatrix}$

$\quad 9R_3 + R_1 \rightarrow R_1$

$(-6)R_3 + R_2 \rightarrow R_2$

Thus, $M^{-1} = \begin{bmatrix} -7 & 15 & 9 \\ 5 & -10 & -6 \\ -1 & 2 & 1 \end{bmatrix}$

$M \cdot M^{-1} = \begin{bmatrix} 2 & 3 & 0 \\ 1 & 2 & 3 \\ 0 & -1 & -5 \end{bmatrix} \begin{bmatrix} -7 & 15 & 9 \\ 5 & -10 & -6 \\ -1 & 2 & 1 \end{bmatrix} = \begin{bmatrix} 1 & 0 & 0 \\ 0 & 1 & 0 \\ 0 & 0 & 1 \end{bmatrix}$

38. $\begin{bmatrix} 1 & 0 & -1 & | & 1 & 0 & 0 \\ 2 & -1 & 0 & | & 0 & 1 & 0 \\ 1 & 1 & -2 & | & 0 & 0 & 1 \end{bmatrix}$ ~ $\begin{bmatrix} 1 & 0 & -1 & | & 1 & 0 & 0 \\ 0 & -1 & 2 & | & -2 & 1 & 0 \\ 0 & 1 & -1 & | & -1 & 0 & 1 \end{bmatrix}$ ~

$(-2)R_1 + R_2 \rightarrow R_2 \qquad\qquad\qquad (-1)R_2 \rightarrow R_2$

$(-1)R_1 + R_3 \rightarrow R_3$

$\begin{bmatrix} 1 & 0 & -1 & | & 1 & 0 & 0 \\ 0 & 1 & -2 & | & 2 & -1 & 0 \\ 0 & 1 & -1 & | & -1 & 0 & 1 \end{bmatrix}$ ~ $\begin{bmatrix} 1 & 0 & -1 & | & 1 & 0 & 0 \\ 0 & 1 & -2 & | & 2 & -1 & 0 \\ 0 & 0 & 1 & | & -3 & 1 & 1 \end{bmatrix}$ ~

$(-1)R_2 + R_3 \rightarrow R_3 \qquad\qquad\qquad R_3 + R_1 \rightarrow R_1$

$\qquad\qquad\qquad\qquad\qquad\qquad 2R_3 + R_2 \rightarrow R_2$

$\begin{bmatrix} 1 & 0 & 0 & | & -2 & 1 & 1 \\ 0 & 1 & 0 & | & -4 & 1 & 2 \\ 0 & 0 & 1 & | & -3 & 1 & 1 \end{bmatrix}$ Thus, $M^{-1} = \begin{bmatrix} -2 & 1 & 1 \\ -4 & 1 & 2 \\ -3 & 1 & 1 \end{bmatrix}$

$M \cdot M^{-1} = \begin{bmatrix} 1 & 0 & -1 \\ 2 & -1 & 0 \\ 1 & 1 & -2 \end{bmatrix} \begin{bmatrix} -2 & 1 & 1 \\ -4 & 1 & 2 \\ -3 & 1 & 1 \end{bmatrix} = \begin{bmatrix} 1 & 0 & 0 \\ 0 & 1 & 0 \\ 0 & 0 & 1 \end{bmatrix}$

40. $\begin{bmatrix} -4 & 3 & | & 1 & 0 \\ -5 & 4 & | & 0 & 1 \end{bmatrix} \sim \begin{bmatrix} 1 & -\frac{3}{4} & | & -\frac{1}{4} & 0 \\ -5 & 4 & | & 0 & 1 \end{bmatrix} \sim \begin{bmatrix} 1 & -\frac{3}{4} & | & -\frac{1}{4} & 0 \\ 0 & \frac{1}{4} & | & -\frac{5}{4} & 1 \end{bmatrix} \sim \begin{bmatrix} 1 & -\frac{3}{4} & | & -\frac{1}{4} & 0 \\ 0 & 1 & | & -5 & 4 \end{bmatrix}$

$\left(-\dfrac{1}{4}\right)R_1 \to R_1 \qquad\qquad 5R_1 + R_2 \to R_2 \qquad\qquad 4R_2 \to R_2 \qquad\qquad \dfrac{3}{4}R_2 + R_1 \to R_1$

$\sim \begin{bmatrix} 1 & 0 & | & -4 & 3 \\ 0 & 1 & | & -5 & 4 \end{bmatrix}$ Thus, $M^{-1} = \begin{bmatrix} -4 & 3 \\ -5 & 4 \end{bmatrix}$

42. $\begin{bmatrix} 2 & -4 & | & 1 & 0 \\ -3 & 6 & | & 0 & 1 \end{bmatrix} \sim \begin{bmatrix} 1 & -2 & | & \frac{1}{2} & 0 \\ -3 & 6 & | & 0 & 1 \end{bmatrix} \sim \begin{bmatrix} 1 & -2 & | & \frac{1}{2} & 0 \\ 0 & 0 & | & \frac{3}{2} & 1 \end{bmatrix}$

$\dfrac{1}{2}R_1 \to R_1 \qquad\qquad 3R_1 + R_2 \to R_2$

The inverse does not exist since the second row on the left matrix consists of only zeros.

44. $\begin{bmatrix} -5 & 3 & | & 1 & 0 \\ 2 & -2 & | & 0 & 1 \end{bmatrix} \sim \begin{bmatrix} 1 & -\frac{3}{5} & | & -\frac{1}{5} & 0 \\ 2 & -2 & | & 0 & 1 \end{bmatrix} \sim \begin{bmatrix} 1 & -\frac{3}{5} & | & -\frac{1}{5} & 0 \\ 0 & -\frac{4}{5} & | & \frac{2}{5} & 1 \end{bmatrix} \sim \begin{bmatrix} 1 & -\frac{3}{5} & | & -\frac{1}{5} & 0 \\ 0 & 1 & | & -\frac{1}{2} & -\frac{5}{4} \end{bmatrix}$

$\left(-\dfrac{1}{5}\right)R_1 \to R_1 \qquad (-2)R_1 + R_2 \to R_2 \qquad \left(-\dfrac{5}{4}\right)R_2 \to R_2 \qquad \dfrac{3}{5}R_2 + R_1 \to R_1$

$\sim \begin{bmatrix} 1 & 0 & | & -\frac{1}{2} & -\frac{3}{4} \\ 0 & 1 & | & -\frac{1}{2} & -\frac{5}{4} \end{bmatrix}$. Thus, $M^{-1} = \begin{bmatrix} -0.5 & -0.75 \\ -0.5 & -1.25 \end{bmatrix}$.

46. $\begin{bmatrix} 2 & -2 & 4 & | & 1 & 0 & 0 \\ 1 & 1 & 1 & | & 0 & 1 & 0 \\ 1 & 0 & 1 & | & 0 & 0 & 1 \end{bmatrix} \sim \begin{bmatrix} 1 & 0 & 1 & | & 0 & 0 & 1 \\ 1 & 1 & 1 & | & 0 & 1 & 0 \\ 2 & -2 & 4 & | & 1 & 0 & 0 \end{bmatrix} \sim$

$\qquad\qquad R_1 \leftrightarrow R_3 \qquad\qquad\qquad (-1)R_1 + R_2 \to R_2$

$\qquad\qquad\qquad\qquad\qquad\qquad\qquad\qquad (-2)R_1 + R_3 \to R_3$

$\begin{bmatrix} 1 & 0 & 1 & | & 0 & 0 & 1 \\ 0 & 1 & 0 & | & 0 & 1 & -1 \\ 0 & -2 & 2 & | & 1 & 0 & 2 \end{bmatrix} \sim \begin{bmatrix} 1 & 0 & 1 & | & 0 & 0 & 1 \\ 0 & 1 & 0 & | & 0 & 1 & -1 \\ 0 & 0 & 2 & | & 1 & 2 & -4 \end{bmatrix} \sim$

$\qquad\qquad 2R_2 + R_3 \to R_3 \qquad\qquad\qquad \dfrac{1}{2}R_3 \to R_3$

$\begin{bmatrix} 1 & 0 & 1 & | & 0 & 0 & 1 \\ 0 & 1 & 0 & | & 0 & 1 & -1 \\ 0 & 0 & 1 & | & \frac{1}{2} & 1 & -2 \end{bmatrix} \sim \begin{bmatrix} 1 & 0 & 0 & | & -\frac{1}{2} & -1 & 3 \\ 0 & 1 & 0 & | & 0 & 1 & -1 \\ 0 & 0 & 1 & | & \frac{1}{2} & 1 & -2 \end{bmatrix}$

$\qquad (-1)R_3 + R_1 \to R_1$

Thus, $M^{-1} = \begin{bmatrix} -0.5 & -1 & 3 \\ 0 & 1 & -1 \\ 0.5 & 1 & -2 \end{bmatrix}$.

48.
$$\begin{bmatrix} 1 & -1 & 0 & | & 1 & 0 & 0 \\ 2 & -1 & 1 & | & 0 & 1 & 0 \\ 0 & 1 & 1 & | & 0 & 0 & 1 \end{bmatrix} \sim \begin{bmatrix} 1 & -1 & 0 & | & 1 & 0 & 0 \\ 0 & 1 & 1 & | & -2 & 1 & 0 \\ 0 & 1 & 1 & | & 0 & 0 & 1 \end{bmatrix} \sim$$

$(-2)R_1 + R_2 \to R_2$ $\qquad\qquad\qquad\qquad$ $(-1)R_2 + R_3 \to R_3$

$$\begin{bmatrix} 1 & -1 & 0 & | & 1 & 0 & 0 \\ 0 & 1 & 1 & | & -2 & 1 & 0 \\ 0 & 0 & 0 & | & 2 & -1 & 1 \end{bmatrix}$$

Thus, there is no inverse since a row with all zeros appeared to the left of the vertical line.

50.
$$\begin{bmatrix} 4 & 2 & 2 & | & 1 & 0 & 0 \\ 4 & 2 & 0 & | & 0 & 1 & 0 \\ 5 & 0 & 5 & | & 0 & 0 & 1 \end{bmatrix} \sim \begin{bmatrix} 5 & 0 & 5 & | & 0 & 0 & 1 \\ 4 & 2 & 0 & | & 0 & 1 & 0 \\ 4 & 2 & 2 & | & 1 & 0 & 0 \end{bmatrix} \sim$$

$\qquad\qquad R_1 \leftrightarrow R_3$ $\qquad\qquad\qquad\qquad$ $\dfrac{1}{5}R_1 \to R_1$

$$\begin{bmatrix} 1 & 0 & 1 & | & 0 & 0 & \frac{1}{5} \\ 4 & 2 & 0 & | & 0 & 1 & 0 \\ 4 & 2 & 2 & | & 1 & 0 & 0 \end{bmatrix} \sim \begin{bmatrix} 1 & 0 & 1 & | & 0 & 0 & \frac{1}{5} \\ 0 & 2 & -4 & | & 0 & 1 & -\frac{4}{5} \\ 0 & 2 & -2 & | & 1 & 0 & -\frac{4}{5} \end{bmatrix} \sim$$

$(-4)R_1 + R_2 \to R_2$ $\qquad\qquad\qquad\qquad$ $\dfrac{1}{2}R_2 \to R_2$

$(-4)R_1 + R_3 \to R_3$

$$\begin{bmatrix} 1 & 0 & 1 & | & 0 & 0 & \frac{1}{5} \\ 0 & 1 & -2 & | & 0 & \frac{1}{2} & -\frac{2}{5} \\ 0 & 2 & -2 & | & 1 & 0 & -\frac{4}{5} \end{bmatrix} \sim \begin{bmatrix} 1 & 0 & 1 & | & 0 & 0 & \frac{1}{5} \\ 0 & 1 & -2 & | & 0 & \frac{1}{2} & -\frac{2}{5} \\ 0 & 0 & 2 & | & 1 & -1 & 0 \end{bmatrix} \sim$$

$\quad(-2)R_2 + R_3 \to R_3$ $\qquad\qquad\qquad\qquad$ $\dfrac{1}{2}R_3 \to R_3$

$$\begin{bmatrix} 1 & 0 & 1 & | & 0 & 0 & \frac{1}{5} \\ 0 & 1 & -2 & | & 0 & \frac{1}{2} & -\frac{2}{5} \\ 0 & 0 & 1 & | & \frac{1}{2} & -\frac{1}{2} & 0 \end{bmatrix} \sim \begin{bmatrix} 1 & 0 & 0 & | & -\frac{1}{2} & \frac{1}{2} & \frac{1}{5} \\ 0 & 1 & 0 & | & 1 & -\frac{1}{2} & -\frac{2}{5} \\ 0 & 0 & 1 & | & \frac{1}{2} & -\frac{1}{2} & 0 \end{bmatrix}$$

$(-1)R_3 + R_1 \to R_1$

$\quad 2R_3 + R_2 \to R_2$

Thus, $M^{-1} = \begin{bmatrix} -0.5 & 0.5 & 0.2 \\ 1 & -0.5 & -0.4 \\ 0.5 & -0.5 & 0 \end{bmatrix}$

52. $\begin{bmatrix} -1 & -1 & 4 & | & 1 & 0 & 0 \\ 3 & 3 & -22 & | & 0 & 1 & 0 \\ -2 & -1 & 19 & | & 0 & 0 & 1 \end{bmatrix} \sim \begin{bmatrix} -2 & -1 & 19 & | & 0 & 0 & 1 \\ 3 & 3 & -22 & | & 0 & 1 & 0 \\ -1 & -1 & 4 & | & 1 & 0 & 0 \end{bmatrix}$

$\qquad\qquad R_1 \leftrightarrow R_3 \qquad\qquad\qquad \left(-\dfrac{1}{2}\right)R_1 \to R_1$

$\begin{bmatrix} 1 & \frac{1}{2} & -\frac{19}{2} & | & 0 & 0 & -\frac{1}{2} \\ 3 & 3 & -22 & | & 0 & 1 & 0 \\ -1 & -1 & 4 & | & 1 & 0 & 0 \end{bmatrix} \sim \begin{bmatrix} 1 & \frac{1}{2} & -\frac{19}{2} & | & 0 & 0 & -\frac{1}{2} \\ 0 & \frac{3}{2} & \frac{13}{2} & | & 0 & 1 & \frac{3}{2} \\ 0 & -\frac{1}{2} & -\frac{11}{2} & | & 1 & 0 & -\frac{1}{2} \end{bmatrix} \sim$

$\qquad (-3)R_1 + R_2 \to R_2 \qquad\qquad\qquad \dfrac{2}{3}R_2 \to R_2$

$\qquad\quad R_1 + R_3 \to R_3$

$\begin{bmatrix} 1 & \frac{1}{2} & -\frac{19}{2} & | & 0 & 0 & -\frac{1}{2} \\ 0 & 1 & \frac{13}{3} & | & 0 & \frac{2}{3} & 1 \\ 0 & -\frac{1}{2} & -\frac{11}{2} & | & 1 & 0 & -\frac{1}{2} \end{bmatrix} \sim \begin{bmatrix} 1 & 0 & -\frac{35}{3} & | & 0 & -\frac{1}{3} & -1 \\ 0 & 1 & \frac{13}{3} & | & 0 & \frac{2}{3} & 1 \\ 0 & 0 & -\frac{10}{3} & | & 1 & \frac{1}{3} & 0 \end{bmatrix} \sim$

$\qquad \left(-\dfrac{1}{2}\right)R_2 + R_1 \to R_1 \qquad\qquad \left(-\dfrac{3}{10}\right)R_3 \to R_3$

$\qquad \dfrac{1}{2}R_2 + R_3 \to R_3$

$\begin{bmatrix} 1 & 0 & -\frac{35}{3} & | & 0 & -\frac{1}{3} & -1 \\ 0 & 1 & \frac{13}{3} & | & 0 & \frac{2}{3} & 1 \\ 0 & 0 & 1 & | & -\frac{3}{10} & -\frac{1}{10} & 0 \end{bmatrix} \sim \begin{bmatrix} 1 & 0 & 0 & | & -3.5 & -1.5 & -1 \\ 0 & 1 & 0 & | & 1.3 & 1.1 & 1 \\ 0 & 0 & 1 & | & -0.3 & -0.1 & 0 \end{bmatrix}$

$\qquad \left(-\dfrac{13}{3}\right)R_3 + R_2 \to R_2$

$\qquad \left(\dfrac{35}{3}\right)R_3 + R_1 \to R_1$

Thus, $M^{-1} = \begin{bmatrix} -3.5 & -1.5 & -1 \\ 1.3 & 1.1 & 1 \\ -0.3 & -0.1 & 0 \end{bmatrix}.$

54. $A = \begin{bmatrix} 4 & 3 \\ 3 & 2 \end{bmatrix};$ $\begin{bmatrix} 4 & 3 & | & 1 & 0 \\ 3 & 2 & | & 0 & 1 \end{bmatrix} \sim \begin{bmatrix} 1 & \frac{3}{4} & | & \frac{1}{4} & 0 \\ 3 & 2 & | & 0 & 1 \end{bmatrix} \sim \begin{bmatrix} 1 & \frac{3}{4} & | & \frac{1}{4} & 0 \\ 0 & -\frac{1}{4} & | & -\frac{3}{4} & 1 \end{bmatrix} \sim$

$\qquad\qquad\quad \dfrac{1}{4}R_1 \to R_1 \qquad (-3)R_1 + R_2 \to R_2 \qquad (-4)R_2 \to R_2$

$\begin{bmatrix} 1 & \frac{3}{4} & | & \frac{1}{4} & 0 \\ 0 & 2 & | & 3 & -4 \end{bmatrix} \sim \begin{bmatrix} 1 & 0 & | & -2 & 3 \\ 0 & 1 & | & 3 & -4 \end{bmatrix}$ Thus, $A^{-1} = \begin{bmatrix} -2 & 3 \\ 3 & -4 \end{bmatrix}.$

$\left(-\dfrac{3}{4}\right)R_2 + R_1 \to R_1$

$$B = \begin{bmatrix} 2 & 5 \\ 3 & 7 \end{bmatrix}; \quad \begin{bmatrix} 2 & 5 & | & 1 & 0 \\ 3 & 7 & | & 0 & 1 \end{bmatrix} \sim \begin{bmatrix} 1 & \frac{5}{2} & | & \frac{1}{2} & 0 \\ 3 & 7 & | & 0 & 1 \end{bmatrix} \sim \begin{bmatrix} 1 & \frac{5}{2} & | & \frac{1}{2} & 0 \\ 0 & -\frac{1}{2} & | & -\frac{3}{2} & 1 \end{bmatrix} \sim$$

$$\frac{1}{2}R_1 \to R_1 \qquad (-3)R_1 + R_2 \to R_2 \qquad (-2)R_2 \to R_2$$

$$\begin{bmatrix} 1 & \frac{5}{2} & | & \frac{1}{2} & 0 \\ 0 & 1 & | & 3 & -2 \end{bmatrix} \sim \begin{bmatrix} 1 & 0 & | & -7 & 5 \\ 0 & 1 & | & 3 & -2 \end{bmatrix} \quad \text{Thus,} \quad B^{-1} = \begin{bmatrix} -7 & 5 \\ 3 & -2 \end{bmatrix}.$$

$$\left(-\frac{5}{2}\right)R_2 + R_1 \to R_1$$

$$AB = \begin{bmatrix} 4 & 3 \\ 3 & 2 \end{bmatrix}\begin{bmatrix} 2 & 5 \\ 3 & 7 \end{bmatrix} = \begin{bmatrix} 17 & 41 \\ 12 & 29 \end{bmatrix};$$

$$\begin{bmatrix} 17 & 41 & | & 1 & 0 \\ 12 & 29 & | & 0 & 1 \end{bmatrix} \sim \begin{bmatrix} 1 & \frac{41}{17} & | & \frac{1}{17} & 0 \\ 12 & 29 & | & 0 & 1 \end{bmatrix} \sim \begin{bmatrix} 1 & \frac{41}{17} & | & \frac{1}{17} & 0 \\ 0 & \frac{1}{17} & | & -\frac{12}{17} & 1 \end{bmatrix} \sim$$

$$\frac{1}{17}R_1 \to R_1 \qquad (-12)R_1 + R_2 \to R_2 \qquad 17R_2 \to R_2$$

$$\begin{bmatrix} 1 & \frac{41}{17} & | & \frac{1}{17} & 0 \\ 0 & 1 & | & -12 & 17 \end{bmatrix} \sim \begin{bmatrix} 1 & 0 & | & 29 & -41 \\ 0 & 1 & | & -12 & 17 \end{bmatrix} \quad \text{Thus,} \quad (AB)^{-1} = \begin{bmatrix} 29 & -41 \\ -12 & 17 \end{bmatrix}.$$

$$\left(-\frac{41}{17}\right)R_2 + R_1 \to R_1$$

We have $B^{-1}A^{-1} = \begin{bmatrix} -7 & 5 \\ 3 & -2 \end{bmatrix}\begin{bmatrix} -2 & 3 \\ 3 & -4 \end{bmatrix} = \begin{bmatrix} 29 & -41 \\ -12 & 17 \end{bmatrix}.$

Therefore, $(AB)^{-1} = B^{-1}A^{-1}$.

56. $\begin{bmatrix} a & b & | & 1 & 0 \\ 0 & d & | & 0 & 1 \end{bmatrix}$

a must be nonzero so that $\left(\frac{1}{a}\right)R_1 \to R_1$ has meaning.

$$\begin{bmatrix} a & b & | & 1 & 0 \\ 0 & d & | & 0 & 1 \end{bmatrix} \sim \begin{bmatrix} 1 & \frac{b}{a} & | & \frac{1}{a} & 0 \\ 0 & d & | & 0 & 1 \end{bmatrix} \sim \begin{bmatrix} 1 & \frac{b}{a} & | & \frac{1}{a} & 0 \\ 0 & 1 & | & 0 & \frac{1}{d} \end{bmatrix}$$

d must be nonzero as well so that we could have operation $\frac{1}{d}R_2 \to R_2$.

$\left(-\frac{b}{a}\right)R_2 + R_1 \to R_1$ implies

$\begin{bmatrix} 1 & 0 & | & \frac{1}{a} & -\frac{b}{ad} \\ 0 & 1 & | & 0 & \frac{1}{d} \end{bmatrix}$. Thus, $M^{-1} = \begin{bmatrix} \frac{1}{a} & -\frac{b}{ad} \\ 0 & \frac{1}{d} \end{bmatrix} = \frac{1}{ad}\begin{bmatrix} d & -b \\ 0 & a \end{bmatrix}$

For an $n \times n$ upper triangular matrix, the inverse exists if and only if all the elements on the main diagonal are nonzero.

58. $A = \begin{bmatrix} -2 & -1 \\ 3 & 2 \end{bmatrix}$

A^{-1}: $\left[\begin{array}{cc|cc} -2 & -1 & 1 & 0 \\ 3 & 2 & 0 & 1 \end{array}\right] \sim \left[\begin{array}{cc|cc} 1 & \frac{1}{2} & -\frac{1}{2} & 0 \\ 3 & 2 & 0 & 1 \end{array}\right] \sim \left[\begin{array}{cc|cc} 1 & \frac{1}{2} & -\frac{1}{2} & 0 \\ 0 & \frac{1}{2} & \frac{3}{2} & 1 \end{array}\right] \sim$

$$\left(-\frac{1}{2}\right)R_1 \rightarrow R_1 \qquad (-3)R_1 + R_2 \rightarrow R_2 \qquad 2R_2 \rightarrow R_2$$

$\left[\begin{array}{cc|cc} 1 & \frac{1}{2} & -\frac{1}{2} & 0 \\ 0 & 1 & 3 & 2 \end{array}\right] \sim \left[\begin{array}{cc|cc} 1 & 0 & -2 & -1 \\ 0 & 1 & 3 & 2 \end{array}\right]$

$$\left(-\frac{1}{2}\right)R_2 + R_1 \rightarrow R_1$$

Therefore, $A^{-1} = A$, so $A^2 = AA = AA^{-1} = I$.

60. If $A = A^{-1}$, then $A^2 = AA = AA^{-1} = A^{-1}A = I$.

62. $A = \begin{bmatrix} -2 & 4 & 0 & -1 \\ 2 & -1 & 2 & 5 \\ 0 & 2 & -1 & 7 \\ 2 & -3 & 0 & 5 \end{bmatrix}$, $A^{-1} = \begin{bmatrix} -3.6 & 0.85 & 1.7 & -3.95 \\ -1.4 & 0.4 & 0.8 & -1.8 \\ 1.4 & 0.1 & -0.8 & 1.3 \\ 0.6 & -0.1 & -0.2 & 0.7 \end{bmatrix}$

64. $A = \begin{bmatrix} 1 & 2 & 3 & 4 & 5 \\ 2 & 6 & 4 & 5 & 6 \\ -1 & -2 & -1 & 2 & 3 \\ 1 & 6 & 1 & 6 & 4 \\ 1 & -4 & 3 & -7 & -4 \end{bmatrix}$, $A^{-1} = \begin{bmatrix} -6.5 & -1.5 & 8.5 & 11.5 & 7.5 \\ 0.75 & 0.625 & -1.5 & -2.125 & -1.375 \\ 3 & 0.25 & -3.5 & -4.25 & -2.75 \\ 0.5 & -0.75 & 0 & 0.75 & 0.25 \\ -1 & 0.5 & 1 & 0.5 & 0.5 \end{bmatrix}$

66. $A = \begin{bmatrix} 1 & 2 \\ 1 & 3 \end{bmatrix}$

Assign the numbers 1 - 26 to the letters of the alphabet, in order, and let 0 correspond to blank space. Then the message "THE GRAPES OF WRATH" corresponds to the sequence

20 8 5 0 7 18 1 16 5 19 0 15 6 0 23 18 1 20 8

To encode this message, divide the numbers into groups of two and use the groups as columns of a matrix B with two rows (we add a blank at the end to make it even).

$B = \begin{bmatrix} 20 & 5 & 7 & 1 & 5 & 0 & 6 & 23 & 1 & 8 \\ 8 & 0 & 18 & 16 & 19 & 15 & 0 & 18 & 20 & 0 \end{bmatrix}$

Now $AB = \begin{bmatrix} 1 & 2 \\ 1 & 3 \end{bmatrix}\begin{bmatrix} 20 & 5 & 7 & 1 & 5 & 0 & 6 & 23 & 1 & 8 \\ 8 & 0 & 18 & 16 & 19 & 15 & 0 & 18 & 20 & 0 \end{bmatrix}$

$= \begin{bmatrix} 36 & 5 & 43 & 33 & 43 & 30 & 6 & 59 & 41 & 8 \\ 44 & 5 & 61 & 49 & 62 & 45 & 6 & 77 & 61 & 8 \end{bmatrix}$

The coded message is:
36 44 5 5 43 61 33 49 43 62 30 45 6 6 59 77 41 61 8 8

68. First we must find the inverse of $A = \begin{bmatrix} 1 & 2 \\ 1 & 3 \end{bmatrix}$

$$\begin{bmatrix} 1 & 2 & | & 1 & 0 \\ 1 & 3 & | & 0 & 1 \end{bmatrix} \sim \begin{bmatrix} 1 & 2 & | & 1 & 0 \\ 0 & 1 & | & -1 & 1 \end{bmatrix} \sim \begin{bmatrix} 1 & 0 & | & 3 & -2 \\ 0 & 1 & | & -1 & 1 \end{bmatrix}$$

$(-1)R_1 + R_2 \rightarrow R_2 \qquad (-2)R_2 + R_1 \rightarrow R_1$

Thus, $A^{-1} = \begin{bmatrix} 3 & -2 \\ -1 & 1 \end{bmatrix}$

Now $\begin{bmatrix} 3 & -2 \\ -1 & 1 \end{bmatrix} \begin{bmatrix} 9 & 40 & 29 & 2 & 22 & 6 & 43 & 29 & 54 \\ 13 & 49 & 34 & 3 & 26 & 9 & 57 & 34 & 74 \end{bmatrix}$

$= \begin{bmatrix} 1 & 22 & 19 & 0 & 14 & 0 & 15 & 19 & 14 \\ 4 & 9 & 5 & 1 & 4 & 3 & 14 & 5 & 20 \end{bmatrix}$

Thus, the decoded message is

1 4 22 9 19 5 0 1 14 4 0 3 15 14 19 5 14 20

which corresponds to "ADVISE AND CONSENT".

70. "THE BRIDGE ON THE RIVER KWAI" corresponds to the sequence

20 8 5 0 2 18 9 4 7 5 0 15 14 0 20 8 5 0 18 9
22 5 18 0 11 23 1 9

We divide the numbers in the sequence into groups of 5 and use these groups as the columns of a matrix with 5 rows, adding blanks at the end to make the columns come out even. Then multiply this matrix on the left by the given matrix B.

$$\begin{bmatrix} 1 & 0 & 1 & 0 & 1 \\ 0 & 1 & 1 & 0 & 3 \\ 2 & 1 & 1 & 1 & 1 \\ 0 & 0 & 1 & 0 & 2 \\ 1 & 1 & 1 & 2 & 1 \end{bmatrix} \begin{bmatrix} 20 & 18 & 0 & 8 & 22 & 23 \\ 8 & 9 & 15 & 5 & 5 & 1 \\ 5 & 4 & 14 & 0 & 18 & 9 \\ 0 & 7 & 0 & 18 & 0 & 0 \\ 2 & 5 & 20 & 9 & 11 & 0 \end{bmatrix} = \begin{bmatrix} 20 & 18 & 0 & 8 & 22 & 23 \\ 8 & 9 & 15 & 5 & 5 & 1 \\ 5 & 4 & 14 & 0 & 18 & 9 \\ 0 & 7 & 0 & 18 & 0 & 0 \\ 2 & 5 & 20 & 9 & 11 & 0 \end{bmatrix}$$

The encoded sequence is:

27 19 55 9 35 27 28 61 14 50 34 89 49 54 49
17 32 48 18 58 51 56 78 40 56 32 10 56 9 33

72. First we must find the inverse of B:

$$B^{-1} = \begin{bmatrix} -2 & -1 & 2 & 2 & -1 \\ 3 & 2 & -2 & -4 & 1 \\ 6 & 2 & -4 & -5 & 2 \\ -2 & -1 & 1 & 2 & 0 \\ -3 & -1 & 2 & 3 & -1 \end{bmatrix}$$

Now, $B^{-1} = \begin{bmatrix} 28 & 30 & 30 & 39 \\ 22 & 27 & 51 & 30 \\ 56 & 75 & 64 & 58 \\ 11 & 15 & 30 & 25 \\ 36 & 78 & 62 & 44 \end{bmatrix} = \begin{bmatrix} 20 & 15 & 15 & 14 \\ 8 & 12 & 6 & 5 \\ 5 & 15 & 0 & 25 \\ 0 & 18 & 13 & 0 \\ 3 & 0 & 15 & 0 \end{bmatrix}$

Thus, the decoded message is:

20 8 5 0 3 15 12 15 18 0 15 6 0 13 15 14 5 25

which corresponds to "THE COLOR OF MONEY".

2. $\begin{bmatrix} -2 & 1 \\ -3 & 4 \end{bmatrix}\begin{bmatrix} x_1 \\ x_2 \end{bmatrix} = \begin{bmatrix} -5 \\ 7 \end{bmatrix}$

$\begin{bmatrix} -2x_1 + x_2 \\ -3x_1 + 4x_2 \end{bmatrix} = \begin{bmatrix} -5 \\ 7 \end{bmatrix}$

Thus, $-2x_1 + x_2 = -5$

$-3x_1 + 4x_2 = 7$

4. $\begin{bmatrix} 2 & -1 & 0 \\ -2 & 3 & -1 \\ 4 & 0 & 3 \end{bmatrix}\begin{bmatrix} x_1 \\ x_2 \\ x_3 \end{bmatrix} = \begin{bmatrix} 6 \\ -4 \\ 7 \end{bmatrix}$

$\begin{bmatrix} 2x_1 - x_2 \\ -2x_1 + 3x_2 - x_3 \\ 4x_1 + 3x_3 \end{bmatrix} = \begin{bmatrix} 6 \\ -4 \\ 7 \end{bmatrix}$

Thus, $2x_1 - x_2 \quad = 6$

$-2x_1 + 3x_2 - x_3 = -4$

$4x_1 \quad + 3x_3 = 7$

6. $2x_1 + x_2 = 8$
$-5x_1 + 3x_2 = -4$

$\begin{bmatrix} 2x_1 + x_2 \\ -5x_1 + 3x_2 \end{bmatrix} = \begin{bmatrix} 8 \\ -4 \end{bmatrix}$ and $\begin{bmatrix} 2 & 1 \\ -5 & 3 \end{bmatrix}\begin{bmatrix} x_1 \\ x_2 \end{bmatrix} = \begin{bmatrix} 8 \\ -4 \end{bmatrix}$

8. $3x_1 \quad + 2x_3 = 9$

$-x_1 + 4x_2 + x_3 = -7$

$-2x_1 + 3x_2 \quad = 6$

$\begin{bmatrix} 3x_1 + 2x_3 \\ -x_1 + 4x_2 + x_3 \\ -2x_1 + 3x_2 \end{bmatrix} = \begin{bmatrix} 9 \\ -7 \\ 6 \end{bmatrix}$ and $\begin{bmatrix} 3 & 0 & 2 \\ -1 & 4 & 1 \\ -2 & 3 & 0 \end{bmatrix}\begin{bmatrix} x_1 \\ x_2 \\ x_3 \end{bmatrix} = \begin{bmatrix} 9 \\ -7 \\ 6 \end{bmatrix}$

10. $\begin{bmatrix} x_1 \\ x_2 \end{bmatrix} = \begin{bmatrix} -2 & 1 \\ -1 & 2 \end{bmatrix}\begin{bmatrix} 3 \\ -2 \end{bmatrix} = \begin{bmatrix} (-2)(3) + (1)(-2) \\ (-1)(3) + (2)(-2) \end{bmatrix} = \begin{bmatrix} -8 \\ -7 \end{bmatrix}$ Thus, $x_1 = -8$
and $x_2 = -7$

12. $\begin{bmatrix} x_1 \\ x_2 \end{bmatrix} = \begin{bmatrix} 3 & -1 \\ 0 & 2 \end{bmatrix}\begin{bmatrix} -2 \\ 1 \end{bmatrix} = \begin{bmatrix} (3)(-2) + (-1)(1) \\ (0)(-2) + (2)(1) \end{bmatrix} = \begin{bmatrix} -7 \\ 2 \end{bmatrix}$ Thus, $x_1 = -7$
and $x_2 = 2$

14. $\begin{bmatrix} 1 & 3 \\ 1 & 4 \end{bmatrix}\begin{bmatrix} x_1 \\ x_2 \end{bmatrix} = \begin{bmatrix} 9 \\ 6 \end{bmatrix}$

If $A = \begin{bmatrix} 1 & 3 \\ 1 & 4 \end{bmatrix}$ has an inverse, then $\begin{bmatrix} x_1 \\ x_2 \end{bmatrix} = A^{-1}\begin{bmatrix} 9 \\ 6 \end{bmatrix}$.

$\begin{bmatrix} 1 & 3 & | & 1 & 0 \\ 1 & 4 & | & 0 & 1 \end{bmatrix} \sim \begin{bmatrix} 1 & 3 & | & 1 & 0 \\ 0 & 1 & | & -1 & 1 \end{bmatrix} \sim \begin{bmatrix} 1 & 0 & | & 4 & -3 \\ 0 & 1 & | & -1 & 1 \end{bmatrix}$

$(-1)R_1 + R_2 \to R_2 \qquad (-3)R_2 + R_1 \to R_1$

Thus, $A^{-1} = \begin{bmatrix} 4 & -3 \\ -1 & 1 \end{bmatrix}$ and $\begin{bmatrix} x_1 \\ x_2 \end{bmatrix} = \begin{bmatrix} 4 & -3 \\ -1 & 1 \end{bmatrix}\begin{bmatrix} 9 \\ 6 \end{bmatrix} = \begin{bmatrix} 18 \\ -3 \end{bmatrix}$

Therefore, $x_1 = 18$, $x_2 = -3$.

16. $\begin{bmatrix} 1 & 1 \\ 3 & -2 \end{bmatrix}\begin{bmatrix} x_1 \\ x_2 \end{bmatrix} = \begin{bmatrix} 10 \\ 20 \end{bmatrix}$

If $A = \begin{bmatrix} 1 & 1 \\ 3 & -2 \end{bmatrix}$ has an inverse, then $\begin{bmatrix} x_1 \\ x_2 \end{bmatrix} = A^{-1}\begin{bmatrix} 10 \\ 20 \end{bmatrix}$

$\left[\begin{array}{cc|cc} 1 & 1 & 1 & 0 \\ 3 & -2 & 0 & 1 \end{array}\right] \sim \left[\begin{array}{cc|cc} 1 & 1 & 1 & 0 \\ 0 & -5 & -3 & 1 \end{array}\right] \sim \left[\begin{array}{cc|cc} 1 & 1 & 1 & 0 \\ 0 & 1 & \frac{3}{5} & -\frac{1}{5} \end{array}\right] \sim \left[\begin{array}{cc|cc} 1 & 0 & \frac{2}{5} & \frac{1}{5} \\ 0 & 1 & \frac{3}{5} & -\frac{1}{5} \end{array}\right]$

$(-3)R_1 + R_2 \rightarrow R_2 \qquad \left(-\dfrac{1}{5}\right)R_2 \rightarrow R_2 \qquad (-1)R_2 + R_1 \rightarrow R_1$

Thus, $A^{-1} = \begin{bmatrix} 0.4 & 0.2 \\ 0.6 & -0.2 \end{bmatrix}$ and $\begin{bmatrix} x_1 \\ x_2 \end{bmatrix} = \begin{bmatrix} 0.4 & 0.2 \\ 0.6 & -0.2 \end{bmatrix}\begin{bmatrix} 10 \\ 20 \end{bmatrix} = \begin{bmatrix} 8 \\ 2 \end{bmatrix}$

Therefore, $x_1 = 8$, $x_2 = 2$.

18. $\begin{bmatrix} 3 & 1 \\ 2 & 1 \end{bmatrix}\begin{bmatrix} x_1 \\ x_2 \end{bmatrix} + \begin{bmatrix} 4 \\ 1 \end{bmatrix} = \begin{bmatrix} 7 \\ 8 \end{bmatrix}$ or $\begin{bmatrix} 3 & 1 \\ 2 & 1 \end{bmatrix}\begin{bmatrix} x_1 \\ x_2 \end{bmatrix} = \begin{bmatrix} 3 \\ 7 \end{bmatrix}$

If $A = \begin{bmatrix} 3 & 1 \\ 2 & 1 \end{bmatrix}$ has an inverse, then $\begin{bmatrix} x_1 \\ x_2 \end{bmatrix} = A^{-1}\begin{bmatrix} 3 \\ 7 \end{bmatrix}$.

$\left[\begin{array}{cc|cc} 3 & 1 & 1 & 0 \\ 2 & 1 & 0 & 1 \end{array}\right] \sim \left[\begin{array}{cc|cc} 3 & 1 & 1 & 0 \\ 0 & \frac{1}{3} & -\frac{2}{3} & 1 \end{array}\right] \sim \left[\begin{array}{cc|cc} 1 & \frac{1}{3} & \frac{1}{3} & 0 \\ 0 & \frac{1}{3} & -\frac{2}{3} & 1 \end{array}\right]$

$\left(-\dfrac{2}{3}\right)R_1 + R_2 \rightarrow R_2 \qquad \dfrac{1}{3}R_1 \rightarrow R_1 \qquad\qquad 3R_2 \rightarrow R_2$

$\sim \left[\begin{array}{cc|cc} 1 & \frac{1}{3} & \frac{1}{3} & 0 \\ 0 & 1 & -2 & 3 \end{array}\right] \sim \left[\begin{array}{cc|cc} 1 & 0 & 1 & -1 \\ 0 & 1 & -2 & 3 \end{array}\right]$

$-R_2 + R_1 \rightarrow R_1$

Thus, $A^{-1} = \begin{bmatrix} 1 & -1 \\ -2 & 3 \end{bmatrix}$ and $\begin{bmatrix} x_1 \\ x_2 \end{bmatrix} = \begin{bmatrix} 1 & -1 \\ -2 & 3 \end{bmatrix}\begin{bmatrix} 3 \\ 7 \end{bmatrix} = \begin{bmatrix} -4 \\ 15 \end{bmatrix}$.

Therefore, $x_1 = -4$, $x_2 = 15$.

20. $\begin{bmatrix} 3 & -4 \\ -6 & 8 \end{bmatrix}\begin{bmatrix} x_1 \\ x_2 \end{bmatrix} + \begin{bmatrix} 1 \\ 0 \end{bmatrix} = \begin{bmatrix} 2 \\ 1 \end{bmatrix}$ or $\begin{bmatrix} 3 & -4 \\ -6 & 8 \end{bmatrix}\begin{bmatrix} x_1 \\ x_2 \end{bmatrix} = \begin{bmatrix} 1 \\ 0 \end{bmatrix}$

Let $A = \begin{bmatrix} 3 & -4 \\ -6 & 8 \end{bmatrix}$ and check to see if A^{-1} exists.

$\left[\begin{array}{cc|cc} 3 & -4 & 1 & 0 \\ -6 & 8 & 0 & 1 \end{array}\right] \sim \left[\begin{array}{cc|cc} 1 & -\frac{4}{3} & \frac{1}{3} & 0 \\ -6 & 8 & 0 & 1 \end{array}\right] \sim \left[\begin{array}{cc|cc} 1 & -\frac{4}{3} & \frac{1}{3} & 0 \\ 0 & 0 & 2 & 1 \end{array}\right]$

$\dfrac{1}{3}R_1 \rightarrow R_1 \qquad\qquad 6R_1 + R_2 \rightarrow R_2$

Since one row consists of only 0, A^{-1} does not exist and hence there are no solutions.

22. $\begin{bmatrix} 3 & -1 \\ 6 & -4 \end{bmatrix}\begin{bmatrix} x_1 \\ x_2 \end{bmatrix} + \begin{bmatrix} -2 \\ -3 \end{bmatrix} = \begin{bmatrix} -2 \\ -3 \end{bmatrix}$ or $\begin{bmatrix} 3 & -1 \\ 6 & -4 \end{bmatrix}\begin{bmatrix} x_1 \\ x_2 \end{bmatrix} = \begin{bmatrix} 0 \\ 0 \end{bmatrix}$

so the only solution is $(0, 0)$, i.e. $x_1 = x_2 = 0$.

24. The matrix equation for the given system is:

$\begin{bmatrix} 2 & 1 \\ 5 & 3 \end{bmatrix}\begin{bmatrix} x_1 \\ x_2 \end{bmatrix} = \begin{bmatrix} k_1 \\ k_2 \end{bmatrix}$

From Exercise 4-5, Problem 32, $\begin{bmatrix} 2 & 1 \\ 5 & 3 \end{bmatrix}^{-1} = \begin{bmatrix} 3 & -1 \\ -5 & 2 \end{bmatrix}$

Thus, $\begin{bmatrix} x_1 \\ x_2 \end{bmatrix} = \begin{bmatrix} 3 & -1 \\ -5 & 2 \end{bmatrix}\begin{bmatrix} k_1 \\ k_2 \end{bmatrix}$

(A) $\begin{bmatrix} x_1 \\ x_2 \end{bmatrix} = \begin{bmatrix} 3 & -1 \\ -5 & 2 \end{bmatrix}\begin{bmatrix} 2 \\ 13 \end{bmatrix} = \begin{bmatrix} -7 \\ 16 \end{bmatrix}$ Thus, $x_1 = -7$ and $x_2 = 16$

(B) $\begin{bmatrix} x_1 \\ x_2 \end{bmatrix} = \begin{bmatrix} 3 & -1 \\ -5 & 2 \end{bmatrix}\begin{bmatrix} 2 \\ 4 \end{bmatrix} = \begin{bmatrix} 2 \\ -2 \end{bmatrix}$ Thus, $x_1 = 2$ and $x_2 = -2$

(C) $\begin{bmatrix} x_1 \\ x_2 \end{bmatrix} = \begin{bmatrix} 3 & -1 \\ -5 & 2 \end{bmatrix}\begin{bmatrix} 1 \\ -3 \end{bmatrix} = \begin{bmatrix} 6 \\ -11 \end{bmatrix}$ Thus, $x_1 = 6$ and $x_2 = -11$

26. The matrix equation for the given system is:

$\begin{bmatrix} 2 & 1 \\ 1 & 1 \end{bmatrix}\begin{bmatrix} x_1 \\ x_2 \end{bmatrix} = \begin{bmatrix} k_1 \\ k_2 \end{bmatrix}$

From Exercise 4-5, Problem 34, $\begin{bmatrix} 2 & 1 \\ 1 & 1 \end{bmatrix}^{-1} = \begin{bmatrix} 1 & -1 \\ -1 & 2 \end{bmatrix}$

Thus, $\begin{bmatrix} x_1 \\ x_2 \end{bmatrix} = \begin{bmatrix} 1 & -1 \\ -1 & 2 \end{bmatrix}\begin{bmatrix} k_1 \\ k_2 \end{bmatrix}$

(A) $\begin{bmatrix} x_1 \\ x_2 \end{bmatrix} = \begin{bmatrix} 1 & -1 \\ -1 & 2 \end{bmatrix}\begin{bmatrix} -1 \\ -2 \end{bmatrix} = \begin{bmatrix} 1 \\ -3 \end{bmatrix}$ Thus, $x_1 = 1$ and $x_2 = -3$

(B) $\begin{bmatrix} x_1 \\ x_2 \end{bmatrix} = \begin{bmatrix} 1 & -1 \\ -1 & 2 \end{bmatrix}\begin{bmatrix} 2 \\ 3 \end{bmatrix} = \begin{bmatrix} -1 \\ 4 \end{bmatrix}$ Thus, $x_1 = -1$ and $x_2 = 4$

(C) $\begin{bmatrix} x_1 \\ x_2 \end{bmatrix} = \begin{bmatrix} 1 & -1 \\ -1 & 2 \end{bmatrix}\begin{bmatrix} 2 \\ 0 \end{bmatrix} = \begin{bmatrix} 2 \\ -2 \end{bmatrix}$ Thus, $x_1 = 2$ and $x_2 = -2$

28. The matrix equation for the given system is:

$\begin{bmatrix} 2 & 3 & 0 \\ 1 & 2 & 3 \\ 0 & -1 & -5 \end{bmatrix}\begin{bmatrix} x_1 \\ x_2 \\ x_3 \end{bmatrix} = \begin{bmatrix} k_1 \\ k_2 \\ k_3 \end{bmatrix}$

From Exercise 4-5, Problem 36, $\begin{bmatrix} 2 & 3 & 0 \\ 1 & 2 & 3 \\ 0 & -1 & -5 \end{bmatrix}^{-1} = \begin{bmatrix} -7 & 15 & 9 \\ 5 & -10 & -6 \\ -1 & 2 & 1 \end{bmatrix}$

Thus,

$\begin{bmatrix} x_1 \\ x_2 \\ x_3 \end{bmatrix} = \begin{bmatrix} -7 & 15 & 9 \\ 5 & -10 & -6 \\ -1 & 2 & 1 \end{bmatrix}\begin{bmatrix} k_1 \\ k_2 \\ k_3 \end{bmatrix}$

(A) $\begin{bmatrix} x_1 \\ x_2 \\ x_3 \end{bmatrix} = \begin{bmatrix} -7 & 15 & 9 \\ 5 & -10 & -6 \\ -1 & 2 & 1 \end{bmatrix} \begin{bmatrix} 0 \\ 2 \\ 1 \end{bmatrix} = \begin{bmatrix} 39 \\ -26 \\ 5 \end{bmatrix}$; $x_1 = 39$, $x_2 = -26$, $x_3 = 5$

(B) $\begin{bmatrix} x_1 \\ x_2 \\ x_3 \end{bmatrix} = \begin{bmatrix} -7 & 15 & 9 \\ 5 & -10 & -6 \\ -1 & 2 & 1 \end{bmatrix} \begin{bmatrix} -2 \\ 0 \\ 1 \end{bmatrix} = \begin{bmatrix} 23 \\ -16 \\ 3 \end{bmatrix}$; $x_1 = 23$, $x_2 = -16$, $x_3 = 3$

(C) $\begin{bmatrix} x_1 \\ x_2 \\ x_3 \end{bmatrix} = \begin{bmatrix} -7 & 15 & 9 \\ 5 & -10 & -6 \\ -1 & 2 & 1 \end{bmatrix} \begin{bmatrix} 3 \\ 1 \\ 0 \end{bmatrix} = \begin{bmatrix} -6 \\ 5 \\ -1 \end{bmatrix}$; $x_1 = -6$, $x_2 = 5$, $x_3 = -1$

30. The matrix equation for the given system is:

$$\begin{bmatrix} 1 & 0 & -1 \\ 2 & -1 & 0 \\ 1 & 1 & -2 \end{bmatrix} \begin{bmatrix} x_1 \\ x_2 \\ x_3 \end{bmatrix} = \begin{bmatrix} k_1 \\ k_2 \\ k_3 \end{bmatrix}$$

From Exercise 4-5, Problem 38, $\begin{bmatrix} 1 & 0 & -1 \\ 2 & -1 & 0 \\ 1 & 1 & -2 \end{bmatrix}^{-1} = \begin{bmatrix} -2 & 1 & 1 \\ -4 & 1 & 2 \\ -3 & 1 & 1 \end{bmatrix}$

Thus,

$$\begin{bmatrix} x_1 \\ x_2 \\ x_3 \end{bmatrix} = \begin{bmatrix} -2 & 1 & 1 \\ -4 & 1 & 2 \\ -3 & 1 & 1 \end{bmatrix} \begin{bmatrix} k_1 \\ k_2 \\ k_3 \end{bmatrix}$$

(A) $\begin{bmatrix} x_1 \\ x_2 \\ x_3 \end{bmatrix} = \begin{bmatrix} -2 & 1 & 1 \\ -4 & 1 & 2 \\ -3 & 1 & 1 \end{bmatrix} \begin{bmatrix} 4 \\ 8 \\ 0 \end{bmatrix} = \begin{bmatrix} 0 \\ -8 \\ -4 \end{bmatrix}$; $x_1 = 0$, $x_2 = -8$, $x_3 = -4$

(B) $\begin{bmatrix} x_1 \\ x_2 \\ x_3 \end{bmatrix} = \begin{bmatrix} -2 & 1 & 1 \\ -4 & 1 & 2 \\ -3 & 1 & 1 \end{bmatrix} \begin{bmatrix} 4 \\ 0 \\ -4 \end{bmatrix} = \begin{bmatrix} -12 \\ -24 \\ -16 \end{bmatrix}$; $x_1 = -12$, $x_2 = -24$, $x_3 = -16$

(C) $\begin{bmatrix} x_1 \\ x_2 \\ x_3 \end{bmatrix} = \begin{bmatrix} -2 & 1 & 1 \\ -4 & 1 & 2 \\ -3 & 1 & 1 \end{bmatrix} \begin{bmatrix} 0 \\ 8 \\ -8 \end{bmatrix} = \begin{bmatrix} 0 \\ -8 \\ 0 \end{bmatrix}$; $x_1 = 0$, $x_2 = -8$, $x_3 = 0$

32. $-2x_1 + 4x_2 = 5 \qquad (1)$
$6x_1 - 12x_2 = 15 \qquad (2)$

Equations (1) and (2) represent two parallel lines
(slope of (1) is $\frac{2}{4}$ and slope of (2) is $\frac{6}{12}$).
Thus, the system has no solution.

34. $x_1 - 3x_2 - 2x_3 = -1$
$-2x_1 + 7x_2 + 3x_3 = 3$

The system is not "square"--2 equations with 3 unknowns. The matrix
of coefficients is 2×3; it does not have an inverse.
Solve the system by Gauss-Jordan elimination:

$$\begin{bmatrix} 1 & -3 & -2 & | & -1 \\ -2 & 7 & 3 & | & 3 \end{bmatrix} \sim \begin{bmatrix} 1 & -3 & -2 & | & -1 \\ 0 & 1 & -1 & | & 1 \end{bmatrix} \sim \begin{bmatrix} 1 & 0 & -5 & | & 2 \\ 0 & 1 & -1 & | & 1 \end{bmatrix}$$

$2R_1 + R_2 \rightarrow R_2 \qquad\quad 3R_2 + R_1 \rightarrow R_1$

$x_1 - 5x_3 = 2$
$x_2 - x_3 = 1$

Letting $x_3 = t$ we get $x_1 = 5t + 2$ and $x_2 = t + 1$.
Solution: $x_1 = 5t + 2$, $x_2 = t + 1$, $x_3 = t$, t any real number.

36.
$$x_1 - 2x_2 + 3x_3 = 1 \qquad (1)$$
$$2x_1 - 3x_2 - 2x_3 = 3 \qquad (2)$$
$$x_1 - x_2 - 5x_3 = 4 \qquad (3)$$

Note that (2) - (3) is
$$(2x_1 - 3x_2 - 2x_3) - (x_1 - x_2 - 5x_3) = 3 - 4 \text{ or}$$
$$x_1 - 2x_2 + 3x_3 = -1 \qquad (4)$$

In view of (1) and (4), we conclude that the system cannot have any solution.

38. $AX + BX = C$
$(A + B)X = C$
$X = (A + B)^{-1}C$
[Note: $X \neq C(A + B)^{-1}$]

40. $AX - X = C$
$(A - I)X = C$
$X = (A - I)^{-1}C$

42. $AX + C = BX + D$
$AX - BX = D - C$
$(A - B)X = (D - C)$
$X = (A - B)^{-1}(D - C)$

44. The matrix equation for the given system is:
$$\begin{bmatrix} 1 & -3.001 \\ 1 & -3 \end{bmatrix}\begin{bmatrix} x_1 \\ x_2 \end{bmatrix} = \begin{bmatrix} k_1 \\ k_2 \end{bmatrix}$$

First we compute the inverse of $\begin{bmatrix} 1 & -3.001 \\ 1 & -3 \end{bmatrix}$

$$\begin{bmatrix} 1 & -3.001 & | & 1 & 0 \\ 1 & -3 & | & 0 & 1 \end{bmatrix} \sim \begin{bmatrix} 1 & -3.001 & | & 1 & 0 \\ 0 & 0.001 & | & -1 & 1 \end{bmatrix} \sim \begin{bmatrix} 1 & -3.001 & | & 1 & 0 \\ 0 & 1 & | & -1000 & 1000 \end{bmatrix}$$

$(-1)R_1 + R_2 \rightarrow R_2$ $\qquad$ $1000R_2 \rightarrow R_2$ $\qquad$ $(3.001)R_2 + R_1 \rightarrow R_1$

$$\begin{bmatrix} 1 & 0 & | & -3000 & 3001 \\ 0 & 1 & | & -1000 & 1000 \end{bmatrix}$$

Thus, $\begin{bmatrix} 1 & -3.001 \\ 1 & -3 \end{bmatrix}^{-1} = \begin{bmatrix} -3000 & 3001 \\ -1000 & 1000 \end{bmatrix}$ and $\begin{bmatrix} x_1 \\ x_2 \end{bmatrix} = \begin{bmatrix} -3000 & 3001 \\ -1000 & 1000 \end{bmatrix}\begin{bmatrix} k_1 \\ k_2 \end{bmatrix}$

(A) $\begin{bmatrix} x_1 \\ x_2 \end{bmatrix} = \begin{bmatrix} -3000 & 3001 \\ -1000 & 1000 \end{bmatrix}\begin{bmatrix} 1 \\ 1 \end{bmatrix} = \begin{bmatrix} 1 \\ 0 \end{bmatrix}$; $x_1 = 1$, $x_2 = 0$

(B) $\begin{bmatrix} x_1 \\ x_2 \end{bmatrix} = \begin{bmatrix} -3000 & 3001 \\ -1000 & 1000 \end{bmatrix}\begin{bmatrix} 1 \\ 0 \end{bmatrix} = \begin{bmatrix} -3000 \\ -1000 \end{bmatrix}$; $x_1 = -3,000$, $x_2 = -1,000$

(C) $\begin{bmatrix} x_1 \\ x_2 \end{bmatrix} = \begin{bmatrix} -3000 & 3001 \\ -1000 & 1000 \end{bmatrix}\begin{bmatrix} 0 \\ 1 \end{bmatrix} = \begin{bmatrix} 3001 \\ 1000 \end{bmatrix}$; $x_1 = 3,001$, $x_2 = 1,000$

46. The matrix equation for the given system is:
$$\begin{bmatrix} 5 & 3 & -2 \\ 7 & 5 & 0 \\ 3 & 1 & -9 \end{bmatrix}\begin{bmatrix} x_1 \\ x_2 \\ x_3 \end{bmatrix} = \begin{bmatrix} 112 \\ 70 \\ 96 \end{bmatrix}$$

Thus, $\begin{bmatrix} x_1 \\ x_2 \\ x_3 \end{bmatrix} = \begin{bmatrix} 5 & 3 & -2 \\ 7 & 5 & 0 \\ 3 & 1 & -9 \end{bmatrix}^{-1}\begin{bmatrix} 112 \\ 70 \\ 96 \end{bmatrix} = \begin{bmatrix} 116.5 \\ -149.1 \\ 11.6 \end{bmatrix}$ and $\begin{matrix} x_1 = 116.5 \\ x_2 = -149.1 \\ x_3 = 11.6 \end{matrix}$

48. The matrix equation for the given system is:

$$\begin{bmatrix} 3 & 3 & 6 & 5 \\ 4 & 5 & 8 & 2 \\ 3 & 6 & 7 & 4 \\ 4 & 1 & 6 & 3 \end{bmatrix}\begin{bmatrix} x_1 \\ x_2 \\ x_3 \\ x_4 \end{bmatrix} = \begin{bmatrix} 10 \\ 15 \\ 30 \\ 25 \end{bmatrix}$$

Thus

$$\begin{bmatrix} x_1 \\ x_2 \\ x_3 \\ x_4 \end{bmatrix} = \begin{bmatrix} 3 & 3 & 6 & 5 \\ 4 & 5 & 8 & 2 \\ 3 & 6 & 7 & 4 \\ 4 & 1 & 6 & 3 \end{bmatrix}^{-1}\begin{bmatrix} 10 \\ 15 \\ 30 \\ 25 \end{bmatrix} = \begin{bmatrix} 81.8 \\ 27.8 \\ -57.8 \\ 5.6 \end{bmatrix} \text{ and } \begin{array}{l} x_1 = 81.8 \\ x_2 = 27.8 \\ x_3 = -57.8 \\ x_4 = 5.6 \end{array}$$

50. (A) Let x_1 = Number of local vehicles

x_2 = Number of non-local vehicles

The mathematical model is:

$$\begin{array}{rl} x_1 + \quad x_2 &= k_1 \quad \text{(vehicles parked)} \\ 5x_1 + 7.5x_2 &= k_2 \quad \text{(Gross receipts)} \end{array}$$

The corresponding matrix equation is:

$$\begin{bmatrix} 1 & 1 \\ 5 & 7.5 \end{bmatrix}\begin{bmatrix} x_1 \\ x_2 \end{bmatrix} = \begin{bmatrix} k_1 \\ k_2 \end{bmatrix}$$

Compute the inverse of the coefficient matrix A.

$$\begin{bmatrix} 1 & 1 & | & 1 & 0 \\ 5 & 7.5 & | & 0 & 1 \end{bmatrix} \sim \begin{bmatrix} 1 & 1 & | & 1 & 0 \\ 0 & 2.5 & | & -5 & 1 \end{bmatrix} \sim \begin{bmatrix} 1 & 1 & | & 1 & 0 \\ 0 & 1 & | & -2 & 0.4 \end{bmatrix}$$

$$(-5)R_1 + R_2 \to R_2 \qquad \left(\dfrac{1}{2.5}\right)R_2 \to R_2 \qquad (-1)R_2 + R_1 \to R_1$$

$$\sim \begin{bmatrix} 1 & 0 & | & 3 & -0.4 \\ 0 & 1 & | & -2 & 0.4 \end{bmatrix} \text{ Thus, } A^{-1} = \begin{bmatrix} 3 & -0.4 \\ -2 & 0.4 \end{bmatrix}$$

Day 1: $k_1 = 1,200$, $k_2 = \$7,125$

$$\begin{bmatrix} x_1 \\ x_2 \end{bmatrix} = \begin{bmatrix} 3 & -0.4 \\ -2 & 0.4 \end{bmatrix}\begin{bmatrix} 1,200 \\ 7,125 \end{bmatrix} = \begin{bmatrix} 750 \\ 450 \end{bmatrix}; \begin{array}{l} 750 \text{ Local} \\ 450 \text{ Non-local} \end{array}$$

Day 2: $k_1 = 1,550$, $k_2 = \$9,825$

$$\begin{bmatrix} x_1 \\ x_2 \end{bmatrix} = \begin{bmatrix} 3 & -0.4 \\ -2 & 0.4 \end{bmatrix}\begin{bmatrix} 1,550 \\ 9,825 \end{bmatrix} = \begin{bmatrix} 720 \\ 830 \end{bmatrix}; \begin{array}{l} 720 \text{ Local} \\ 830 \text{ Non-local} \end{array}$$

Day 3: $k_1 = 1,740$, $k_2 = \$11,100$

$$\begin{bmatrix} x_1 \\ x_2 \end{bmatrix} = \begin{bmatrix} 3 & -0.4 \\ -2 & 0.4 \end{bmatrix}\begin{bmatrix} 1,740 \\ 11,100 \end{bmatrix} = \begin{bmatrix} 780 \\ 960 \end{bmatrix}; \begin{array}{l} 780 \text{ Local} \\ 960 \text{ Non-local} \end{array}$$

Day 4: $k_1 = 1,400$, $k_2 = \$8,650$

$$\begin{bmatrix} x_1 \\ x_2 \end{bmatrix} = \begin{bmatrix} 3 & -0.4 \\ -2 & 0.4 \end{bmatrix}\begin{bmatrix} 1,400 \\ 8,650 \end{bmatrix} = \begin{bmatrix} 740 \\ 660 \end{bmatrix}; \begin{array}{l} 740 \text{ Local} \\ 660 \text{ Non-local} \end{array}$$

(B) $k_2 = \$5,000$

$$\begin{bmatrix} x_1 \\ x_2 \end{bmatrix} \overset{?}{=} \begin{bmatrix} 3 & -0.4 \\ -2 & 0.4 \end{bmatrix} \begin{bmatrix} 1,200 \\ 5,000 \end{bmatrix} = \begin{bmatrix} 1,600 \\ -400 \end{bmatrix}$$

This is not possible; x_2 cannot be negative.

$k_2 = \$10,000$

$$\begin{bmatrix} x_1 \\ x_2 \end{bmatrix} \overset{?}{=} \begin{bmatrix} 3 & -0.4 \\ -2 & 0.4 \end{bmatrix} \begin{bmatrix} 1,200 \\ 10,000 \end{bmatrix} = \begin{bmatrix} -400 \\ 1,600 \end{bmatrix}$$

This is not possible; x_1 cannot be negative.

(C) $\quad x_1 + \quad x_2 = 1200 \qquad (1)$

$\quad 5x_1 + 7.5x_2 = k_2 \qquad (2)$

Letting $x_2 = t$, we have $x_1 = 1200 - t$. Substituting for x_1 and x_2 in (2) we obtain

$k_2 = 5(1200 - t) + 7.5t = 6,000 + 2.5t$, where t is an integer satisfying $0 \le t \le 1,200$.

52. (A) Let x_1 = number of model A guitars produced

$\qquad\quad x_2$ = number of model B guitars produced

Then, the mathematical model is:

$\qquad 30x_1 + 40x_2 = k_1$ (Labor allocation)

$\qquad 20x_1 + 30x_2 = k_2$ (Materials allocation)

The corresponding matrix equation is:

$$\begin{bmatrix} 30 & 40 \\ 20 & 30 \end{bmatrix} \begin{bmatrix} x_1 \\ x_2 \end{bmatrix} = \begin{bmatrix} k_1 \\ k_2 \end{bmatrix}$$

First we compute the inverse of $\begin{bmatrix} 30 & 40 \\ 20 & 30 \end{bmatrix}$

$$\begin{bmatrix} 30 & 40 & | & 1 & 0 \\ 20 & 30 & | & 0 & 1 \end{bmatrix} \sim \begin{bmatrix} 1 & \frac{4}{3} & | & \frac{1}{30} & 0 \\ 20 & 30 & | & 0 & 1 \end{bmatrix} \sim \begin{bmatrix} 1 & \frac{4}{3} & | & \frac{1}{30} & 0 \\ 0 & \frac{10}{3} & | & -\frac{2}{3} & 1 \end{bmatrix}$$

$\qquad \frac{1}{30}R_1 \rightarrow R_1 \qquad\qquad (-20)R_1 + R_2 \rightarrow R_2 \qquad\qquad \frac{3}{10}R_2 \rightarrow R_2$

$$\sim \begin{bmatrix} 1 & \frac{4}{3} & | & \frac{1}{30} & 0 \\ 0 & 1 & | & -0.2 & 0.3 \end{bmatrix} \sim \begin{bmatrix} 1 & 0 & | & 0.3 & -0.4 \\ 0 & 1 & | & -0.2 & 0.3 \end{bmatrix}$$

$\qquad \left(-\frac{4}{3}\right)R_2 + R_1 \rightarrow R_1$

Thus $\begin{bmatrix} 30 & 40 \\ 20 & 30 \end{bmatrix}^{-1} = \begin{bmatrix} 0.3 & -0.4 \\ -0.2 & 0.3 \end{bmatrix}$ and $\begin{bmatrix} x_1 \\ x_2 \end{bmatrix} = \begin{bmatrix} 0.3 & -0.4 \\ -0.2 & 0.3 \end{bmatrix} \begin{bmatrix} k_1 \\ k_2 \end{bmatrix}$

Now, for week 1: $k_1 = \$1,800$, $k_2 = \$1,200$

$$\begin{bmatrix} x_1 \\ x_2 \end{bmatrix} = \begin{bmatrix} 0.3 & -0.4 \\ -0.2 & 0.3 \end{bmatrix} \begin{bmatrix} 1,800 \\ 1,200 \end{bmatrix} = \begin{bmatrix} 60 \\ 0 \end{bmatrix}; \quad \begin{array}{l} 60 \text{ model } A \\ 0 \text{ model } B \end{array}$$

For week 2: $k_1 = \$1,700$, $k_2 = \$1,250$

$$\begin{bmatrix} x_1 \\ x_2 \end{bmatrix} = \begin{bmatrix} 0.3 & -0.4 \\ -0.2 & 0.3 \end{bmatrix}\begin{bmatrix} 1,700 \\ 1,250 \end{bmatrix} = \begin{bmatrix} 25 \\ 25 \end{bmatrix}; \quad \begin{matrix} 25 \text{ model } A \\ 25 \text{ model } B \end{matrix}$$

For week 3: $k_1 = \$1,700$, $k_2 = \$1,280$

$$\begin{bmatrix} x_1 \\ x_2 \end{bmatrix} = \begin{bmatrix} 0.3 & -0.4 \\ -0.2 & 0.3 \end{bmatrix}\begin{bmatrix} 1,700 \\ 1,280 \end{bmatrix} = \begin{bmatrix} 4 \\ 40 \end{bmatrix}; \quad \begin{matrix} 4 \text{ model } A \\ 40 \text{ model } B \end{matrix}$$

(B) For $k_1 = \$1,600$ and $k_2 = \$1,400$

$$\begin{bmatrix} x_1 \\ x_2 \end{bmatrix} \overset{?}{=} \begin{bmatrix} 0.3 & -0.4 \\ -0.2 & 0.3 \end{bmatrix}\begin{bmatrix} 1,600 \\ 1,400 \end{bmatrix} = \begin{bmatrix} -80 \\ 100 \end{bmatrix}$$

This is not possible; x_1 cannot be negative.

For $k_1 = \$2,000$ and $k_2 = \$1,000$

$$\begin{bmatrix} x_1 \\ x_2 \end{bmatrix} \overset{?}{=} \begin{bmatrix} 0.3 & -0.4 \\ -0.2 & 0.3 \end{bmatrix}\begin{bmatrix} 2,000 \\ 1,000 \end{bmatrix} = \begin{bmatrix} 200 \\ -100 \end{bmatrix}$$

This is not possible; x_2 cannot be negative.

54. Let x_1 = President's bonus

x_2 = Executive Vice President's bonus

x_3 = Associate Vice President's bonus

x_4 = Assistant Vice President's bonus

x_5 = Sales Manager's bonus

Then, the mathematical model is:

$$x_1 + 0.03x_2 + 0.03x_3 + 0.03x_4 + 0.03x_5 = 60,000$$
$$0.025x_1 + x_2 + 0.025x_3 + 0.025x_4 + 0.025x_5 = 50,000$$
$$0.02x_1 + 0.02x_2 + x_3 + 0.02x_4 + 0.02x_5 = 40,000$$
$$0.015x_1 + 0.015x_2 + 0.015x_3 + x_4 + 0.015x_5 = 30,000$$
$$0.01x_1 + 0.01x_2 + 0.01x_3 + 0.01x_4 + x_5 = 20,000$$

and

$$\begin{bmatrix} 1 & 0.03 & 0.03 & 0.03 & 0.03 \\ 0.025 & 1 & 0.025 & 0.025 & 0.025 \\ 0.02 & 0.02 & 1 & 0.02 & 0.02 \\ 0.015 & 0.015 & 0.015 & 1 & 0.015 \\ 0.01 & 0.01 & 0.01 & 0.01 & 1 \end{bmatrix}\begin{bmatrix} x_1 \\ x_2 \\ x_3 \\ x_4 \\ x_5 \end{bmatrix} = \begin{bmatrix} 60,000 \\ 50,000 \\ 40,000 \\ 30,000 \\ 20,000 \end{bmatrix}$$

Thus $$\begin{bmatrix} x_1 \\ x_2 \\ x_3 \\ x_4 \\ x_5 \end{bmatrix} = \begin{bmatrix} 1 & 0.03 & 0.03 & 0.03 & 0.03 \\ 0.025 & 1 & 0.025 & 0.025 & 0.025 \\ 0.02 & 0.02 & 1 & 0.02 & 0.02 \\ 0.015 & 0.015 & 0.015 & 1 & 0.015 \\ 0.01 & 0.01 & 0.01 & 0.01 & 1 \end{bmatrix}^{-1}\begin{bmatrix} 60,000 \\ 50,000 \\ 40,000 \\ 30,000 \\ 20,000 \end{bmatrix}$$

or $x_1 = \$56,100$, $x_2 = \$46,500$, $x_3 = \$37,000$, $x_4 = \$27,600$, $x_5 = \$18,300$

56. Let x_1 = Number of lecturers hired

x_2 = Number of instructors hired

The mathematical model is:

$$3x_1 + 4x_2 = k_1 \quad \text{(sections)}$$
$$20x_1 + 25x_2 = k_2 \quad \text{(salaries)}$$

and $\begin{bmatrix} 3 & 4 \\ 20 & 25 \end{bmatrix} \begin{bmatrix} x_1 \\ x_2 \end{bmatrix} = \begin{bmatrix} k_1 \\ k_2 \end{bmatrix}$

Thus, $\begin{bmatrix} x_1 \\ x_2 \end{bmatrix} = \begin{bmatrix} 3 & 4 \\ 20 & 25 \end{bmatrix}^{-1} \begin{bmatrix} k_1 \\ k_2 \end{bmatrix}$

$\left[\begin{array}{cc|cc} 3 & 4 & 1 & 0 \\ 20 & 25 & 0 & 1 \end{array}\right] \sim \left[\begin{array}{cc|cc} 1 & \frac{4}{3} & \frac{1}{3} & 0 \\ 20 & 25 & 0 & 1 \end{array}\right] \sim \left[\begin{array}{cc|cc} 1 & \frac{4}{3} & \frac{1}{3} & 0 \\ 0 & -\frac{5}{3} & -\frac{20}{3} & 1 \end{array}\right] \sim$

$\quad \frac{1}{3}R_1 \rightarrow R_1 \qquad\qquad (-20)R_1 + R_2 \rightarrow R_2 \qquad \left(-\frac{3}{5}\right)R_2 \rightarrow R_2$

$\left[\begin{array}{cc|cc} 1 & \frac{4}{3} & \frac{1}{3} & 0 \\ 0 & 1 & 4 & -\frac{3}{5} \end{array}\right] \sim \left[\begin{array}{cc|cc} 1 & 0 & -5 & 0.8 \\ 0 & 1 & 4 & -0.6 \end{array}\right]$ Thus, $\begin{bmatrix} 3 & 4 \\ 20 & 25 \end{bmatrix}^{-1} = \begin{bmatrix} -5 & 0.8 \\ 4 & -0.6 \end{bmatrix}$

$\left(-\frac{4}{3}\right)R_2 + R_1 \rightarrow R_1$

College 1: $k_1 = 30$, $k_2 = 200$

$\begin{bmatrix} x_1 \\ x_2 \end{bmatrix} = \begin{bmatrix} -5 & 0.8 \\ 4 & -0.6 \end{bmatrix} \begin{bmatrix} 30 \\ 200 \end{bmatrix} = \begin{bmatrix} 10 \\ 0 \end{bmatrix}$; $x_1 = 10$, $x_2 = 0$

College 2: $k_1 = 33$, $k_2 = 210$

$\begin{bmatrix} x_1 \\ x_2 \end{bmatrix} = \begin{bmatrix} -5 & 0.8 \\ 4 & -0.6 \end{bmatrix} \begin{bmatrix} 33 \\ 210 \end{bmatrix} = \begin{bmatrix} 3 \\ 6 \end{bmatrix}$; $x_1 = 3$, $x_2 = 6$

College 3: $k_1 = 35$, $k_2 = 220$

$\begin{bmatrix} x_1 \\ x_2 \end{bmatrix} = \begin{bmatrix} -5 & 0.8 \\ 4 & -0.6 \end{bmatrix} \begin{bmatrix} 35 \\ 220 \end{bmatrix} = \begin{bmatrix} 1 \\ 8 \end{bmatrix}$; $x_1 = 1$, $x_2 = 8$

EXERCISE 4-7

2. 20¢ from A and 10¢ from E

4. $I - M = \begin{bmatrix} 1 & 0 \\ 0 & 1 \end{bmatrix} - \begin{bmatrix} 0.4 & 0.2 \\ 0.2 & 0.1 \end{bmatrix} = \begin{bmatrix} 0.6 & -0.2 \\ -0.2 & 0.9 \end{bmatrix}$

From Problem 3, $(I - M)^{-1} = \begin{bmatrix} 1.8 & 0.4 \\ 0.4 & 1.2 \end{bmatrix}$.

$X = (I - M)^{-1}D_1 = \begin{bmatrix} 1.8 & 0.4 \\ 0.4 & 1.2 \end{bmatrix} \begin{bmatrix} 6 \\ 4 \end{bmatrix} = \begin{bmatrix} 12.4 \\ 7.2 \end{bmatrix}$. Thus

$\begin{bmatrix} x_1 \\ x_2 \end{bmatrix} = \begin{bmatrix} 12.4 \\ 7.2 \end{bmatrix}$ and $x_1 = 12.4$, $x_2 = 7.2$.

6. $X = \begin{bmatrix} x_1 \\ x_2 \end{bmatrix} = (I - M)^{-1}D_2 = \begin{bmatrix} 1.8 & 0.4 \\ 0.4 & 1.2 \end{bmatrix} \begin{bmatrix} 8 \\ 5 \end{bmatrix} = \begin{bmatrix} 25.2 \\ 15.6 \end{bmatrix}$.

Thus, $x_1 = 25.2$, $x_2 = 15.6$.

8. 10¢ for each sector.

10. $I - M = \begin{bmatrix} 1 & 0 & 0 \\ 0 & 1 & 0 \\ 0 & 0 & 1 \end{bmatrix} - \begin{bmatrix} 0.3 & 0.2 & 0.2 \\ 0.1 & 0.1 & 0.1 \\ 0.2 & 0.1 & 0.1 \end{bmatrix} = \begin{bmatrix} 0.7 & -0.2 & -0.2 \\ -0.1 & 0.9 & -0.1 \\ -0.2 & -0.1 & 0.9 \end{bmatrix}$

Given $(I - M)^{-1} = \begin{bmatrix} 1.6 & 0.4 & 0.4 \\ 0.22 & 1.18 & 0.18 \\ 0.38 & 0.22 & 1.22 \end{bmatrix}$

$(I - M)^{-1}(I - M) = \begin{bmatrix} 1 & 0 & 0 \\ 0 & 1 & 0 \\ 0 & 0 & 1 \end{bmatrix} = I$

12. $X = (I - M)^{-1}D_2$

Therefore, $\begin{bmatrix} x_1 \\ x_2 \\ x_3 \end{bmatrix} = \begin{bmatrix} 1.6 & 0.4 & 0.4 \\ 0.22 & 1.18 & 0.18 \\ 0.38 & 0.22 & 1.22 \end{bmatrix}\begin{bmatrix} 20 \\ 15 \\ 10 \end{bmatrix} = \begin{bmatrix} 42 \\ 23.9 \\ 23.1 \end{bmatrix}$

Thus, agriculture, \$42 billion; building, \$23.9 billion; and energy, \$23.1 billion.

14. $I - M = \begin{bmatrix} 1 & 0 \\ 0 & 1 \end{bmatrix} - \begin{bmatrix} 0.4 & 0.2 \\ 0.6 & 0.8 \end{bmatrix} = \begin{bmatrix} 0.6 & -0.2 \\ -0.6 & 0.2 \end{bmatrix}$

$\begin{bmatrix} 0.6 & -0.2 & | & 1 & 0 \\ -0.6 & 0.2 & | & 0 & 1 \end{bmatrix} \sim \begin{bmatrix} 1 & -\frac{1}{3} & | & \frac{5}{3} & 0 \\ -0.6 & 0.2 & | & 0 & 1 \end{bmatrix} \sim \begin{bmatrix} 1 & -\frac{1}{3} & | & \frac{5}{3} & 0 \\ 0 & 0 & | & 1 & 1 \end{bmatrix}$

$\quad\quad \frac{1}{0.6}R_1 \to R_1 \quad\quad\quad (0.6)R_1 + R_2 \to R_2$

Thus, $I - M$ is singular and hence x does not exist.

16. $I - M = \begin{bmatrix} 1 & 0 \\ 0 & 1 \end{bmatrix} - \begin{bmatrix} 0.4 & 0.1 \\ 0.2 & 0.3 \end{bmatrix} = \begin{bmatrix} 0.6 & -0.1 \\ -0.2 & 0.7 \end{bmatrix}$

$\begin{bmatrix} 0.6 & -0.1 & | & 1 & 0 \\ -0.2 & 0.7 & | & 0 & 1 \end{bmatrix} \sim \begin{bmatrix} 1 & -\frac{1}{6} & | & \frac{5}{3} & 0 \\ -0.2 & 0.7 & | & 0 & 1 \end{bmatrix} \sim \begin{bmatrix} 1 & -\frac{1}{6} & | & \frac{5}{3} & 0 \\ 0 & \frac{2}{3} & | & \frac{1}{3} & 1 \end{bmatrix} \sim$

$\quad\quad \frac{1}{0.6}R_1 \to R_1 \quad\quad\quad 0.2R_1 + R_2 \to R_2 \quad\quad\quad \frac{3}{2}R_2 \to R_2$

$\begin{bmatrix} 1 & -\frac{1}{6} & | & \frac{5}{3} & 0 \\ 0 & 1 & | & \frac{1}{2} & \frac{3}{2} \end{bmatrix} \sim \begin{bmatrix} 1 & 0 & | & \frac{7}{4} & \frac{1}{4} \\ 0 & 1 & | & \frac{1}{2} & \frac{3}{2} \end{bmatrix}$. Thus, $(I - M)^{-1} = \begin{bmatrix} 1.75 & 0.25 \\ 0.5 & 1.5 \end{bmatrix}$

$\frac{1}{6}R_2 + R_1 \to R_1$

$X = \begin{bmatrix} x_1 \\ x_2 \end{bmatrix} = (I - M)^{-1}D = \begin{bmatrix} 1.75 & 0.25 \\ 0.5 & 1.5 \end{bmatrix}\begin{bmatrix} 15 \\ 20 \end{bmatrix} = \begin{bmatrix} 31.25 \\ 37.5 \end{bmatrix}; \quad \begin{array}{l} x_1 = 31.25 \\ x_2 = 37.5 \end{array}$

18. $I - M = \begin{bmatrix} 1 & 0 & 0 \\ 0 & 1 & 0 \\ 0 & 0 & 1 \end{bmatrix} - \begin{bmatrix} 0.3 & 0.2 & 0.3 \\ 0.1 & 0.1 & 0.1 \\ 0.1 & 0.2 & 0.1 \end{bmatrix} = \begin{bmatrix} 0.7 & -0.2 & -0.3 \\ -0.1 & 0.9 & -0.1 \\ -0.1 & -0.2 & 0.9 \end{bmatrix}$

$\begin{bmatrix} 0.7 & -0.2 & -0.3 & | & 1 & 0 & 0 \\ -0.1 & 0.9 & -0.1 & | & 0 & 1 & 0 \\ -0.1 & -0.2 & 0.9 & | & 0 & 0 & 1 \end{bmatrix} \sim \begin{bmatrix} 7 & -2 & -3 & | & 10 & 0 & 0 \\ -1 & 9 & -1 & | & 0 & 10 & 0 \\ 1 & 2 & -9 & | & 0 & 0 & -10 \end{bmatrix}$

$\quad\quad 10R_1 \to R_1 \quad\quad\quad\quad\quad\quad R_1 \leftrightarrow R_3$
$\quad\quad 10R_2 \to R_2$
$\quad\quad -10R_3 \to R_3$

$$\sim \begin{bmatrix} 1 & 2 & -9 & | & 0 & 0 & -10 \\ -1 & 9 & -1 & | & 0 & 10 & 0 \\ 7 & -2 & -3 & | & 10 & 0 & 0 \end{bmatrix} \sim \begin{bmatrix} 1 & 2 & -9 & | & 0 & 0 & -10 \\ 0 & 11 & -10 & | & 0 & 10 & -10 \\ 0 & -16 & 60 & | & 10 & 0 & 70 \end{bmatrix}$$

$$R_1 + R_2 \to R_2 \qquad\qquad\qquad \frac{1}{11} R_2 \to R_2$$
$$(-7) R_1 + R_3 \to R_3$$

$$\begin{bmatrix} 1 & 2 & -9 & | & 0 & 0 & -10 \\ 0 & 1 & -\frac{1}{11} & | & 0 & \frac{1}{11} & -\frac{1}{11} \\ 0 & -16 & 60 & | & 10 & 0 & 70 \end{bmatrix} \sim \begin{bmatrix} 1 & 0 & -\frac{79}{11} & | & 0 & -\frac{20}{11} & -\frac{90}{11} \\ 0 & 1 & -\frac{1}{11} & | & 0 & \frac{1}{11} & -\frac{1}{11} \\ 0 & 0 & \frac{500}{11} & | & 10 & \frac{160}{11} & \frac{610}{11} \end{bmatrix}$$

$$(-2) R_2 + R_1 \to R_1 \qquad\qquad\qquad \frac{11}{500} R_3 \to R_3$$
$$(16) R_2 + R_3 \to R_3$$

$$\begin{bmatrix} 1 & 0 & -\frac{79}{11} & | & 0 & -\frac{20}{11} & -\frac{90}{11} \\ 0 & 1 & -\frac{1}{11} & | & 0 & \frac{1}{11} & -\frac{1}{11} \\ 0 & 0 & 1 & | & 0.22 & 0.32 & 1.22 \end{bmatrix} \sim \begin{bmatrix} 1 & 0 & 0 & | & 1.58 & 0.48 & 0.58 \\ 0 & 1 & 0 & | & 0.2 & 1.2 & 0.2 \\ 0 & 0 & 1 & | & 0.22 & 0.32 & 1.22 \end{bmatrix}$$

$$\frac{79}{11} R_3 + R_1 \to R_1$$
$$\frac{10}{11} R_3 + R_2 \to R_2$$

$$X = \begin{bmatrix} x_1 \\ x_2 \\ x_3 \end{bmatrix} = (I - M)^{-1} D = \begin{bmatrix} 1.58 & 0.48 & 0.58 \\ 0.2 & 1.2 & 0.2 \\ 0.22 & 0.32 & 1.22 \end{bmatrix} \begin{bmatrix} 10 \\ 25 \\ 15 \end{bmatrix} = \begin{bmatrix} 36.5 \\ 35 \\ 28.5 \end{bmatrix}$$

20. (A) The technology matrix $M = \begin{bmatrix} 0.25 & 0.25 \\ 0.4 & 0.2 \end{bmatrix}$ and the final demand matrix

$D = \begin{bmatrix} 50 \\ 50 \end{bmatrix}$. The input-output matrix equation is $X = MX + D$ or

$X = \begin{bmatrix} 0.25 & 0.25 \\ 0.4 & 0.2 \end{bmatrix} X + \begin{bmatrix} 50 \\ 50 \end{bmatrix}$, where $X = \begin{bmatrix} x_1 \\ x_2 \end{bmatrix}$.

The solution is $X = (I - M)^{-1} D$, provided $I - M$ has an inverse.
Now,

$$I - M = \begin{bmatrix} 1 & 0 \\ 0 & 1 \end{bmatrix} - \begin{bmatrix} 0.25 & 0.25 \\ 0.4 & 0.2 \end{bmatrix} = \begin{bmatrix} 0.75 & -0.25 \\ -0.4 & 0.8 \end{bmatrix}$$

$$(I - M)^{-1}: \begin{bmatrix} 0.75 & -0.25 & | & 1 & 0 \\ -0.4 & 0.8 & | & 0 & 1 \end{bmatrix} \sim \begin{bmatrix} 1 & -\frac{1}{3} & | & \frac{4}{3} & 0 \\ -0.4 & 0.8 & | & 0 & 1 \end{bmatrix} \sim$$

$$\frac{1}{0.75} R_1 \to R_1 \qquad\qquad (0.4) R_1 + R_2 \to R_2$$

$$\begin{bmatrix} 1 & -\frac{1}{3} & | & \frac{4}{3} & 0 \\ 0 & \frac{2}{3} & | & \frac{8}{15} & 1 \end{bmatrix} \sim \begin{bmatrix} 1 & -\frac{1}{3} & | & \frac{4}{3} & 0 \\ 0 & 1 & | & \frac{4}{5} & \frac{3}{2} \end{bmatrix} \sim \begin{bmatrix} 1 & 0 & | & \frac{8}{5} & \frac{1}{2} \\ 0 & 1 & | & \frac{4}{5} & \frac{3}{2} \end{bmatrix}.$$

$$\frac{3}{2} R_2 \to R_2 \qquad\qquad \frac{1}{3} R_2 + R_1 \to R_1$$

Thus, $(I - M)^{-1} = \begin{bmatrix} 1.6 & 0.5 \\ 0.8 & 1.5 \end{bmatrix}$.

$$X = \begin{bmatrix} x_1 \\ x_2 \end{bmatrix} = (I - M)^{-1}D = \begin{bmatrix} 1.6 & 0.5 \\ 0.8 & 1.5 \end{bmatrix}\begin{bmatrix} 50 \\ 50 \end{bmatrix} = \begin{bmatrix} 105 \\ 115 \end{bmatrix}. \text{ Thus}$$

Energy: \$105 million; Transportation: \$115 million.

(B) If the transportation output is increased by \$40 million and energy output remains at \$50 million, then the final demand D is given by

$$D = (I - M)X = \begin{bmatrix} 0.25 & 0.25 \\ 0.4 & 0.2 \end{bmatrix}\begin{bmatrix} 50 \\ 90 \end{bmatrix} = \begin{bmatrix} 40 \\ 82 \end{bmatrix}$$

The final demand for energy decreases to \$40 million and the final demand for transportation decreases to \$82 million.

22. The technology matrix $T = \begin{bmatrix} 0.2 & 0.4 \\ 0.25 & 0.25 \end{bmatrix}$ and the final demand D is given

by $D = \begin{bmatrix} 50 \\ 50 \end{bmatrix}$ (see Problem 20). The input-output matrix equation is

$$X = Tx + D \text{ or } X = \begin{bmatrix} 0.2 & 0.4 \\ 0.25 & 0.25 \end{bmatrix}X + \begin{bmatrix} 50 \\ 50 \end{bmatrix} \text{ where } X = \begin{bmatrix} x_1 \\ x_2 \end{bmatrix}.$$

The solution $X = (I - T)^{-1}D$, provided $(I - T)$ has an inverse. Now,

$$I - T = \begin{bmatrix} 1 & 0 \\ 0 & 1 \end{bmatrix} - \begin{bmatrix} 0.2 & 0.4 \\ 0.25 & 0.25 \end{bmatrix} = \begin{bmatrix} 0.8 & -0.4 \\ -0.25 & 0.75 \end{bmatrix}$$

$$(I - T)^{-1}: \begin{bmatrix} 0.8 & -0.4 & | & 1 & 0 \\ -0.25 & 0.75 & | & 0 & 1 \end{bmatrix} \sim \begin{bmatrix} 1 & -\frac{1}{2} & | & 1.25 & 0 \\ -0.25 & 0.75 & | & 0 & 1 \end{bmatrix}$$

$$\left(\frac{1}{0.8}\right)R_1 \rightarrow R_1 \qquad\qquad (0.25)R_1 + R_2 \rightarrow R_2$$

$$\begin{bmatrix} 1 & -\frac{1}{2} & | & 1.25 & 0 \\ 0 & 0.625 & | & 0.3125 & 1 \end{bmatrix} \sim \begin{bmatrix} 1 & -0.5 & | & 1.25 & 0 \\ 0 & 1 & | & 0.5 & 1.6 \end{bmatrix} \sim \begin{bmatrix} 1 & 0 & | & 1.5 & 0.8 \\ 0 & 1 & | & 0.5 & 1.6 \end{bmatrix}$$

$$\left(\frac{1}{0.625}\right)R_2 \rightarrow R_2 \qquad\qquad (0.5)R_2 + R_1 \rightarrow R_1$$

Thus, $(I - T)^{-1} = \begin{bmatrix} 1.5 & 0.8 \\ 0.5 & 1.6 \end{bmatrix}$ and $X = \begin{bmatrix} x_1 \\ x_2 \end{bmatrix} = \begin{bmatrix} 1.5 & 0.8 \\ 0.5 & 1.6 \end{bmatrix}\begin{bmatrix} 50 \\ 50 \end{bmatrix} = \begin{bmatrix} 115 \\ 105 \end{bmatrix}.$

The answers are switched around. In Problem 20, we have $x_1 = 105$, $x_2 = 115$ and here we have $x_1 = 115$, $x_2 = 105$.

24. Let x_1 = total output of automobiles, and
x_2 = total output of construction

Then the final demand matrix $D = \begin{bmatrix} 0.70x_1 \\ 0.70x_2 \end{bmatrix}$ and the input-output matrix

equation is:

$$\begin{bmatrix} x_1 \\ x_2 \end{bmatrix} = \begin{bmatrix} 0.1 & 0.4 \\ 0.1 & 0.1 \end{bmatrix}\begin{bmatrix} x_1 \\ x_2 \end{bmatrix} + \begin{bmatrix} 0.70x_1 \\ 0.70x_2 \end{bmatrix}$$

This yields the dependent system of equations

$$x_1 = 0.1x_1 + 0.4x_2 + 0.70x_1$$
$$x_2 = 0.1x_1 + 0.1x_2 + 0.7x_2$$

$$0.2x_1 = 0.4x_2$$
or $0.2x_2 = 0.1x_1$ or $x_1 = 2x_2$ which is a dependent case.

So the total output of the automobile sector should be twice the output of the construction sector.

26. Each column sum should be between 0 and 1, inclusive. If every column sum is 1, all output would be consumed in the production process and there would be nothing left for the final demand.

28. The technology matrix $M = \begin{bmatrix} 0.1 & 0.4 \\ 0.1 & 0.4 \end{bmatrix}$ and the final demand matrix

$D = \begin{bmatrix} 5 \\ 20 \end{bmatrix}$.

The input-output matrix equation is $X = MX + D$ or

$X = \begin{bmatrix} 0.1 & 0.4 \\ 0.1 & 0.4 \end{bmatrix} X + \begin{bmatrix} 5 \\ 20 \end{bmatrix}$ where $X = \begin{bmatrix} x_1 \\ x_2 \end{bmatrix}$.

The solution is $X = (I - M)^{-1}D$, provided $(I - M)$ has an inverse. Now,

$I - M = \begin{bmatrix} 1 & 0 \\ 0 & 1 \end{bmatrix} - \begin{bmatrix} 0.1 & 0.4 \\ 0.1 & 0.4 \end{bmatrix} = \begin{bmatrix} 0.9 & -0.4 \\ -0.1 & 0.6 \end{bmatrix}$

$(I - M)^{-1}$: $\begin{bmatrix} 0.9 & -0.4 & | & 1 & 0 \\ -0.1 & 0.6 & | & 0 & 1 \end{bmatrix} \sim \begin{bmatrix} 1 & -\frac{4}{9} & | & \frac{10}{9} & 0 \\ -0.1 & 0.6 & | & 0 & 1 \end{bmatrix} \sim$

$$\frac{1}{0.9}R_1 \to R_1 \qquad\qquad (0.1)R_1 + R_2 \to R_2$$

$\begin{bmatrix} 1 & -\frac{4}{9} & | & \frac{10}{9} & 0 \\ 0 & \frac{5}{9} & | & \frac{1}{9} & 1 \end{bmatrix} \sim \begin{bmatrix} 1 & -\frac{4}{9} & | & \frac{10}{9} & 0 \\ 0 & 1 & | & \frac{1}{5} & \frac{9}{5} \end{bmatrix} \sim \begin{bmatrix} 1 & 0 & | & 1.2 & 0.8 \\ 0 & 1 & | & 0.2 & 1.8 \end{bmatrix}$

$$\frac{9}{5}R_2 \to R_2 \qquad\qquad \frac{4}{9}R_2 + R_1 \to R_1$$

Thus, $(I - M)^{-1} = \begin{bmatrix} 1.2 & 0.8 \\ 0.2 & 1.8 \end{bmatrix}$ and $X = \begin{bmatrix} 1.2 & 0.8 \\ 0.2 & 1.8 \end{bmatrix}\begin{bmatrix} 5 \\ 20 \end{bmatrix} = \begin{bmatrix} 22 \\ 37 \end{bmatrix}$;

Transportation: \$22 billion; Manufacturing: \$37 billion

30. The technology matrix $M = \begin{bmatrix} 0.40 & 0.20 \\ 0.35 & 0.05 \end{bmatrix}$ and the final demand matrix

$D = \begin{bmatrix} 40 \\ 250 \end{bmatrix}$. $X = \begin{bmatrix} x_1 \\ x_2 \end{bmatrix} = (I - M)^{-1}D$ if $(I - M)^{-1}$ exists.

$I - M = \begin{bmatrix} 1 & 0 \\ 0 & 1 \end{bmatrix} - \begin{bmatrix} 0.40 & 0.20 \\ 0.35 & 0.05 \end{bmatrix} = \begin{bmatrix} 0.60 & -0.20 \\ -0.35 & 0.95 \end{bmatrix}$

$(I - M)^{-1}$: $\begin{bmatrix} 0.6 & -0.20 & | & 1 & 0 \\ -0.35 & 0.95 & | & 0 & 1 \end{bmatrix} \sim \begin{bmatrix} 1 & -\frac{1}{3} & | & \frac{5}{3} & 0 \\ -0.35 & 0.95 & | & 0 & 1 \end{bmatrix} \sim$

$$\frac{1}{0.6}R_1 \to R_1 \qquad\qquad (0.35)R_1 + R_2 \to R_2$$

$$\begin{bmatrix} 1 & -\frac{1}{3} & \Big| & \frac{5}{3} & 0 \\ 0 & \frac{5}{6} & \Big| & \frac{7}{12} & 1 \end{bmatrix} \sim \begin{bmatrix} 1 & -\frac{1}{3} & \Big| & \frac{5}{3} & 0 \\ 0 & 1 & \Big| & \frac{7}{12} & \frac{6}{5} \end{bmatrix} \sim \begin{bmatrix} 1 & 0 & \Big| & 1.9 & 0.4 \\ 0 & 1 & \Big| & 0.7 & 1.2 \end{bmatrix}$$

$$\frac{6}{5}R_2 \to R_2 \qquad\qquad \frac{1}{3}R_2 + R_1 \to R_1$$

Thus, $(I - M)^{-1} = \begin{bmatrix} 1.9 & 0.4 \\ 0.7 & 1.2 \end{bmatrix}$ and $X = \begin{bmatrix} x_1 \\ x_2 \end{bmatrix} = \begin{bmatrix} 1.9 & 0.4 \\ 0.7 & 1.2 \end{bmatrix}\begin{bmatrix} 40 \\ 250 \end{bmatrix} = \begin{bmatrix} 176 \\ 328 \end{bmatrix}.$

Thus, Agriculture: \$176 million; Oil: \$328 million

32. The technology matrix $M = \begin{bmatrix} 0.3 & 0.3 & 0.1 \\ 0.1 & 0.1 & 0.1 \\ 0.2 & 0.2 & 0.1 \end{bmatrix}$ and the final demand matrix

$D = \begin{bmatrix} 25 \\ 15 \\ 20 \end{bmatrix}.$

The input-output matrix equation is $X = MX + D$.

The solution is $X = (I - M)^{-1}D$, provided $I - M$ has an inverse.

$I - M = \begin{bmatrix} 1 & 0 & 0 \\ 0 & 1 & 0 \\ 0 & 0 & 1 \end{bmatrix} - \begin{bmatrix} 0.3 & 0.3 & 0.1 \\ 0.1 & 0.1 & 0.1 \\ 0.2 & 0.2 & 0.1 \end{bmatrix} = \begin{bmatrix} 0.7 & -0.3 & -0.1 \\ -0.1 & 0.9 & -0.1 \\ -0.2 & -0.2 & 0.9 \end{bmatrix}.$

$(I - M)^{-1}$:

$$\begin{bmatrix} 0.7 & -0.3 & -0.1 & \Big| & 1 & 0 & 0 \\ -0.1 & 0.9 & -0.1 & \Big| & 0 & 1 & 0 \\ -0.2 & -0.2 & 0.9 & \Big| & 0 & 0 & 1 \end{bmatrix} \sim \begin{bmatrix} 1 & -\frac{3}{7} & -\frac{1}{7} & \Big| & \frac{10}{7} & 0 & 0 \\ -0.1 & 0.9 & -0.1 & \Big| & 0 & 1 & 0 \\ -0.2 & -0.2 & 0.9 & \Big| & 0 & 0 & 1 \end{bmatrix}$$

$$\frac{1}{0.7}R_1 \to R_1 \qquad\qquad\qquad 0.1R_1 + R_2 \to R_2$$
$$0.2R_1 + R_3 \to R_3$$

$$\begin{bmatrix} 1 & -\frac{3}{7} & -\frac{1}{7} & \Big| & \frac{10}{7} & 0 & 0 \\ 0 & \frac{6}{7} & -\frac{4}{35} & \Big| & \frac{1}{7} & 1 & 0 \\ 0 & -\frac{2}{7} & \frac{61}{70} & \Big| & \frac{2}{7} & 0 & 1 \end{bmatrix} \sim \begin{bmatrix} 1 & -\frac{3}{7} & -\frac{1}{7} & \Big| & \frac{10}{7} & 0 & 0 \\ 0 & 1 & -\frac{2}{15} & \Big| & \frac{1}{6} & \frac{7}{6} & 0 \\ 0 & -\frac{2}{7} & \frac{61}{70} & \Big| & \frac{2}{7} & 0 & 1 \end{bmatrix} \sim$$

$$\frac{7}{6}R_2 \to R_2 \qquad\qquad \frac{3}{7}R_2 + R_1 \to R_2$$
$$\frac{2}{7}R_2 + R_3 \to R_3$$

$$\begin{bmatrix} 1 & 0 & -\frac{1}{5} & \Big| & \frac{3}{2} & \frac{1}{2} & 0 \\ 0 & 1 & -\frac{2}{15} & \Big| & \frac{1}{6} & \frac{7}{6} & 0 \\ 0 & 0 & -\frac{5}{6} & \Big| & \frac{1}{3} & \frac{1}{3} & 1 \end{bmatrix} \sim \begin{bmatrix} 1 & 0 & \frac{1}{5} & \Big| & \frac{3}{2} & \frac{1}{2} & 0 \\ 0 & 1 & -\frac{2}{15} & \Big| & \frac{1}{6} & \frac{7}{6} & 0 \\ 0 & 0 & 1 & \Big| & \frac{1}{10} & \frac{1}{10} & \frac{6}{5} \end{bmatrix} \sim \begin{bmatrix} 1 & 0 & 0 & \Big| & 1.48 & 0.48 & -0.24 \\ 0 & 1 & 0 & \Big| & 0.18 & 1.18 & 0.08 \\ 0 & 0 & 1 & \Big| & 0.1 & 0.1 & 1.2 \end{bmatrix}$$

$$\frac{6}{5}R_3 \to R_3 \qquad\qquad \left(-\frac{1}{5}\right)R_3 + R_1 \to R_1$$
$$\left(\frac{2}{15}\right)R_3 + R_2 \to R_2$$

Thus, $(I - M)^{-1} = \begin{bmatrix} 1.48 & 0.48 & -0.24 \\ 0.18 & 1.18 & 0.08 \\ 0.1 & 0.1 & 1.2 \end{bmatrix}$ and

$$X = \begin{bmatrix} x_1 \\ x_2 \\ x_3 \end{bmatrix} = \begin{bmatrix} 1.48 & 0.48 & -0.24 \\ 0.18 & 1.18 & 0.08 \\ 0.1 & 0.1 & 1.2 \end{bmatrix} \begin{bmatrix} 25 \\ 15 \\ 20 \end{bmatrix} = \begin{bmatrix} 53 \\ 27 \\ 40 \end{bmatrix}.$$

Therefore,
Electricity: $53 billion; natural gas: $27 billion; Oil: $40 billion.

34. The technology matrix is $M = \begin{bmatrix} 0.07 & 0.09 & 0.27 & 0.12 \\ 0.14 & 0.07 & 0.21 & 0.24 \\ 0.17 & 0.06 & 0.02 & 0.21 \\ 0.15 & 0.13 & 0.31 & 0.19 \end{bmatrix}.$

The input-output matrix equation is $X = MX + D$

where $X = \begin{bmatrix} A \\ E \\ L \\ M \end{bmatrix}$ and D is the final demand matrix. Thus, $X = (I - M)^{-1}D$,

where $I - M = \begin{bmatrix} 0.93 & -0.09 & -0.27 & -0.12 \\ -0.14 & 0.93 & -0.21 & -0.24 \\ -0.17 & -0.06 & 0.98 & -0.21 \\ -0.15 & -0.13 & -0.31 & 0.81 \end{bmatrix}$

$X = (I - M)^{-1}D$

Year 1: $D = \begin{bmatrix} 18 \\ 26 \\ 12 \\ 41 \end{bmatrix}$ and $(I - M)^{-1}D = \begin{bmatrix} 50 \\ 68 \\ 44 \\ 88 \end{bmatrix}$

Agriculture: $50 billion; Energy: $68 billion; Labor: $44 billion;
Manufacturing: $88 billion

Year 2: $D = \begin{bmatrix} 22 \\ 31 \\ 19 \\ 45 \end{bmatrix}$ and $(I - M)^{-1}D = \begin{bmatrix} 61 \\ 82 \\ 57 \\ 102 \end{bmatrix}$

Agriculture: $61 billion; Energy: $82 billion; Labor: $57 billion;
Manufacturing: $102 billion

Year 3: $D = \begin{bmatrix} 37 \\ 42 \\ 28 \\ 49 \end{bmatrix}$ and $(I - M)^{-1}D = \begin{bmatrix} 89 \\ 108 \\ 77 \\ 124 \end{bmatrix}$

Agriculture: $89 billion; Energy: $108 billion; Labor: $77 billion;
Manufacturing: $124 billion

5 LINEAR INEQUALITIES AND LINEAR PROGRAMMING

2. $y > x + 1$

Graph $y = x + 1$ as a broken line.

Test point $(0, 0)$:

$0 > 0 + 1 = 1$

The inequality is false. Thus, the graph is above the line $y = x + 1$, not including the line.

x	y
0	1
−1	0

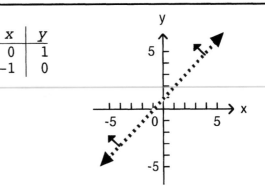

4. $2x - 5y \leq 10$

Graph the line $2x - 5y = 10$ as a solid line.

Test point $(0, 0)$:

$2 \cdot 0 - 5 \cdot 0 \leq 10$

$ 0 \leq 10$

The inequality is true. Thus, the graph is above the line $2x - 5y = 10$, including the line.

x	y
0	−2
5	0

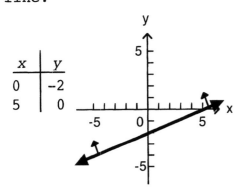

6. $y < 5$

Graph $y = 5$ [the horizontal line through $(0, 5)$] as a broken line.

Test point $(0, 0)$:

$0 < 5$

The inequality is true. Thus, the graph is below the line $y = 5$, not including the line.

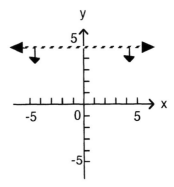

8. $4x + 8y \geq 32$

Graph $4x + 8y = 32$ as a solid line.

Test point $(0, 0)$:

$4 \cdot 0 + 8 \cdot 0 \geq 32$

$ 0 \geq 32$

The inequality is false. Thus, the graph is above the line $4x + 8y = 32$, including the line.

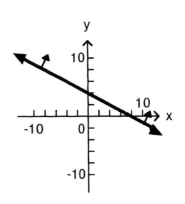

10. $6x \geq 4y$

Graph $6x - 4y = 0$ or $y = \dfrac{3}{2}x$ as a solid

line. Test point $(1, 0)$:

$6 \cdot 1 \geq 4 \cdot 0$

$\quad 6 \geq 0$

This inequality is true. Thus, the graph

is below the line $y = \dfrac{3}{2}x$, including the

line.

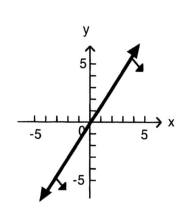

12. (A) 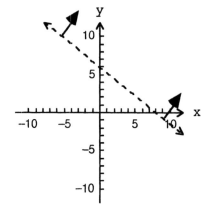 (B)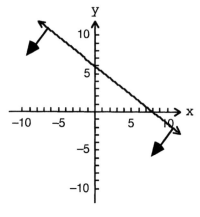

14. (A) 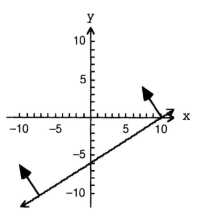 (B)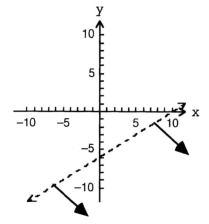

16. The boundary line passes through the points $(0, -1)$ and $(2, 0)$. We
use the slope-intercept form to find the equation of this line:

Slope: $m = \dfrac{0 - (-1)}{2 - 0} = \dfrac{1}{2}$

y intercept: $b = -1$

Boundary line equation: $y = \dfrac{1}{2}x - 1$

Multiplying both sides by 2 we arrive at:

$\qquad 2y = x - 2$

or $\qquad x - 2y = 2$

Since $(0, 0)$ is not in the shaded area and the boundary line is not
solid, we have:

$\qquad x - 2y > 2$.

18. The boundary line passes through the point (-2, 0) and is parallel to the y axis. So, its equation is:

$x = -2$

Since (-5, 0) is in the shaded area and the boundary line is a broken line, we have

$x < -2$

20. The boundary line passes through the points (0, 0) and (-1, 4). We only need its slope, since it passes through the origin.

Slope: $m = \dfrac{4 - 0}{-1 - 0} = -4$

Boundary line equation: $y = -4x$ or $4x + y = 0$

Since the point (1, 1) is in the shaded area and the boundary line is solid, we have:

$4x + y \geq 0$

22. Let k = the daily dose of vitamin K. Then $k \leq 1,500$.

24. Let P = profit. The $P > 100,000$.

26. Let b = the number of board feet used in table production. Then $b \leq 4,000$.

28. Let N = percentage of nitrogen in the mix. Then $N \geq 10$.

30.

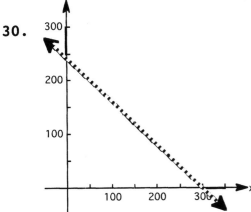

32.

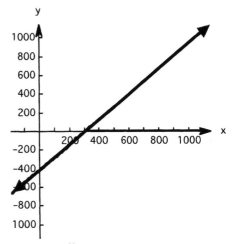

34.

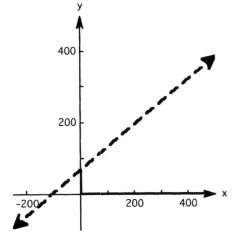

36.

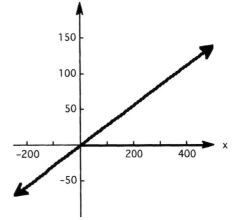

38.

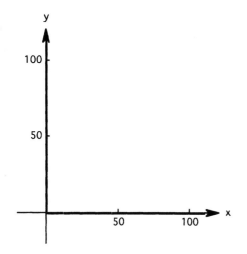

40. Let x = number of acres planted with corn.
Let y = number of acres planted with soybeans.
$55x + 45y \le 6{,}900$, $x \ge 0$, $y \ge 0$

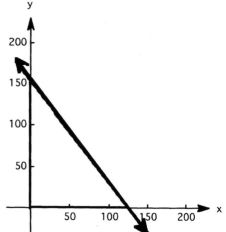

42. Let x = the number of pounds of brand A.
Let y = number of pounds of brand B.
(A) $0.24x + 0.1y \ge 50$, $x \ge 0$, $y \ge 0$

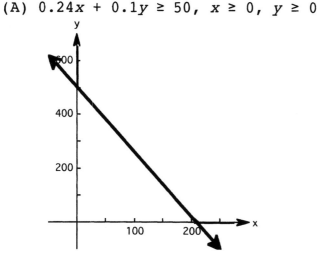

(B) $0.12x + 0.15y \le 60$, $x \ge 0$, $y \ge 0$.

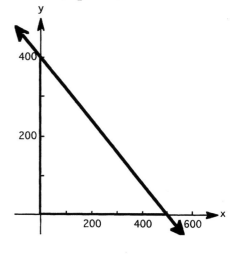

44. Let x = number of pounds of the standard blend.
Let y = number of pounds of the deluxe blend.
$0.40x + 0.52y \ge 1000(0.45)$,
$x \ge 0$, $y \ge 0$

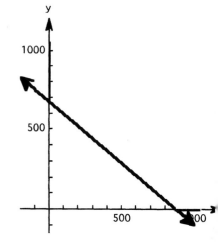

46. Let x = number of weeks Plant A is operated.
Let y = number of weeks Plant B is operated.
$8x + 6y \geq 480$,
$x \geq 0$, $y \geq 0$.

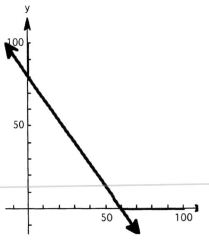

48. Let x = number of radio spots.
Let y = number of newspapers ads.
$200x + 500y \leq 10,000$,
$x \geq 0$, $y \geq 0$

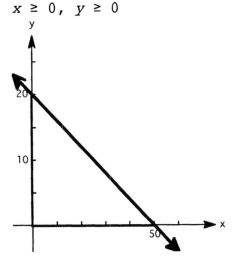

50. Let x = number of regular mattresses covered per day.
Let y = number of king size mattresses covered per day.
$15x + 20y \leq 9,600$,
$x \geq 0$, $y \geq 0$.

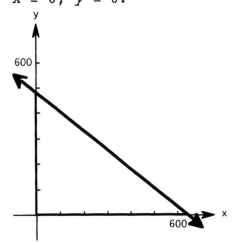

EXERCISE 5-2

2. The graph of $x + 2y \geq 8$ is the region above the line $x + 2y = 8$ [e.g., $(0, 0)$ does not satisfy the inequality]. The graph of $3x - 2y \leq 0$ is the region above the line $3x - 2y = 0$ [e.g., $(1, 0)$ does not satisfy the inequality]. The intersection of these two regions is region II.

4. The graph of $x + 2y \leq 8$ is the region below the line $x + 2y = 8$ [e.g., $(0, 0)$ satisfies the inequality]. The graph of $3x - 2y \leq 0$ is the region above the line $3x - 2y = 0$ [e.g., $(1, 0)$ does not satisfy the inequality]. The intersection of these two regions is region III.

6. The graphs of the inequalities $3x + y \leq 12$ and $y \geq -3$ are:

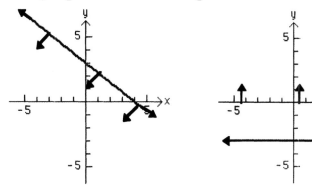

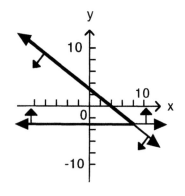

The intersection of these regions is shown in the graph with the shaded area.

8. The graphs of the inequalities $2x + 5y \leq 20$ and $x - 5y \geq -5$ are:

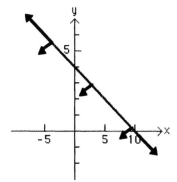
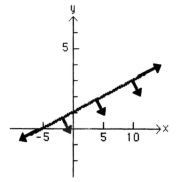

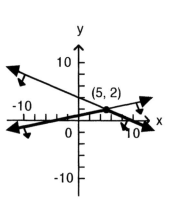

The intersection of these regions is shown in the graph with the shaded area.

10. $x - 2y \leq 1$
$x + 3y \geq 12$

The first inequality is equivalent to $y \geq \frac{1}{2}x - \frac{1}{2}$. The second inequality is equivalent to $y \geq -\frac{1}{3}x + 4$. Graph the two inequalities using the shading option.

(A)

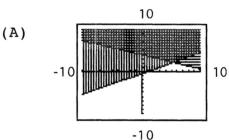

The solution region is the double-shaded region.

(B)

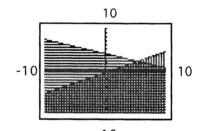

The solution region is the unshaded region.

12. $3x + y \geq -2$
$x - 2y \geq -6$
The first inequality is equivalent to $y \geq -3x - 2$. The second inequality is equivalent to $y \leq \frac{1}{2}x + 3$. Graph the two inequalities using the shading option.

(A)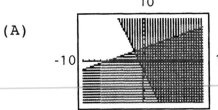

The solution region is the double-shaded region.

(B)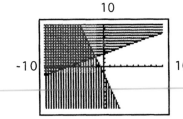

The solution region is the unshaded region.

14. The graph of $x + 3y \leq 18$ is the region below the line $x + 3y = 18$ and the graph of $2x + y \leq 16$ is the region below the line $2x + y = 16$. The graph of $x \geq 0$, $y \geq 0$ is the first quadrant. The intersection of these regions is region III. The corner points are $(0, 0)$, $(8, 0)$, $(6, 4)$, and $(0, 6)$.

16. The graph of $x + 3y \geq 18$ is the region above the line $x + 3y = 18$ and the graph of $2x + y \leq 16$ is the region below the line $2x + y = 16$. The graph of $x \geq 0$, $y \geq 0$ is the first quadrant. The intersection of these regions is region II. The corner points are $(0, 6)$, $(6, 4)$, and $(0, 16)$.

18. The graphs of the inequalities are shown at the right. The solution region is indicated by the shaded region. The solution region is *bounded*.

The corner points of the solution region are:

$(0, 0)$, the intersection of $x = 0$, $y = 0$;
$(8, 0)$, the intersection of $y = 0$,
  $3x + 4y = 24$;
$(0, 6)$, the intersection of $x = 0$,
  $3x + 4y = 24$.

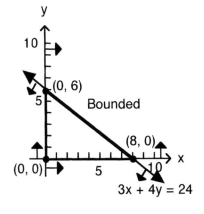

20. The graphs of the inequalities are shown at the right. The solution region is shaded. The solution region is *bounded*.

The corner points of the solution region are:

$(0, 0)$, the intersection of $x = 0$, $y = 0$;
$(4, 0)$, the intersection of $y = 0$, $6x + 3y = 24$;
$(2, 4)$, the intersection of $3x + 6y = 30$,
  $6x + 3y = 24$;
$(0, 5)$, the intersection of $x = 0$,
  $3x + 6y = 30$.

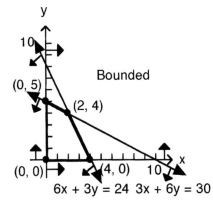

22. The graphs of the inequalities are shown at the right. The solution region is shaded. The solution region is *unbounded*.

The corner points of the solution region are:

(6, 0), the intersection of $y = 0$,
$\quad$ $4x + 3y = 24$;
(0, 8), the intersection of $x = 0$,
$\quad$ $4x + 3y = 24$.

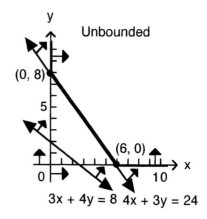

24. The graphs of the inequalities are shown at the right. The solution is indicated by the shaded region. The solution region is *bounded*.

The corner points of the solution region are:
(0, 0), the intersection of $x = 0$, $y = 0$,
(7, 0), the intersection of $y = 0$,
$\quad$ $3x + y = 21$;
(6, 3), the intersection of $3x + y = 21$,
$\quad$ $x + y = 9$;
(3, 6), the intersection of $x + 3y = 21$,
$\quad$ $x + y = 9$;
(0, 7), the intersection of $x = 0$,
$\quad$ $x + 3y = 21$.

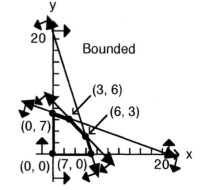

26. The graphs of the inequalities are shown at the right. The solution is indicated by the shaded region, which is *unbounded*.

The corner points are:

(30, 0), the intersection of $y = 0$,
$\quad$ $x + 3y = 30$;
(9, 7), the intersection of $x + 3y = 30$,
$\quad$ $x + y = 16$;
(4, 12), the intersection of $3x + y = 24$,
$\quad$ $x + y = 16$;
(0, 24), the intersection of $x = 0$,
$\quad$ $3x + y = 24$.

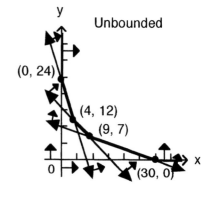

28. The graphs of the inequalities are shown at the right. The solution is indicated by the shaded region, which is *bounded*.

The corner points are (10, 1), (1, 10), and (5, 2).

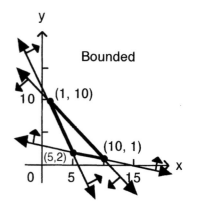

30. The graphs of the inequalities are shown at the right. The solution region is empty.

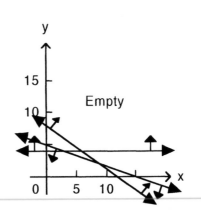

32. The graphs of the inequalities are shown at the right. The solution is indicated by the shaded region, which is *unbounded*.

The corner points are (6, 0), (3, 2), and (12, 5).

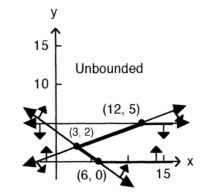

34. The graphs of the inequalities are shown at the right. The solution is indicated by the shaded region, which is *bounded*.

The corner points are (3, 0), (8, 2), (3, 7), and (0, 5).

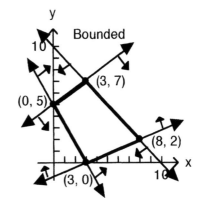

36. The graphs of the inequalities are shown at the right. The solution is indicated by the shaded region, which is *bounded*. The corner points are (7.75, 2.75), (1, 6.8), and (1.9, 8.6).

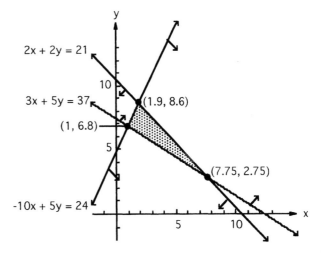

38. (A)

$2x + y = 16$
$2x + 3y = 36$ subtract
$2y = 20$
$y = 10$
$x = 3$

intersection point: (10, 3)

$2x + y = 16$
$x = 0$
$y = 16$

intersection point: (0, 16)

$2x + 3y = 16$
$y = 0$
$2x = 16$
$x = 8$

intersection point: (8, 0)

$2x + 3y = 36$
$x = 0$
$3y = 36$
$y = 12$

intersection point: (0, 12)

$2x + 3y = 36$
$y = 0$
$2x = 36$
$x = 18$

intersection point: (18, 0)

$x = 0$
$y = 0$

intersection point: (0, 0)

(B) The corner points are: (3, 10), (8, 0), (0, 12), (0, 0);
(0, 16) does not satisfy $2x + 3y \leq 36$, and
(18, 0) does not satisfy $2x + y \leq 16$.

40. Let x = the number of dining room tables and y = the number of chairs produced per day. The information is summarized in the following table.

	Hours per item		Maximum labor-hours per day available
	Table	Chair	
Assembling	8 hrs	2 hrs	400 hrs
Finishing	2 hrs	1 hr	120 hrs

We have the following inequalities:

$8x + 2y \leq 400$
$2x + y \leq 120$

Also, $x \geq 0$ and $y \geq 0$.

The graphs of these inequalities are shown at the right. The shaded region indicates the set of feasible solutions.

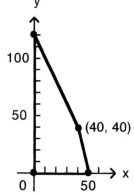

42. (A) All the production schedules in the feasible region that are on the graph of $50x + 15y = 1,300$ will result in a profit of $1,300.

(B) There are many possible choices. For example, producing 30 tables and 30 chairs per day will produce a profit of $1,950. The graph of the line $50x + 15y = 1,950$ includes all the production schedules in the feasible region that result in a profit of $1,950.

44. Let x = the number of ounces of food M and
y = the number of ounces of food N.
The information is summarized in the following table:

	An ounce of Food M	An ounce of Food N	Minimum Monthly requirement
Calcium	30 units	10 units	360 units
Iron	10 units	10 units	160 units
Vitamin A	10 units	30 units	240 units

EXERCISE 5-3

2. Evaluate the profit function at each corner point

Corner Point	$P = 4x_1 + x_2$
$(0, 0)$	0
$(0, 12)$	12
$(7, 9)$	37
$(10, 0)$	40

The maximum value of P is 40 at $x_1 = 10$ and $x_2 = 0$.

4. Evaluate the profit function at each corner point.

Corner Point	$P = 9x_1 + 3x_2$
$(0, 0)$	0
$(0, 12)$	36
$(7, 9)$	90
$(10, 0)$	90

The maximum value of P is 90 at $x_1 = 7$ and $x_2 = 9$, at $x_1 = 10$, $x_2 = 0$, and at every point on the line segment joining the preceding two points.

6. Evaluate the cost function at each corner point.

Corner Point	$C = 7x_1 + 9x_2$
$(4, 3)$	55
$(0, 8)$	72
$(0, 15)$	135
$(15, 15)$	240
$(15, 0)$	105

The minimum value of C is 55 at $x_1 = 4$ and $x_2 = 3$.

8. Evaluate the cost function at each corner point.

Corner Point	$C = 2x_1 + 11x_2$
(4, 3)	41
(0, 8)	88
(0, 15)	165
(15, 15)	195
(15, 0)	30

The minimum value of C is 30 at $x_1 = 15$ and $x_2 = 0$.

10. Graph the feasible region and find the corner points.

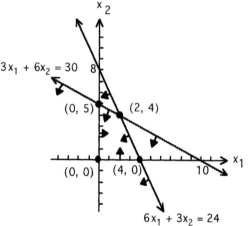

The feasible region S is the solution set of the given inequalities. This region is indicated by the shading in the graph at the right.

The corner points are (0, 0), (4, 0), (2, 4), and (0, 5).

Since S is bounded, it follows that P has a maximum value.

Corner Point	$P = 3x_1 + 2x_2$
(0, 0)	0
(4, 0)	12
(2, 4)	14
(0, 5)	10

The maximum value of P is 14 at (2, 4).

12. Graph the feasible region and find the corner points.

The feasible region S is the solution set of the given inequalities. This region is indicated by the shading in the graph at the right. Since S is unbounded, there is no maximum value of P.

The corner points are (6, 0) and (0, 8).

Corner Point	$P = 8x_1 + 7x_2$
(6, 0)	48
(0, 8)	56

The minimum value of P is 48 at (6, 0).

14. Graph the feasible region and find the corner points.
The feasible region S is the solution set of the given inequalities.
This region is indicated by the shading in the graph on the following
page. Since S is bounded, P has a maximum value.
The corner points are $(0, 0)$, $(7, 0)$, $(6, 3)$, $(3, 6)$, and $(0, 7)$.

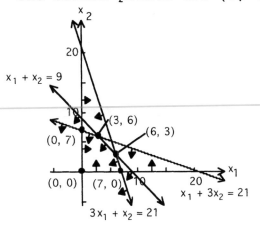

Corner Point	$P = 20x_1 + 10x_2$
$(0, 0)$	0
$(7, 0)$	140
$(6, 3)$	150
$(3, 6)$	120
$(0, 7)$	70

The maximum value of P is 150 at $(6, 3)$.

16. Graph the feasible region and find the corner points.
The feasible region S is the solution set of the given inequalities.
This region is indicated by the shading in the graph below.
z does not have a maximum value.
The corner points are $(30, 0)$,
$(9, 7)$, $(4, 12)$, and $(0, 24)$.

Corner Point	$z = 400x_1 + 100x_2$
$(30, 0)$	12,000
$(9, 7)$	4,300
$(4, 12)$	2,800
$(0, 24)$	2,400

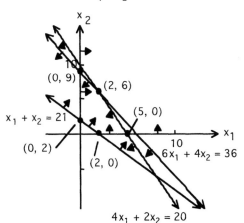

The minimum value of z is 2,400
at $(0, 24)$.

18. Graph the feasible region and find the
corner points.

The feasible region S is the solution
set of the given inequalities, and is
indicated by the shading in the graph
at the right.

The corner points are $(2, 0)$, $(5, 0)$,
$(2, 6)$, $(0, 9)$, and $(0, 2)$.

Corner Point	$P = 2x_1 + x_2$
$(2, 0)$	4
$(5, 0)$	10
$(2, 6)$	10
$(0, 9)$	9
$(0, 2)$	2

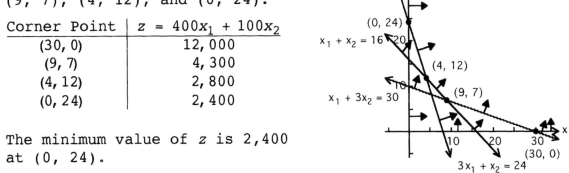

The minimum value of P is 2 at $(0, 2)$; the maximum value of P is 10 at
$(5, 0)$ or $(2, 6)$ or any point on the line segment joining the two
points.

20. Graph the feasible region and find the corner points.

The feasible region is the shaded region shown at the right.

The corner points are $(2, 0)$, $(8, 6)$, $(4, 4)$.

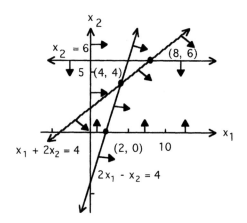

Corner Point	$P = -x_1 + 3x_2$
$(2, 0)$	-2
$(8, 6)$	10
$(4, 4)$	8

The maximum value of P is 10 at $(8, 6)$; there is no minimum value since the region is unbounded.

22. Graph the feasible region and find the corner points.

The feasible region is empty. No optimal solutions exist.

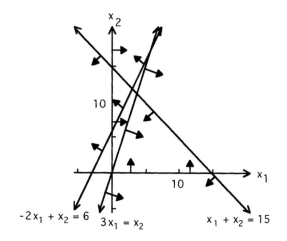

24. Graph the feasible region and find the corner points. The feasible region is the shaded region on the right, which is unbounded.

The corner points are $(300, 0)$, $(120, 90)$, $(60, 180)$, and $(0, 300)$.

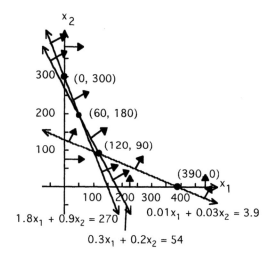

Corner Point	$C = 30x_1 + 10x_2$
$(390, 0)$	$11,700$
$(120, 90)$	$4,500$
$(60, 180)$	$3,600$
$(0, 300)$	$3,000$

The minimum of C is 3,000 at $(0, 300)$.

26. Graph the feasible region and find the corner points. The feasible region is the shaded region on the right, which is bounded.

The corner points are $(11.3, 0)$, $(8.3, 3.9)$, $(4.52, 6.8)$, $(0, 9.3)$.

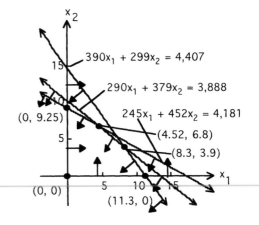

Corner Point	$P = 300x_1 + 460x_2$
$(11.3, 0)$	$3,390$
$(8.3, 3.9)$	$4,284$
$(4.52, 6.8)$	$4,484$
$(0, 9.25)$	$4,255$

The maximum of P is $4,484$ at $(4.52, 6.8)$.

28. Minimize and maximize $z = x_1 - x_2$

Subject to
$$x_1 - 2x_2 \geq -6$$
$$2x_1 - x_2 \geq 0$$
$$x_1, x_2 \geq 0$$

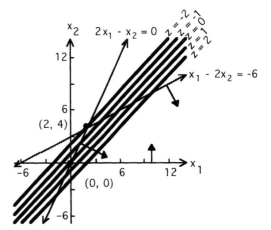

The feasible region and several values of the objective function are shown in the figure.

The points $(0, 0)$ and $(2, 4)$ are the corner points; $z = x_1 - x_2$ does not have a maximum value. Its minimum value is -2 at $(2, 4)$.

30. The value of $C = ax_1 + bx_2$, $a > 0$, $b > 0$, at each corner point is:

Corner Point	$C = ax_1 + bx_2$
A: $(0, 24)$	$24b$
B: $(6, 6)$	$6a + 6b$
D: $(30, 0)$	$30a$

(A) For the minimum value of C to occur at A only, we must have $24b < 6a + 6b$ and $24b < 30a$. Solving the first inequality, we get $a > 3b$; from the second inequality, we get $a > \frac{4}{5}b$. Therefore, we must have $a > 3b$ in order for C to have its minimum value at A only.

(B) For the minimum value of C to occur at B only, we must have $6a + 6b < 24b$ and $6a + 6b < 30a$. Solving this pair of inequalities, we get $a < 3b$ and $b < 4a$, which is the same as $\frac{a}{3} < b < 4a$ (or $\frac{b}{4} < a < 3b$).

(C) For the minimum value of C to occur at D only, we must have $30a < 6a + 6b$ and $30a < 24b$. This pair of inequalities implies that $b > 4a$ (or $a < \frac{1}{4}b$).

(D) For the minimum value of C to occur at both A and B, we must have $a = 3b$.

(E) For the minimum value of C to occur at both B and D, we must have $a = \frac{1}{4}b$.

32. (A) Form a mathematical model for the problem.

Let x_1 = the number of tables

and x_2 = the number of chairs produced per day.

The mathematical model for this problem is:

$$\text{Maximize } P = 90x_1 + 25x_2$$
$$\text{Subject to: } 8x_1 + 2x_2 \le 400$$
$$2x_1 + x_2 \le 120$$
$$x_1 \ge 0, \ x_2 \ge 0$$

Graph the feasible region and find the corner points.

The feasible region S is the solution set of the given system of inequalities, and is indicated by the shading in the graph at the right.

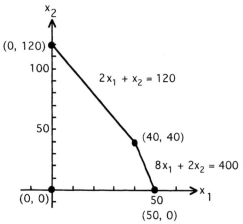

The corner points are $(0, 0)$, $(50, 0)$, $(40, 40)$, and $(0, 120)$.

Since S is bounded, P has a maximum value.

Evaluate the objective function each corner point.

Corner Point	$P = 90x_1 + 25x_2$
$(0, 0)$	0
$(50, 0)$	4,500
$(40, 40)$	4,600
$(0, 120)$	3,000

The maximum occurs at $(40, 40)$ and the maximum value of P is $4,600.

(B) The mathematical model for this problem is:

$$\text{Maximize } P = 90x_1 + 25x_2$$
$$\text{Subject to: } 8x_1 + 2x_2 \le 400$$
$$2x_1 + x_2 \le 120$$
$$x_2 \ge 4x_1$$
$$x_1, \ x_2 \ge 0$$

The feasible region is the shaded region shown on the graph at the right. The corner points are (0, 0), (20, 80), and (0, 120).

Evaluate the objective function at each corner point.

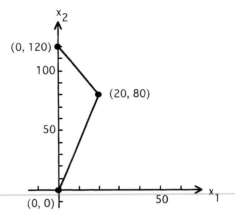

Corner Point	$P = 90x_1 + 25x_2$
(0, 0)	0
(20, 80)	3,800
(0, 120)	3,000

The maximum value of P is \$3,800 at (20, 80).

34. Summarize relevant material in table form.

	Standard computer	Portable computer
Capital expenditure	\$400	\$250
Labor	40 hours	30 hours

Form a mathematical model for the problem.

Let x_1 = the number of standard computers

and x_2 = the number of portable computers produced.

The mathematical model for this problem is:

Maximize $z = x_1 + x_2$

Subject to: $400x_1 + 250x_2 \leq 20,000$

$40x_1 + 30x_2 \leq 2,160$

$x_1 \geq 0, \ x_2 \geq 0$

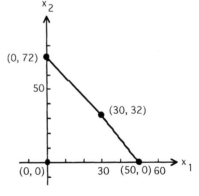

Graph the feasible region and find the corner points.

The feasible region is the shaded region shown on the right.
The corner points are (0, 0), (50, 0), (30, 32), and (0, 72).

Evaluate the objective function at each corner point.

Corner Point	$z = x_1 + x_2$
(0, 0)	0
(50, 0)	50
(30, 32)	62
(0, 72)	72

The maximum value of z is 72 at (0, 72); i.e. 72 portable and 0 standard.

Let P be the profit function. Then $P = 320x_1 + 220x_2$.

Profit on 72 portable computers is $15,840. The maximum value of P is $16,640 at (30, 32); i.e. 30 standard and 32 portable computers.

Corner Point	$P = 320x_1 + 220x_2$
(0, 0)	0
(50, 0)	16,000
(30, 32)	16,640
(0, 72)	15,840

36. The changes in the data for Problem 35 change the model to:
Minimize $C = 1200x_1 + 100x_2$

Subject to:
$$40x_1 + 7x_2 \geq 400$$
$$3x_1 + x_2 \leq 35$$
$$x_1,\ x_2 \geq 0$$

The feasible region is shown in figure (a) and the values of the objective function are shown in the table.

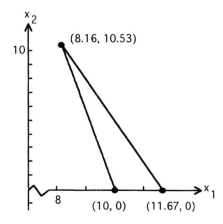

Corner Point	$C = 1200x_1 + 100x_2$
(10, 0)	12,000
(11.67, 0)	14,004
(8.16, 10.53)	10,845

The minimum value of C is 10,845 at (8.16, 10.53). But decimal solutions do not make sense in this problem. If we round the coordinates of this corner point to (8, 11), then we can accommodate only $40(8) + 7(11) = 397$ students; that is, (8, 11) is not a feasible solution. Since a meaningful solution must have integer coordinates, we must consider only the points in the feasible solution with integer solutions, as shown in figure (b). Evaluating the objective function at each of these points (details omitted), we find that the minimal value of C is $11,400 at $x_1 = 9$ and $x_2 = 6$.

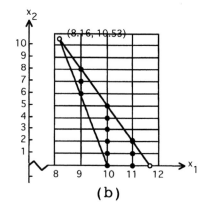

(b)

38. Let x_1 = amount invested in bonds of AAA quality and x_2 = amount invested in bonds of B quality.

The mathematical model for this problem is
Maximize $P = 0.06x_1 + 0.10x_2$
Subject to: $x_1 + x_2 \leq 24,000$
$$x_1 \geq 3x_2$$
$$x_1, x_2 \geq 0$$

Graph the feasible region and find the corner points.

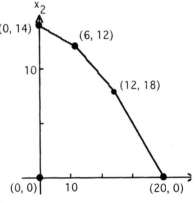

The corner points are (0, 0), (24,000, 0), and (18,000, 6,000).

Now, evaluate objective function at each corner point.

Corner Point	$P = 0.06x_1 + 0.10x_2$
(0, 0)	0
(24,000, 0)	1,440
(18,000, 6,000)	1,680

The maximum value of P is \$1,680 at (18,000, 6,000); i.e. invest 18,000 in AAA bonds and 6,000 in B bonds.

40. Let x_1 = the number of drive-through restaurants and x_2 = the number of full-service restaurants.

The mathematical model for this problem is:
Maximize $P = 200,000x_1 + 500,000x_2$
Subject to: $100,000x_1 + 150,000x_2 \leq 2,400,000$
$$5x_1 + 15x_2 \leq 210$$
$$x_1 + x_2 \leq 20$$
$$x_1 \geq 0, \ x_2 \geq 0$$

Graph the feasible region and find the corner points.
The feasible region is indicated by shading the region in the graph above. The corner points are (0, 0), (20, 0), (12, 8), (6, 12), and (0, 14).

Evaluate expected revenue function P at each corner point.

The maximum of P is \$7,200,000 at (6, 12); i.e. 6 drive-through and 12 full-service restaurants. Capital expenditure is \$2,400,000. The number of employees is $6 \times 5 + 15 \times 12 = 210$.

Corner point	$P = 200,000x_1 + 500,000x_2$
(0,0)	0
(20,0)	4,000,000
(12,8)	6,400,000
(6,12)	7,200,000
(0,14)	7,000,000

42. Let x_1 = the number of ounces of food M
and x_2 = the number of ounces of food N.

The mathematical model for this problem is:
Minimize $z = 8x_1 + 4x_2$
Subject to: $30x_1 + 10x_2 \geq 360$
$$10x_1 + 10x_2 \geq 160$$
$$10x_1 + 30x_2 \geq 240$$
$$x_1 \geq 0, \ x_2 \geq 0$$

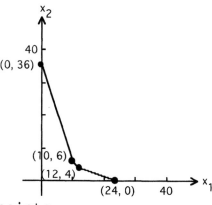

Graph the feasible region and find the corner points.
The feasible region is indicated by the shading of a region in the above graph. The corner points are: (24, 0), (12, 4), (10, 6), and (0, 36).

Now, evaluate z at each corner point.

The minimum value of z is 104 at (10, 6); i.e. 10 oz of M and 6 oz of N; 104 units of cholesterol.

Corner point	$z = 8x_1 + 4x_2$
(24,0)	192
(12,4)	112
(10,6)	104
(0,36)	144

44. Let x_1 = the number of ounces of food A
and x_2 = the number of ounces of food B.

The mathematical model for this problem is:
Maximize $z = 0.05x_1 + 0.05x_2$
Subject to: $8x_1 + 4x_2 \geq 176$
$$16x_1 + 32x_2 \geq 1,024$$
$$2x_1 + 8x_2 \geq 384$$

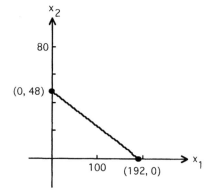

Graph the feasible region and find the corner points.
The feasible region is indicated by shading the region in the above graph. The corner points are: (192, 0) and (0, 48).

Evaluate the cost function $z = 0.05x_1 + 0.05x_2$ at each corner point.

The minimum value of z is $2.40 at (0, 48); i.e. 0 oz of A and 48 oz of B.

Corner point	$z = 0.05x_1 + 0.05x_2$
(192,0)	$9.60
(0,48)	$2.40

46. Let x_1 = the number of Sociologists and x_2 = the number of Research assistants.

The mathematical model for this problem is:

Maximize $C = 500x_1 + 300x_2$

Subject to: $10x_1 + 30x_2 \geq 180$

$\qquad\qquad 30x_1 + 10x_2 \geq 140$

$\qquad\qquad x_1 \geq 0, \; x_2 \geq 0$

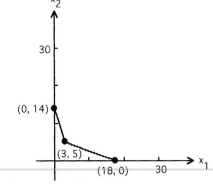

Graph the feasible region and find the corner points.

The feasible region is indicated by shading the region in the above graph. The corner points are: (18, 0), (3, 5), and (0, 14).

Now, evaluate the objective function at each corner point.

The minimum cost is \$3,000 at (3, 5); i.e. 3 Sociologists and 5 Research assistants.

Corner point	$C = 500x_1 + 300x_2$
(18,0)	9,000
(3,5)	3,000
(0,14)	4,200

6 LINEAR PROGRAMMING—SIMPLEX METHOD

2. (A) Since there are 3 problem constraints, 3 slack variables are introduced.

   (B) Since there are three equations (from the three problem constraints) and four decision variables, there are three basic variables and four nonbasic variables.

   (C) There will be three linear equations and three variables.

4. (A) There are 4 constraint equations; the number of equations is the same as the number of slack variables.

   (B) There are 6 decision variables since there are 10 variables altogether, and 4 of them are slack variables.

   (C) There are 4 basic variables and 6 nonbasic variables; the number of basic variables equals the number of equations.

   (D) Four linear equations with 4 variables.

6.

	Nonbasic	Basic	Feasible?
(A)	x_1, x_2	s_1, s_2	Yes, all values are nonnegative.
(B)	x_1, s_1	x_2, s_2	No, $s_2 = -90 < 0$.
(C)	x_1, s_2	x_2, s_1	Yes, all values are nonnegative.
(D)	x_2, s_1	x_1, s_2	Yes, all values are nonnegative.
(E)	x_2, s_2	x_1, s_1	No, $s_1 = -90 < 0$.
(F)	s_1, s_2	x_1, x_2	Yes, all values are nonnegative.

8.

	x_1	x_2	s_1	s_2	Feasible?
(A)	0	0	12	24	Yes, all values are nonnegative.
(B)	0	6	0	12	Yes, all values are nonnegative
(C)	0	12	-12	0	No, $s_1 = -12 < 0$.
(D)	12	0	0	-12	No, $s_2 = -12 < 0$.
(E)	8	0	4	0	Yes, all values are nonnegative.
(F)	6	3	0	0	Yes, all values are nonnegative.

10.

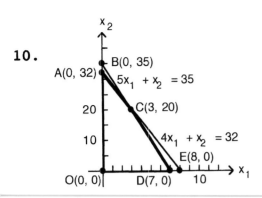

Introduce slack variables s_1 and s_2 to obtain the system of equations:

$$5x_1 + x_2 + s_1 \qquad = 35$$
$$4x_1 + x_2 \qquad + s_2 = 32$$

x_1	x_2	s_1	s_2	Intersection Point	Feasible?
0	0	35	32	O	Yes
0	35	0	-3	B	No, $s_2 = -3 < 0$
0	32	3	0	A	Yes
7	0	0	4	D	Yes
8	0	-5	0	E	No, $s_1 = -5 < 0$
3	20	0	0	C	Yes

12.

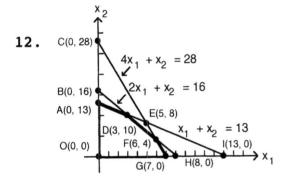

Introduce slack variables s_1, s_2, and s_3 to obtain the system of equations:

$$4x_1 + x_2 + s_1 \qquad\qquad = 28$$
$$2x_1 + x_2 \qquad + s_2 \qquad = 16$$
$$x_1 + x_2 \qquad\qquad + s_3 = 13$$

x_1	x_2	s_1	s_2	s_3	Intersection Point	Feasible?
0	0	28	16	13	O	Yes
0	28	0	-12	-15	C	No, $s_2 = -12 < 0$, $s_3 = -15 < 0$
0	16	12	0	-3	B	No, $s_3 = -3 < 0$
0	13	15	3	0	A	Yes
7	0	0	2	6	G	Yes
8	0	-4	0	5	H	No, $s_1 = -4 < 0$
13	0	-24	-10	0	I	No, $s_1 = -24 < 0$, $s_3 = -10 < 0$
6	4	0	0	3	F	Yes
5	8	0	-2	0	E	No, $s_2 = -2 < 0$
3	10	0	0	0	D	Yes

EXERCISE 6-2

2. Given the simplex tableau:

$$
\begin{array}{ccccc|c}
x_1 & x_2 & s_1 & s_2 & P & \\
1 & 4 & -2 & 0 & 0 & 10 \\
0 & 2 & 3 & 1 & 0 & 25 \\
\hline
0 & 5 & 6 & 0 & 1 & 35
\end{array}
$$

which corresponds to the system of equations:

$$(I) \begin{cases} x_1 + 4x_2 - 2s_1 = 10 \\ \quad\quad 2x_2 + 3s_1 + s_2 = 25 \\ \quad\quad 5x_2 + 6s_1 \quad\quad + P = 35 \end{cases}$$

(A) The basic variables are x_1, s_2, and P, and the nonbasic variables are x_2 and s_1.

(B) The corresponding basic feasible solution is found by setting the nonbasic variables equal to 0 in system (I). This yields:

$$x_1 = 10, \ x_2 = 0, \ s_1 = 0, \ s_2 = 25, \ P = 35$$

(C) Optimal solution.

4. Given the simplex tableau:

$$\begin{array}{ccccccc} x_1 & x_2 & x_3 & s_1 & s_2 & s_3 & P \\ \end{array}$$
$$\left[\begin{array}{ccccccc|c} 0 & 2 & -1 & 1 & 4 & 0 & 0 & 5 \\ 0 & 1 & 2 & 0 & -2 & 1 & 0 & 2 \\ 1 & 3 & 0 & 0 & 5 & 0 & 0 & 11 \\ \hline 0 & -5 & 4 & 0 & -3 & 0 & 1 & 27 \end{array} \right]$$

which corresponds to the system of equations:

$$(I) \begin{cases} 2x_2 - x_3 + s_1 + 4s_2 = 5 \\ \quad x_2 + 2x_3 \quad\quad - 2s_2 + s_3 = 2 \\ x_1 + 3x_2 \quad\quad\quad + 5s_2 = 11 \\ \quad -5x_2 + 4x_3 \quad\quad - 3s_2 \quad\quad + P = 27 \end{cases}$$

(A) The basic variables are x_1, s_1, s_3, and P, and the nonbasic variables are x_2, x_3, and s_2.

(B) The corresponding basic feasible solution is found by setting the nonbasic variables equal to 0 in system (I). This yields:

$$x_1 = 11, \ x_2 = 0, \ x_3 = 0, \ s_1 = 5, \ s_2 = 0, \ s_3 = 2, \ P = 27$$

(C) An additional pivot is required, since the last row of the tableau has a negative indicator, the -5 in the second column.

6. Given the simplex tableau:

$$\begin{array}{ccccc} x_1 & x_2 & s_1 & s_2 & P \\ \end{array}$$
$$\left[\begin{array}{ccccc|c} 1 & 6 & 1 & 0 & 0 & 36 \\ 3 & 1 & 0 & 1 & 0 & 5 \\ \hline -1 & -2 & 0 & 0 & 1 & 0 \end{array} \right]$$

The most negative indicator is -2 in the second column.

Now, $\dfrac{36}{6} = 6$ and $\dfrac{5}{1} = 5$. Thus, the second row is the pivot row and the pivot element is the element in the second row, second column. These are indicated in the following tableau.

$$\begin{array}{c} \\ s_1 \\ \text{Exit}\;\; s_2 \\ \\ P \end{array}
\begin{array}{c} x_1 \;\; x_2 \;\; s_1 \;\; s_2 \;\; P \\
\left[\begin{array}{ccccc|c}
1 & 6 & 1 & 0 & 0 & 36 \\
3 & \textcircled{1} & 0 & 1 & 0 & 5 \\
\hline
-1 & -2 & 0 & 0 & 1 & 0
\end{array}\right]
\end{array}
\begin{array}{c}
\frac{36}{6} = 6 \\[4pt]
\frac{5}{1} = 5 \;\text{(minimum)}
\end{array}
\sim
\left[\begin{array}{ccccc|c}
-17 & 0 & 1 & -6 & 0 & 6 \\
3 & 1 & 0 & 1 & 0 & 5 \\
\hline
5 & 0 & 0 & 2 & 1 & 10
\end{array}\right]$$

$$(-6)R_2 + R_1 \rightarrow R_1$$
$$2R_2 + R_3 \rightarrow R_3$$

8. Given the simplex tableau:

$$\begin{array}{c}
x_1 \;\; x_2 \;\; s_1 \;\; s_2 \;\; s_3 \;\; P \\
\left[\begin{array}{cccccc|c}
0 & 0 & 2 & 1 & 1 & 0 & 2 \\
1 & 0 & -4 & 0 & 1 & 0 & 3 \\
0 & 1 & 5 & 0 & 2 & 0 & 11 \\
\hline
0 & 0 & -6 & 0 & -5 & 1 & 18
\end{array}\right]
\end{array}$$

The most negative indicator is -6 in the third column.
Now, $\dfrac{2}{2} = 1$, $\dfrac{3}{-4} = -\dfrac{3}{4}$, and $\dfrac{11}{5} = 2.2$. Thus, the first row is the pivot row, and the pivot element is the element in the first row, third column. These are indicated in the following tableau.

Enter

$$\begin{array}{c}
\text{Exit}\;\; s_2 \\
x_1 \\
x_2 \\
P
\end{array}
\begin{array}{c}
x_1 \;\; x_2 \;\; s_1 \;\; s_2 \;\; s_3 \;\; P \\
\left[\begin{array}{cccccc|c}
0 & 0 & \textcircled{2} & 1 & 1 & 0 & 2 \\
1 & 0 & -4 & 0 & 1 & 0 & 3 \\
0 & 1 & 5 & 0 & 2 & 0 & 11 \\
0 & 0 & -6 & 0 & -5 & 1 & 18
\end{array}\right]
\end{array}
\sim
\begin{array}{c}
s_1 \\
x_1 \\
x_2 \\
P
\end{array}
\left[\begin{array}{cccccc|c}
0 & \textcircled{0} & 1 & \frac{1}{2} & \frac{1}{2} & 0 & 1 \\
1 & 0 & 0 & 2 & 3 & 0 & 7 \\
0 & 1 & 0 & -\frac{5}{2} & -\frac{1}{2} & 0 & 6 \\
0 & 0 & 0 & 3 & -2 & 1 & 24
\end{array}\right]$$

10. (A) Introduce slack variables s_1 and s_2 to obtain:

Maximize $P = 3x_1 + 2x_2$

Subject to:
$$5x_1 + 2x_2 + s_1 \quad\quad = 20$$
$$3x_1 + 2x_2 \quad\quad + s_2 = 16$$
$$x_1,\; x_2,\; s_1,\; s_2 \geq 0$$

This system can be written in initial form:

$$5x_1 + 2x_2 + s_1 \quad\quad\quad = 20$$
$$3x_1 + 2x_2 \quad\quad + s_2 \quad\quad = 16$$
$$-3x_1 - 2x_2 \quad\quad\quad\quad + P = 0$$
$$x_1,\; x_2,\; s_1,\; s_2 \geq 0$$

(B) The simplex tableau for this problem is:

Enter

$$
\begin{array}{c}
\\
\text{Exit } s_1 \\
s_2 \\
P
\end{array}
\begin{array}{c}
x_1 \quad x_2 \quad s_1 \quad s_2 \quad P \\
\left[\begin{array}{ccccc|c}
\circledm{5} & 2 & 1 & 0 & 0 & 20 \\
3 & 2 & 0 & 1 & 0 & 16 \\
\hline
-3 & -2 & 0 & 0 & 1 & 0
\end{array}\right]
\end{array}
\quad
\begin{array}{c}
\frac{20}{5} = 4 \\[2mm]
\frac{16}{3} = 5.3\overline{3}
\end{array}
$$

Column 1 is the pivot column (-3 is the most negative indicator). Row 1 is the pivot row (4 is the smallest positive quotient). Thus, the pivot element is the circled 5.

(C) We use the simplex method as outlined above. The pivot elements are circled.

$$
\left[\begin{array}{ccccc|c}
\circledm{5} & 2 & 1 & 0 & 0 & 20 \\
3 & 2 & 0 & 1 & 0 & 16 \\
\hline
-3 & -2 & 0 & 0 & 1 & 0
\end{array}\right]
\sim
\left[\begin{array}{ccccc|c}
\circledm{1} & \frac{2}{5} & \frac{1}{5} & 0 & 0 & 4 \\
3 & 2 & 0 & 1 & 0 & 16 \\
\hline
-3 & -2 & 0 & 0 & 1 & 0
\end{array}\right]
\sim
$$

$$\frac{1}{5}R_1 \to R_1 \qquad\qquad\qquad (-3)R_1 + R_2 \to R_2$$
$$3R_1 + R_3 \to R_3$$

$$
\left[\begin{array}{ccccc|c}
1 & \frac{2}{5} & \frac{1}{5} & 0 & 0 & 4 \\
0 & \circledm{\frac{4}{5}} & -\frac{3}{5} & 1 & 0 & 4 \\
\hline
0 & -\frac{4}{5} & \frac{3}{5} & 0 & 1 & 12
\end{array}\right]
\sim
\left[\begin{array}{ccccc|c}
1 & \frac{2}{5} & \frac{1}{5} & 0 & 0 & 4 \\
0 & \circledm{1} & -\frac{3}{4} & -\frac{5}{4} & 0 & 5 \\
\hline
0 & -\frac{4}{5} & \frac{3}{5} & 0 & 1 & 12
\end{array}\right]
\sim
$$

$$\left(\frac{5}{4}\right)R_2 \to R_2 \qquad\qquad \left(-\frac{2}{5}\right)R_2 + R_1 \to R_1$$
$$\left(\frac{4}{5}\right)R_2 + R_3 \to R_3$$

$$
\begin{array}{c}
x_1 \\
x_2 \\
P
\end{array}
\begin{array}{c}
x_1 \quad\ x_2 \quad\ s_1 \qquad s_2 \quad\ p \\
\left[\begin{array}{ccccc|c}
1 & 0 & 0.5 & -0.5 & 0 & 2 \\
0 & 1 & -\frac{3}{4} & -\frac{5}{4} & 0 & 5 \\
\hline
0 & 1 & 0 & 1 & 1 & 16
\end{array}\right]
\end{array}
$$

All elements in the last row are nonnegative. Thus, max $P = 16$ at $x_1 = 2$, $x_2 = 5$, $s_1 = 0$, $s_2 = 0$.

12. (A) Introduce slack variables s_1 and s_2 to obtain:

Maximize $P = x_1 + 3x_2$
Subject to:
$$
\begin{aligned}
5x_1 + 2x_2 + s_1 \quad\ &= 20 \\
3x_1 + 2x_2 \quad\ + s_2 &= 16 \\
x_1,\ x_2,\ s_1,\ s_2 &\geq 0
\end{aligned}
$$

This system can be written in the initial form:

$$
\begin{aligned}
5x_1 + 2x_2 + s_1 \qquad\qquad &= 20 \\
3x_1 + 2x_2 \qquad + s_2 \qquad &= 16 \\
-x_1 - 3x_2 \qquad\qquad + P &= 0 \\
x_1,\ x_2,\ s_1,\ s_2 &\geq 0
\end{aligned}
$$

(B) The simplex tableau for this problem is:

$$
\begin{array}{c}
\\
s_1 \\
\text{Exit } s_2 \\
P
\end{array}
\begin{array}{c}
\begin{array}{ccccc}
x_1 & x_2 & s_1 & s_2 & P
\end{array}\\
\left[\begin{array}{ccccc|c}
5 & 2 & 1 & 0 & 0 & 20 \\
3 & ② & 0 & 1 & 0 & 16 \\
\hline
-1 & -3 & 0 & 0 & 1 & 0
\end{array}\right]
\end{array}
\begin{array}{c}
\frac{20}{2} = 10 \\
\frac{16}{2} = 8
\end{array}
\sim
$$

Enter (above x_2); Pivot column (below x_2)

$\frac{1}{2} R_2 \rightarrow R_2$

$$
\left[\begin{array}{ccccc|c}
5 & 2 & 1 & 0 & 0 & 20 \\
\frac{3}{2} & ① & 0 & \frac{1}{2} & 0 & 8 \\
\hline
-1 & -3 & 0 & 0 & 1 & 0
\end{array}\right]
\sim
\left[\begin{array}{ccccc|c}
2 & 0 & 1 & -1 & 0 & 4 \\
\frac{3}{2} & 1 & 0 & \frac{1}{2} & 0 & 8 \\
\hline
-\frac{7}{2} & 0 & 0 & \frac{3}{2} & 1 & 24
\end{array}\right]
$$

$(-2) R_2 + R_1 \rightarrow R_1$

$3 R_2 + R_3 \rightarrow R_3$

(C) Max $P = 24$ at $x_1 = 0$ and $x_2 = 8$.

14. The simplex tableau for this problem is:

$$
\begin{array}{c}
\\
\\
s_1 \\
s_2 \\
\text{pivot} \rightarrow s_3 \\
\text{row} \\
\text{Exit}
\end{array}
\begin{array}{c}
\begin{array}{cccccc}
x_1 & x_2 & s_1 & s_2 & s_3 & P
\end{array}\\
\left[\begin{array}{cccccc|c}
2 & 1 & 1 & 0 & 0 & 0 & 9 \\
1 & 1 & 0 & 1 & 0 & 0 & 6 \\
1 & ② & 0 & 0 & 1 & 0 & 10 \\
\hline
-15 & -20 & 0 & 0 & 0 & 1 & 0
\end{array}\right]
\end{array}
\begin{array}{c}
9 \\
6 \\
5
\end{array}
\sim
$$

Enter (above x_2); pivot column (below x_2)

$\frac{1}{2} R_3 \rightarrow R_3$

$$
\left[\begin{array}{cccccc|c}
2 & 1 & 1 & 0 & 0 & 0 & 9 \\
1 & 1 & 0 & 1 & 0 & 0 & 6 \\
\frac{1}{2} & ① & 0 & 0 & \frac{1}{2} & 0 & 5 \\
\hline
-15 & -20 & 0 & 0 & 0 & 1 & 0
\end{array}\right]
\sim
$$

$(-1) R_3 + R_1 \rightarrow R_1, \quad (-1) R_3 + R_1 \rightarrow R_2, \quad 20 R_3 + R_4 \rightarrow R_4$

$$
\begin{array}{c}
\\
\\
\text{pivot} \rightarrow \\
\text{row}
\end{array}
\left[\begin{array}{cccccc|c}
\frac{3}{2} & 0 & 1 & 0 & -\frac{1}{2} & 0 & 4 \\
①\frac{1}{2} & 0 & 0 & 1 & -\frac{1}{2} & 0 & 1 \\
\frac{1}{2} & 1 & 0 & 0 & \frac{1}{2} & 0 & 5 \\
\hline
-5 & 0 & 0 & 0 & 10 & 1 & 100
\end{array}\right]
\begin{array}{c}
\frac{4}{3/2} = \frac{8}{3} \\
\frac{1}{1/2} = 2 \\
\frac{5}{1/2} = 10
\end{array}
\sim
$$

pivot column (below x_1)

$2 R_2 \rightarrow R_2$

$$\begin{bmatrix} \frac{3}{2} & 0 & 1 & 0 & -\frac{1}{2} & 0 & 4 \\ 1 & 0 & 0 & 2 & -1 & 0 & 2 \\ \frac{1}{2} & ① & 0 & 0 & \frac{1}{2} & 0 & 5 \\ \hline -5 & 0 & 0 & 0 & 10 & 1 & 100 \end{bmatrix} \sim \begin{matrix} \\ x_1 \\ x_2 \\ \\ \end{matrix} \begin{bmatrix} 0 & 0 & 1 & -3 & 1 & 0 & 1 \\ 1 & 0 & 0 & 2 & -1 & 0 & 2 \\ 0 & 1 & 0 & -1 & 1 & 0 & 4 \\ 0 & 0 & 0 & 10 & 5 & 1 & 110 \end{bmatrix}$$

$$\left(-\frac{3}{2}\right)R_2 + R_1 \to R_1, \quad \left(-\frac{1}{2}\right)R_2 + R_3 \to R_3,$$

$$5R_2 + R_4 \to R_4$$

Max $P = 110$ at $x_1 = 2$ and $x_2 = 4$.

16. The simplex tableau for the problem is:

$$\begin{array}{c} \text{Enter} \\ \text{Exit} \quad x_1 \quad x_2 \quad s_1 \quad s_2 \quad s_3 \quad P \end{array}$$

$$\begin{matrix} \text{pivot} \to s_1 \\ \text{row} \\ s_2 \\ s_3 \\ P \end{matrix} \begin{bmatrix} -2 & ① & 1 & 0 & 0 & 0 & 2 \\ -1 & 1 & 0 & 1 & 0 & 0 & 5 \\ 0 & 1 & 0 & 0 & 1 & 0 & 6 \\ \hline 1 & -3 & 0 & 0 & 0 & 1 & 0 \end{bmatrix} \begin{matrix} \frac{2}{1} = 2 \\ \frac{5}{1} = 5 \\ \frac{6}{1} = 6 \\ \\ \end{matrix} \sim$$

$$\begin{matrix} \uparrow \\ \text{pivot} \\ \text{column} \end{matrix}$$

$$(-1)R_1 + R_2 \to R_2, \quad (-1)R_1 + R_3 \to R_3, \quad \text{and} \quad 3R_1 + R_4 \to R_4$$

$$\begin{matrix} \\ \\ \text{pivot} \to \\ \text{row} \\ \\ \end{matrix} \begin{bmatrix} -2 & 1 & 1 & 0 & 0 & 0 & 2 \\ 1 & 0 & -1 & 1 & 0 & 0 & 3 \\ ② & 0 & -1 & 0 & 1 & 0 & 4 \\ \hline -5 & 0 & 3 & 0 & 0 & 1 & 6 \end{bmatrix} \begin{matrix} \\ \frac{3}{1} = 3 \\ \frac{4}{2} = 2 \ (\text{minimum}) \\ \\ \end{matrix}$$

$$\begin{matrix} \uparrow \\ \text{pivot} \\ \text{column} \end{matrix} \qquad \frac{1}{2}R_3 \to R_3$$

$$\sim \begin{bmatrix} -2 & 1 & 1 & 0 & 0 & 0 & 2 \\ 1 & 0 & -1 & 1 & 0 & 0 & 3 \\ ① & 0 & -\frac{1}{2} & 0 & \frac{1}{2} & 0 & 2 \\ \hline -5 & 0 & 3 & 0 & 0 & 1 & 6 \end{bmatrix} \sim \begin{bmatrix} 0 & 2 & 0 & 0 & 1 & 0 & 6 \\ 0 & 0 & -\frac{1}{2} & 1 & -\frac{1}{2} & 0 & 1 \\ 1 & 0 & -\frac{1}{2} & 0 & \frac{1}{2} & 0 & 2 \\ \hline 0 & 0 & \frac{1}{2} & 0 & \frac{5}{2} & 1 & 16 \end{bmatrix}$$

$$2R_3 + R_1 \to R_1$$
$$(-1)R_3 + R_2 \to R_2$$
$$5R_3 + R_4 \to R_4$$

Max $P = 16$ at $x_1 = 2$ and $x_2 = 6$.

18. The simplex tableau for this problem is:

$$\begin{array}{c} \text{pivot} \\ \text{row} \end{array} \rightarrow \begin{array}{c} \\ s_1 \\ s_2 \\ s_3 \\ P \end{array} \begin{array}{cccccc} x_1 & x_2 & s_1 & s_2 & s_3 & P \end{array}$$

$$\begin{array}{c} \text{pivot} \\ \text{row} \end{array} \rightarrow \begin{array}{c} s_1 \\ s_2 \\ s_3 \\ \\ P \end{array} \left[\begin{array}{cccccc|c} -1 & ① & 1 & 0 & 0 & 0 & 2 \\ -1 & 3 & 0 & 1 & 0 & 0 & 12 \\ 1 & -4 & 0 & 0 & 1 & 0 & 4 \\ \hdashline -1 & -2 & 0 & 0 & 0 & 1 & 0 \end{array}\right] \begin{array}{l} \frac{2}{1} = 2 \text{ (minimum)} \\ \frac{12}{3} = 4 \end{array}$$

$$\uparrow$$
pivot column $(-3)R_1 + R_2 \rightarrow R_2,\ 4R_1 + R_3 \rightarrow R_3,\ \text{and } 2R_1 + R_4 \rightarrow R_4$

$$\begin{array}{c} \text{pivot} \\ \text{row} \end{array} \rightarrow \sim \left[\begin{array}{cccccc|c} -1 & 1 & 1 & 0 & 0 & 0 & 2 \\ ② & 0 & -3 & 1 & 0 & 0 & 6 \\ -3 & 0 & 4 & 0 & 1 & 0 & 12 \\ \hdashline -3 & 0 & 2 & 0 & 0 & 1 & 4 \end{array}\right] \begin{array}{l} \\ \frac{6}{2} = 3 \\ \\ \end{array}$$

$$\uparrow$$
pivot column $\frac{1}{2}R_2 \rightarrow R_2$

$$\sim \left[\begin{array}{cccccc|c} -1 & 1 & 1 & 0 & 0 & 0 & 2 \\ ① & 0 & -\frac{3}{2} & \frac{1}{2} & 0 & 0 & 3 \\ -3 & 0 & 4 & 0 & 1 & 0 & 12 \\ -3 & 0 & 2 & 1 & 0 & 1 & 4 \end{array}\right] \sim \left[\begin{array}{cccccc|c} 0 & 1 & -\frac{1}{2} & \frac{1}{2} & 0 & 0 & 5 \\ 1 & 0 & -\frac{3}{2} & \frac{1}{2} & 0 & 0 & 3 \\ 0 & 0 & -\frac{1}{2} & \frac{3}{2} & 1 & 0 & 21 \\ \hline 0 & 0 & -\frac{5}{2} & \frac{3}{2} & 0 & 1 & 13 \end{array}\right]$$

$R_2 + R_1 \rightarrow R_1,\ 3R_2 + R_3 \rightarrow R_3$ $\uparrow$
$3R_2 + R_4 \rightarrow R_4$ pivot column

Since all the elements of the pivot column are negative, no optimal solution exists.

20. The simplex tableau for the problem is:

$$\begin{array}{cccccc} x_1 & x_2 & x_3 & s_1 & s_2 & P \end{array}$$

$$\begin{array}{c} \text{pivot} \\ \text{row} \end{array} \rightarrow \begin{array}{c} s_1 \\ s_2 \\ \\ P \end{array} \left[\begin{array}{cccccc|c} ① & 2 & -1 & 1 & 0 & 0 & 5 \\ 3 & 2 & 2 & 0 & 1 & 0 & 22 \\ \hdashline -4 & 3 & -2 & 0 & 0 & 1 & 0 \end{array}\right] \begin{array}{l} \frac{5}{1} = 5 \text{ (minimum)} \\ \frac{22}{3} = 15 \end{array}$$

$$\uparrow$$
pivot column $(-3)R_1 + R_2 \rightarrow R_2,\ 4R_1 + R_3 \rightarrow R_3$

$$\begin{array}{c} \text{pivot} \\ \text{row} \rightarrow \end{array} \sim \left[\begin{array}{cccccc|c} 1 & 2 & -1 & 1 & 0 & 0 & 5 \\ 0 & -4 & ⑤ & -3 & 1 & 0 & 7 \\ 0 & 7 & -6 & 4 & 0 & 1 & 20 \end{array}\right] \sim \left[\begin{array}{cccccc|c} 1 & 2 & -1 & 1 & 0 & 0 & 5 \\ 0 & -\frac{4}{5} & ① & -\frac{3}{5} & \frac{1}{5} & 0 & \frac{7}{5} \\ 0 & 7 & -6 & 4 & 0 & 1 & 20 \end{array}\right]$$

$$\uparrow$$
pivot column $R_1 + R_2 \rightarrow R_2$
                $6R_2 + R_3 \rightarrow R_3$

$\frac{1}{5}R_2 \rightarrow R_2$

$$\sim \begin{bmatrix} 1 & \frac{6}{5} & 0 & \frac{2}{5} & \frac{1}{5} & 0 & \bigm| & \frac{32}{5} \\ 0 & -\frac{4}{5} & 1 & -\frac{3}{5} & \frac{1}{5} & 0 & \bigm| & \frac{7}{5} \\ \hline 0 & \frac{11}{7} & 0 & \frac{2}{5} & \frac{6}{5} & 1 & \bigm| & \frac{142}{5} \end{bmatrix}$$

Max $P = \dfrac{142}{5}$ at $x_1 = \dfrac{32}{5}$, $x_2 = 0$, and $x_3 = \dfrac{7}{5}$.

22. The simplex tableau for this problem is:

$$\begin{array}{c} \\ \text{pivot} \to \\ \text{row} \\ \\ \end{array} \begin{array}{c} s_1 \\ s_2 \\ P \end{array} \begin{bmatrix} x_1 & x_2 & x_3 & s_1 & s_2 & P \\ 1 & -2 & \textcircled{1} & 1 & 0 & 0 & \bigm| & 9 \\ 2 & 1 & 2 & 0 & 1 & 0 & \bigm| & 28 \\ \hline -1 & -1 & -2 & 0 & 0 & 1 & \bigm| & 0 \end{bmatrix} \begin{array}{l} \frac{9}{1} = 9 \\ \frac{28}{2} = 14 \end{array}$$

pivot column $(-2)R_1 + R_2 \to R_2$, $2R_1 + R_3 \to R_3$

$$\begin{array}{c} \text{pivot} \\ \text{row} \to \end{array} \sim \begin{bmatrix} 1 & -2 & 1 & 1 & 0 & 0 & \bigm| & 9 \\ 0 & \textcircled{5} & 0 & -2 & 1 & 0 & \bigm| & 10 \\ \hline 1 & -5 & 0 & 2 & 0 & 1 & \bigm| & 18 \end{bmatrix}$$

pivot column $\quad \frac{1}{5}R_2 \to R_2$

$$\sim \begin{bmatrix} 1 & \boxed{-2} & 1 & 1 & 0 & 0 & \bigm| & 9 \\ 0 & 1 & 0 & -\frac{2}{5} & \frac{1}{5} & 0 & \bigm| & 2 \\ \hline 1 & -5 & 0 & 2 & 0 & 1 & \bigm| & 18 \end{bmatrix} \sim \begin{bmatrix} 1 & 0 & 1 & \frac{1}{5} & \frac{2}{5} & 0 & \bigm| & 13 \\ 0 & 1 & 0 & -\frac{2}{5} & \frac{1}{5} & 0 & \bigm| & 2 \\ \hline 1 & 0 & 0 & 0 & 1 & 1 & \bigm| & 28 \end{bmatrix}$$

$2R_2 + R_1 \to R_1$
$5R_2 + R_3 \to R_3$

Max $P = 28$ at $x_1 = 0$, $x_2 = 2$, and $x_3 = 13$.

24. The simplex tableau for this problem is:

$$\begin{array}{c} \\ \\ \text{pivot} \to \\ \text{row} \\ \\ \end{array} \begin{array}{c} s_1 \\ s_2 \\ s_3 \\ \\ \end{array} \begin{bmatrix} x_1 & x_2 & x_3 & s_1 & s_2 & s_3 & P \\ 1 & 1 & 1 & 1 & 0 & 0 & 0 & \bigm| & 11 \\ \textcircled{2} & 3 & 1 & 0 & 1 & 0 & 0 & \bigm| & 20 \\ 1 & 3 & 2 & 0 & 0 & 1 & 0 & \bigm| & 20 \\ \hline -4 & -2 & -3 & 0 & 0 & 0 & 1 & \bigm| & 0 \end{bmatrix} \begin{array}{l} 11 \\ 10 \\ 20 \end{array}$$

pivot column $\quad \frac{1}{2}R_2 \to R_2$

$$\sim \begin{bmatrix} 1 & 1 & 1 & 1 & 0 & 0 & 0 & | & 11 \\ ① & \frac{3}{2} & \frac{1}{2} & 0 & \frac{1}{2} & 0 & 0 & | & 10 \\ 1 & 3 & 2 & 0 & 0 & 1 & 0 & | & 20 \\ 4 & -2 & -3 & 0 & 0 & 0 & 1 & | & 0 \end{bmatrix}$$

$(-1)R_2 + R_1 \rightarrow R_1, \quad (-1)R_2 + R_3 \rightarrow R_3, \quad 4R_2 + R_4 \rightarrow R_4$

$$\sim \begin{bmatrix} 0 & -\frac{1}{2} & ⑴{\tfrac{1}{2}} & 1 & -\frac{1}{2} & 0 & 0 & | & 1 \\ 1 & \frac{3}{2} & \frac{1}{2} & 0 & \frac{1}{2} & 0 & 0 & | & 10 \\ 0 & \frac{3}{2} & \frac{3}{2} & 0 & -\frac{1}{2} & 1 & 0 & | & 10 \\ 0 & 4 & -1 & 0 & 2 & 0 & 1 & | & 40 \end{bmatrix} \quad \begin{array}{l} \frac{1}{1/2} = 2 \text{ (minimum)} \\ \frac{10}{1/2} = 20 \\ \frac{10}{3/2} = \frac{20}{3} \end{array}$$

$\uparrow$ pivot column $\qquad 2R_1 \rightarrow R_1$

$$\sim \begin{bmatrix} 0 & -1 & ① & 2 & -1 & 0 & 0 & | & 2 \\ 1 & \frac{3}{2} & \frac{1}{2} & 0 & \frac{1}{2} & 0 & 0 & | & 10 \\ 0 & \frac{3}{2} & \frac{3}{2} & 0 & -\frac{1}{2} & 1 & 0 & | & 10 \\ 0 & 4 & -1 & 0 & 2 & 0 & 1 & | & 40 \end{bmatrix}$$

$\left(-\frac{1}{2}\right)R_1 + R_2 \rightarrow R_2, \quad \left(-\frac{3}{2}\right)R_1 + R_3 \rightarrow R_3, \quad R_1 + R_4 \rightarrow R_4$

$$\sim \begin{bmatrix} 0 & -1 & 1 & 2 & -1 & 0 & 0 & | & 2 \\ 1 & 2 & 0 & -1 & 1 & 0 & 0 & | & 9 \\ 0 & 3 & 0 & -3 & 1 & 1 & 0 & | & 7 \\ 0 & 3 & 0 & 2 & 1 & 0 & 1 & | & 42 \end{bmatrix}$$

Max $P = 42$ at $x_1 = 9$, $x_2 = 0$, and $x_3 = 2$.

26. Multiply the first constraint by $\dfrac{10}{6}$, the second by 100, and the third by 10 to clear fractions. Then, the simplex tableau for this problem is:

	x_1	x_2	s_1	s_2	s_3	P		
s_1	1	2	1	0	0	0	1,600	1,600
s_2	③	4	0	1	0	0	3,600	3,600
s_3	3	2	0	0	1	0	2,700	900
P	-20	-20	0	0	0	1	0	

pivot row $\rightarrow s_3$

$\uparrow$ pivot column $\qquad \dfrac{1}{3} R_3 \rightarrow R_3$

$$\sim \begin{bmatrix} 1 & 2 & 1 & 0 & 0 & 0 & | & 1,600 \\ 3 & 4 & 0 & 1 & 0 & 0 & | & 3,600 \\ ① & \frac{2}{3} & 0 & 0 & \frac{1}{3} & 0 & | & 900 \\ \hline -20 & -20 & 0 & 0 & 0 & 1 & | & 0 \end{bmatrix}$$

$(-1)R_3 + R_1 \rightarrow R_1$, $(-3)R_3 + R_2 \rightarrow R_2$, and $20R_3 + R_4 \rightarrow R_4$

pivot row $\rightarrow$

$$\sim \begin{bmatrix} 0 & \frac{4}{3} & 1 & 0 & -\frac{1}{3} & 0 & | & 700 \\ 0 & ② & 0 & 1 & -1 & 0 & | & 900 \\ 1 & \frac{2}{3} & 0 & 0 & \frac{1}{3} & 0 & | & 900 \\ \hline 0 & -\frac{20}{3} & 0 & 0 & \frac{20}{3} & 1 & | & 1,800 \end{bmatrix} \begin{matrix} \frac{700}{4/3} = \frac{2100}{4} = 525 \\ \frac{900}{2} = 450 \\ \frac{900}{2/3} = \frac{2700}{2} = 1,350 \end{matrix}$$

$\uparrow$ pivot column

$\frac{1}{2}R_2 \rightarrow R_2$

$$\sim \begin{bmatrix} 0 & \frac{4}{3} & 1 & 0 & -\frac{1}{3} & 0 & | & 700 \\ 0 & ① & 0 & \frac{1}{2} & -\frac{1}{2} & 0 & | & 450 \\ 1 & \frac{2}{3} & 0 & 0 & \frac{1}{3} & 0 & | & 900 \\ \hline 0 & -\frac{20}{3} & 0 & 0 & \frac{20}{3} & 1 & | & 1,800 \end{bmatrix}$$

$\left(-\frac{4}{3}\right)R_2 + R_1 \rightarrow R_1$, $\left(-\frac{2}{3}\right)R_2 + R_3 \rightarrow R_3$, $\frac{20}{3}R_2 + R_4 \rightarrow R_4$

$$\sim \begin{bmatrix} 0 & 0 & 1 & -\frac{2}{3} & \frac{1}{3} & 0 & | & 100 \\ 0 & 1 & 0 & \frac{1}{2} & -\frac{1}{2} & 0 & | & 450 \\ 1 & 0 & 0 & -\frac{1}{3} & \frac{2}{3} & 0 & | & 600 \\ \hline 0 & 0 & 0 & \frac{10}{3} & \frac{10}{3} & 1 & | & 21,000 \end{bmatrix}$$

Max $P = 21,000$ at $x_1 = 600$, $x_2 = 450$.

28. The simplex tableau for this problem is:

$$\begin{array}{c} \\ s_1 \\ s_2 \\ \text{pivot} \rightarrow s_3 \\ \text{row} \\ P \end{array} \begin{array}{cccccc} x_1 & x_2 & x_3 & s_1 & s_2 & s_3 & P \end{array}$$

$$\begin{bmatrix} 3 & 3 & 3 & 1 & 0 & 0 & 0 & | & 66 \\ 6 & -2 & 4 & 0 & 1 & 0 & 0 & | & 48 \\ 3 & ⑥ & 9 & 0 & 0 & 1 & 0 & | & 108 \\ \hline -10 & -50 & -10 & 0 & 0 & 0 & 1 & | & 0 \end{bmatrix} \begin{matrix} \frac{66}{3} = 22 \\ \\ \frac{108}{6} = 18 \end{matrix}$$

$\uparrow$ pivot column $\qquad \frac{1}{6}R_3 \rightarrow R_3$

$$\sim \begin{bmatrix} 3 & 3 & 3 & 1 & 0 & 0 & 0 & | & 66 \\ 6 & -2 & 4 & 0 & 1 & 0 & 0 & | & 48 \\ \frac{1}{2} & ① & \frac{3}{2} & 0 & 0 & \frac{1}{6} & 0 & | & 18 \\ \hline 10 & -50 & -10 & 0 & 0 & 0 & 1 & | & 0 \end{bmatrix}$$

$(-3)R_3 + R_1 \rightarrow R_1$, $2R_3 + R_2 \rightarrow R_2$, and $50R_3 + R_4 \rightarrow R_4$

$$\sim \begin{bmatrix} \frac{3}{2} & 0 & -\frac{3}{2} & 1 & 0 & -\frac{1}{2} & 0 & 60 \\ 7 & 0 & 7 & 0 & 1 & \frac{1}{3} & 0 & 84 \\ \frac{1}{2} & 1 & \frac{3}{2} & 0 & 0 & \frac{1}{6} & 0 & 18 \\ \hline 15 & 0 & 65 & 0 & 0 & \frac{25}{3} & 1 & 900 \end{bmatrix}$$

Max $P = 900$ at $x_1 = 0$, $x_2 = 18$, and $x_3 = 0$.

30. The simplex tableau for this problem is:

$$\begin{array}{c} \\ s_1 \\ s_2 \\ s_3 \\ \text{pivot} \to s_4 \\ \text{row} \\ P \end{array} \begin{array}{c} x_1 \quad x_2 \quad s_1 \quad s_2 \quad s_3 \quad s_4 \quad P \\ \begin{bmatrix} 5 & 4 & 1 & 0 & 0 & 0 & 0 & 100 \\ 2 & 1 & 0 & 1 & 0 & 0 & 0 & 28 \\ 4 & 1 & 0 & 0 & 1 & 0 & 0 & 42 \\ ① & 0 & 0 & 0 & 0 & 1 & 0 & 10 \\ \hdashline -5 & -3 & 0 & 0 & 0 & 0 & 1 & 0 \end{bmatrix} \end{array} \begin{array}{l} \frac{100}{5} = 20 \\ \frac{28}{2} = 14 \\ \frac{42}{4} = 10.5 \\ \frac{10}{1} = 10 \\ \\ \end{array}$$

pivot column

$(-5)R_4 + R_1 \to R_1,\ (-2)R_4 + R_2 \to R_2,\ (-4)R_4 + R_3 \to R_3,\ \text{and } 5R_4 + R_5 \to R_5$

$$\begin{array}{c} \\ \\ \text{pivot} \\ \text{row} \to \end{array} \sim \begin{bmatrix} 0 & 4 & 1 & 0 & 0 & -5 & 0 & 50 \\ 0 & 1 & 0 & 1 & 0 & -2 & 0 & 8 \\ 0 & ① & 0 & 0 & 1 & -4 & 0 & 2 \\ 1 & 0 & 0 & 0 & 0 & 1 & 0 & 10 \\ \hline 0 & -3 & 0 & 0 & 0 & 5 & 1 & 50 \end{bmatrix} \begin{array}{l} 12.5 \\ 8 \\ 2 \\ \\ \end{array}$$

pivot column

$(-4)R_3 + R_1 \to R_1,\ (-1)R_3 + R_2 \to R_2,\ \text{and } 3R_3 + R_5 \to R_5$

$$\begin{array}{c} \\ \text{pivot} \to \\ \text{row} \\ \\ \\ \end{array} \sim \begin{bmatrix} 0 & 0 & 1 & 0 & -4 & 11 & 0 & 42 \\ 0 & 0 & 0 & 1 & -1 & ② & 0 & 6 \\ 0 & 1 & 0 & 0 & 1 & -4 & 0 & 2 \\ 1 & 0 & 0 & 0 & 0 & 1 & 0 & 10 \\ \hdashline 0 & 0 & 0 & 0 & 3 & -7 & 1 & 56 \end{bmatrix} \begin{array}{l} \frac{42}{11} \\ 3 \\ \\ 10 \\ \\ \end{array}$$

pivot column

$\frac{1}{2}R_2 \to R_2$

$$\sim \begin{bmatrix} 0 & 0 & 1 & 0 & -4 & 11 & 0 & \vline & 42 \\ 0 & 0 & 0 & \frac{1}{2} & -\frac{1}{2} & \boxed{1} & 0 & \vline & 3 \\ 0 & 1 & 0 & 0 & 1 & -4 & 0 & \vline & 2 \\ 1 & 0 & 0 & 0 & 0 & 1 & 0 & \vline & 10 \\ \hdashline 0 & 0 & 0 & 0 & 3 & -7 & 1 & \vline & 56 \end{bmatrix}$$

$(-11)R_2 + R_1 \rightarrow R_1$, $4R_2 + R_3 \rightarrow R_3$, $(-1)R_2 + R_4 \rightarrow R_4$, and $7R_2 + R_5 \rightarrow R_5$

pivot row $\rightarrow$
$$\sim \begin{bmatrix} 0 & 0 & 1 & -\frac{11}{2} & \boxed{\frac{3}{2}} & 0 & 0 & \vline & 9 \\ 0 & 0 & 0 & \frac{1}{2} & -\frac{1}{2} & 1 & 0 & \vline & 3 \\ 0 & 1 & 0 & 2 & -1 & 0 & 0 & \vline & 14 \\ 1 & 0 & 0 & -\frac{1}{2} & \frac{1}{2} & 0 & 0 & \vline & 7 \\ \hdashline 0 & 0 & 0 & \frac{7}{2} & -\frac{1}{2} & 0 & 1 & \vline & 77 \end{bmatrix} \begin{matrix} \frac{9}{3/2} = 6 \\ \\ \\ \frac{7}{1/2} = 14 \\ \\ \end{matrix}$$

$\uparrow$
pivot column

$\frac{2}{3}R_1 \rightarrow R_1$

$$\sim \begin{bmatrix} 0 & 0 & \frac{2}{3} & -\frac{11}{3} & \boxed{1} & 0 & 0 & \vline & 6 \\ 0 & 0 & 0 & \frac{1}{2} & -\frac{1}{2} & 1 & 0 & \vline & 3 \\ 0 & 1 & 0 & 2 & -1 & 0 & 0 & \vline & 14 \\ 1 & 0 & 0 & -\frac{1}{2} & \frac{1}{2} & 0 & 0 & \vline & 7 \\ \hdashline 0 & 0 & 0 & \frac{7}{2} & -\frac{1}{2} & 0 & 1 & \vline & 77 \end{bmatrix}$$

$\frac{1}{2}R_1 + R_2 \rightarrow R_2$, $R_1 + R_3 \rightarrow R_3$, $\left(-\frac{1}{2}\right)R_1 + R_4 \rightarrow R_4$, and $\frac{1}{2}R_1 + R_5 \rightarrow R_5$

$$\sim \begin{bmatrix} 0 & 0 & \frac{2}{3} & -\frac{11}{3} & 1 & 0 & 0 & \vline & 6 \\ 0 & 0 & \frac{1}{3} & -\frac{4}{3} & 0 & 1 & 0 & \vline & 6 \\ 0 & 1 & \frac{2}{3} & -\frac{5}{3} & 0 & 0 & 0 & \vline & 20 \\ 1 & 0 & -\frac{1}{3} & \frac{4}{3} & 0 & 0 & 0 & \vline & 4 \\ \hdashline 0 & 0 & \frac{1}{3} & \frac{5}{3} & 0 & 0 & 1 & \vline & 80 \end{bmatrix}$$

Max $P = 80$ at $x_1 = 4$, and $x_2 = 20$.

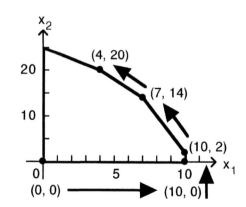

32. The simplex tableau for the problem is:

$$
\begin{array}{c}
 \\
s_1 \\
s_2 \\
s_3 \\
P
\end{array}
\begin{array}{c}
\begin{array}{cccccc}
x_1 & x_2 & s_1 & s_2 & s_3 & P
\end{array} \\
\left[\begin{array}{cccccc|c}
1 & 2 & 1 & 0 & 0 & 0 & 10 \\
1 & 0 & 0 & 1 & 0 & 0 & 6 \\
0 & 1 & 0 & 0 & 1 & 0 & 4 \\
\hline
-1 & -1 & 0 & 0 & 0 & 1 & 0
\end{array}\right]
\end{array}
$$

(A) Solution using the first column as the pivot column

$$
\begin{array}{c}
\begin{array}{cccccc}
x_1 & x_2 & s_1 & s_2 & s_3 & P
\end{array} \\
\left[\begin{array}{cccccc|c}
1 & 2 & 1 & 0 & 0 & 0 & 10 \\
① & 0 & 0 & 1 & 0 & 0 & 6 \\
0 & 1 & 0 & 0 & 1 & 0 & 4 \\
\hline
-1 & -1 & 0 & 0 & 0 & 1 & 0
\end{array}\right]
\end{array}
\quad
\begin{array}{l}
\dfrac{10}{1} = 10 \\[2mm]
\dfrac{6}{1} = 6
\end{array}
$$

$$(-1)R_2 + R_1 \rightarrow R_1, \quad R_2 + R_4 \rightarrow R_4$$

$$
\sim
\left[\begin{array}{cccccc|c}
0 & ② & 1 & -1 & 0 & 0 & 4 \\
1 & 0 & 0 & 1 & 0 & 0 & 6 \\
0 & 1 & 0 & 0 & 1 & 0 & 4 \\
\hline
0 & -1 & 0 & 1 & 0 & 1 & 6
\end{array}\right]
\begin{array}{l} 2 \\ \\ 4 \\ \\ \end{array}
$$

$$\frac{1}{2}R_1 \rightarrow R_1$$

$$
\sim
\left[\begin{array}{cccccc|c}
0 & ① & \frac{1}{2} & -\frac{1}{2} & 0 & 0 & 2 \\
1 & 0 & 0 & 1 & 0 & 0 & 6 \\
0 & 1 & 0 & 0 & 1 & 0 & 4 \\
\hline
0 & -1 & 0 & 1 & 0 & 1 & 6
\end{array}\right]
\sim
\left[\begin{array}{cccccc|c}
0 & 1 & \frac{1}{2} & -\frac{1}{2} & 0 & 0 & 2 \\
1 & 0 & 0 & 1 & 0 & 0 & 6 \\
0 & 0 & -\frac{1}{2} & \frac{1}{2} & 1 & 0 & 2 \\
\hline
0 & 0 & \frac{1}{2} & \frac{1}{2} & 0 & 1 & 8
\end{array}\right]
$$

$$(-1)R_1 + R_3 \rightarrow R_3, \quad R_1 + R_4 \rightarrow R_4$$

Max $P = 8$ at $x_1 = 6$ and $x_2 = 2$.

(B) Using the second column as the pivot column

$$
\begin{array}{c}
\begin{array}{cccccc}
x_1 & x_2 & s_1 & s_2 & s_3 & P
\end{array} \\
\left[\begin{array}{cccccc|c}
1 & 2 & 1 & 0 & 0 & 0 & 10 \\
1 & 0 & 0 & 1 & 0 & 0 & 6 \\
0 & ① & 0 & 0 & 1 & 0 & 4 \\
\hline
-1 & -1 & 0 & 0 & 0 & 1 & 0
\end{array}\right]
\end{array}
\quad
\begin{array}{l}
\dfrac{10}{2} = 5 \\[3mm]
\dfrac{4}{1} = 4
\end{array}
$$

$$(-2)R_3 + R_1 \rightarrow R_1, \quad R_3 + R_4 \rightarrow R_4$$

$$\sim \begin{bmatrix} ① & 0 & 1 & 0 & -2 & 0 & 2 \\ 1 & 0 & 0 & 1 & 0 & 0 & 6 \\ \hline 0 & 1 & 0 & 0 & 1 & 0 & 4 \\ \hline -1 & 0 & 0 & 0 & 1 & 1 & 4 \end{bmatrix} \begin{matrix} 2 \\ 6 \\ \\ \end{matrix}$$

$$(-1)R_1 + R_2 \rightarrow R_2, \; R_1 + R_4 \rightarrow R_4$$

$$\sim \begin{bmatrix} 1 & 0 & 1 & 0 & -2 & 0 & 2 \\ 0 & 0 & -1 & 1 & ② & 0 & 4 \\ 0 & 1 & 0 & 0 & 1 & 0 & 4 \\ \hdashline 0 & 0 & 1 & 0 & -1 & 1 & 6 \end{bmatrix} \begin{matrix} \\ 2 \\ 4 \\ \end{matrix} \qquad \sim \begin{bmatrix} 1 & 0 & 1 & 0 & -2 & 0 & 2 \\ 0 & 0 & -\frac{1}{2} & \frac{1}{2} & ① & 0 & 2 \\ 0 & 1 & 0 & 0 & 1 & 0 & 4 \\ \hdashline 0 & 0 & 1 & 0 & -1 & 1 & 6 \end{bmatrix}$$

$$\frac{1}{2}R_2 \rightarrow R_2 \qquad\qquad\qquad 2R_2 + R_1 \rightarrow R_1, \; (-1)R_2 + R_3 \rightarrow R_3,$$
$$\text{and } R_2 + R_4 \rightarrow R_4$$

$$\sim \begin{bmatrix} 1 & 0 & 0 & 1 & 0 & 0 & 6 \\ 0 & 0 & -\frac{1}{2} & \frac{1}{2} & 1 & 0 & 2 \\ 0 & 1 & \frac{1}{2} & -\frac{1}{2} & 0 & 0 & 2 \\ \hline 0 & 0 & \frac{1}{2} & \frac{1}{2} & 0 & 1 & 8 \end{bmatrix}$$

Max $P = 8$ at $x_1 = 6$ and $x_2 = 2$. The same result as in (A).

34. The simplex tableau for this problem is:

$$\begin{array}{c} \\ s_1 \\ s_2 \\ \\ P \end{array} \begin{array}{cccccc} x_1 & x_2 & x_3 & s_1 & s_2 & P \\ \end{array}$$

$$\begin{array}{c} s_1 \\ s_2 \\ \\ P \end{array} \left[\begin{array}{cccccc|c} 1 & 1 & 3 & 1 & 0 & 0 & 10 \\ 2 & 4 & 5 & 0 & 1 & 0 & 24 \\ \hline -2 & -2 & -1 & 0 & 0 & 1 & 0 \end{array} \right]$$

(A) Solution using the first column as the pivot column

$$\begin{array}{cccccc} x_1 & x_2 & x_3 & s_1 & s_2 & P \\ \end{array}$$

$$\left[\begin{array}{cccccc|c} ① & 1 & 3 & 1 & 0 & 0 & 10 \\ 2 & 4 & 5 & 0 & 1 & 0 & 24 \\ \hline -2 & -2 & -1 & 0 & 0 & 1 & 0 \end{array} \right] \begin{array}{l} \frac{10}{1} = 10 \\[2mm] \frac{24}{2} = 12 \end{array}$$

pivot column $\qquad (-2)R_1 + R_2 \rightarrow R_2, \; 2R_1 + R_3 \rightarrow R_3$

$$\sim \left[\begin{array}{cccccc|c} 1 & 1 & 3 & 1 & 0 & 0 & 10 \\ 0 & 2 & -1 & -2 & 1 & 0 & 4 \\ \hline 0 & 0 & 5 & 2 & 0 & 1 & 20 \end{array} \right]$$

Max $P = 20$ at $x_1 = 10$, $x_2 = 0$, and $x_3 = 0$.

(B) Solution using second column as the pivot column

$$
\begin{array}{cccccc}
x_1 & x_2 & x_3 & s_1 & s_2 & P
\end{array}
$$

$$
\begin{bmatrix}
1 & 1 & 3 & 1 & 0 & 0 & | & 10 \\
2 & \boxed{4} & 5 & 0 & 1 & 0 & | & 24 \\
\hdashline
-2 & -2 & -1 & 0 & 0 & 1 & | & 0
\end{bmatrix}
\quad
\begin{array}{l}
\dfrac{10}{1} = 10 \\[4pt]
\dfrac{24}{4} = 6
\end{array}
$$

$\uparrow$
pivot column $\quad \dfrac{1}{4}R_2 \to R_2$

$$
\sim
\begin{bmatrix}
1 & 1 & 3 & 1 & 0 & 0 & | & 10 \\
\frac{1}{2} & \boxed{1} & \frac{5}{4} & 0 & \frac{1}{4} & 0 & | & 6 \\
-2 & -2 & -1 & 0 & 0 & 1 & | & 0
\end{bmatrix}
\sim
\begin{bmatrix}
\boxed{\frac{1}{2}} & 0 & \frac{7}{4} & 1 & -\frac{1}{4} & 0 & | & 4 \\
\frac{1}{2} & 1 & \frac{5}{4} & 0 & \frac{1}{4} & 0 & | & 6 \\
-1 & 0 & \frac{3}{2} & 0 & \frac{1}{2} & 1 & | & 12
\end{bmatrix}
\quad
\begin{array}{l}
\dfrac{4}{1/2} = 8 \\[4pt]
\dfrac{6}{1/2} = 12
\end{array}
$$

$(-1)R_2 + R_1 \to R_1, \quad 2R_2 + R_3 \to R_3 \qquad\qquad 2R_1 \to R_1$

$$
\sim
\begin{bmatrix}
\boxed{1} & 0 & \frac{7}{2} & 2 & -\frac{1}{2} & 0 & | & 8 \\
\frac{1}{2} & 1 & \frac{5}{4} & 0 & \frac{1}{4} & 0 & | & 6 \\
-1 & 0 & \frac{3}{2} & 0 & \frac{1}{2} & 1 & | & 12
\end{bmatrix}
\sim
\begin{bmatrix}
1 & 0 & \frac{7}{2} & 2 & -\frac{1}{2} & 0 & | & 8 \\
0 & 1 & -\frac{1}{2} & -1 & \frac{1}{2} & 0 & | & 2 \\
0 & 0 & 5 & 2 & 0 & 1 & | & 20
\end{bmatrix}
$$

$\left(-\dfrac{1}{2}\right)R_1 + R_2 \to R_2, \quad R_1 + R_3 \to R_3$

Max $P = 20$ at $x_1 = 8$, $x_2 = 2$, and $x_3 = 0$.

36. Let x_1 = the number of A components
$\quad\quad x_2$ = the number of B components
$\quad\quad x_3$ = the number of C components

The mathematical model for this problem is:
Maximize $P = 7x_1 + 8x_2 + 10x_3$

Subject to
$$
\begin{aligned}
2x_1 + 3x_2 + 2x_3 &\le 1000 \\
x_1 + x_2 + 2x_3 &\le 800 \\
x_1 + x_2 + x_3 &\le 420 \\
x_1, x_2, x_3 &\ge 0
\end{aligned}
$$

We introduce slack variables s_1, s_2, s_3 to obtain the equivalent form:
$$
\begin{aligned}
2x_1 + 3x_2 + 2x_3 + s_1 \qquad\qquad\qquad &= 1000 \\
x_1 + x_2 + 2x_3 \qquad + s_2 \qquad\qquad &= 800 \\
x_1 + x_2 + x_3 \qquad\qquad + s_3 \qquad &= 420 \\
-7x_1 - 8x_2 - 10x_3 \qquad\qquad\qquad + P &= 0
\end{aligned}
$$

The simplex tableau for this problem is:

$$
\begin{array}{c}
 \\
s_1 \\
s_2 \\
s_3 \\
P
\end{array}
\begin{array}{c}
\begin{array}{ccccccc}
x_1 & x_2 & x_3 & s_1 & s_2 & s_3 & P
\end{array} \\
\left[\begin{array}{ccccccc|c}
2 & 3 & 2 & 1 & 0 & 0 & 0 & 1,000 \\
1 & 1 & ② & 0 & 1 & 0 & 0 & 800 \\
1 & 1 & 1 & 0 & 0 & 1 & 0 & 420 \\
-7 & -8 & -10 & 0 & 0 & 0 & 1 & 0
\end{array}\right]
\end{array}
\begin{array}{l}
1000/2 = 500 \\
800/2 = 400 \\
420/1 = 420 \\

\end{array}
$$

$$\tfrac{1}{2}R_2 \rightarrow R_2$$

$$
\sim
\left[\begin{array}{ccccccc|c}
2 & 3 & 2 & 1 & 0 & 0 & 0 & 1,000 \\
\tfrac{1}{2} & \tfrac{1}{2} & ① & 0 & \tfrac{1}{2} & 0 & 0 & 400 \\
1 & 1 & 1 & 0 & 0 & 1 & 0 & 420 \\
-7 & -8 & -10 & 0 & 0 & 0 & 1 & 0
\end{array}\right]
$$

$$(-2)R_2 + R_1 \rightarrow R_1, \quad (-1)R_2 + R_3 \rightarrow R_3, \quad \text{and} \quad 10R_2 + R_4 \rightarrow R_4$$

$$
\sim
\left[\begin{array}{ccccccc|c}
1 & 2 & 0 & 1 & -1 & 0 & 0 & 200 \\
\tfrac{1}{2} & \tfrac{1}{2} & 1 & 0 & \tfrac{1}{2} & 0 & 0 & 400 \\
\tfrac{1}{2} & ⓵\tfrac{1}{2} & 0 & 0 & -\tfrac{1}{2} & 1 & 0 & 20 \\
-2 & -3 & 0 & 0 & 5 & 0 & 1 & 4,000
\end{array}\right]
\begin{array}{l}
\tfrac{200}{2} = 100 \\
\tfrac{400}{1/2} = 800 \\
\tfrac{20}{1/2} = 40 \\

\end{array}
$$

$$2R_3 \rightarrow R_3$$

$$
\sim
\left[\begin{array}{ccccccc|c}
1 & 2 & 0 & 1 & -1 & 0 & 0 & 200 \\
\tfrac{1}{2} & \tfrac{1}{2} & 1 & 0 & \tfrac{1}{2} & 0 & 0 & 400 \\
1 & ① & 0 & 0 & -1 & 2 & 0 & 40 \\
-2 & -3 & 0 & 0 & 5 & 0 & 1 & 4,000
\end{array}\right]
$$

$$(-2)R_3 + R_1 \rightarrow R_1, \quad \left(-\tfrac{1}{2}\right)R_3 + R_2 \rightarrow R_2, \quad \text{and} \quad 3R_3 + R_4 \rightarrow R_4$$

$$
\sim
\left[\begin{array}{ccccccc|c}
-1 & 0 & 0 & 1 & 1 & -4 & 0 & 120 \\
0 & 0 & 1 & 0 & 1 & -1 & 0 & 380 \\
1 & 1 & 0 & 0 & -1 & 2 & 0 & 40 \\
1 & 0 & 0 & 0 & 2 & 6 & 1 & 4,120
\end{array}\right]
$$

Max $P = \$4,120$ at $x_1 = 0$, $x_2 = 40$, $x_3 = 380$, i.e. 0 A components, 40 B components, and 380 C components produce a maximum profit of $\$4,120$; 120 unused labor hours for fabrication.

38. Let x_1 = the amount invested in government bonds,
x_2 = the amount invested in mutual funds,
and x_3 = the amount invested in money market funds.
The mathematical model for this problem is:

$$
\begin{aligned}
&\text{Maximize } P = 0.08x_1 + 0.13x_2 + 0.15x_3 \\
&\text{Subject to: } x_1 + x_2 + x_3 \leq 100,000 \\
&\qquad\qquad\quad -x_1 + x_2 + x_3 \leq 0 \\
&\qquad\qquad\qquad\qquad\qquad x_3 \leq 30,000 \\
&\qquad\qquad\quad x_1, \ x_2, \ x_3 \geq 0
\end{aligned}
$$

We introduce slack variables s_1, s_2 and s_3 to obtain the equivalent form:

$$
\begin{aligned}
x_1 + x_2 + x_3 + s_1 &= 100{,}000 \\
-x_1 + x_2 + x_3 \quad\ + s_2 &= 0 \\
x_3 \quad\ + s_3 &= 30{,}000 \\
-0.08x_1 - 0.13x_2 - 0.15x_3 \quad\ + P &= 0
\end{aligned}
$$

The simplex tableau for this problem is:

$$
\begin{array}{c}
\begin{array}{ccccccc}
\ x_1 & \ x_2 & \ x_3 & \ s_1 & s_2 & s_3 & P
\end{array}\\
\begin{array}{c}
s_1 \\ s_2 \\ s_3 \\ P
\end{array}
\left[
\begin{array}{ccccccc|c}
1 & 1 & \boxed{1} & 1 & 0 & 0 & 0 & 100{,}000 \\
-1 & 1 & 1 & 0 & 1 & 0 & 0 & 0 \\
0 & 0 & 1 & 0 & 0 & 1 & 0 & 30{,}000 \\
-0.08 & -0.13 & -0.15 & 0 & 0 & 0 & 1 & 0
\end{array}
\right]
\begin{array}{c}
100{,}000 \\ 0 \\ 30{,}000 \\ \
\end{array}
\end{array}
$$

$(-1)R_2 + R_1 \to R_1$, $(-1)R_2 + R_3 \to R_3$, and $0.15R_2 + R_4 \to R_4$

$$
\sim
\left[
\begin{array}{ccccccc|c}
2 & 0 & 0 & 1 & -1 & 0 & 0 & 100{,}000 \\
-1 & 1 & 1 & 0 & 1 & 0 & 0 & 0 \\
\boxed{1} & -1 & 0 & 0 & -1 & 1 & 0 & 30{,}000 \\
-0.23 & 0.02 & 0 & 0 & 0.15 & 0 & 1 & 0
\end{array}
\right]
\begin{array}{c}
50{,}000 \\ 0 \\ 30{,}000 \\ \
\end{array}
$$

$(-2)R_3 + R_1 \to R_1$, $R_3 + R_2 \to R_2$, and $0.23R_3 + R_4 \to R_4$

$$
\sim
\left[
\begin{array}{ccccccc|c}
0 & \boxed{2} & 0 & 1 & 1 & -2 & 0 & 40{,}000 \\
0 & 0 & 1 & 0 & 0 & 1 & 0 & 30{,}000 \\
1 & -1 & 0 & 0 & -1 & 1 & 0 & 30{,}000 \\
0 & -0.21 & 0 & 0 & -0.08 & 0.23 & 1 & 6{,}900
\end{array}
\right]
$$

$\dfrac{1}{2}R_1 \to R_1$

$$
\sim
\left[
\begin{array}{ccccccc|c}
0 & \boxed{1} & 0 & \frac{1}{2} & \frac{1}{2} & -1 & 0 & 20{,}000 \\
0 & 0 & 1 & 0 & 0 & 1 & 0 & 30{,}000 \\
1 & -1 & 0 & 0 & -1 & 1 & 0 & 50{,}000 \\
0 & -0.21 & 0 & 0 & -0.08 & 0.23 & 1 & 11{,}100
\end{array}
\right]
$$

$R_1 + R_3 \to R_3$, $0.21R_1 + R_4 \to R_4$

Max $P = \$11{,}100$ at $x_1 = 50{,}000$, $x_2 = 20{,}000$, and $x_3 = 30{,}000$; i.e. invest \$50,000 in government bonds, \$20,000 in mutual funds, \$30,000 in money market funds.

40. Let x_1 = the number of ads placed in daytime shows,

x_2 = the number of ads placed in prime-time shows,

and x_3 = the number of ads placed in late-night shows.

The mathematical model for this problem is:

Maximize $P = 14,000x_1 + 24,000x_2 + 18,000x_3$

Subject to:
$$x_1 + x_2 + x_3 \leq 15$$
$$1,000x_1 + 2,000x_2 + 1,500x_3 \leq 24,000$$
$$x_1 - x_2 + x_3 \leq 0$$
$$x_1, \ x_2, \ x_3 \geq 0$$

We introduce slack variables s_1, s_2, s_3 to obtain the following initial form:

$$x_1 + x_2 + x_3 + s_1 \qquad\qquad = 15$$
$$1,000x_1 + 2,000x_2 + 1,500x_3 \qquad + s_2 \qquad = 24,000$$
$$x_1 - x_2 + x_3 \qquad\qquad + s_3 = 0$$
$$-14,000x_1 - 24,000x_2 - 18,000x_3 \qquad\qquad\qquad + P = 0$$

The simplex tableau for this problem is:

	x_1	x_2	x_3	s_1	s_2	s_3	P	
s_1	1	1	1	1	0	0	0	15
s_2	1000	(2000)	1500	0	1	0	0	24,000
s_3	1	−1	1	0	0	1	0	0
P	−14,000	−24,000	−18,000	0	0	0	1	0

$$\frac{1}{2000}R_2 \rightarrow R_2$$

$$\sim
\begin{bmatrix}
1 & 1 & 1 & 1 & 0 & 0 & 0 & 15 \\
\frac{1}{2} & (1) & \frac{3}{4} & 0 & \frac{1}{2000} & 0 & 0 & 12 \\
1 & -1 & 1 & 0 & 0 & 1 & 0 & 0 \\
-14,000 & -24,000 & -18,000 & 0 & 0 & 0 & 1 & 0
\end{bmatrix}$$

$(-1)R_2 + R_1 \rightarrow R_1$, $R_2 + R_3 \rightarrow R_3$, and $24,000R_2 + R_4 \rightarrow R_4$

$$\sim
\begin{bmatrix}
(\frac{1}{2}) & 0 & \frac{1}{4} & 1 & -\frac{1}{2000} & 0 & 0 & 3 & 6 \\
\frac{1}{2} & 1 & \frac{3}{4} & 0 & \frac{1}{2000} & 0 & 0 & 12 & 24 \\
\frac{3}{2} & 0 & \frac{7}{4} & 0 & \frac{1}{2000} & 1 & 0 & 12 & 8 \\
-2,000 & 0 & 0 & 0 & 12 & 0 & 1 & 288,000
\end{bmatrix}$$

$$2R_1 \rightarrow R_1$$

$$\sim \begin{bmatrix} \textcircled{1} & 0 & \frac{1}{2} & 2 & -\frac{1}{1000} & 0 & 0 & 6 \\ \frac{1}{2} & 1 & \frac{3}{4} & 0 & \frac{1}{2000} & 0 & 0 & 12 \\ \frac{3}{2} & 0 & \frac{7}{4} & 0 & \frac{1}{2000} & 1 & 0 & 12 \\ \hline -2{,}000 & 0 & 0 & 0 & 12 & 0 & 1 & 288{,}000 \end{bmatrix}$$

$$\left(-\frac{1}{2}\right)R_1 + R_2 \rightarrow R_2, \quad \left(-\frac{3}{2}\right)R_1 + R_3 \rightarrow R_3, \quad \text{and} \quad 2000R_1 + R_4 \rightarrow R_4$$

$$\sim \begin{bmatrix} 1 & 0 & \frac{1}{2} & 2 & -\frac{1}{1000} & 0 & 0 & 6 \\ 0 & 1 & \frac{1}{2} & -1 & \frac{1}{2000} & 0 & 0 & 9 \\ 0 & 0 & 1 & -3 & \frac{1}{500} & 1 & 0 & 3 \\ \hline 0 & 0 & 1000 & 4000 & 14 & 0 & 1 & 300{,}000 \end{bmatrix}$$

6 daytime ads, 9 prime-time ads, 0 late-night ads; maximum number of potential customers 300,000; 50% prime-time requirement is exceeded by 3 ads.

42. Let x_1 = the number of three-speed bicycles,

x_2 = the number of five-speed bicycles,

and x_3 = the number of ten-speed bicycles.

(A) The mathematical model for this problem is:

Maximize $P = 80x_1 + 70x_2 + 100x_3$

Subject to: $3x_1 + 4x_2 + 5x_3 \le 120$

$\qquad\qquad 5x_1 + 3x_2 + 5x_3 \le 130$

$\qquad\qquad 4x_1 + 3x_2 + 5x_3 \le 120$

$\qquad\qquad\qquad x_1,\ x_2,\ x_3 \ge 0$

We introduce slack variables s_1, s_2, s_3 to obtain the equivalent form:

$$3x_1 + 4x_2 + 5x_3 + s_1 \qquad\qquad\qquad = 120$$
$$5x_1 + 3x_2 + 5x_3 \qquad + s_2 \qquad\quad = 130$$
$$4x_1 + 3x_2 + 5x_3 \qquad\qquad + s_3 \qquad = 120$$
$$-80x_1 - 70x_2 - 100x_3 \qquad\qquad\qquad + P = 0$$

The simplex tableau for this problem is:

	x_1	x_2	x_3	s_1	s_2	s_3	P		
s_1	3	4	⑤	1	0	0	0	120	24
s_2	5	3	5	0	1	0	0	130	26
s_3	4	3	5	0	0	1	0	120	24
P	-80	-70	-100	0	0	0	1	0	

$$\frac{1}{5}R_1 \rightarrow R_1$$

$$\sim \begin{bmatrix} 0.6 & 0.8 & \boxed{1} & 0.2 & 0 & 0 & 0 & | & 24 \\ 5 & 3 & \circled{5} & 0 & 1 & 0 & 0 & | & 130 \\ 4 & 3 & 5 & 0 & 0 & 1 & 0 & | & 120 \\ \hline -80 & -70 & -100 & 0 & 0 & 0 & 1 & | & 0 \end{bmatrix}$$

$(-5)R_1 + R_2 \to R_2$, $(-5)R_1 + R_3 \to R_3$, and $100R_1 + R_4 \to R_4$

$$\sim \begin{bmatrix} 0.6 & 0.8 & 1 & 0.2 & 0 & 0 & 0 & | & 24 \\ 2 & -1 & 0 & -1 & 1 & 0 & 0 & | & 10 \\ \circled{1} & -1 & 0 & -1 & 0 & 1 & 0 & | & 0 \\ \hline -20 & 10 & 0 & 20 & 0 & 0 & 1 & | & 2,400 \end{bmatrix} \begin{matrix} 40 \\ 5 \\ 0 \\ \end{matrix}$$

$(-0.6)R_3 + R_1 \to R_1$, $(-2)R_3 + R_2 \to R_2$, and $20R_3 + R_4 \to R_4$

$$\sim \begin{bmatrix} 0 & 1.4 & 1 & 0.8 & 0 & -0.6 & 0 & | & 24 \\ 0 & \circled{1} & 0 & 1 & 1 & -2 & 0 & | & 10 \\ 1 & -1 & 0 & -1 & 0 & 1 & 0 & | & 0 \\ \hline 0 & -10 & 0 & 0 & 0 & 20 & 1 & | & 2,400 \end{bmatrix}$$

$(-1.4)R_2 + R_1 \to R_1$, $R_2 + R_3 \to R_3$, and $10R_2 + R_4 \to R_4$

$$\sim \begin{bmatrix} 0 & 0 & 1 & -0.6 & -1.4 & 2.2 & 0 & | & 10 \\ 0 & 1 & 0 & 1 & 1 & -2 & 0 & | & 10 \\ 1 & 0 & 0 & 0 & 1 & -1 & 0 & | & 10 \\ \hline 0 & 0 & 0 & 10 & 10 & 0 & 1 & | & 2,500 \end{bmatrix}$$

Thus, 10 three-speed, 10 five-speed, and 10 ten-speed bicycles; maximum profit is $2,500.

(B) In this case, $P = 80x_1 + 70x_2 + 110x_3$. The simplex tableau for this problem is:

$$\begin{array}{c} \\ s_1 \\ s_2 \\ s_3 \\ P \end{array} \begin{array}{cccccccc} x_1 & x_2 & x_3 & s_1 & s_2 & s_3 & P & \\ \begin{bmatrix} 3 & 4 & 5 & 1 & 0 & 0 & 0 & | & 120 \\ 5 & 3 & 5 & 0 & 1 & 0 & 0 & | & 130 \\ 4 & 3 & \circled{5} & 0 & 0 & 1 & 0 & | & 120 \\ \hline -80 & -70 & -110 & 0 & 0 & 0 & 1 & | & 0 \end{bmatrix} & \begin{matrix} 24 \\ 26 \\ 24 \\ \end{matrix} \end{array}$$

$\dfrac{1}{5}R_3 \to R_3$

$$\sim \begin{bmatrix} 3 & 4 & 5 & 1 & 0 & 0 & 0 & | & 120 \\ 5 & 3 & 5 & 0 & 1 & 0 & 0 & | & 130 \\ 0.8 & 0.6 & \circled{1} & 0 & 0 & 0.2 & 0 & | & 24 \\ \hline -80 & -70 & -110 & 0 & 0 & 0 & 1 & | & 0 \end{bmatrix}$$

$(-5)R_3 + R_1 \to R_1$, $(-5)R_3 + R_2 \to R_2$, and $110R_3 + R_4 \to R_4$

$$\sim \begin{bmatrix} -1 & 1 & 0 & 1 & 0 & -1 & 0 & | & 0 \\ 1 & \circled{0} & 0 & 0 & 1 & -1 & 0 & | & 10 \\ 0.8 & 0.6 & 1 & 0 & 0 & 0.2 & 0 & | & 24 \\ \hline 8 & -4 & 0 & 0 & 0 & 22 & 1 & | & 2,640 \end{bmatrix}$$

$(-0.6)R_1 + R_3 \to R_3$, and $4R_1 + R_4 \to R_4$

$$\sim \begin{bmatrix} -1 & 1 & 0 & 1 & 0 & -1 & 0 & | & 0 \\ 1 & 0 & 0 & 0 & 1 & -1 & 0 & | & 10 \\ 1.4 & 0 & 1 & -0.6 & 0 & 0.8 & 0 & | & 24 \\ \hline 4 & 0 & 0 & 4 & 0 & 18 & 1 & | & 2,640 \end{bmatrix}$$

Thus, 0 three-speed, 0 five-speed, and 24 ten-speed bicycles; maximum profit $2,640; 10 labor-hours in painting and plating department are not used.

(C) In this case, $P = 80x_1 + 110x_2 + 100x_3$. The simplex tableau for this problem is:

$$
\begin{array}{c}
 \\
S_1 \\
S_2 \\
S_3 \\
P
\end{array}
\begin{array}{c}
\begin{array}{ccccccc}
x_1 & x_2 & x_3 & s_1 & s_2 & s_3 & P
\end{array} \\
\left[\begin{array}{ccccccc|c}
3 & \textcircled{4} & 5 & 1 & 0 & 0 & 0 & 120 \\
5 & 3 & 5 & 0 & 1 & 0 & 0 & 130 \\
4 & 3 & 5 & 0 & 0 & 1 & 0 & 120 \\
-80 & -110 & -100 & 0 & 0 & 0 & 1 & 0
\end{array}\right]
\end{array}
\begin{array}{l}
120/4 = 30 \\
130/3 = 43.\overline{3} \\
120/3 = 40
\end{array}
$$

$$\frac{1}{4}R_1 \to R_1$$

$$
\sim
\left[\begin{array}{ccccccc|c}
\frac{3}{4} & \textcircled{1} & \frac{5}{4} & \frac{1}{4} & 0 & 0 & 0 & 30 \\
5 & 3 & 5 & 0 & 1 & 0 & 0 & 130 \\
4 & 3 & 5 & 0 & 0 & 1 & 0 & 120 \\
-80 & -110 & -100 & 0 & 0 & 0 & 1 & 0
\end{array}\right]
$$

$(-3)R_1 + R_2 \to R_2$, $(-3)R_1 + R_3 \to R_3$, and $110R_1 + R_4 \to R_4$

$$
\sim
\left[\begin{array}{ccccccc|c}
\frac{3}{4} & 1 & \frac{5}{4} & \frac{1}{4} & 0 & 0 & 0 & 30 \\
\frac{11}{4} & 0 & \frac{5}{4} & -\frac{3}{4} & 1 & 0 & 0 & 40 \\
\frac{7}{4} & 0 & \frac{5}{4} & -\frac{3}{4} & 0 & 1 & 0 & 30 \\
\frac{5}{2} & 0 & \frac{75}{2} & \frac{55}{2} & 0 & 0 & 1 & 3,300
\end{array}\right]
$$

Thus, 0 three-speed, 30 five-speed, and 0 ten-speed bicycles; maximum profit $3,300; 30 labor-hours in the final assembly department and 40 labor-hours in the painting and plating department are not used.

44. (A) Let x_1 = the number of individual customers,
       x_2 = the number of commercial customers,
   and x_3 = the number of industrial customers.

The mathematical model for this problem is:

Maximize $P = 50x_1 + 65x_2 + 60x_3$

Subject to:
$$
\begin{aligned}
x_1 + x_2 + x_3 &\le 50 \\
x_1 + 2x_2 + 1.5x_3 &\le 80 \\
10x_1 + 25x_2 + 20x_3 &\le 1{,}025 \\
x_1, x_2, x_3 &\ge 0
\end{aligned}
$$

We introduce slack variables to obtain the initial form:

$$
\begin{aligned}
x_1 + x_2 + x_3 + s_1 &= 50 \\
x_1 + 2x_2 + 1.5x_3 + s_2 &= 80 \\
10x_1 + 25x_2 + 20x_3 + s_3 &= 1{,}025 \\
-50x_1 - 65x_2 - 60x_3 + P &= 0
\end{aligned}
$$

The simplex tableau for this problem is:

$$
\begin{array}{c}
 \\
s_1 \\
s_2 \\
s_3 \\
P
\end{array}
\begin{array}{c}
\begin{array}{ccccccc}
x_1 & x_2 & x_3 & s_1 & s_2 & s_3 & P
\end{array} \\
\left[
\begin{array}{ccccccc|c}
1 & 1 & 1 & 1 & 0 & 0 & 0 & 50 \\
1 & ② & 1.5 & 0 & 1 & 0 & 0 & 80 \\
10 & 25 & 20 & 0 & 0 & 1 & 0 & 1,025 \\
\hline
-50 & -65 & -60 & 0 & 0 & 0 & 1 & 0
\end{array}
\right]
\end{array}
\begin{array}{l}
50/1 = 50 \\
80/2 = 40 \\
1025/25 = 41 \\

\end{array}
$$

$$\frac{1}{2}R_2 \;\to\; R_2$$

$$
\sim
\left[
\begin{array}{ccccccc|c}
1 & 1 & 1 & 1 & 0 & 0 & 0 & 50 \\
\frac{1}{2} & ① & \frac{3}{4} & 0 & \frac{1}{2} & 0 & 0 & 40 \\
10 & 25 & 20 & 0 & 0 & 1 & 0 & 1,025 \\
\hline
-50 & -65 & -60 & 0 & 0 & 0 & 1 & 0
\end{array}
\right]
$$

$(-1)R_2 + R_1 \to R_1$, $(-25)R_2 + R_3 \to R_3$, and $65R_2 + R_4 \to R_4$

$$
\sim
\left[
\begin{array}{ccccccc|c}
②\!\!\frac{1}{2} & 0 & \frac{1}{4} & 1 & -\frac{1}{2} & 0 & 0 & 10 \\
\frac{1}{2} & 1 & \frac{3}{4} & 0 & \frac{1}{2} & 0 & 0 & 40 \\
-2.5 & 0 & \frac{5}{4} & 0 & -12.5 & 1 & 0 & 25 \\
\hline
-17.5 & 0 & -11.25 & 0 & 32.5 & 0 & 1 & 2,600
\end{array}
\right]
\begin{array}{l}
20 \\
80 \\
 \\

\end{array}
$$

$$2R_1 \;\to\; R_1$$

$$
\sim
\left[
\begin{array}{ccccccc|c}
① & 0 & \frac{1}{2} & 2 & -1 & 0 & 0 & 20 \\
\frac{1}{2} & 0 & \frac{3}{4} & 0 & \frac{1}{2} & 0 & 0 & 40 \\
-2.5 & 0 & \frac{5}{4} & 0 & -12.5 & 1 & 0 & 25 \\
\hline
-17.5 & 0 & -11.25 & 0 & 32.5 & 0 & 1 & 2,600
\end{array}
\right]
$$

$\left(-\dfrac{1}{2}\right)R_1 + R_2 \to R_2$, $2.5R_1 + R_3 \to R_3$, and $17.5R_1 + R_4 \to R_4$

$$
\sim
\left[
\begin{array}{ccccccc|c}
1 & 0 & \frac{1}{2} & 2 & -1 & 0 & 0 & 20 \\
0 & 0 & \frac{1}{2} & -1 & 1 & 0 & 0 & 30 \\
0 & 0 & ②\!\!\frac{5}{2} & 5 & -14.5 & 1 & 0 & 75 \\
\hline
0 & 0 & -2.5 & 35 & 15 & 0 & 1 & 2,950
\end{array}
\right]
\begin{array}{l}
\frac{20}{1/2} = 40 \\
\frac{30}{1/2} = 60 \\
\frac{75}{5/2} = 30 \\

\end{array}
$$

$$\frac{2}{5}R_3 \;\to\; R_3$$

$$
\sim
\left[
\begin{array}{ccccccc|c}
1 & 0 & \frac{1}{2} & 2 & -1 & 0 & 0 & 20 \\
0 & 0 & \frac{1}{2} & -1 & 1 & 0 & 0 & 30 \\
0 & 0 & ① & 2 & -5.8 & \frac{2}{5} & 0 & 30 \\
\hline
0 & 0 & -2.5 & 35 & 15 & 0 & 1 & 2,950
\end{array}
\right]
$$

$\left(-\dfrac{1}{2}\right)R_3 + R_1 \to R_1$, $\left(-\dfrac{1}{2}\right)R_3 + R_2 \to R_2$, and $2.5R_3 + R_4 \to R_4$

$$\sim \begin{bmatrix} 1 & 0 & 0 & 1 & 1.9 & -\frac{1}{5} & 0 & \bigm| & 5 \\ 0 & 0 & 0 & -2 & 2.9 & -\frac{1}{5} & 0 & \bigm| & 15 \\ 0 & 0 & 1 & 2 & -5.8 & \frac{2}{5} & 0 & \bigm| & 30 \\ \hline 0 & 0 & 0 & 40 & 0.5 & 1 & 1 & \bigm| & 3,025 \end{bmatrix}$$

Thus, 5 individual, 15 commercial, and 30 industrial customers; maximum profit $3,025.

(B) In the initial form in part A, replace 50 in the first equation by 35. The simplex tableau for this problem is:

	x_1	x_2	x_3	s_1	s_2	s_3	P		
s_1	1	①1	1	1	0	0	0	35	35
s_2	1	2	1.5	0	1	0	0	80	40
s_3	10	25	20	0	0	1	0	1,025	41
P	−50	−65	−60	0	0	0	1	0	

$$(-2)R_1 + R_2 \to R_2, \quad (-25)R_1 + R_3 \to R_3, \quad \text{and} \quad 65R_1 + R_4 \to R_4$$

$$\sim \begin{bmatrix} 1 & 1 & 1 & 1 & 0 & 0 & 0 & \bigm| & 35 \\ -1 & 0 & -0.5 & -2 & 1 & 0 & 0 & \bigm| & 10 \\ -15 & 0 & -5 & -25 & 0 & 1 & 0 & \bigm| & 150 \\ \hline 15 & 0 & 5 & 65 & 0 & 0 & 1 & \bigm| & 2,275 \end{bmatrix}$$

Thus, 0 individual, 35 commercial, and 0 industrial customers; maximum profit $2,275; 10 hours for data-entry and 150 minutes of computer time are not used.

(C) In the third equation of the initial form in part A, replace 1,025 by 450. The simplex tableau for this problem is:

	x_1	x_2	x_3	s_1	s_2	s_3	P		
s_1	1	1	1	1	0	0	0	50	50
s_2	1	2	1.5	0	1	0	0	80	40
s_3	10	㉕25	20	0	0	1	0	450	18
P	−50	−65	−60	0	0	0	1	0	

$$\frac{1}{25}R_3 \to R_3$$

$$\sim \begin{bmatrix} 1 & 1 & 1 & 1 & 0 & 0 & 0 & \bigm| & 50 \\ 1 & 2 & 1.5 & 0 & 1 & 0 & 0 & \bigm| & 80 \\ \frac{2}{5} & ①1 & \frac{4}{5} & 0 & 0 & \frac{1}{25} & 0 & \bigm| & 18 \\ \hline -50 & -65 & -60 & 0 & 0 & 0 & 1 & \bigm| & 0 \end{bmatrix}$$

$$(-1)R_3 + R_1 \to R_1, \quad (-2)R_3 + R_2 \to R_2, \quad \text{and} \quad 65R_3 + R_4 \to R_4$$

$$\sim \begin{bmatrix} \frac{3}{5} & 0 & \frac{1}{5} & 1 & 0 & -\frac{1}{25} & 0 & \bigm| & 32 & \frac{32}{3/5} = 53.\overline{3} \\ \frac{1}{5} & 0 & -0.1 & 0 & 1 & -\frac{2}{25} & 0 & \bigm| & 44 & \frac{44}{1/5} = 220 \\ ⓶\frac{2}{5} & 1 & \frac{4}{5} & 0 & 0 & \frac{1}{25} & 0 & \bigm| & 18 & \frac{18}{2/5} = 45 \\ \hline -24 & 0 & -8 & 0 & 0 & \frac{13}{5} & 1 & \bigm| & 1,170 \end{bmatrix}$$

$$\frac{5}{2}R_3 \to R_3$$

$$\sim \begin{bmatrix} \frac{3}{5} & 0 & \frac{1}{5} & 1 & 0 & -\frac{1}{25} & 0 & 32 \\ \frac{1}{5} & 0 & -0.1 & 0 & 1 & -\frac{2}{25} & 0 & 44 \\ \textcircled{1} & \frac{5}{2} & 2 & 0 & 0 & \frac{1}{10} & 0 & 45 \\ \hline -24 & 0 & -8 & 0 & 0 & \frac{13}{5} & 1 & 1,170 \end{bmatrix}$$

$$\left(-\frac{3}{5}\right)R_3 + R_1 \to R_1, \quad \left(-\frac{1}{5}\right)R_3 + R_2 \to R_2, \quad \text{and} \quad 24R_3 + R_4 \to R_4$$

$$\sim \begin{bmatrix} 0 & -\frac{3}{2} & -1 & 1 & 0 & -\frac{1}{10} & 0 & 5 \\ 0 & -\frac{1}{2} & -0.5 & 0 & 1 & -\frac{1}{10} & 0 & 35 \\ 1 & \frac{5}{2} & 2 & 0 & 0 & \frac{1}{10} & 0 & 45 \\ \hline 0 & 60 & 40 & 0 & 0 & 5 & 1 & 2,250 \end{bmatrix}$$

Thus, 45 individual, 0 commercial, and 0 industrial customers; maximum profit \$2,250; 5 hours for interviewing and 35 hours for data-entry are not used.

46. Let x_1 = the number of grams of food A,
    x_2 = the number of grams of food B,
and x_3 = the number of grams of food C.

The mathematical model for this problem is:

Maximize $P = x_1 + 3x_2 + 2x_3$

Subject to:
$$2x_1 + x_2 + 2x_3 \le 24$$
$$3x_1 + 4x_2 + 5x_3 \le 60$$
$$x_1, x_2, x_3 \ge 0$$

We introduce slack variables s_1 and s_2 to obtain the initial form:
$$2x_1 + x_2 + 2x_3 + s_1 \qquad\qquad = 24$$
$$3x_1 + 4x_2 + 5x_3 \qquad + s_2 \qquad = 60$$
$$-x_1 - 3x_2 - 2x_3 \qquad\qquad + P = 0$$

The simplex tableau for this problem is:

$$\begin{array}{c} \\ s_1 \\ s_2 \\ P \end{array} \begin{array}{cccccc} x_1 & x_2 & x_3 & s_1 & s_2 & P \\ \end{array}$$

$$\begin{matrix} s_1 \\ s_2 \\ P \end{matrix} \begin{bmatrix} 2 & 1 & 2 & 1 & 0 & 0 & 24 \\ 3 & \textcircled{4} & 5 & 0 & 1 & 0 & 60 \\ -1 & -3 & -2 & 0 & 0 & 1 & 0 \end{bmatrix} \begin{matrix} 24 \\ 15 \\ \end{matrix}$$

$$\frac{1}{4}R_2 \to R_2$$

$$\sim \begin{bmatrix} 2 & 1 & 2 & 1 & 0 & 0 & 24 \\ \frac{3}{4} & \textcircled{1} & \frac{5}{4} & 0 & \frac{1}{4} & 0 & 15 \\ -1 & -3 & -2 & 0 & 0 & 1 & 0 \end{bmatrix} \sim \begin{bmatrix} \frac{5}{4} & 0 & \frac{3}{4} & 1 & -\frac{1}{4} & 0 & 9 \\ \frac{3}{4} & 1 & \frac{5}{4} & 0 & \frac{1}{4} & 0 & 15 \\ \frac{5}{4} & 0 & \frac{7}{4} & 0 & \frac{3}{4} & 1 & 45 \end{bmatrix}$$

$$(-1)R_2 + R_1 \to R_1 \quad \text{and} \quad 3R_2 + R_3 \to R_3$$

Thus, 0 grams of food A, 15 grams of food B, and 0 grams of food C; maximum calcium 45 units; iron intake is 9 units below daily average.

48. Let x_1 = the number of undergraduate students,

x_2 = the number of graduate students,

and x_3 = the number of faculty members.

The mathematical model for this problem is:

Maximize $P = 18x_1 + 25x_2 + 35x_3$

Subject to:

$$x_1 + x_2 + x_3 \leq 20$$
$$100x_1 + 150x_2 + 200x_3 \leq 3{,}200$$
$$-x_1 + x_2 + x_3 \leq 0$$
$$x_1,\ x_2,\ x_3 \geq 0$$

We introduce slack variables s_1, s_2, and s_2 to obtain the initial form:

$$x_1 + x_2 + x_3 + s_1 = 20$$
$$100x_1 + 150x_2 + 200x_3 + s_2 = 3{,}200$$
$$-x_1 + x_2 + x_3 + s_3 = 0$$
$$-18x_1 - 25x_2 - 35x_3 + P = 0$$

The simplex tableau for this problem is:

$$
\begin{array}{ccccccc|c}
x_1 & x_2 & x_3 & s_1 & s_2 & s_3 & P & \\
\hline
1 & 1 & 1 & 1 & 0 & 0 & 0 & 20 \\
100 & 150 & 200 & 0 & 1 & 0 & 0 & 3{,}200 \\
-1 & 1 & ① & 0 & 0 & 1 & 0 & 0 \\
\hline
-18 & -25 & -30 & 0 & 0 & 0 & 1 & 0 \\
\end{array}
\quad
\begin{array}{c}
20 \\ 16 \\ 0 \\ \\
\end{array}
$$

$(-1)R_3 + R_1 \rightarrow R_1$, $(-200)R_3 + R_2 \rightarrow R_2$, and $30R_3 + R_4 \rightarrow R_4$

$$
\sim
\begin{array}{ccccccc|c}
② & 0 & 0 & 1 & 0 & -1 & 0 & 20 \\
300 & -50 & 0 & 0 & 1 & -200 & 0 & 3{,}200 \\
-1 & 1 & 1 & 0 & 0 & 1 & 0 & 0 \\
\hline
-48 & 5 & 0 & 0 & 0 & 30 & 1 & 0 \\
\end{array}
\quad
\begin{array}{c}
10 \\ 10.\overline{6} \\ 0 \\ \\
\end{array}
$$

$\dfrac{1}{2}R_1 \rightarrow R_1$

$$
\sim
\begin{array}{ccccccc|c}
① & 0 & 0 & \frac{1}{2} & 0 & -\frac{1}{2} & 0 & 10 \\
300 & -50 & 0 & 0 & 1 & -200 & 0 & 3{,}200 \\
-1 & 1 & 1 & 0 & 0 & 1 & 0 & 0 \\
\hline
-48 & 5 & 0 & 0 & 0 & 30 & 1 & 0 \\
\end{array}
$$

$(-300)R_1 + R_2 \rightarrow R_2$, $R_1 + R_3 \rightarrow R_3$, and $48R_1 + R_4 \rightarrow R_4$

$$
\sim
\begin{array}{ccccccc|c}
1 & 0 & 0 & \frac{1}{2} & 0 & -\frac{1}{2} & 0 & 10 \\
0 & -50 & 0 & -150 & 1 & -50 & 0 & 200 \\
0 & 1 & 1 & \frac{1}{2} & 0 & \frac{1}{2} & 0 & 10 \\
\hline
0 & 5 & 0 & 24 & 0 & 6 & 1 & 480 \\
\end{array}
$$

Thus, 10 undergraduate students, 0 graduate students, 10 faculty members; maximum number of interviews 480; $200 in the budget is not used.

2. $A = [1 \quad 0 \quad -7 \quad 3 \quad -2]$; $A^T = \begin{bmatrix} 1 \\ 0 \\ -7 \\ 3 \\ -2 \end{bmatrix}$

4. $A = \begin{bmatrix} 9 \\ 5 \\ -4 \\ 0 \end{bmatrix}$; $A^T = [9 \quad 5 \quad -4 \quad 0]$

6. $A = \begin{bmatrix} 7 & 3 & -1 & 3 \\ -6 & 1 & 0 & -9 \end{bmatrix}$; $A^T = \begin{bmatrix} 7 & -6 \\ 3 & 1 \\ -1 & 0 \\ 3 & 9 \end{bmatrix}$

8. $A = \begin{bmatrix} 1 & -1 & 3 & 2 \\ 1 & -4 & 0 & 2 \\ 4 & -5 & 6 & 1 \\ -3 & 8 & 0 & -1 \\ 2 & 7 & -3 & 1 \end{bmatrix}$; $A^T = \begin{bmatrix} 1 & 1 & 4 & -3 & 2 \\ -1 & -4 & -5 & 8 & 7 \\ 3 & 0 & 6 & 0 & -3 \\ 2 & 2 & 1 & -1 & 1 \end{bmatrix}$

10. (A) Given the minimization problem:

Minimize $C = 12x_1 + 5x_2$
Subject to: $2x_1 + x_2 \geq 7$
$3x_1 + x_2 \geq 9$
$x_1,\ x_2 \geq 0$

The matrix corresponding to this problem is: $A = \begin{bmatrix} 2 & 1 & 7 \\ 3 & 1 & 9 \\ 12 & 5 & 1 \end{bmatrix}$

The matrix A^T corresponding to the dual problem has the rows of A as its columns. Thus:

$A^T = \begin{bmatrix} 2 & 3 & 12 \\ 1 & 1 & 5 \\ 7 & 9 & 1 \end{bmatrix}$

The dual problem is: Maximize $P = 7y_1 + 9y_2$
Subject to: $2y_1 + 3y_2 \leq 12$
$y_1 + y_2 \leq 5$
$y_1,\ y_2 \geq 0$

(B) Letting x_1 and x_2 be slack variables, the initial system for the dual problem is:

$$2y_1 + 3y_2 + x_1 \qquad\quad = 12$$
$$y_1 + y_2 \qquad\ + x_2 \quad = 5$$
$$-7y_1 - 9y_2 \qquad\qquad + P = 0$$

(C) The simplex tableau for this problem is:

$$
\begin{array}{c}
\quad\ y_1\ \ y_2\ \ x_1\ \ x_2\ \ \ P \\
\begin{array}{c} x_1 \\ x_2 \\ P \end{array}
\left[
\begin{array}{ccccc|c}
2 & 3 & 1 & 0 & 0 & 12 \\
1 & 1 & 0 & 1 & 0 & 5 \\
\hline
-7 & -9 & 0 & 0 & 1 & 0
\end{array}
\right]
\end{array}
$$

12. From the final simplex tableau,

$$
\begin{array}{c}
\quad\ y_1\ \ y_2\ \ x_1\ \ x_2\ \ P \\
\begin{array}{c} y_2 \\ y_1 \\ P \end{array}
\left[
\begin{array}{ccccc|c}
0 & 1 & 5 & -3 & 0 & 5 \\
1 & 0 & -3 & 2 & 0 & 2 \\
\hline
0 & 0 & 5 & 3 & 1 & 155
\end{array}
\right]
\end{array}
$$

(A) The optimal solution of the dual problem is: maximum value of $P = 155$ at $y_1 = 2$ and $y_2 = 5$;

(B) The optimal solution of the minimization problem is: minimum value of $C = 155$ at $x_1 = 5$, $x_2 = 3$.

14. (A) The matrix corresponding to the given problem is: $A = \begin{bmatrix} 1 & 2 & 5 \\ 1 & 3 & 6 \\ 1 & 4 & 1 \end{bmatrix}$

The matrix A^T corresponding to the dual problem has the rows of A as its columns, that is:

$$A^T = \begin{bmatrix} 1 & 1 & 1 \\ 2 & 3 & 4 \\ 5 & 6 & 1 \end{bmatrix}$$

Thus, the dual problem is: Maximize $P = 5y_1 + 6y_2$

$$\text{Subject to:}\quad y_1 + y_2 \le 1$$
$$2y_1 + 3y_2 \le 4$$
$$y_1,\ y_2 \ge 0$$

(B) We introduce slack variables x_1 and x_2 to obtain the initial system for the dual problem:

$$y_1 + y_2 + x_1 \qquad\quad = 1$$
$$2y_1 + 3y_2 \qquad\ + x_2 \quad = 4$$
$$-5y_1 - 6y_2 \qquad\qquad + P = 0$$

The simplex tableau for this problem is:

$$
\begin{array}{c}
\quad\; y_1 \quad y_2 \quad x_1 \quad x_2 \quad P \\
\begin{array}{c} x_1 \\ x_2 \\ \\ P \end{array}
\left[\begin{array}{ccccc|c}
1 & \boxed{1} & 1 & 0 & 0 & 1 \\
2 & 3 & 0 & 1 & 0 & 4 \\
\hline
-5 & -6 & 0 & 0 & 1 & 0
\end{array}\right]
\begin{array}{c} 1 \\ \frac{4}{3} \\ \\ \end{array}
\end{array}
\sim
\begin{array}{c}
\quad\; y_1 \quad y_2 \quad x_1 \quad x_2 \quad P \\
\begin{array}{c} x_1 \\ y_1 \\ \\ P \end{array}
\left[\begin{array}{ccccc|c}
1 & 1 & 1 & 0 & 0 & 1 \\
-1 & 0 & -3 & 1 & 0 & 1 \\
\hline
1 & 0 & 6 & 0 & 1 & 6
\end{array}\right]
\end{array}
$$

$(-3)R_1 + R_2 \to R_2$ and $6R_1 + R_3 \to R_3$

Optimal solution: min $C = 6$ at $x_1 = 6$, $x_2 = 0$.

16. (A) The matrix corresponding to the given problem is: $A = \begin{bmatrix} 2 & 3 & 7 \\ 1 & 2 & 4 \\ 3 & 5 & 1 \end{bmatrix}$

The matrix A^T corresponding to the dual problem has the rows of A as its columns, that is:

$$A^T = \begin{bmatrix} 2 & 1 & 3 \\ 3 & 2 & 5 \\ 7 & 4 & 1 \end{bmatrix}$$

Thus, the dual problem is: Maximize $P = 7y_1 + 4y_2$

Subject to: $2y_1 + y_2 \le 3$

$3y_1 + 2y_2 \le 5$

$y_1, y_2 \ge 0$

(B) We introduce slack variables x_1 and x_2 to obtain the initial system for the dual problem:

$$
\begin{aligned}
2y_1 + y_2 + x_1 \qquad\quad &= 3 \\
3y_1 + 2y_2 \qquad + x_2 \quad &= 5 \\
-7y_1 - 4y_2 \qquad\qquad + P &= 0
\end{aligned}
$$

The simplex tableau for this problem is:

$$
\begin{array}{c}
\quad\; y_1 \quad y_2 \quad x_1 \quad x_2 \quad P \\
\begin{array}{c} x_1 \\ x_2 \\ \\ P \end{array}
\left[\begin{array}{ccccc|c}
\boxed{2} & 1 & 1 & 0 & 0 & 3 \\
3 & 2 & 0 & 1 & 0 & 5 \\
\hline
-7 & -4 & 0 & 0 & 1 & 0
\end{array}\right]
\begin{array}{c} \frac{3}{2} \\ \frac{5}{3} \\ \\ \end{array}
\end{array}
\sim
\left[\begin{array}{ccccc|c}
\boxed{1} & \frac{1}{2} & \frac{1}{2} & 0 & 0 & \frac{3}{2} \\
3 & 2 & 0 & 1 & 0 & 5 \\
\hline
-7 & -4 & 0 & 0 & 1 & 0
\end{array}\right]
$$

$\frac{1}{2}R_1 \to R_1$ $\qquad\qquad\qquad\qquad$ $(-3)R_1 + R_2 \to R_2$ and $7R_1 + R_3 \to R_3$

$$
\sim
\left[\begin{array}{ccccc|c}
1 & \frac{1}{2} & \frac{1}{2} & 0 & 0 & \frac{3}{2} \\
0 & \boxed{\frac{1}{2}} & -\frac{3}{2} & 1 & 0 & \frac{1}{2} \\
\hline
0 & -\frac{1}{2} & \frac{7}{2} & 0 & 1 & 10.5
\end{array}\right]
\begin{array}{c} 3 \\ 1 \\ \\ \end{array}
\sim
\left[\begin{array}{ccccc|c}
1 & \frac{1}{2} & \frac{1}{2} & 0 & 0 & \frac{3}{2} \\
0 & \boxed{1} & -3 & 2 & 0 & 1 \\
\hline
0 & -\frac{1}{2} & \frac{7}{2} & 0 & 1 & 10.5
\end{array}\right]
$$

$2R_2 \to R_2$ $\qquad\qquad\qquad\qquad$ $\left(-\frac{1}{2}\right)R_2 + R_1 \to R_1$ and $\frac{1}{2}R_2 + R_3 \to R_3$

$$
\begin{array}{c}
\quad\quad y_1\ \ y_2\ \ x_1\ \ x_2\ \ P \\
\begin{array}{c} y_1 \\ \sim\ y_2 \\ P \end{array}
\left[
\begin{array}{ccccc|c}
1 & 0 & 2 & -1 & 0 & 1 \\
0 & 1 & -3 & 2 & 0 & 1 \\
\hline
0 & 0 & 2 & 1 & 1 & 11
\end{array}
\right]
\end{array}
$$

Optimal solution: min $C = 11$ at $x_1 = 2$, $x_2 = 1$.

18. (A) The matrix corresponding to the given problem is:

$$
A = \begin{bmatrix}
2 & 1 & 12 \\
3 & -1 & 3 \\
40 & 10 & 1
\end{bmatrix}
$$

The matrix A^T corresponding to the dual problem is:

$$
A^T = \begin{bmatrix}
2 & 3 & 40 \\
1 & -1 & 10 \\
12 & 3 & 1
\end{bmatrix}
$$

Thus, the dual problem is: Maximize $P = 12y_1 + 3y_2$

$$
\begin{aligned}
\text{Subject to: } 2y_1 + 3y_2 &\le 40 \\
y_1 - y_2 &\le 10 \\
y_1,\ y_2 &\ge 0
\end{aligned}
$$

(B) We introduce slack variables x_1 and x_2 to obtain the initial system for the dual problem:

$$
\begin{aligned}
2y_1 + 3y_2 + x_1 \qquad\qquad &= 40 \\
y_1 - y_2 \qquad + x_2 \qquad &= 10 \\
-12y_1 - 3y_2 \qquad\qquad + P &= 0
\end{aligned}
$$

The simplex tableau for this problem is:

$$
\begin{array}{c}
\quad\quad y_1\ \ y_2\ \ x_1\ \ x_2\ \ P \\
\begin{array}{c} x_1 \\ \sim\ x_2 \\ P \end{array}
\left[
\begin{array}{ccccc|c}
2 & 3 & 1 & 0 & 0 & 40 \\
\boxed{1} & -1 & 0 & 1 & 0 & 10 \\
\hline
-12 & -3 & 0 & 0 & 1 & 0
\end{array}
\right]
\begin{array}{l}
\frac{40}{2} = 20 \\[4pt]
\frac{10}{1} = 10
\end{array}
\end{array}
$$

$(-2)R_2 + R_1 \rightarrow R_1$ and $12R_2 + R_3 \rightarrow R_3$

$$
\sim
\left[
\begin{array}{ccccc|c}
0 & \boxed{5} & 1 & -2 & 0 & 20 \\
1 & -1 & 0 & 1 & 0 & 10 \\
\hline
0 & -15 & 0 & 12 & 1 & 120
\end{array}
\right]
$$

$\dfrac{1}{5}R_1 \rightarrow R_1$

$$
\sim
\left[
\begin{array}{ccccc|c}
0 & \boxed{1} & \frac{1}{5} & -\frac{2}{5} & 0 & 4 \\
1 & -1 & 0 & 1 & 0 & 10 \\
\hline
0 & -15 & 0 & 12 & 1 & 120
\end{array}
\right]
\sim
\left[
\begin{array}{ccccc|c}
0 & 1 & \frac{1}{5} & -\frac{2}{5} & 0 & 4 \\
1 & 0 & \frac{1}{5} & \frac{3}{5} & 0 & 14 \\
\hline
0 & 0 & 3 & 6 & 1 & 180
\end{array}
\right]
$$

$R_1 + R_2 \rightarrow R_2$ and $15R_1 + R_3 \rightarrow R_3$

Optimal solution: min $C = 180$ at $x_1 = 3$, $x_2 = 6$.

20. (A) The matrix corresponding to the given problem is:

$$A = \begin{bmatrix} -4 & 1 & | & 12 \\ 12 & -3 & | & 10 \\ 10 & 15 & | & 1 \end{bmatrix}$$

The matrix A^T corresponding to the dual problem is:

$$A^T = \begin{bmatrix} -4 & 12 & | & 10 \\ 1 & -3 & | & 15 \\ 12 & 10 & | & 1 \end{bmatrix}$$

Thus, the dual problem is: Maximize $P = 12y_1 + 10y_2$

$$\text{Subject to: } -4y_1 + 12y_2 \le 10$$
$$y_1 - 3y_2 \le 15$$
$$y_1, \ y_2 \ge 0$$

(B) We introduce slack variables x_1 and x_2 to obtain the initial system for the dual problem:

$$-4y_1 + 12y_2 + x_1 \qquad = 10$$
$$y_1 - 3y_2 \qquad + x_2 \qquad = 15$$
$$-12y_1 - 10y_2 \qquad + P = 0$$

The simplex tableau for this problem is:

$$\begin{array}{c} \\ x_1 \\ x_2 \\ P \end{array} \begin{array}{cccccc} y_1 & y_2 & x_1 & x_2 & P & \\ \left[\begin{array}{ccccc|c} -4 & 12 & 1 & 0 & 0 & 10 \\ \textcircled{1} & -3 & 0 & 1 & 0 & 15 \\ \hline -12 & -10 & 0 & 0 & 1 & 0 \end{array}\right] \end{array} \sim \begin{array}{cccccc} y_1 & y_2 & x_1 & x_2 & P & \\ \left[\begin{array}{ccccc|c} 0 & 0 & 1 & 4 & 0 & 70 \\ 1 & -3 & 0 & 1 & 0 & 15 \\ \hline 0 & -46 & 0 & 12 & 1 & 180 \end{array}\right] \end{array}$$

$4R_2 + R_1 \rightarrow R_1$ and $12R_2 + R_3 \rightarrow R_3$ $\qquad\qquad\uparrow$
pivot column

Since there are no positive entries in the pivot column, no optimal solution exists.

22. The matrices corresponding to the given problem and the dual problem are:

$$A = \begin{bmatrix} 1 & 1 & | & 8 \\ 1 & 2 & | & 4 \\ 2 & 1 & | & 1 \end{bmatrix} \text{ and } A^T = \begin{bmatrix} 1 & 1 & | & 3 \\ 1 & 2 & | & 1 \\ 8 & 4 & | & 1 \end{bmatrix} \text{ respectively.}$$

Thus, the dual problem is: Maximize $P = 8y_1 + 4y_2$

$$\text{Subject to: } y_1 + y_2 \le 2$$
$$y_1 + 2y_2 \le 1$$
$$y_1, \ y_2 \ge 0$$

We introduce slack variables x_1 and x_2 to obtain the initial system:

$$y_1 + y_2 + x_1 \qquad\qquad = 2$$
$$y_1 + 2y_2 \qquad + x_2 \qquad = 1$$
$$-8y_1 - 4y_2 \qquad\qquad + P = 0$$

The simplex tableau for this problem is:

$$
\begin{array}{c}
x_1 \\ \sim\ x_2 \\ P
\end{array}
\begin{array}{c}
\begin{array}{ccccc} y_1 & y_2 & x_1 & x_2 & P \end{array} \\
\left[\begin{array}{ccccc|c}
1 & 2 & 1 & 0 & 0 & 2 \\
① & 2 & 0 & 1 & 0 & 1 \\
\hline
-8 & -4 & 0 & 0 & 1 & 0
\end{array}\right]
\end{array}
\begin{array}{c} 2 \\ 1 \end{array}
\sim
\begin{array}{c}
\begin{array}{ccccc} y_1 & y_2 & x_1 & x_2 & P \end{array} \\
\left[\begin{array}{ccccc|c}
0 & 0 & 1 & -1 & 0 & 1 \\
1 & 2 & 0 & 1 & 0 & 1 \\
\hline
0 & 12 & 0 & 8 & 1 & 8
\end{array}\right]
\end{array}
$$

$(-1)R_2 + R_1 \rightarrow R_1$ and $8R_2 + R_3 \rightarrow R_3$ Optimal solution: min $C = 8$ at $x_1 = 0$,
$$x_2 = 8.$$

24. The matrices corresponding to the given problem and the dual problem are:

$$
A = \begin{bmatrix} 2 & 1 & 6 \\ 1 & -4 & -24 \\ -8 & 5 & -24 \\ 10 & 4 & 1 \end{bmatrix}
\quad \text{and} \quad
A^T = \begin{bmatrix} 2 & 1 & -8 & 10 \\ 1 & -4 & 5 & 4 \\ 6 & -24 & -24 & 1 \end{bmatrix}
\quad \text{respectively.}
$$

Thus, the dual problem is: Maximize $P = 6y_1 - 24y_2 - 24y_3$

Subject to: $2y_1 + y_2 - 8y_3 \le 10$
$$y_1 - 4y_2 + 5y_3 \le 4$$
$$y_1,\ y_2,\ y_3 \ge 0$$

We introduce slack variables x_1 and x_2 to obtain the initial system:

$$2y_1 + y_2 - 8y_3 + x_1 \qquad\qquad = 10$$
$$y_1 - 4y_2 + 5y_3 \qquad + x_2 \qquad = 4$$
$$-6y_1 + 24y_2 + 24y_3 \qquad\qquad + P = 0$$

The simplex tableau for this problem is:

$$
\begin{array}{c}
x_1 \\ x_2 \\ P
\end{array}
\begin{array}{c}
\begin{array}{cccccc} y_1 & y_2 & y_3 & x_1 & x_2 & P \end{array} \\
\left[\begin{array}{cccccc|c}
2 & 1 & -8 & 1 & 0 & 0 & 10 \\
① & -4 & 5 & 0 & 1 & 0 & 4 \\
\hline
-6 & 24 & 24 & 0 & 0 & 1 & 0
\end{array}\right]
\end{array}
\begin{array}{c} 5 \\ 4 \end{array}
\sim
\begin{array}{c}
\begin{array}{cccccc} y_1 & y_2 & y_3 & x_1 & x_2 & P \end{array} \\
\left[\begin{array}{cccccc|c}
0 & 9 & -18 & 1 & -2 & 0 & 2 \\
1 & -4 & 5 & 0 & 1 & 0 & 4 \\
\hline
0 & 0 & 54 & 0 & 6 & 1 & 24
\end{array}\right]
\end{array}
$$

$(-2)R_2 + R_1 \rightarrow R_1$ and $6R_2 + R_3 \rightarrow R_3$ Optimal solution: min $C = 24$ at $x_1 = 0$,
$$x_2 = 6.$$

26. The matrices corresponding to the given problem and the dual problem are:

$$A = \begin{bmatrix} 3 & 1 & | & 24 \\ 1 & 1 & | & 16 \\ 1 & 4 & | & 30 \\ \hline 40 & 10 & | & 1 \end{bmatrix} \quad \text{and} \quad A^T = \begin{bmatrix} 3 & 1 & 1 & | & 40 \\ 1 & 1 & 4 & | & 10 \\ \hline 24 & 16 & 30 & | & 1 \end{bmatrix} \quad \text{respectively.}$$

Thus, the dual problem is: Maximize $P = 24y_1 + 16y_2 + 30y_3$

Subject to: $3y_1 + y_2 + y_3 \leq 40$

$y_1 + y_2 + 4y_3 \leq 10$

$y_1, y_2, y_3 \geq 0$

We introduce slack variables x_1 and x_2 to obtain the initial system:

$$3y_1 + y_2 + y_3 + x_1 \qquad\quad = 40$$
$$y_1 + y_2 + 4y_3 \qquad + x_2 \quad = 10$$
$$-24y_1 - 16y_2 - 30y_3 \qquad\quad + P = 0$$

The simplex tableau for this problem is:

$$\begin{array}{c} \\ x_1 \\ x_2 \\ P \end{array} \begin{array}{cccccc} y_1 & y_2 & y_3 & x_1 & x_2 & P \\ \end{array}$$

$$\begin{bmatrix} 3 & 1 & 1 & 1 & 0 & 0 & | & 40 \\ 1 & 1 & ④ & 0 & 1 & 0 & | & 10 \\ \hdashline -24 & -16 & -30 & 0 & 0 & 1 & | & 0 \end{bmatrix} \begin{array}{c} 40 \\ 2.5 \\ \\ \end{array}$$

$$\frac{1}{4}R_2 \rightarrow R_2$$

$$\sim \begin{bmatrix} 3 & 1 & 1 & 1 & 0 & 0 & | & 40 \\ \frac{1}{4} & \frac{1}{4} & ① & 0 & \frac{1}{4} & 0 & | & 2.5 \\ \hline -24 & -16 & -30 & 0 & 0 & 1 & | & 0 \end{bmatrix}$$

$$(-1)R_2 + R_1 \rightarrow R_1, \quad 30R_2 + R_4 \rightarrow R_4$$

$$\sim \begin{bmatrix} \frac{11}{4} & \frac{3}{4} & 0 & 1 & -\frac{1}{4} & 0 & | & 37.5 \\ ④\!\!\!\frac{1}{4} & \frac{1}{4} & 1 & 0 & \frac{1}{4} & 0 & | & 2.5 \\ \hdashline -16.5 & -8.5 & 0 & 0 & 7.5 & 1 & | & 75 \end{bmatrix} \begin{array}{c} 13.\overline{36} \\ 10 \\ \\ \end{array}$$

$$4R_2 \rightarrow R_2$$

$$\sim \begin{bmatrix} \frac{11}{4} & \frac{3}{4} & 0 & 1 & -\frac{1}{4} & 0 & | & 37.5 \\ ① & 1 & 4 & 0 & 1 & 0 & | & 10 \\ \hdashline -16.5 & -8.5 & 0 & 0 & 7.5 & 1 & | & 75 \end{bmatrix}$$

$$\left(-\frac{11}{4}\right)R_2 + R_1 \rightarrow R_1, \quad 16.5R_2 + R_3 \rightarrow R_3$$

$$\sim \begin{bmatrix} 0 & -2 & -11 & 1 & -3 & 0 & | & 10 \\ 1 & 1 & 4 & 0 & 1 & 0 & | & 10 \\ 0 & 8 & 66 & 0 & 24 & 1 & | & 240 \end{bmatrix}$$

Thus, min $C = 240$ at $x_1 = 0$ and $x_2 = 24$.

28. The matrices corresponding to the given problem and the dual problem are:

$$A = \begin{bmatrix} 2 & 1 & | & 12 \\ 1 & 1 & | & 9 \\ 0 & 1 & | & 4 \\ 4 & 5 & | & 1 \end{bmatrix} \quad \text{and} \quad A^T = \begin{bmatrix} 2 & 1 & 0 & | & 4 \\ 1 & 1 & 1 & | & 5 \\ 12 & 9 & 4 & | & 1 \end{bmatrix} \text{ respectively.}$$

Thus, the dual problem is: Maximize $P = 12y_1 + 9y_2 + 4y_3$

$$\begin{aligned} \text{Subject to: } 2y_1 + y_2 &\le 4 \\ y_1 + y_2 + y_3 &\le 5 \\ y_1, \ y_2, \ y_3 &\ge 0 \end{aligned}$$

We introduce slack variables x_1 and x_2 to obtain the initial system:

$$\begin{aligned} 2y_1 + y_2 + \quad + x_1 \quad &= 4 \\ y_1 + y_2 + y_3 \quad + x_2 \quad &= 5 \\ -12y_1 - 9y_2 - 4y_3 \quad + P &= 0 \end{aligned}$$

The simplex tableau for this problem is:

$$\begin{array}{c} \quad\ y_1 \quad y_2 \ \ y_3 \ \ x_1 \ x_2 \ x_3 \ \ P \\ \begin{array}{c} x_1 \\ x_2 \\ P \end{array} \begin{bmatrix} ② & 1 & 0 & 1 & 0 & 0 & | & 4 \\ 1 & 1 & 1 & 0 & 1 & 0 & | & 5 \\ -12 & -9 & -4 & 0 & 0 & 1 & | & 0 \end{bmatrix} \begin{array}{c} \frac{4}{2} = 2 \\ \frac{5}{1} = 5 \\ \ \end{array} \end{array}$$

$$\frac{1}{2}R_1 \to R_1$$

$$\sim \begin{bmatrix} ① & \frac{1}{2} & 0 & \frac{1}{2} & 0 & 0 & | & 2 \\ 1 & 1 & 1 & 0 & 1 & 0 & | & 5 \\ -12 & -9 & -4 & 0 & 0 & 1 & | & 0 \end{bmatrix} \sim \begin{bmatrix} 1 & \frac{1}{2} & 0 & \frac{1}{2} & 0 & 0 & | & 2 \\ 0 & \frac{1}{2} & ① & -\frac{1}{2} & 1 & 0 & | & 3 \\ 0 & -3 & -4 & 6 & 0 & 1 & | & 24 \end{bmatrix}$$

$(-1)R_1 + R_2 \to R_2, \quad 12R_1 + R_3 \to R_3 \qquad\qquad 4R_2 + R_3 \to R_3$

$$\sim \begin{bmatrix} 1 & ⓵⁄₂ & 0 & \frac{1}{2} & 0 & 0 & | & 2 \\ 0 & \frac{1}{2} & 1 & -\frac{1}{2} & 1 & 0 & | & 3 \\ 0 & -1 & 0 & 4 & 4 & 1 & | & 36 \end{bmatrix} \begin{array}{c} 4 \\ 6 \\ \ \end{array} \sim \begin{bmatrix} 2 & ① & 0 & 1 & 0 & 0 & | & 4 \\ 0 & \frac{1}{2} & 1 & -\frac{1}{2} & 1 & 0 & | & 3 \\ 0 & -1 & 0 & 4 & 4 & 1 & | & 36 \end{bmatrix}$$

$$2R_1 \to R_1 \qquad\qquad\qquad \left(-\frac{1}{2}\right)R_1 + R_2 \to R_2, \quad R_1 + R_3 \to R_3$$

$$\sim \begin{bmatrix} 2 & 1 & 0 & 1 & 0 & 0 & | & 4 \\ -1 & 0 & 1 & -1 & 1 & 0 & | & 1 \\ 2 & 0 & 0 & 5 & 4 & 1 & | & 40 \end{bmatrix}$$

Thus, min $C = 40$ at $x_1 = 5$ and $x_2 = 4$.

30. The matrices corresponding to the given problem and the dual problem are:

$$A = \begin{bmatrix} 1 & 1 & 3 & | & 6 \\ 2 & 1 & 1 & | & 9 \\ \hline 14 & 8 & 20 & | & 1 \end{bmatrix} \quad \text{and} \quad A^T = \begin{bmatrix} 1 & 2 & | & 14 \\ 1 & 1 & | & 8 \\ 3 & 1 & | & 20 \\ \hline 6 & 9 & | & 1 \end{bmatrix} \quad \text{respectively.}$$

Thus, the dual problem is: Maximize $P = 6y_1 + 9y_2$

$$\begin{aligned} \text{Subject to:} \quad y_1 + 2y_2 &\le 14 \\ y_1 + y_2 &\le 8 \\ 3y_1 + y_2 &\le 20 \\ y_1, y_2 &\ge 0 \end{aligned}$$

We introduce slack variables x_1, x_2, and x_3 to obtain the initial system:

$$\begin{aligned} y_1 + 2y_2 + x_1 &&&&= 14 \\ y_1 + y_2 &+ x_2 &&&= 8 \\ 3y_1 + y_2 &&+ x_3 &&= 20 \\ -6y_1 - 9y_2 &&&+ P &= 0 \end{aligned}$$

The simplex tableau for this problem is:

$$\begin{array}{c} \quad\; y_1 \;\; y_2 \;\; x_1 \;\, x_2 \; x_3 \;\; P \\ \begin{array}{c} x_1 \\ x_2 \\ x_3 \\ P \end{array} \begin{bmatrix} 1 & ② & 1 & 0 & 0 & 0 & | & 14 \\ 1 & 1 & 0 & 1 & 0 & 0 & | & 8 \\ 3 & 1 & 0 & 0 & 1 & 0 & | & 20 \\ \hline -6 & -9 & 0 & 0 & 0 & 1 & | & 0 \end{bmatrix} \begin{array}{l} 7 \\ 8 \\ 20 \end{array} \end{array}$$

$$\frac{1}{2} R_1 \rightarrow R_1$$

$$\sim \begin{bmatrix} \frac{1}{2} & ① & \frac{1}{2} & 0 & 0 & 0 & | & 7 \\ 1 & 1 & 0 & 1 & 0 & 0 & | & 8 \\ 3 & 1 & 0 & 0 & 1 & 0 & | & 20 \\ \hline -6 & -9 & 0 & 0 & 0 & 1 & | & 0 \end{bmatrix}$$

$$(-1)R_1 + R_2 \rightarrow R_2, \quad (-1)R_1 + R_3 \rightarrow R_3,$$
$$\text{and } 9R_1 + R_4 \rightarrow R_4$$

$$\sim \begin{bmatrix} \frac{1}{2} & 1 & \frac{1}{2} & 0 & 0 & 0 & | & 7 \\ ①\!\!/2 & 0 & -\frac{1}{2} & 1 & 0 & 0 & | & 1 \\ \frac{5}{2} & 0 & -\frac{1}{2} & 0 & 1 & 0 & | & 13 \\ \hline -\frac{3}{2} & 0 & \frac{9}{2} & 0 & 0 & 1 & | & 63 \end{bmatrix} \begin{array}{l} 14 \\ 2 \\ \frac{26}{5} \end{array}$$

$$2R_2 \rightarrow R_2$$

$$\sim \begin{bmatrix} \frac{1}{2} & 1 & \frac{1}{2} & 0 & 0 & 0 & | & 7 \\ ① & 0 & -1 & 2 & 0 & 0 & | & 2 \\ \frac{5}{2} & 0 & -\frac{1}{2} & 0 & 1 & 0 & | & 13 \\ \hline -\frac{3}{2} & 0 & \frac{9}{2} & 0 & 0 & 1 & | & 63 \end{bmatrix}$$

$$\left(-\frac{1}{2}\right)R_2 + R_1 \rightarrow R_1, \quad \left(-\frac{5}{2}\right)R_2 + R_3 \rightarrow R_3,$$
$$\text{and } \frac{3}{2}R_2 + R_4 \rightarrow R_4$$

$$\sim \begin{bmatrix} 0 & 1 & 1 & -1 & 0 & 0 & | & 6 \\ 1 & 0 & -1 & 2 & 0 & 0 & | & 2 \\ 0 & 0 & 2 & -5 & 1 & 0 & | & 8 \\ 0 & 0 & 3 & 3 & 0 & 1 & | & 66 \end{bmatrix}$$

Thus, min $C = 66$ at $x_1 = 3$, $x_2 = 3$, and $x_3 = 0$.

32. The matrices corresponding to the given problem and the dual problem are:

$$A = \begin{bmatrix} -3 & -2 & 1 & | & 4 \\ 1 & 1 & -1 & | & 2 \\ \hline 6 & 8 & 3 & | & 1 \end{bmatrix} \quad \text{and} \quad A^T = \begin{bmatrix} -3 & 1 & | & 6 \\ -2 & 1 & | & 8 \\ 1 & -1 & | & 3 \\ \hline 4 & 2 & | & 1 \end{bmatrix} \quad \text{respectively.}$$

Thus, the dual problem is: Maximize $P = 4y_1 + 2y_2$

Subject to: $-3y_1 + y_2 \leq 6$
$-2y_1 + y_2 \leq 8$
$y_1 - y_2 \leq 3$
$y_1, \ y_2 \geq 0$

We introduce slack variables x_1, x_2, and x_3 to obtain the initial system:

$-3y_1 + y_2 + x_1 \qquad\qquad = 6$
$-2y_1 + y_2 \qquad + x_2 \qquad = 8$
$y_1 - y_2 \qquad\qquad + x_3 \quad = 3$
$-4y_1 - 2y_2 \qquad\qquad\qquad + P = 0$

The simplex tableau for this problem is:

$$\begin{array}{c} \\ x_1 \\ x_2 \\ x_3 \\ P \end{array} \begin{array}{cccccc} y_1 & y_2 & x_1 & x_2 & x_3 & P \\ \left[\begin{array}{cccccc|c} -3 & 1 & 1 & 0 & 0 & 0 & 6 \\ -2 & 1 & 0 & 1 & 0 & 0 & 8 \\ \textcircled{1} & -1 & 0 & 0 & 1 & 0 & 3 \\ -4 & -2 & 0 & 0 & 0 & 1 & 0 \end{array} \right] \end{array} \sim \begin{bmatrix} 0 & -2 & 1 & 0 & 3 & 0 & | & 15 \\ 0 & -1 & 0 & 1 & 2 & 0 & | & 14 \\ 1 & -1 & 0 & 0 & 1 & 0 & | & 3 \\ 0 & -6 & 0 & 0 & 4 & 1 & | & 12 \end{bmatrix}$$

$3R_3 + R_1 \rightarrow R_1$, $2R_3 + R_2 \rightarrow R_2$, and $4R_3 + R_4 \rightarrow R_4$

pivot column

Since all the entries on the pivot column, above the broken line, are negative, there is no optimal solution.

34. The dual problem has 5 variables and 3 problem constraints.

36. The original problem must have two variables and any number of constraints.

38. Yes. No modifications are necessary.

40. Yes. No modifications are necessary.

42. The matrices corresponding to the given problem and the dual problem are:

$$A = \begin{bmatrix} 1 & 3 & 3 & | & 6 \\ 1 & 5 & 5 & | & 4 \\ 2 & 2 & 3 & | & 8 \\ 6 & 8 & 12 & | & 1 \end{bmatrix} \quad \text{and} \quad A^T = \begin{bmatrix} 1 & 1 & 2 & | & 6 \\ 3 & 5 & 2 & | & 8 \\ 3 & 5 & 3 & | & 12 \\ 6 & 4 & 8 & | & 1 \end{bmatrix} \quad \text{respectively.}$$

Thus, the dual problem is: Maximize $P = 6y_1 + 4y_2 + 8y_3$

$$\begin{aligned} \text{Subject to:} \quad y_1 + y_2 + 2y_3 &\le 6 \\ 3y_1 + 5y_2 + 2y_3 &\le 8 \\ 3y_1 + 5y_2 + 3y_3 &\le 12 \\ y_1, \; y_2, \; y_3 &\ge 0 \end{aligned}$$

We introduce slack variables x_1, x_2, and x_3 to obtain the initial system:

$$\begin{aligned} y_1 + y_2 + 2y_3 + x_1 &= 6 \\ 3y_1 + 5y_2 + 2y_3 \quad + x_2 &= 8 \\ 3y_1 + 5y_2 + 3y_3 \quad\quad + x_3 &= 12 \\ -6y_1 - 4y_2 - 8y_3 \quad\quad\quad + P &= 0 \end{aligned}$$

The simplex tableau for this problem is:

$$
\begin{array}{c}
\begin{array}{ccccccc} y_1 & y_2 & y_3 & x_1 & x_2 & x_3 & P \end{array} \\
\begin{array}{c} x_1 \\ x_2 \\ x_3 \\ P \end{array}
\left[\begin{array}{ccccccc|c}
1 & 1 & ② & 1 & 0 & 0 & 0 & 6 \\
3 & 5 & 2 & 0 & 1 & 0 & 0 & 8 \\
3 & 5 & 3 & 0 & 0 & 1 & 0 & 12 \\
\hline
-6 & -4 & -8 & 0 & 0 & 0 & 1 & 0
\end{array} \right]
\begin{array}{l} 6/2 = 3 \\ 8/2 = 4 \\ 12/3 = 4 \\ {} \end{array}
\end{array}
$$

$$\tfrac{1}{2}R_1 \to R_1$$

$$
\sim \left[\begin{array}{ccccccc|c}
\tfrac{1}{2} & \tfrac{1}{2} & ① & \tfrac{1}{2} & 0 & 0 & 0 & 3 \\
3 & 5 & 2 & 0 & 1 & 0 & 0 & 8 \\
3 & 5 & 3 & 0 & 0 & 1 & 0 & 12 \\
\hline
-6 & -4 & -8 & 0 & 0 & 0 & 1 & 0
\end{array} \right]
\sim \left[\begin{array}{ccccccc|c}
\tfrac{1}{2} & \tfrac{1}{2} & 1 & \tfrac{1}{2} & 0 & 0 & 0 & 3 \\
② & 4 & 0 & -1 & 1 & 0 & 0 & 2 \\
\tfrac{3}{2} & \tfrac{7}{2} & 0 & -\tfrac{3}{2} & 0 & 1 & 0 & 3 \\
\hline
-2 & 0 & 0 & 4 & 0 & 0 & 1 & 24
\end{array} \right]
\begin{array}{l} 6 \\ 1 \\ 2 \end{array}
$$

$(-2)R_1 + R_2 \to R_2, \quad (-3)R_1 + R_3 \to R_3, \qquad \tfrac{1}{2}R_2 \to R_2$

and $8R_1 + R_4 \to R_4$

$$
\sim \left[\begin{array}{ccccccc|c}
\tfrac{1}{2} & \tfrac{1}{2} & 1 & \tfrac{1}{2} & 0 & 0 & 0 & 3 \\
① & 2 & 0 & -\tfrac{1}{2} & \tfrac{1}{2} & 0 & 0 & 1 \\
\tfrac{3}{2} & \tfrac{7}{2} & 0 & -\tfrac{3}{2} & 0 & 1 & 0 & 3 \\
\hline
-2 & 0 & 0 & 4 & 0 & 0 & 1 & 24
\end{array} \right]
\sim \left[\begin{array}{ccccccc|c}
0 & -\tfrac{1}{2} & 1 & \tfrac{3}{4} & -\tfrac{1}{4} & 0 & 0 & \tfrac{5}{2} \\
1 & 2 & 0 & -\tfrac{1}{2} & \tfrac{1}{2} & 0 & 0 & 1 \\
0 & \tfrac{1}{2} & 0 & -\tfrac{3}{4} & -\tfrac{3}{4} & 1 & 0 & \tfrac{3}{2} \\
\hline
0 & 4 & 0 & 3 & 1 & 0 & 1 & 26
\end{array} \right]
$$

$\left(-\tfrac{1}{2}\right)R_2 + R_1 \to R_1, \quad \left(-\tfrac{3}{2}\right)R_2 + R_3 \to R_3,$

and $2R_2 + R_4 \to R_4$

Thus, min $C = 26$ at $x_1 = 3$, $x_2 = 1$, and $x_3 = 0$.

44. The first and second inequalities must be rewritten before forming the dual.

$$\text{Minimize } C = 4x_1 + 7x_2 + 5x_3 + 6x_4$$

$$
\begin{aligned}
\text{Subject to: } -x_1 - x_2 \qquad\qquad &\geq -12\\
- x_3 - x_4 &\geq -25\\
x_1 \qquad + x_3 \qquad &\geq 20\\
x_2 \qquad + x_4 &\geq 15\\
x_1,\ x_2,\ x_3,\ x_4 &\geq 0
\end{aligned}
$$

The matrices corresponding to the given problem and the dual problem are:

$$
A = \left[\begin{array}{cccc|c}
-1 & -1 & 0 & 0 & -12\\
0 & 0 & -1 & -1 & -25\\
1 & 0 & 1 & 0 & 20\\
0 & 1 & 0 & 1 & 15\\
4 & 7 & 5 & 6 & 1
\end{array}\right]
\quad\text{and}\quad
A^T = \left[\begin{array}{cccc|c}
-1 & 0 & 1 & 0 & 4\\
-1 & 0 & 0 & 1 & 7\\
0 & -1 & 1 & 0 & 5\\
0 & -1 & 0 & 1 & 6\\
-12 & -25 & 20 & 15 & 1
\end{array}\right]
$$

The dual problem is: Maximize $P = -12y_1 - 25y_2 + 20y_3 + 15y_4$

$$
\begin{aligned}
\text{Subject to: } -y_1 \qquad + y_3 \qquad &\leq 4\\
-y_1 \qquad\qquad + y_4 &\leq 7\\
-y_2 + y_3 \qquad &\leq 5\\
-y_2 \qquad + y_4 &\leq 6\\
y_1,\ y_2,\ y_3,\ y_4 &\geq 0
\end{aligned}
$$

We introduce the slack variables x_1, x_2, x_3, and x_4 to obtain the initial system:

$$
\begin{aligned}
-y_1 \qquad + y_3 \qquad\qquad + x_1 \qquad\qquad\qquad &= 4\\
-y_1 \qquad\qquad + y_4 \qquad + x_2 \qquad\qquad &= 7\\
-y_2 + y_3 \qquad\qquad\qquad + x_3 \qquad &= 5\\
-y_2 \qquad + y_4 \qquad\qquad\qquad + x_4 &= 6\\
12y_1 + 25y_2 - 20y_3 - 15y_4 \qquad\qquad\qquad\qquad + P &= 0
\end{aligned}
$$

The simplex tableau for this problem is:

	y_1	y_2	y_3	y_4	x_1	x_2	x_3	x_4	P		
x_1	-1	0	①	0	1	0	0	0	0	4	4
x_2	-1	0	0	1	0	1	0	0	0	7	
x_3	0	-1	1	0	0	0	1	0	0	5	5
x_4	0	-1	0	1	0	0	0	1	0	6	
P	12	25	-20	-15	0	0	0	0	1	0	

$$(-1)R_1 + R_3 \rightarrow R_3 \quad\text{and}\quad 20R_1 + R_5 \rightarrow R_5$$

$$
\sim \left[\begin{array}{ccccccccc|c}
-1 & 0 & 1 & 0 & 1 & 0 & 0 & 0 & 0 & 4\\
-1 & 0 & 0 & 1 & 0 & 1 & 0 & 0 & 0 & 7\\
1 & -1 & 0 & 0 & -1 & 0 & 1 & 0 & 0 & 1\\
0 & -1 & 0 & ① & 0 & 0 & 0 & 1 & 0 & 6\\
-8 & 25 & 0 & -15 & 20 & 0 & 0 & 0 & 1 & 80
\end{array}\right]
\begin{array}{c} \\ 7 \\ \\ 6 \\ \\ \end{array}
$$

$$(-1)R_4 + R_2 \rightarrow R_2 \quad\text{and}\quad 15R_4 + R_5 \rightarrow R_5$$

$$\sim \begin{bmatrix} -1 & 0 & 1 & 0 & 1 & 0 & 0 & 0 & 0 & | & 4 \\ -1 & 1 & 0 & 0 & 0 & 1 & -1 & 0 & 0 & | & 6 \\ \textcircled{1} & -1 & 0 & 0 & -1 & 0 & 1 & 0 & 0 & | & 1 \\ 0 & -1 & 0 & 1 & 0 & 0 & 0 & 1 & 0 & | & 6 \\ -8 & 10 & 0 & 0 & 20 & 0 & 0 & 15 & 1 & | & 170 \end{bmatrix}$$

$R_3 + R_1 \to R_1$, $R_3 + R_2 \to R_2$, and $8R_3 + R_5 \to R_5$

$$\sim \begin{bmatrix} 0 & -1 & 1 & 0 & 0 & 0 & 1 & 0 & 0 & | & 5 \\ 0 & 0 & 0 & 0 & -1 & 1 & 0 & 0 & 0 & | & 7 \\ 1 & -1 & 0 & 0 & -1 & 0 & 1 & 0 & 0 & | & 1 \\ 0 & -1 & 0 & 1 & 0 & 0 & 0 & 1 & 0 & | & 6 \\ 0 & 2 & 0 & 0 & 12 & 0 & 8 & 15 & 1 & | & 178 \end{bmatrix}$$

Thus, min $C = 178$ at $x_1 = 12$, $x_2 = 0$, $x_3 = 8$, and $x_4 = 15$.

46. (A) Let x_1 = the number of hours the West Summit mine is operated, and x_2 = the number of hours the North Ridge mine is operated. The mathematical model for this problem is:

Minimize $C = 400x_1 + 600x_2$

Subject to: $2x_1 + 2x_2 \geq 100$

$3x_1 + x_2 \geq 60$

$x_1 + 2x_2 \geq 80$

$x_1,\ x_2 \geq 0$

The matrices corresponding to the given problem and the dual problem are:

$$A = \begin{bmatrix} 2 & 2 & | & 100 \\ 3 & 1 & | & 60 \\ 1 & 2 & | & 80 \\ 400 & 600 & | & 1 \end{bmatrix} \quad \text{and} \quad A^T = \begin{bmatrix} 2 & 3 & 1 & | & 400 \\ 2 & 1 & 2 & | & 600 \\ 100 & 60 & 80 & | & 1 \end{bmatrix}$$

Thus, the dual problem is: Maximize $P = 100y_1 + 60y_2 + 80y_3$

Subject to: $2y_1 + 3y_2 + y_3 \leq 400$

$2y_1 + y_2 + 2y_3 \leq 600$

$y_1,\ y_2,\ y_3 \geq 0$

We introduce slack variables x_1 and x_2 to obtain the initial system:

$$2y_1 + 3y_2 + y_3 + x_1 \qquad = 400$$
$$2y_1 + y_2 + 2y_3 \quad + x_2 = 600$$
$$-100y_1 - 60y_2 - 80y_3 \qquad + P = 0$$

The simplex tableau for this problem is:

$$
\begin{array}{c}
\\
X_1\\
X_2\\
P
\end{array}
\begin{array}{c}
\begin{array}{cccccc}
Y_1 & Y_2 & Y_3 & X_1 & X_2 & P
\end{array}\\
\left[\begin{array}{cccccc|c}
② & 3 & 1 & 1 & 0 & 0 & 400\\
2 & 1 & 2 & 0 & 1 & 0 & 600\\
\hline
-100 & -60 & -80 & 0 & 0 & 1 & 0
\end{array}\right]
\begin{array}{c}
200\\
300\\

\end{array}
\end{array}
$$

$$\frac{1}{2}R_1 \rightarrow R_1$$

$$
\sim
\left[\begin{array}{cccccc|c}
① & \frac{3}{2} & \frac{1}{2} & \frac{1}{2} & 0 & 0 & 200\\
2 & 1 & 2 & 0 & 1 & 0 & 600\\
\hline
-100 & -60 & -80 & 0 & 0 & 1 & 0
\end{array}\right]
$$

$$(-2)R_1 + R_2 \rightarrow R_2 \text{ and } 100R_1 + R_3 \rightarrow R_3$$

$$
\sim
\left[\begin{array}{cccccc|c}
1 & \frac{3}{2} & \frac{1}{2} & \frac{1}{2} & 0 & 0 & 200\\
0 & -2 & ① & -1 & 1 & 0 & 200\\
\hline
0 & 90 & -30 & 50 & 0 & 1 & 20,000
\end{array}\right]
\begin{array}{c}
400\\
200\\
200
\end{array}
$$

$$\left(-\frac{1}{2}\right)R_2 + R_1 \rightarrow R_1 \text{ and } 30R_2 + R_3 \rightarrow R_3$$

$$
\sim
\left[\begin{array}{cccccc|c}
0 & \frac{5}{2} & 0 & 1 & -\frac{1}{2} & 0 & 100\\
0 & -2 & 1 & -1 & 1 & 0 & 200\\
\hline
0 & 30 & 0 & 20 & 30 & 1 & 26,000
\end{array}\right]
$$

Thus, min $C = \$26,000$ at $x_1 = 20$ and $x_2 = 30$; i.e. operate the West Summit mine 20 hours and the North Ridge mine 30 hours.

(B) In this case, the matrices for the given problem and the dual problem are:

$$
A = \left[\begin{array}{cc|c}
2 & 2 & 100\\
3 & 1 & 60\\
1 & 2 & 80\\
\hline
300 & 700 & 1
\end{array}\right]
\text{ and }
A^T = \left[\begin{array}{ccc|c}
2 & 3 & 1 & 300\\
2 & 1 & 2 & 700\\
\hline
100 & 60 & 80 & 1
\end{array}\right]
\text{ respectively.}
$$

Thus, the dual problem is: Maximize $P = 100y_1 + 60y_2 + 80y_3$

Subject to: $2y_1 + 3y_2 + y_3 \le 300$
$2y_1 + y_2 + 2y_3 \le 700$
$y_1, y_2, y_3 \ge 0$

The simplex tableau for this problem is:

$$
\begin{array}{c}
\\
X_1\\
X_2\\
P
\end{array}
\begin{array}{c}
\begin{array}{cccccc}
Y_1 & Y_2 & Y_3 & X_1 & X_2 & P
\end{array}\\
\left[\begin{array}{cccccc|c}
② & 3 & 1 & 1 & 0 & 0 & 300\\
2 & 1 & 2 & 0 & 1 & 0 & 700\\
\hline
-100 & -60 & -80 & 0 & 0 & 1 & 0
\end{array}\right]
\end{array}
$$

$$\frac{1}{2}R_1 \rightarrow R_1$$

$$\sim \begin{bmatrix} \textcircled{1} & \frac{3}{2} & \frac{1}{2} & \frac{1}{2} & 0 & 0 & 150 \\ 2 & 1 & 2 & 0 & 1 & 0 & 700 \\ \hline -100 & -60 & -80 & 0 & 0 & 1 & 0 \end{bmatrix}$$

$(-2)R_1 + R_2 \rightarrow R_2$ and $100R_1 + R_3 \rightarrow R_3$

$$\sim \begin{bmatrix} 1 & \frac{3}{2} & \textcircled{\frac{1}{2}} & \frac{1}{2} & 0 & 0 & 150 \\ 0 & -2 & 1 & -1 & 1 & 0 & 400 \\ \hline 0 & 90 & -30 & 50 & 0 & 1 & 15,000 \end{bmatrix}$$

$2R_1 \rightarrow R_1$

$$\sim \begin{bmatrix} 2 & 3 & \textcircled{1} & 1 & 0 & 0 & 300 \\ 0 & -2 & 1 & -1 & 1 & 0 & 400 \\ \hline 0 & 90 & -30 & 50 & 0 & 1 & 15,000 \end{bmatrix}$$

$(-1)R_1 + R_2 \rightarrow R_2$ and $30R_1 + R_3 \rightarrow R_3$

$$\sim \begin{bmatrix} 2 & 3 & 1 & 1 & 0 & 0 & 300 \\ -2 & -5 & 0 & -2 & 1 & 0 & 100 \\ \hline 60 & 180 & 0 & 80 & 0 & 1 & 24,000 \end{bmatrix}$$

Thus, operate West Summit mine 80 hours, the North Ridge mine is not used; min $C = \$24,000$.

(C) In this case, the simplex tableau is:

$$\begin{array}{c} \\ x_1 \\ x_2 \\ P \end{array} \begin{array}{cccccc} Y_1 & Y_2 & Y_3 & x_1 & x_2 & P \\ \end{array}$$

$$\begin{bmatrix} 2 & 3 & 1 & 1 & 0 & 0 & 800 \\ \textcircled{2} & 1 & 2 & 0 & 1 & 0 & 200 \\ \hline -100 & -60 & -80 & 0 & 0 & 1 & 0 \end{bmatrix}$$

$\frac{1}{2}R_2 \rightarrow R_2$

$$\sim \begin{bmatrix} 2 & 3 & 1 & 1 & 0 & 0 & 800 \\ \textcircled{1} & \frac{1}{2} & 1 & 0 & \frac{1}{2} & 0 & 100 \\ \hline -100 & -60 & -80 & 0 & 0 & 1 & 0 \end{bmatrix}$$

$(-2)R_2 + R_1 \rightarrow R_1$ and $100R_2 + R_3 \rightarrow R_3$

$$\sim \begin{bmatrix} 0 & 2 & -1 & 1 & -1 & 0 & 600 \\ 1 & \textcircled{\frac{1}{2}} & 1 & 0 & \frac{1}{2} & 0 & 100 \\ \hline 0 & -10 & 20 & 0 & 50 & 1 & 10,000 \end{bmatrix}$$

$2R_2 \rightarrow R_2$

$$\sim \begin{bmatrix} 0 & 2 & -1 & 1 & -1 & 0 & 600 \\ 2 & \textcircled{1} & 2 & 0 & 1 & 0 & 200 \\ \hline 0 & -10 & 20 & 0 & 50 & 1 & 10,000 \end{bmatrix}$$

$(-2)R_2 + R_1 \rightarrow R_1$ and $10R_2 + R_3 \rightarrow R_3$

$$\sim \begin{bmatrix} -4 & 0 & -5 & 1 & -3 & 0 & 200 \\ 2 & 1 & 2 & 0 & 2 & 0 & 200 \\ \hline 20 & 0 & 40 & 0 & 60 & 1 & 12,000 \end{bmatrix}$$

Thus, operate the North Ridge mine 60 hours, the West Summit mine is not used; min $C = \$12,000$.

48. Let x_1 = the number of tons shipped from Ames to Columbia,
x_2 = the number of tons shipped from Ames to Danville,
x_3 = the number of tons shipped from Bedford to Columbia,
and x_4 = the number of tons shipped from Bedford to Danville.

The mathematical model is: Minimize $C = 22x_1 + 38x_2 + 46x_3 + 24x_4$
Subject to:
$$x_1 + x_2 \leq 700$$
$$x_3 + x_4 \leq 500$$
$$x_1 + x_3 \geq 400$$
$$x_2 + x_4 \geq 600$$
$$x_1, \ x_2, \ x_3, \ x_4 \geq 0$$

We multiply the first two problem constraints by -1 to obtain inequalities of the $\geq$ type.

Minimize $C = 22x_1 + 38x_2 + 46x_3 + 24x_4$
Subject to:
$$-x_1 - x_2 \geq -700$$
$$-x_3 - x_4 \geq -500$$
$$x_1 + x_3 \geq 400$$
$$x_2 + x_4 \geq 600$$
$$x_1, \ x_2, \ x_3, \ x_4 \geq 0$$

The matrices for this problem and the dual problem are:

$$A = \begin{bmatrix} -1 & -1 & 0 & 0 & -700 \\ 0 & 0 & -1 & -1 & -500 \\ 1 & 0 & 1 & 0 & 400 \\ 0 & 1 & 0 & 1 & 600 \\ 22 & 38 & 46 & 24 & 1 \end{bmatrix} \quad \text{and} \quad A^T = \begin{bmatrix} -1 & 0 & 1 & 0 & 22 \\ -1 & 0 & 0 & 1 & 38 \\ 0 & -1 & 1 & 0 & 46 \\ 0 & -1 & 0 & 1 & 24 \\ -700 & -500 & 400 & 600 & 1 \end{bmatrix}$$

Thus, the dual problem is:
Maximize $P = -700y_1 - 500y_2 + 400y_3 + 600y_4$
Subject to:
$$-y_1 + y_3 \leq 22$$
$$-y_1 + y_4 \leq 38$$
$$-y_2 + y_3 \leq 46$$
$$-y_2 + y_4 \leq 24$$
$$y_1, \ y_2, \ y_3, \ y_4 \geq 0$$

We introduce slack variables x_1, x_2, x_3, and x_4 to obtain the initial system:

$$-y_1 + y_3 + x_1 = 22$$
$$-y_1 + y_4 + x_2 = 38$$
$$-y_2 + y_3 + x_3 = 46$$
$$-y_2 + y_4 + x_4 = 24$$
$$700y_1 + 500y_2 - 400y_3 - 600y_4 + P = 0$$

The simplex tableau for this problem is:

$$
\begin{array}{c}
\\
x_1 \\
x_2 \\
x_3 \\
x_4 \\
P
\end{array}
\begin{array}{ccccccccc}
y_1 & y_2 & y_3 & y_4 & x_1 & x_2 & x_3 & x_4 & P \\
\end{array}
$$

$$
\begin{array}{c}
x_1 \\
x_2 \\
x_3 \\
x_4 \\
P
\end{array}
\left[\begin{array}{ccccccccc|c}
-1 & 0 & 1 & 0 & 1 & 0 & 0 & 0 & 0 & 22 \\
-1 & 0 & 0 & 1 & 0 & 1 & 0 & 0 & 0 & 38 \\
0 & -1 & 1 & 0 & 0 & 0 & 1 & 0 & 0 & 46 \\
0 & -1 & 0 & \textcircled{1} & 0 & 0 & 0 & 1 & 0 & 24 \\
\hline
700 & 500 & -400 & -600 & 0 & 0 & 0 & 0 & 1 & 0
\end{array}\right]
$$

$(-1)R_4 + R_2 \rightarrow R_2$ and $600R_4 + R_5 \rightarrow R_5$

$$
\sim
\left[\begin{array}{ccccccccc|c}
-1 & 0 & \textcircled{1} & 0 & 1 & 0 & 0 & 0 & 0 & 22 \\
-1 & 1 & 0 & 0 & 0 & 1 & 0 & -1 & 0 & 14 \\
0 & -1 & 1 & 0 & 0 & 0 & 1 & 0 & 0 & 46 \\
0 & -1 & 0 & 1 & 0 & 0 & 0 & 1 & 0 & 24 \\
\hline
700 & -100 & -400 & 0 & 0 & 0 & 0 & 600 & 1 & 14{,}000
\end{array}\right]
$$

$(-1)R_1 + R_3 \rightarrow R_3$ and $400R_1 + R_5 \rightarrow R_5$

$$
\sim
\left[\begin{array}{ccccccccc|c}
-1 & 0 & 1 & 0 & 1 & 0 & 0 & 0 & 0 & 22 \\
-1 & \textcircled{1} & 0 & 0 & 0 & 1 & 0 & -1 & 0 & 14 \\
1 & -1 & 0 & 0 & -1 & 0 & 1 & 0 & 0 & 24 \\
0 & -1 & 0 & 1 & 0 & 0 & 0 & 1 & 0 & 24 \\
\hline
300 & -100 & 0 & 0 & 400 & 0 & 0 & 600 & 1 & 23{,}200
\end{array}\right]
$$

$R_2 + R_3 \rightarrow R_3$, $R_2 + R_4 \rightarrow R_4$, and $100R_2 + R_5 \rightarrow R_5$

$$
\sim
\left[\begin{array}{ccccccccc|c}
-1 & 0 & 1 & 0 & 1 & 0 & 0 & 0 & 0 & 22 \\
-1 & 1 & 0 & 0 & 0 & 1 & 0 & -1 & 0 & 14 \\
0 & 0 & 0 & 0 & -1 & 1 & 1 & -1 & 0 & 38 \\
-1 & 0 & 0 & 1 & 0 & 1 & 0 & 0 & 0 & 38 \\
\hline
200 & 0 & 0 & 0 & 400 & 100 & 0 & 500 & 1 & 24{,}600
\end{array}\right]
$$

Thus, ship 400 tons from Ames to Columbia ($x_1 = 400$), 100 tons from Ames to Danville ($x_2 = 100$), 500 tons from Bedford to Danville ($x_4 = 500$); minimal cost is \$24,600.

50. Let x_1 = the number of cubic yards of mix A,
$\quad\quad x_2$ = the number of cubic yards of mix B,
$\quad\quad x_3$ = the number of cubic yards of mix C.

Mathematical model: Minimize $C = 30x_1 + 36x_2 + 39x_3$

$$
\begin{aligned}
\text{Subject to: } & 20x_1 + 10x_2 + 20x_3 \geq 480 \\
& 10x_1 + 10x_2 + 20x_3 \geq 320 \\
& 10x_1 + 15x_2 + 5x_3 \geq 225 \\
& x_1,\ x_2,\ x_3 \geq 0
\end{aligned}
$$

Divide the first two problem constraints by 10 and the third by 5. This will simplify the calculations.

$$A = \begin{bmatrix} 2 & 1 & 2 & 48 \\ 1 & 1 & 2 & 32 \\ 2 & 3 & 1 & 45 \\ 30 & 36 & 39 & 1 \end{bmatrix} \quad \text{and} \quad A^T = \begin{bmatrix} 2 & 1 & 2 & 30 \\ 1 & 1 & 3 & 36 \\ 2 & 2 & 1 & 39 \\ 48 & 32 & 45 & 1 \end{bmatrix}$$

The dual problem is: Maximize $P = 48y_1 + 32y_2 + 45y_3$

Subject to:
$$2y_1 + y_2 + 2y_3 \leq 30$$
$$y_1 + y_2 + 3y_3 \leq 36$$
$$2y_1 + 2y_2 + y_3 \leq 39$$
$$y_1,\ y_2,\ y_3 \geq 0$$

We introduce slack variables x_1, x_2, and x_3 to obtain the initial system:

$$
\begin{aligned}
2y_1 + y_2 + 2y_3 + x_1 \quad\quad\quad\quad &= 30 \\
y_1 + y_2 + 3y_3 \quad + x_2 \quad\quad &= 36 \\
2y_1 + 2y_2 + y_3 \quad\quad + x_3 \quad &= 39 \\
-48y_1 - 32y_2 - 45y_3 \quad\quad\quad\quad + P &= 0
\end{aligned}
$$

The simplex tableau for this problem is:

$$
\begin{array}{c} \\ x_1 \\ x_2 \\ x_3 \\ P \end{array}
\begin{array}{cccccccc}
y_1 & y_2 & y_3 & x_1 & x_2 & x_3 & P & \\
\end{array}
$$

	y_1	y_2	y_3	x_1	x_2	x_3	P		
x_1	②	1	2	1	0	0	0	30	15
x_2	1	1	3	0	1	0	0	36	36
x_3	2	2	1	0	0	1	0	39	19.5
P	-48	-32	-45	0	0	0	1	0	

$$\tfrac{1}{2}R_1 \to R_1$$

$$
\sim \begin{bmatrix}
① & \tfrac{1}{2} & 1 & \tfrac{1}{2} & 0 & 0 & 0 & 15 \\
1 & 1 & 3 & 0 & 1 & 0 & 0 & 36 \\
2 & 2 & 1 & 0 & 0 & 1 & 0 & 39 \\
-48 & -32 & -45 & 0 & 0 & 0 & 1 & 0
\end{bmatrix}
$$

$$(-1)R_1 + R_2 \to R_2, \quad (-2)R_1 + R_3 \to R_3, \quad \text{and} \quad 48R_1 + R_4 \to R_4$$

$$
\sim \begin{bmatrix}
1 & \tfrac{1}{2} & 1 & \tfrac{1}{2} & 0 & 0 & 0 & 15 \\
0 & \tfrac{1}{2} & 2 & -\tfrac{1}{2} & 1 & 0 & 0 & 21 \\
0 & ① & -1 & -1 & 0 & 1 & 0 & 9 \\
0 & -8 & 3 & 24 & 0 & 0 & 1 & 720
\end{bmatrix}
$$

$$\left(-\tfrac{1}{2}\right)R_3 + R_1 \to R_1, \quad \left(-\tfrac{1}{2}\right)R_3 + R_2 \to R_2, \quad \text{and} \quad 8R_3 + R_4 \to R_4$$

$$\sim \begin{bmatrix} 1 & 0 & \frac{3}{2} & 1 & 0 & -1 & 0 & | & 11.5 \\ 0 & 0 & \boxed{2.5} & 0 & 1 & -\frac{1}{2} & 0 & | & 16.5 \\ 0 & 1 & -1 & -1 & 0 & 1 & 0 & | & 9 \\ 0 & 0 & -5 & 16 & 0 & 8 & 1 & | & 792 \end{bmatrix} \begin{matrix} 7.\overline{6} \\ 6.6 \\ \\ \end{matrix}$$

$$\frac{1}{2.5} R_2 \to R_2$$

$$\sim \begin{bmatrix} 1 & 0 & 1.5 & 1 & 0 & -1 & 0 & | & 11.5 \\ 0 & 0 & \boxed{1} & 0 & 0.4 & -0.2 & 0 & | & 6.6 \\ 0 & 1 & -1 & -1 & 0 & 1 & 0 & | & 9 \\ 0 & 0 & -5 & 16 & 0 & 8 & 1 & | & 792 \end{bmatrix}$$

$(-1.5)R_2 + R_1 \to R_1$, $R_2 + R_3 \to R_3$, and $5R_2 + R_4 \to R_4$

$$\sim \begin{bmatrix} 1 & 0 & 0 & 1 & -0.6 & -0.7 & 0 & | & 1.6 \\ 0 & 0 & 1 & 0 & 0.4 & -0.2 & 0 & | & 6.6 \\ 0 & 1 & 0 & -1 & 0.4 & 0.8 & 0 & | & 15.6 \\ 0 & 0 & 0 & 16 & 2 & 7 & 1 & | & 825 \end{bmatrix}$$

Thus, blend 16 cu yd A, 2 cu yd B, 7 cu yd C; min $C = \$825$.

52. Let x_1 = the number of students bused from North Division to Central,

x_2 = the number of students bused from North Division to Washington,

x_3 = the number of students bused from South Division to Central,

and x_4 = the number of students bused from South Division to Washington.

The mathematical model for this problem is:

Minimize $C = 5x_1 + 7x_2 + 3x_3 + 4x_4$

Subject to: $x_1 + x_2 \qquad\qquad \ge 300$

$\qquad\qquad x_3 + x_4 \ge 500$

$\qquad x_1 \qquad + x_3 \qquad \le 400$

$\qquad\qquad x_2 \qquad + x_4 \le 500$

$\qquad x_1, \; x_2, \; x_3, \; x_4 \ge 0$

We multiply the last two problem constraints by -1 so that all the constraints are of the $\ge$ type. The model becomes:

Minimize $C = 5x_1 + 7x_2 + 3x_3 + 4x_4$

Subject to: $x_1 + x_2 \qquad\qquad \ge \quad 300$

$\qquad\qquad x_3 + x_4 \ge \quad 500$

$\qquad -x_1 \qquad - x_3 \qquad \ge -400$

$\qquad\qquad -x_2 \qquad - x_4 \ge -500$

$\qquad x_1, \; x_2, \; x_3, \; x_4 \ge \quad 0$

The matrices for this problem and the dual problem are:

$$A = \begin{bmatrix} 1 & 1 & 0 & 0 & | & 300 \\ 0 & 0 & 1 & 1 & | & 500 \\ -1 & 0 & -1 & 0 & | & -400 \\ 0 & -1 & 0 & -1 & | & -500 \\ 5 & 7 & 3 & 4 & | & 1 \end{bmatrix} \quad \text{and} \quad A^T = \begin{bmatrix} 1 & 0 & -1 & 0 & | & 5 \\ 1 & 0 & 0 & -1 & | & 7 \\ 0 & 1 & -1 & 0 & | & 3 \\ 0 & 1 & 0 & -1 & | & 4 \\ 300 & 500 & -400 & -500 & | & 1 \end{bmatrix}$$

The dual problem is: Maximize $P = 300y_1 + 500y_2 - 400y_3 - 500y_4$

Subject to:
$$y_1 \quad\quad - y_3 \quad\quad \leq 5$$
$$y_1 \quad\quad\quad - y_4 \leq 7$$
$$y_2 - y_3 \quad\quad \leq 3$$
$$y_2 \quad\quad - y_4 \leq 4$$
$$y_1, \; y_2, \; y_3, \; y_4 \geq 0$$

We introduce slack variables x_1, x_2, x_3, and x_4 to obtain the initial system:

$$y_1 \quad\quad - y_3 \quad\quad + x_1 \quad\quad\quad\quad\quad = 5$$
$$y_1 \quad\quad\quad - y_4 \quad + x_2 \quad\quad\quad\quad = 7$$
$$y_2 \quad - y_3 \quad\quad\quad\quad + x_3 \quad\quad = 3$$
$$y_2 \quad\quad - y_4 \quad\quad\quad\quad + x_4 = 4$$
$$-300y_1 - 500y_2 + 400y_3 + 500y_4 \quad\quad\quad\quad\quad + P = 0$$

The simplex tableau for this problem is:

	y_1	y_2	y_3	y_4	x_1	x_2	x_3	x_4	P	
x_1	1	0	-1	0	1	0	0	0	0	5
x_2	1	0	0	-1	0	1	0	0	0	7
x_3	0	①	-1	0	0	0	1	0	0	3
x_4	0	1	0	-1	0	0	0	1	0	4
P	-300	-500	400	500	0	0	0	0	1	0

$(-1)R_3 + R_4 \rightarrow R_4$ and $500R_3 + R_5 \rightarrow R_5$

$$\sim \begin{bmatrix} ① & 0 & -1 & 0 & 1 & 0 & 0 & 0 & 0 & | & 5 \\ 1 & 0 & 0 & -1 & 0 & 1 & 0 & 0 & 0 & | & 7 \\ 0 & 1 & -1 & 0 & 0 & 0 & 1 & 0 & 0 & | & 3 \\ 0 & 0 & 1 & -1 & 0 & 0 & -1 & 1 & 0 & | & 1 \\ -300 & 0 & -100 & 500 & 0 & 0 & 500 & 0 & 1 & | & 1500 \end{bmatrix}$$

$(-1)R_1 + R_2 \rightarrow R_2$ and $300R_1 + R_5 \rightarrow R_5$

$$\sim \begin{bmatrix} 1 & 0 & -1 & 0 & 1 & 0 & 0 & 0 & 0 & | & 5 \\ 0 & 0 & 1 & -1 & -1 & 1 & 0 & 0 & 0 & | & 2 \\ 0 & 1 & -1 & 0 & 0 & 0 & 1 & 0 & 0 & | & 3 \\ 0 & 0 & ① & -1 & 0 & 0 & -1 & 1 & 0 & | & 1 \\ 0 & 0 & -400 & 500 & 300 & 300 & 500 & 0 & 1 & | & 3000 \end{bmatrix}$$

$400R_4 + R_5 \rightarrow R_5$, $R_4 + R_1 \rightarrow R_1$, $R_4 + R_3 \rightarrow R_3$, and $(-1)R_4 + R_2 \rightarrow R_2$

$$\sim \begin{bmatrix} 1 & 0 & 0 & -1 & 1 & 0 & -1 & 1 & 0 & | & 6 \\ 1 & 0 & 0 & 0 & -1 & 1 & 1 & -1 & 0 & | & 1 \\ 0 & 1 & 0 & -1 & 0 & 0 & 0 & 1 & 0 & | & 4 \\ 0 & 0 & 1 & -1 & 0 & 0 & -1 & 1 & 0 & | & 1 \\ \hline 0 & 0 & 0 & 100 & 0 & 300 & 100 & 400 & 1 & | & 3400 \end{bmatrix}$$

Thus, bus 300 students from North Division to Washington, 100 from South Division to Central, 400 from South Division to Washington; minimal cost is $3,400.

EXERCISE 6-4

2. (A) We introduce a slack variable s_1 to convert the first inequality ($\leq$) into an equation, and we use a surplus variable s_2 and an artificial variable a_1 to convert the second inequality ($\geq$) into an equation.

The modified problem is: Maximize $P = 3x_1 + 7x_2 - Ma_1$

$$\text{Subject to: } 2x_1 + x_2 + s_1 \qquad\quad = 16$$
$$x_1 + x_2 \quad\ - s_2 + a_1 = 6$$
$$x_1,\ x_2,\ s_1,\ s_2,\ a_1\ \geq\ 0$$

(B) The preliminary simplex tableau for the modified problem is:

$$\begin{array}{cccccc} x_1 & x_2 & s_1 & s_2 & a_1 & P \end{array}$$

$$\begin{bmatrix} 2 & 1 & 1 & 0 & 0 & 0 & | & 16 \\ 1 & 1 & 0 & -1 & 1 & 0 & | & 6 \\ \hline -3 & -7 & 0 & 0 & M & 1 & | & 0 \end{bmatrix} \sim \begin{bmatrix} 2 & 1 & 1 & 0 & 0 & 0 & | & 16 \\ 1 & 1 & 0 & -1 & 1 & 0 & | & 6 \\ \hline -M-3 & -M-7 & 0 & M & 0 & 1 & | & -6M \end{bmatrix}$$

$$(-M)R_2 + R_3 \rightarrow R_3$$

Thus, the initial simplex tableau is:

$$\begin{array}{cccccc} x_1 & x_2 & s_1 & s_2 & a_1 & P \end{array}$$

$$\begin{bmatrix} 2 & 1 & 1 & 0 & 0 & 0 & | & 16 \\ 1 & 1 & 0 & -1 & 1 & 0 & | & 6 \\ \hline -M-3 & -M-7 & 0 & M & 0 & 1 & | & -6M \end{bmatrix}$$

(C) We use the simplex method to solve the modified problem.

$$\begin{array}{c} \\ s_1 \\ a_1 \\ P \end{array} \begin{array}{cccccc} x_1 & x_2 & s_1 & s_2 & a_1 & P \end{array}$$

$$\begin{array}{c} s_1 \\ a_1 \\ P \end{array} \begin{bmatrix} 2 & 1 & 1 & 0 & 0 & 0 & | & 16 \\ 1 & \textcircled{1} & 0 & -1 & 1 & 0 & | & 6 \\ \hline -M-3 & -M-7 & 0 & M & 0 & 1 & | & -6M \end{bmatrix} \begin{array}{l} \frac{16}{1} = 16 \\ \frac{6}{1} = 6 \end{array}$$

$$(-1)R_2 + R_1 \rightarrow R_1 \text{ and } (M+7)R_2 + R_3 \rightarrow R_3$$

$$\sim \begin{bmatrix} 1 & 0 & 1 & \boxed{1} & -1 & 0 & | & 10 \\ 1 & 1 & 0 & -1 & 1 & 0 & | & 6 \\ \hline 4 & 0 & M+7 & -7 & M+7 & 1 & | & 42 \end{bmatrix}$$

$R_1 + R_2 \to R_2$ and $7R_1 + R_3 \to R_3$

$$\sim \begin{bmatrix} 1 & 0 & 1 & 1 & -2 & 0 & | & 10 \\ 2 & 1 & 1 & 0 & 0 & 0 & | & 16 \\ \hline 11 & 0 & M+14 & 0 & M & 1 & | & 112 \end{bmatrix}$$

Thus, the optimal solution of the modified problem is: max $P = 112$ at $x_1 = 0$, $x_2 = 16$, $s_1 = 0$, $s_2 = 10$, $a_1 = 0$.

(D) The optimal solution of the original problem is: max $P = 112$ at $x_1 = 0$, $x_2 = 16$.

4. (A) We introduce the slack variable s_1 and the artificial variable a_1 to obtain the modified problem: Maximize $P = 4x_1 + 3x_2 - Ma_1$

$$\begin{aligned} \text{Subject to: } x_1 + 3x_2 + s_1 &= 24 \\ x_1 + x_2 + a_1 &= 12 \\ x_1, \; x_2, \; s_1, \; a_1 &\geq 0 \end{aligned}$$

(B) The preliminary simplex tableau for the modified problem is:

$$\begin{array}{ccccc} x_1 & x_2 & s_1 & a_1 & P \end{array}$$

$$\begin{bmatrix} 1 & 3 & 1 & 0 & 0 & | & 24 \\ 1 & 1 & 0 & 1 & 0 & | & 12 \\ \hline -4 & -3 & 0 & M & 1 & | & 0 \end{bmatrix} \sim \begin{bmatrix} 1 & 3 & 1 & 0 & 0 & | & 24 \\ 1 & 1 & 0 & 1 & 0 & | & 12 \\ \hline -M-4 & -M-3 & 0 & 0 & 1 & | & -12M \end{bmatrix}$$

$(-M)R_2 + R_3 \to R_3$

Thus, the initial simplex tableau is:

$$\begin{array}{c c c c c c} & x_1 & x_2 & s_1 & a_1 & P \end{array}$$

$$\begin{array}{c} s_1 \\ a_1 \\ P \end{array} \begin{bmatrix} 1 & 3 & 1 & 0 & 0 & | & 24 \\ 1 & 1 & 0 & 1 & 0 & | & 12 \\ \hline -M-4 & -M-3 & 0 & 0 & 1 & | & -12M \end{bmatrix}$$

(C) We use the simplex method to solve the modified problem.

$$\begin{array}{c c c c c c} & x_1 & x_2 & s_1 & a_1 & P \end{array}$$

$$\begin{array}{c} s_1 \\ a_1 \\ P \end{array} \begin{bmatrix} 1 & 3 & 1 & 0 & 0 & | & 24 \\ \boxed{1} & 1 & 0 & 1 & 0 & | & 12 \\ \hline -M-4 & -M-3 & 0 & 0 & 1 & | & -12M \end{bmatrix} \begin{array}{l} \frac{24}{1} = 24 \\ \frac{12}{1} = 12 \end{array}$$

$(-1)R_2 + R_1 \to R_1$ and $(M+4)R_2 + R_3 \to R_3$

$$\sim \begin{bmatrix} 0 & 2 & 1 & -1 & 0 & | & 12 \\ 1 & 1 & 0 & 1 & 0 & | & 12 \\ \hline 0 & 1 & 0 & M+4 & 1 & | & 48 \end{bmatrix}$$

Thus, the optimal solution of the modified problem is max $P = 48$ at $x_1 = 12$, $x_2 = 0$, $s_1 = 12$, $a_1 = 0$.

(D) The optimal solution of the original problem is: max $P = 48$ at $x_1 = 12$, $x_2 = 0$.

6. (A) We introduce slack, surplus, and artificial variables to obtain the modified problem: Maximize $P = 3x_1 + 4x_2 - Ma_1$

Subject to:
$$x_1 - 2x_2 + s_1 \qquad\qquad = 2$$
$$x_1 + x_2 \qquad - s_2 + a_1 = 5$$
$$x_1,\ x_2,\ s_1,\ s_2,\ a_1 \geq 0$$

(B) The preliminary simplex tableau for the modified problem is:

$$
\begin{array}{cccccc}
x_1 & x_2 & s_1 & s_2 & a_1 & P \\
\end{array}
$$

$$
\left[\begin{array}{cccccc|c}
1 & -2 & 1 & 0 & 0 & 0 & 2 \\
1 & 1 & 0 & -1 & 1 & 0 & 5 \\
\hline
-3 & -4 & 0 & 0 & M & 1 & 0
\end{array}\right]
\sim
\left[\begin{array}{cccccc|c}
1 & -2 & 1 & 0 & 0 & 0 & 2 \\
1 & 1 & 0 & -1 & 1 & 0 & 5 \\
\hline
-M-3 & -M-4 & 0 & M & 0 & 1 & -5M
\end{array}\right]
$$

$(-M)R_2 + R_3 \rightarrow R_3$

Thus, the initial simplex tableau is:

$$
\begin{array}{ccccccc}
 & x_1 & x_2 & s_1 & s_2 & a_1 & P \\
\end{array}
$$

$$
\begin{array}{c}
s_1 \\
a_1 \\
\\
P
\end{array}
\left[\begin{array}{cccccc|c}
1 & -2 & 1 & 0 & 0 & 0 & 2 \\
1 & 1 & 0 & -1 & 1 & 0 & 5 \\
\hline
-M-3 & -M-4 & 0 & M & 0 & 1 & -5M
\end{array}\right]
$$

(C) We use the simplex method to solve the modified problem:

$$
\begin{array}{cccccc}
x_1 & x_2 & s_1 & s_2 & a_1 & P \\
\end{array}
$$

$$
\left[\begin{array}{cccccc|c}
1 & -2 & 1 & 0 & 0 & 0 & 2 \\
1 & \textcircled{1} & 0 & -1 & 1 & 0 & 5 \\
\hline
-M-3 & -M-4 & 0 & M & 0 & 1 & -5M
\end{array}\right]
\sim
\left[\begin{array}{cccccc|c}
3 & 0 & 1 & -2 & 2 & 0 & 12 \\
1 & 1 & 0 & -1 & 1 & 0 & 5 \\
\hline
1 & 0 & 0 & -4 & M+4 & 1 & 20
\end{array}\right]
$$

$2R_2 + R_1 \rightarrow R_1$ and $(M+4)R_2 + R_3 \rightarrow R_3$

No optimal solution exists because the elements in the pivot column (the s_2 column) above the dashed line are negative.

(D) No optimal solution exists.

8. (A) We introduce slack, surplus, and artificial variables to obtain the modified problem: Maximize $P = 4x_1 + 6x_2 - Ma_1$

$$\text{Subject to:} \quad x_1 + x_2 + s_1 \qquad\qquad = 2$$
$$3x_1 + 5x_2 \qquad - s_2 + a_1 = 15$$
$$x_1, \; x_2, \; s_1, \; s_2, \; a_1 \geq 0$$

(B) The preliminary simplex tableau for the modified problem is:

$$
\begin{array}{c}
\quad x_1 \quad x_2 \quad s_1 \quad s_2 \quad a_1 \quad P \\
\begin{array}{c} s_1 \\ a_1 \\ P \end{array}
\left[
\begin{array}{cccccc|c}
1 & 1 & 1 & 0 & 0 & 0 & 2 \\
3 & 5 & 0 & -1 & 1 & 0 & 15 \\
\hline
-4 & -6 & 0 & 0 & M & 1 & 0
\end{array}
\right]
\sim
\left[
\begin{array}{cccccc|c}
1 & 1 & 1 & 0 & 0 & 0 & 2 \\
3 & 5 & 0 & -1 & 1 & 0 & 15 \\
\hline
-3M-4 & -5M-6 & 0 & M & 0 & 1 & -15M
\end{array}
\right]
\end{array}
$$

$$(-M)R_2 + R_3 \rightarrow R_3$$

Thus, the initial simplex tableau is:

$$
\begin{array}{c}
\qquad x_1 \qquad\quad x_2 \qquad\quad s_1 \quad s_2 \quad a_1 \quad P \\
\begin{array}{c} s_1 \\ a_1 \\ P \end{array}
\left[
\begin{array}{cccccc|c}
1 & 1 & 1 & 0 & 0 & 0 & 2 \\
3 & 5 & 0 & -1 & 1 & 0 & 15 \\
\hline
-3M-4 & -5M-6 & 0 & M & 0 & 1 & -15M
\end{array}
\right]
\end{array}
$$

(C) Applying the simplex method to the initial tableau, we have:

$$
\left[
\begin{array}{cccccc|c}
1 & \textcircled{1} & 1 & 0 & 0 & 0 & 2 \\
3 & 5 & 0 & -1 & 1 & 0 & 15 \\
\hline
-3M-4 & -5M-6 & 0 & M & 0 & 1 & -15M
\end{array}
\right]
\begin{array}{l} \frac{2}{1} = 2 \\[4pt] \frac{15}{5} = 3 \end{array}
$$

$$(-5)R_1 + R_2 \rightarrow R_2 \text{ and } (5M + 6)R_1 + R_3 \rightarrow R_3$$

$$
\begin{array}{c}
\qquad\quad x_1 \qquad x_2 \qquad s_1 \qquad s_2 \quad a_1 \quad P \\
\sim\begin{array}{c} x_2 \\ a_1 \\ P \end{array}
\left[
\begin{array}{cccccc|c}
1 & 1 & 1 & 0 & 0 & 0 & 2 \\
-2 & 0 & -5 & -1 & 1 & 0 & 5 \\
\hline
2M+2 & 0 & 5M+6 & M & 0 & 1 & -5M+12
\end{array}
\right]
\end{array}
$$

The optimal solution of the modified problem is: max $P = -5M + 12$ at $x_1 = 0$, $x_2 = 2$, $s_1 = 0$, $s_2 = 0$, and $a_1 = 5$.

(D) The original problem does not have an optimal solution, since the artificial variable a_1 in the solution of the modified problem has a nonzero value.

10. To minimize $P = -4x_1 + 16x_2$, we maximize $T = -P = 4x_1 - 16x_2$. Introducing slack, surplus, and artificial variables, we obtain the modified problem:

Maximize $T = 4x_1 - 16x_2 - Ma_1$

Subject to:
$$3x_1 + x_2 + s_1 \qquad\qquad = 28$$
$$x_1 + 2x_2 \qquad - s_2 + a_1 = 16$$
$$x_1,\ x_2,\ s_1,\ s_2,\ a_1 \geq 0$$

The preliminary simplex tableau for this problem is:

$$
\begin{array}{cccccc}
x_1 & x_2 & s_1 & s_2 & a_1 & T \\
\end{array}
$$

$$
\left[
\begin{array}{cccccc|c}
3 & 1 & 1 & 0 & 0 & 0 & 28 \\
1 & 2 & 0 & -1 & 1 & 0 & 16 \\
\hline
-4 & 16 & 0 & 0 & M & 1 & 0
\end{array}
\right]
$$

$$(-M)R_2 + R_3 \rightarrow R_3$$

$$
\begin{array}{c}
\\
s_1 \\
\sim \quad a_1 \\
\\
T
\end{array}
\left[
\begin{array}{cccccc|c}
x_1 & x_2 & s_1 & s_2 & a_1 & T & \\
3 & 1 & 1 & 0 & 0 & 0 & 28 \\
1 & ② & 0 & -1 & 1 & 0 & 16 \\
\hline
-M-4 & -2M+16 & 0 & M & 0 & 1 & -16M
\end{array}
\right]
$$

(This is the initial simplex tableau.) $\dfrac{1}{2}R_2 \rightarrow R_2$

$$
\sim
\left[
\begin{array}{cccccc|c}
3 & 1 & 1 & 0 & 0 & 0 & 28 \\
\frac{1}{2} & ① & 0 & -\frac{1}{2} & \frac{1}{2} & 0 & 8 \\
\hline
-M-4 & -2M+16 & 0 & M & 0 & 1 & -16M
\end{array}
\right]
$$

$$(-1)R_2 + R_1 \rightarrow R_1 \quad \text{and} \quad (2M-16)R_2 + R_3 \rightarrow R_3$$

$$
\sim
\left[
\begin{array}{cccccc|c}
⑤\!\!\!\frac{5}{2} & 0 & 1 & \frac{1}{2} & -\frac{1}{2} & 0 & 20 \\
\frac{1}{2} & 1 & 0 & -\frac{1}{2} & \frac{1}{2} & 0 & 8 \\
\hline
-12 & 0 & 0 & 8 & M-8 & 1 & -128
\end{array}
\right]
\begin{array}{l}
\frac{20}{5/2} = 8 \\[6pt]
\frac{8}{1/2} = 16
\end{array}
$$

$$\frac{2}{5}R_1 \rightarrow R_1$$

$$
\sim
\left[
\begin{array}{cccccc|c}
① & 0 & \frac{2}{5} & \frac{1}{5} & -\frac{1}{5} & 0 & 8 \\
\frac{1}{2} & 1 & 0 & -\frac{1}{2} & \frac{1}{2} & 0 & 8 \\
\hline
-12 & 0 & 0 & 8 & M-8 & 1 & -128
\end{array}
\right]
$$

$$\left(-\frac{1}{2}\right)R_1 + R_2 \rightarrow R_2 \quad \text{and} \quad 12R_1 + R_3 \rightarrow R_3$$

$$\sim \begin{bmatrix} 1 & 0 & \frac{2}{5} & \frac{1}{5} & -\frac{1}{5} & 0 & 8 \\ 0 & 1 & -\frac{1}{5} & -\frac{3}{5} & \frac{3}{5} & 0 & 4 \\ 0 & 0 & \frac{24}{5} & \frac{52}{5} & M - \frac{52}{5} & 1 & -32 \end{bmatrix}$$

Thus, the optimal solution is: max $T = -32$ at $x_1 = 8$, $x_2 = 4$, and min $P = -$max $T = 32$.

The modified problem for maximizing $P = -4x_1 + 16x_2$ subject to the given constraints is: Maximize $P = -4x_1 + 16x_2 - Ma_1$

$$\text{Subject to: } 3x_1 + x_2 + s_1 \qquad = 28$$
$$x_1 + 2x_2 \qquad - s_2 + a_1 = 16$$
$$x_1, \ x_2, \ s_1, \ s_2, \ a_1 \ \geq \ 0$$

The preliminary simplex tableau for the modified problem is:

$$\begin{array}{cccccc} x_1 & x_2 & s_1 & s_2 & a_1 & P \end{array}$$
$$\begin{bmatrix} 3 & 1 & 1 & 0 & 0 & 0 & 28 \\ 1 & 2 & 0 & -1 & 1 & 0 & 16 \\ \hline 4 & -16 & 0 & 0 & M & 1 & 0 \end{bmatrix}$$

$$(-M)R_2 + R_3 \rightarrow R_3$$

$$\begin{array}{ccccccc} & x_1 & x_2 & s_1 & s_2 & a_1 & P \end{array}$$
$$\sim \begin{array}{c} s_1 \\ a_1 \\ \\ P \end{array} \begin{bmatrix} 3 & 1 & 1 & 0 & 0 & 0 & 28 \\ 1 & ② & 0 & -1 & 1 & 0 & 16 \\ \hline -M+4 & -2M-16 & 0 & M & 0 & 1 & -16M \end{bmatrix}$$

$$\frac{1}{2}R_2 \rightarrow R_2$$

$$\sim \begin{bmatrix} 3 & 1 & 1 & 0 & 0 & 0 & 28 \\ \frac{1}{2} & ① & 0 & -\frac{1}{2} & \frac{1}{2} & 0 & 8 \\ \hline -M+4 & -2M-16 & 0 & M & 0 & 1 & -16M \end{bmatrix}$$

$$(-1)R_2 + R_1 \rightarrow R_1 \text{ and } (2M+16)R_2 + R_3 \rightarrow R_3$$

$$\sim \begin{bmatrix} \frac{5}{2} & 0 & 1 & ⓵\!\!\frac{1}{2} & -\frac{1}{2} & 0 & 20 \\ \frac{1}{2} & 1 & 0 & -\frac{1}{2} & \frac{1}{2} & 0 & 8 \\ \hline 12 & 0 & 0 & -8 & M+8 & 1 & 128 \end{bmatrix}$$

$$2R_1 \rightarrow R_1$$

$$\sim \begin{bmatrix} 5 & 0 & 2 & ① & -1 & 0 & 40 \\ \frac{1}{2} & 1 & 0 & -\frac{1}{2} & \frac{1}{2} & 0 & 8 \\ \hline 12 & 0 & 0 & -8 & M+8 & 1 & 128 \end{bmatrix}$$

$$\frac{1}{2}R_1 + R_2 \rightarrow R_2 \text{ and } 8R_1 + R_3 \rightarrow R_3$$

$$\sim \begin{bmatrix} 5 & 0 & 2 & 1 & -1 & 0 & | & 40 \\ 3 & 1 & 1 & 0 & 0 & 0 & | & 28 \\ \hline 52 & 0 & 16 & 0 & M & 1 & | & 448 \end{bmatrix}$$

Thus, max $P = 448$ at $x_1 = 0$, $x_2 = 28$.

12. We introduce slack, surplus, and artificial variables to obtain the modified problem: Maximize $P = 6x_1 + 2x_2 - Ma_1$

$$\text{Subject to:} \quad \begin{array}{rcrcrcrcrcl} x_1 & + & 2x_2 & + & s_1 & & & & & = & 20 \\ 2x_1 & + & x_2 & & & + & s_2 & & & = & 16 \\ x_1 & + & x_2 & & & & & - s_3 + a_1 & = & 9 \end{array}$$
$$x_1, \; x_2, \; s_1, \; s_2, \; s_3, \; a_1 \geq 0$$

The preliminary simplex tableau for this problem is:

$x_1 \quad x_2 \quad s_1 \quad s_2 \quad s_3 \quad a_1 \quad P$

$$\begin{bmatrix} 1 & 2 & 1 & 0 & 0 & 0 & 0 & | & 20 \\ 2 & 1 & 0 & 1 & 0 & 0 & 0 & | & 16 \\ 1 & 1 & 0 & 0 & -1 & 1 & 0 & | & 9 \\ \hdashline -6 & -2 & 0 & 0 & 0 & M & 1 & | & 0 \end{bmatrix}$$

$(-M)R_3 + R_4 \rightarrow R_4$

	x_1	x_2	s_1	s_2	s_3	a_1	P		
s_1	1	2	1	0	0	0	0	20	20
s_2	②	1	0	1	0	0	0	16	8
a_1	1	1	0	0	-1	1	0	9	9
P	$-M-6$	$-M-2$	0	0	M	0	1	$-9M$	

$\dfrac{1}{2}R_2 \rightarrow R_2$

$$\sim \begin{bmatrix} 1 & 2 & 1 & 0 & 0 & 0 & 0 & | & 20 \\ ① & \frac{1}{2} & 0 & \frac{1}{2} & 0 & 0 & 0 & | & 8 \\ 1 & 1 & 0 & 0 & -1 & 1 & 0 & | & 9 \\ \hline -M-6 & -M-2 & 0 & 0 & M & 0 & 1 & | & -9M \end{bmatrix}$$

$(-1)R_2 + R_1 \rightarrow R_1$, $(-1)R_2 + R_3 \rightarrow R_3$, and $(M+6)R_2 + R_4 \rightarrow R_4$

$$\sim \begin{bmatrix} 0 & \frac{3}{2} & 1 & -\frac{1}{2} & 0 & 0 & 0 & | & 12 \\ 1 & ①\frac{1}{2} & 0 & \frac{1}{2} & 0 & 0 & 0 & | & 8 \\ 0 & \frac{1}{2} & 0 & -\frac{1}{2} & -1 & 1 & 0 & | & 1 \\ \hline 0 & -\frac{1}{2}M+1 & 0 & \frac{1}{2}M+3 & M & 0 & 1 & | & -M+48 \end{bmatrix} \begin{matrix} 8 \\ 4 \\ 2 \\ \\ \end{matrix}$$

$2R_3 \rightarrow R_3$

$$\sim \begin{bmatrix} 0 & \frac{3}{2} & 1 & -\frac{1}{2} & 0 & 0 & 0 & | & 12 \\ 1 & \boxed{\frac{1}{2}} & 0 & \frac{1}{2} & 0 & 0 & 0 & | & 8 \\ 0 & 1 & 0 & -1 & -2 & 2 & 0 & | & 2 \\ 0 & -\frac{1}{2}M+1 & 0 & \frac{1}{2}M+3 & M & 0 & 1 & | & -M+48 \end{bmatrix}$$

$$\left(-\frac{3}{2}\right)R_3 + R_1 \to R_1, \quad \left(-\frac{1}{2}\right)R_3 + R_2 \to R_2, \text{ and } \left(\frac{M}{2}-1\right)R_3 + R_4 \to R_4$$

$$\sim \begin{bmatrix} 0 & 1 & 1 & 1 & 3 & -3 & 0 & | & 9 \\ 1 & 0 & 0 & 1 & 1 & -1 & 0 & | & 7 \\ 0 & 1 & 0 & -1 & -2 & 2 & 0 & | & 2 \\ 0 & 0 & 0 & 4 & 2 & M-2 & 1 & | & 46 \end{bmatrix}$$

Optimal solution: max $P = 46$ at $x_1 = 7$, $x_2 = 2$.

14. We introduce surplus and artificial variables to obtain the modified problem: Maximize $P = 5x_1 + 7x_2 + 9x_3 - Ma_1 - Ma_2$

$$\begin{aligned} \text{Subject to: } & x_1 - x_2 + x_3 - s_1 + a_1 = 20 \\ & 2x_1 + x_2 + 5x_3 + a_2 = 35 \\ & x_1, \ x_2, \ x_3, \ s_1, \ a_1, \ a_2 \geq 0 \end{aligned}$$

The preliminary simplex tableau for the modified problem is:

$$\begin{array}{ccccccc} x_1 & x_2 & x_3 & s_1 & a_1 & a_2 & P \end{array}$$
$$\begin{bmatrix} 1 & -1 & 1 & -1 & 1 & 0 & 0 & | & 20 \\ 2 & 1 & 5 & 0 & 0 & 1 & 0 & | & 35 \\ \hline -5 & -7 & -9 & 0 & M & M & 1 & | & 0 \end{bmatrix}$$

$(-M)R_1 + R_3 \to R_3$

$$\sim \begin{bmatrix} 1 & -1 & 1 & -1 & 1 & 0 & 0 & | & 20 \\ 2 & 1 & 5 & 0 & 0 & 1 & 0 & | & 35 \\ \hline -M-5 & M-7 & -M-9 & M & 0 & M & 1 & | & -20M \end{bmatrix}$$

$(-M)R_2 + R_3 \to R_3$

$$\sim \begin{bmatrix} 1 & -1 & 1 & -1 & 1 & 0 & 0 & | & 20 & \rvert 20 \\ 2 & 1 & \boxed{5} & 0 & 0 & 1 & 0 & | & 35 & \rvert 7 \\ \hline -3M-5 & -7 & -6M-9 & M & 0 & 0 & 1 & | & -55M \end{bmatrix}$$

$\frac{1}{5}R_2 \to R_2$

$$\sim \begin{bmatrix} 1 & -1 & 1 & -1 & 1 & 0 & 0 & | & 20 \\ \frac{2}{5} & \frac{1}{5} & \boxed{1} & 0 & 0 & \frac{1}{5} & 0 & | & 7 \\ \hline -3M-5 & -7 & -6M-9 & M & 0 & 0 & 1 & | & -55M \end{bmatrix}$$

$(-1)R_2 + R_1 \to R_1$ and $(6M+9)R_2 + R_3 \to R_3$

$$\sim \left[\begin{array}{ccccccc|c} \frac{3}{5} & -\frac{6}{5} & 0 & -1 & 1 & -\frac{1}{5} & 0 & 13 \\ \boxed{\frac{2}{5}} & \frac{1}{5} & 1 & 0 & 0 & \frac{1}{5} & 0 & 7 \\ \hline -\left(\frac{3M+7}{5}\right) & \frac{6M-26}{5} & 0 & M & 0 & \frac{6M+9}{5} & 1 & -13M+63 \end{array}\right]$$

$$\frac{5}{2}R_2 \;\to\; R_2$$

$$\sim \left[\begin{array}{ccccccc|c} \frac{3}{5} & -\frac{6}{5} & 0 & -1 & 1 & -\frac{1}{5} & 0 & 13 \\ \boxed{1} & 2 & \frac{5}{2} & 0 & 0 & \frac{1}{2} & 0 & 17.5 \\ \hline -\left(\frac{3M+7}{5}\right) & \frac{6M-26}{5} & 0 & M & 0 & \frac{6M+9}{5} & 1 & -13M+63 \end{array}\right]$$

$$\left(-\frac{3}{5}\right)R_2 + R_1 \;\to\; R_1 \quad \text{and} \quad \left(\frac{3M+7}{5}\right)R_2 + R_3 \;\to\; R_3$$

$$\sim \left[\begin{array}{ccccccc|c} 1 & -\frac{12}{5} & -\frac{3}{2} & -1 & 1 & -\frac{1}{2} & 0 & 2.5 \\ 1 & 2 & \frac{5}{2} & 0 & 0 & \frac{1}{2} & 0 & 17.5 \\ \hline 0 & \frac{12M-12}{5} & \frac{3M+7}{2} & M & 0 & \frac{15M+25}{5} & 1 & \frac{-5M+175}{2} \end{array}\right]$$

Since $a_2 \neq 0$, there is no optimal solution.

16. We will maximize $P = -C = 3x_1 - 15x_2 + 4x_3$ subject to the given constraints. Introduce slack, surplus, and artificial variables to obtain the modified problem:

Maximize $P = 3x_1 - 15x_2 + 4x_3 - Ma_1 - Ma_2$

Subject to:
$$\begin{aligned}
2x_1 + x_2 + 3x_3 + s_1 &= 24 \\
x_1 + 2x_2 + x_3 - s_2 + a_1 &= 6 \\
x_1 - 3x_2 + x_3 + a_2 &= 2 \\
x_1,\ x_2,\ x_3,\ s_1,\ s_2,\ a_1,\ a_2 &\geq 0
\end{aligned}$$

The preliminary simplex tableau for the modified problem is:

x_1	x_2	x_3	s_1	s_2	a_1	a_2	P	
2	1	3	1	0	0	0	0	24
1	2	1	0	-1	1	0	0	6
1	-3	1	0	0	0	1	0	2
-3	15	-4	0	0	M	M	1	0

$$(-M)R_2 + R_4 \;\to\; R_4$$

$$\sim \left[\begin{array}{cccccccc|c}
2 & 1 & 3 & 1 & 0 & 0 & 0 & 0 & 24 \\
1 & 2 & 1 & 0 & -1 & 1 & 0 & 0 & 6 \\
1 & -3 & 1 & 0 & 0 & 0 & 1 & 0 & 2 \\
\hline
-M-3 & -2M+15 & -M-4 & 0 & M & 0 & M & 1 & -6M
\end{array}\right]$$

$(-M)R_3 + R_4 \to R_4$

$$\sim \left[\begin{array}{cccccccc|c}
2 & 1 & 3 & 1 & 0 & 0 & 0 & 0 & 24 \\
1 & 2 & 1 & 0 & -1 & 1 & 0 & 0 & 6 \\
1 & -3 & \textcircled{1} & 0 & 0 & 0 & 1 & 0 & 2 \\
\hline
-2M-3 & M+15 & -2M-4 & 0 & M & 0 & 0 & 1 & -8M
\end{array}\right]\begin{array}{l} 8 \\ 6 \\ 2 \end{array}$$

$(-3)R_3 + R_1 \to R_1$, $(-1)R_3 + R_2 \to R_2$, and $(2M+4)R_3 + R_4 \to R_4$

$$\sim \left[\begin{array}{cccccccc|c}
-1 & 10 & 0 & 1 & 0 & 0 & -3 & 0 & 18 \\
0 & \textcircled{5} & 0 & 0 & -1 & 1 & -1 & 0 & 4 \\
1 & -3 & 1 & 0 & 0 & 0 & 1 & 0 & 2 \\
\hline
1 & -5M+3 & 0 & 0 & M & 0 & 2M+4 & 1 & -4M+8
\end{array}\right]$$

$\dfrac{1}{5}R_2 \to R_2$

$$\sim \left[\begin{array}{cccccccc|c}
-1 & 10 & 0 & 1 & 0 & 0 & -3 & 0 & 18 \\
0 & \textcircled{1} & 0 & 0 & -\frac{1}{5} & \frac{1}{5} & -\frac{1}{5} & 0 & \frac{4}{5} \\
1 & -3 & 1 & 0 & 0 & 0 & 1 & 0 & 2 \\
\hline
1 & -5M+3 & 0 & 0 & M & 0 & 2M+4 & 1 & -4M+8
\end{array}\right]$$

$(-10)R_2 + R_1 \to R_1$, $3R_2 + R_3 \to R_3$, and $(5M-3)R_2 + R_4 \to R_4$

$$\sim \left[\begin{array}{cccccccc|c}
-1 & 0 & 0 & 1 & 2 & -2 & -1 & 0 & \frac{4}{5} \\
0 & 1 & 0 & 0 & -\frac{1}{5} & \frac{1}{5} & -\frac{1}{5} & 0 & \frac{4}{5} \\
1 & 0 & 1 & 0 & -\frac{3}{5} & \frac{3}{5} & \frac{2}{5} & 0 & \frac{22}{5} \\
\hline
1 & 0 & 0 & 0 & \frac{3}{5} & M-\frac{3}{5} & M+\frac{23}{5} & 1 & \frac{28}{5}
\end{array}\right]$$

Thus, $\min C = -\dfrac{28}{5}$ at $x_1 = 0$, $x_2 = \dfrac{4}{5}$, and $x_3 = \dfrac{22}{5}$.

18. We introduce a slack and an artificial variable to obtain the modified problem: Maximize $P = 3x_1 + 6x_2 + 2x_3 - Ma_1$

$$\begin{aligned}
\text{Subject to: } \quad 2x_1 + 2x_2 + 3x_3 + s_1 \quad\;\;\, &= 12 \\
2x_1 - 2x_2 + x_3 \qquad\quad + a_1 &= 0 \\
x_1,\ x_2,\ x_3,\ s_1,\ a_1 &\geq 0
\end{aligned}$$

The preliminary simplex tableau for the modified problem is:

$$
\begin{array}{c}
\quad\;\; x_1 \quad x_2 \quad x_3 \quad s_1 \quad a_1 \quad P \\
\begin{array}{c} s_1 \\ a_1 \\ P \end{array}
\left[
\begin{array}{ccccccc|c}
2 & 2 & 3 & 1 & 0 & 0 & & 12 \\
2 & -2 & 1 & 0 & 1 & 0 & & 0 \\
\hline
-3 & -6 & -2 & 0 & M & 1 & & 0
\end{array}
\right]
\begin{array}{c} 6 \\ 0 \end{array}
\end{array}
$$

$$
\sim
\left[
\begin{array}{cccccc|c}
2 & 2 & 3 & 1 & 0 & 0 & 12 \\
②\, & -2 & 1 & 0 & 1 & 0 & 0 \\
\hline
-2M-3 & 2M-6 & -M-2 & 0 & 0 & 1 & 0
\end{array}
\right]
$$

$$(-M)R_2 + R_3 \to R_3 \qquad\qquad \tfrac{1}{2}R_2 \to R_2$$

$$
\sim
\left[
\begin{array}{cccccc|c}
2 & 2 & 3 & 1 & 0 & 0 & 12 \\
①\, & -1 & \tfrac{1}{2} & 0 & \tfrac{1}{2} & 0 & 0 \\
\hline
-2M-3 & 2M-6 & -M-2 & 0 & 0 & 1 & 0
\end{array}
\right]
$$

$$(-2)R_2 + R_1 \to R_1 \text{ and } (2M+3)R_2 + R_3 \to R_3$$

$$
\sim
\left[
\begin{array}{cccccc|c}
0 & ④\, & 2 & 1 & -1 & 0 & 12 \\
1 & -1 & \tfrac{1}{2} & 0 & \tfrac{1}{2} & 0 & 0 \\
\hline
0 & -9 & -\tfrac{1}{2} & 0 & M+\tfrac{3}{2} & 1 & 0
\end{array}
\right]
$$

$$\tfrac{1}{4}R_1 \to R_1$$

$$
\sim
\left[
\begin{array}{cccccc|c}
0 & ①\, & \tfrac{1}{2} & \tfrac{1}{4} & -\tfrac{1}{4} & 0 & 3 \\
1 & -1 & \tfrac{1}{2} & 0 & \tfrac{1}{2} & 0 & 0 \\
\hline
0 & -9 & -\tfrac{1}{2} & 0 & M+\tfrac{3}{2} & 1 & 0
\end{array}
\right]
$$

$$R_1 + R_2 \to R_2 \text{ and } 9R_1 + R_3 \to R_3$$

$$
\sim
\left[
\begin{array}{cccccc|c}
0 & 1 & \tfrac{1}{2} & \tfrac{1}{4} & -\tfrac{1}{4} & 0 & 3 \\
1 & 0 & 1 & \tfrac{1}{4} & \tfrac{1}{4} & 0 & 3 \\
\hline
0 & 0 & 4 & \tfrac{9}{4} & M-\tfrac{3}{4} & 0 & 27
\end{array}
\right]
$$

Thus, max $P = 27$ at $x_1 = 3$, $x_2 = 3$, and $x_3 = 0$.

20. We introduce slack, surplus, and artificial variables to obtain the
modified problem: Maximize $P = 5x_1 + 2x_2 + 9x_3 - Ma_1$

$$
\begin{aligned}
\text{Subject to: } 2x_1 + 4x_2 + x_3 + s_1 &= 150 \\
3x_1 + 3x_2 + x_3 + s_2 &= 90 \\
-x_1 + 5x_2 + x_3 - s_3 + a_1 &= 120 \\
x_1,\ x_2,\ x_3,\ s_1,\ s_2,\ s_3,\ a_1 &\ge 0
\end{aligned}
$$

The preliminary simplex tableau for the modified problem is:

$$
\begin{array}{c}
x_1 \quad x_2 \quad x_3 \quad s_1 \quad s_2 \quad s_3 \quad a_1 \quad P \\
\left[
\begin{array}{cccccccc|c}
2 & 4 & 1 & 1 & 0 & 0 & 0 & 0 & 150 \\
3 & 3 & 1 & 0 & 1 & 0 & 0 & 0 & 90 \\
-1 & 5 & 1 & 0 & 0 & -1 & 1 & 0 & 120 \\
\hline
-5 & -2 & -9 & 0 & 0 & 0 & M & 1 & 0
\end{array}
\right]
\end{array}
$$

$$(-M)R_3 + R_4 \to R_4$$

$$\sim \quad \begin{array}{c} \\ s_1 \\ s_2 \\ a_1 \\ P \end{array} \begin{array}{cccccccc} x_1 & x_2 & x_3 & s_1 & s_2 & s_3 & a_1 & P \\ \left[\begin{array}{cccccccc|c} 2 & 4 & 1 & 1 & 0 & 0 & 0 & 0 & 150 \\ 3 & 3 & 1 & 0 & 1 & 0 & 0 & 0 & 90 \\ -1 & ⑤ & 1 & 0 & 0 & -1 & 1 & 0 & 120 \\ \hdashline M-5 & -5M-2 & -M-9 & 0 & 0 & M & 0 & 1 & -120M \end{array}\right] \end{array}$$

$$\frac{1}{5}R_3 \rightarrow R_3$$

$$\sim \quad \left[\begin{array}{cccccccc|c} 2 & 4 & 1 & 1 & 0 & 0 & 0 & 0 & 150 \\ 3 & 3 & 1 & 0 & 1 & 0 & 0 & 0 & 90 \\ -\frac{1}{5} & ① & \frac{1}{5} & 0 & 0 & -\frac{1}{5} & \frac{1}{5} & 0 & 24 \\ \hline M-5 & -5M-2 & -M-9 & 0 & 0 & M & 0 & 1 & -120M \end{array}\right]$$

$$(-4)R_3 + R_1 \rightarrow R_1, \quad (-3)R_3 + R_2 \rightarrow R_2, \quad \text{and} \quad (5M+2)R_3 + R_4 \rightarrow R_4$$

$$\sim \quad \left[\begin{array}{cccccccc|c} \frac{14}{5} & 0 & \frac{1}{5} & 1 & 0 & \frac{4}{5} & -\frac{4}{5} & 0 & 54 \\ \frac{18}{5} & 0 & ②\!\!/\!\!⑤ & 0 & 1 & \frac{3}{5} & -\frac{3}{5} & 0 & 18 \\ -\frac{1}{5} & 1 & \frac{1}{5} & 0 & 0 & -\frac{1}{5} & \frac{1}{5} & 0 & 24 \\ \hline -\frac{27}{5} & 0 & -\frac{43}{5} & 0 & 0 & -\frac{2}{5} & M+\frac{2}{5} & 1 & 48 \end{array}\right]$$

$$\frac{5}{2}R_2 \rightarrow R_2$$

$$\sim \quad \left[\begin{array}{cccccccc|c} \frac{14}{5} & 0 & \frac{1}{5} & 1 & 0 & \frac{4}{5} & -\frac{4}{5} & 0 & 54 \\ 9 & 0 & ① & 0 & \frac{5}{2} & \frac{3}{2} & -\frac{3}{2} & 0 & 45 \\ -\frac{1}{5} & 1 & \frac{1}{5} & 0 & 0 & -\frac{1}{5} & \frac{1}{5} & 0 & 24 \\ \hline -\frac{27}{5} & 0 & -\frac{43}{5} & 0 & 0 & -\frac{2}{5} & M+\frac{2}{5} & 1 & 48 \end{array}\right]$$

$$\left(-\frac{1}{5}\right)R_2 + R_1 \rightarrow R_1, \quad \left(-\frac{1}{5}\right)R_2 + R_3 \rightarrow R_3, \quad \text{and} \quad \frac{43}{5}R_2 + R_4 \rightarrow R_4$$

$$\sim \quad \left[\begin{array}{cccccccc|c} 1 & 0 & 0 & 1 & -\frac{1}{2} & \frac{1}{2} & -\frac{1}{2} & 0 & 45 \\ 9 & 0 & 1 & 0 & \frac{5}{2} & \frac{3}{2} & -\frac{3}{2} & 0 & 24 \\ -2 & 1 & 0 & 0 & -\frac{1}{2} & \frac{1}{2} & -\frac{1}{2} & 0 & 15 \\ \hline 72 & 0 & 0 & 0 & \frac{43}{2} & \frac{25}{2} & M-\frac{25}{2} & 1 & 435 \end{array}\right]$$

Optimal solution: max $P = 435$ at $x_1 = 0$, $x_2 = 15$, and $x_3 = 45$.

22. We introduce slack, surplus, and artificial variables to obtain the modified problem:

Maximize $P = 2x_1 + 4x_2 + x_3 - Ma_1 - Ma_2$

Subject to:
$$\begin{aligned} 2x_1 + 3x_2 + 5x_3 + s_1 \qquad\qquad\qquad &= 280 \\ 2x_1 + 2x_2 + x_3 \qquad - s_2 \qquad + a_1 \qquad &= 140 \\ 2x_1 + x_2 \qquad\qquad\qquad - s_3 \qquad + a_2 &= 150 \\ x_1, \ x_2, \ x_3, \ s_1, \ s_2, \ s_3, \ a_1, \ a_2 &\geq 0 \end{aligned}$$

The preliminary simplex tableau for the modified problem is:

$$\begin{array}{ccccccccc} x_1 & x_2 & x_3 & s_1 & s_2 & s_3 & a_1 & a_2 & P \end{array}$$

$$\left[\begin{array}{ccccccccc|c} 2 & 3 & 5 & 1 & 0 & 0 & 0 & 0 & 0 & 280 \\ 2 & 2 & 1 & 0 & -1 & 0 & 1 & 0 & 0 & 140 \\ 2 & 1 & 0 & 0 & 0 & -1 & 0 & 1 & 0 & 150 \\ \hdashline -2 & -4 & -1 & 0 & 0 & 0 & M & M & 1 & 0 \end{array}\right]$$

$(-M)R_2 + R_4 \rightarrow R_4$

$$\sim\left[\begin{array}{ccccccccc|c} 2 & 3 & 5 & 1 & 0 & 0 & 0 & 0 & 0 & 280 \\ 2 & 2 & 1 & 0 & -1 & 0 & 1 & 0 & 0 & 140 \\ 2 & 1 & 0 & 0 & 0 & -1 & 0 & 1 & 0 & 150 \\ \hdashline -2M-2 & -2M-4 & -M-1 & 0 & M & 0 & 0 & M & 1 & -140M \end{array}\right]$$

$(-M)R_3 + R_4 \rightarrow R_4$

$$\sim\left[\begin{array}{ccccccccc|c} 2 & 3 & 5 & 1 & 0 & 0 & 0 & 0 & 0 & 280 \\ ②\,2 & 2 & 1 & 0 & -1 & 0 & 1 & 0 & 0 & 140 \\ 2 & 1 & 0 & 0 & 0 & -1 & 0 & 1 & 0 & 150 \\ \hdashline -4M-2 & -3M-4 & -M-1 & 0 & M & M & 0 & 0 & 1 & -290M \end{array}\right]$$

$\dfrac{1}{2}R_2 \rightarrow R_2$

$$\sim\left[\begin{array}{ccccccccc|c} 2 & 3 & 5 & 1 & 0 & 0 & 0 & 0 & 0 & 280 \\ ①\,1 & 1 & \frac{1}{2} & 0 & -\frac{1}{2} & 0 & \frac{1}{2} & 0 & 0 & 70 \\ 2 & 1 & 0 & 0 & 0 & -1 & 0 & 1 & 0 & 150 \\ \hline -4M-2 & -3M-4 & -M-1 & 0 & M & M & 0 & 0 & 1 & -290M \end{array}\right]$$

$(-2)R_2 + R_1 \rightarrow R_1$, $(-2)R_2 + R_3 \rightarrow R_3$, and $(4M+2)R_2 + R_4 \rightarrow R_4$

$$\sim\left[\begin{array}{ccccccccc|c} 0 & 1 & 4 & 1 & 1 & 0 & 1 & 0 & 0 & 140 \\ 1 & 1 & \frac{1}{2} & 0 & -\frac{1}{2} & 0 & \frac{1}{2} & 0 & 0 & 70 \\ 0 & -1 & -1 & 0 & ①\,1 & -1 & -1 & 1 & 0 & 10 \\ \hline 0 & -M-2 & M & 0 & -M-1 & M & 2M+1 & 0 & 1 & -10M+140 \end{array}\right]$$

$(-1)R_3 + R_1 \rightarrow R_1$, $\dfrac{1}{2}R_3 + R_2 \rightarrow R_2$, and $(M+1)R_3 + R_4 \rightarrow R_4$

$$\sim\left[\begin{array}{ccccccccc|c} 0 & ②\,2 & 5 & 1 & 0 & 1 & 2 & -1 & 0 & 130 \\ 1 & \frac{1}{2} & 0 & 0 & 0 & -\frac{1}{2} & 0 & \frac{1}{2} & 0 & 75 \\ 0 & -1 & -1 & 0 & 1 & -1 & -1 & 1 & 0 & 10 \\ \hline 0 & -3 & -1 & 0 & 0 & -1 & M & M+1 & 1 & 150 \end{array}\right]$$

$\dfrac{1}{2}R_1 \rightarrow R_1$

$$\sim \begin{bmatrix} 0 & ① & \frac{5}{2} & \frac{1}{2} & 0 & \frac{1}{2} & 2 & -\frac{1}{2} & 0 & | & 65 \\ 1 & \frac{1}{2} & 0 & 0 & 0 & -\frac{1}{2} & 0 & \frac{1}{2} & 0 & | & 75 \\ 0 & -1 & -1 & 0 & 1 & -1 & -1 & 1 & 0 & | & 10 \\ 0 & -3 & -1 & 0 & 0 & -1 & M & M+1 & 1 & | & 150 \end{bmatrix}$$

$\left(-\frac{1}{2}\right)R_1 + R_2 \to R_2,\; R_1 + R_3 \to R_3,$ and $3R_1 + R_4 \to R_4$

$$\sim \begin{bmatrix} 0 & 1 & \frac{5}{2} & \frac{1}{2} & 0 & \frac{1}{2} & 1 & -\frac{1}{2} & 0 & | & 65 \\ 1 & 0 & -5 & -1 & 0 & -\frac{3}{4} & -\frac{1}{2} & \frac{3}{4} & 0 & | & \frac{85}{2} \\ 0 & 0 & \frac{3}{2} & \frac{1}{2} & 1 & -\frac{1}{2} & 0 & \frac{1}{2} & 0 & | & 75 \\ 0 & 0 & \frac{13}{2} & \frac{3}{2} & 0 & -\frac{1}{2} & M+\frac{3}{2} & M-\frac{1}{2} & 1 & | & 345 \end{bmatrix}$$

Optimal solution: max $P = 345$ at $x_1 = 42.5$, $x_2 = 65$, and $x_3 = 0$.

24. (A) Refer to Problem 6.
The graph of the feasible region
$P = 3x_1 + 4x_2$ does not have a
maximum value by Theorem 2(B)
in Section 5.2.

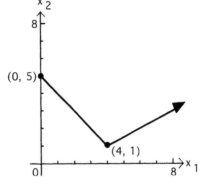

(B) Refer to Problem 8.
The graph of the feasible region
$P = 4x_1 + 6x_2$ does not have a
maximum value, by Theorem 2(C)
in Section 5.2.

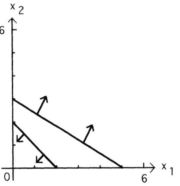

26. Observe that the first constraint can be written as $-x_1 + 2x_2 - x_3 \le 8$.
We will maximize $P = 7x_1 - 5x_2 + 2x_3$

$$\begin{aligned} \text{Subject to: } -x_1 + 2x_2 - x_3 + s_1 &= 8 \\ x_1 - x_2 + x_3 + s_2 &= 10 \\ x_1,\; x_2,\; x_3,\; s_1,\; s_2 &\ge 0 \end{aligned}$$

where s_1, s_2 are slack variables.

The simplex tableau for this problem is:

$$\begin{array}{c} & x_1 & x_2 & x_3 & s_1 & s_2 & P \\ \begin{array}{c} s_1 \\ s_2 \\ P \end{array} & \left[\begin{array}{cccccc|c} -1 & 2 & -1 & 1 & 0 & 0 & 8 \\ ① & -1 & 1 & 0 & 1 & 0 & 10 \\ \hline -7 & 5 & -2 & 0 & 0 & 1 & 0 \end{array}\right] \end{array} \sim \left[\begin{array}{cccccc|c} 0 & ① & 0 & 1 & 1 & 0 & 18 \\ 1 & -1 & 1 & 0 & 1 & 0 & 10 \\ \hline 0 & -2 & 5 & 0 & 7 & 1 & 70 \end{array}\right]$$

$\quad R_1 + R_2 \to R_2$ and $7R_2 + R_3 \to R_3 \qquad R_1 + R_2 \to R_2$ and $2R_1 + R_3 \to R_3$

$$\sim \begin{bmatrix} 0 & 1 & 0 & 1 & 1 & 0 & | & 18 \\ 1 & 0 & 1 & 1 & 2 & 0 & | & 28 \\ \hdashline 0 & 0 & 5 & 2 & 9 & 1 & | & 106 \end{bmatrix}$$

Thus, max $P = 106$ at $x_1 = 28$, $x_2 = 18$, and $x_3 = 0$.

28. We will maximize $P = -C = 5x_1 - 10x_2 - 15x_3$

$$\begin{aligned} \text{Subject to: } 2x_1 + 3x_2 + x_3 &\le 24 \\ x_1 - 2x_2 - 2x_3 &\ge 1 \\ x_1, \ x_2, \ x_3 &\ge 0 \end{aligned}$$

We introduce slack, surplus, and artificial variables to obtain the modified problem: Maximize $P = 5x_1 - 10x_2 - 15x_3 - Ma_1$

$$\begin{aligned} \text{Subject to: } 2x_1 + 3x_2 + x_3 + s_1 &= 24 \\ x_1 - 2x_2 - 2x_3 - s_2 + a_1 &= 1 \\ x_1, \ x_2, \ x_3, \ s_1, \ s_2, \ a_1 &\ge 0 \end{aligned}$$

The preliminary simplex tableau for the modified problem is:

x_1	x_2	x_3	s_1	s_2	a_1	P	
2	3	1	1	0	0	0	24
1	-2	-2	0	-1	1	0	1
-5	10	10	0	0	M	1	0

$(-M)R_2 + R_3 \to R_3$

$$\sim \begin{bmatrix} 2 & 3 & 1 & 1 & 0 & 0 & 0 & | & 24 \\ ① & -2 & -2 & 0 & -1 & 1 & 0 & | & 1 \\ \hline -M-5 & 2M+10 & 2M+15 & 0 & M & 0 & 1 & | & -M \end{bmatrix}$$

$(-2)R_2 + R_1 \to R_1$ and $(M+5)R_2 + R_3 \to R_3$

$$\sim \begin{bmatrix} 0 & 7 & 5 & 1 & ② & -2 & 0 & | & 22 \\ 1 & -2 & -2 & 0 & -1 & 1 & 0 & | & 1 \\ \hline 0 & 0 & 5 & 0 & -5 & M+5 & 1 & | & 5 \end{bmatrix}$$

$\dfrac{1}{2}R_1 \to R_1$

$$\sim \begin{bmatrix} 0 & \frac{7}{2} & \frac{5}{2} & \frac{1}{2} & ① & -1 & 0 & | & 11 \\ 1 & -2 & -2 & 0 & -1 & 1 & 0 & | & 1 \\ \hline 0 & 0 & 5 & 0 & -5 & M+5 & 1 & | & 5 \end{bmatrix}$$

$R_1 + R_2 \to R_2$ and $5R_1 + R_3 \to R_3$

$$\sim \begin{bmatrix} 0 & \frac{7}{2} & \frac{5}{2} & \frac{1}{2} & 1 & -1 & 0 & | & 11 \\ 1 & \frac{3}{2} & \frac{1}{2} & \frac{1}{2} & 0 & 0 & 0 & | & 12 \\ \hdashline 0 & \frac{35}{2} & \frac{35}{2} & \frac{5}{2} & 0 & M & 1 & | & 60 \end{bmatrix}$$

Thus, min $C = 60$ at $x_1 = 12$, $x_2 = 0$, and $x_3 = 0$.

30. We maximize $P = 8x_1 + 2x_2 - 10x_3$
Subject to: $\quad x_1 + x_2 - 3x_3 \le 6$
$\quad\quad -4x_1 + x_2 - 2x_3 \ge 7$
$\quad\quad\quad x_1, \; x_2, \; x_3 \ge 0$

We introduce slack, surplus, and artificial variables to obtain the modified problem: Maximize $P = 8x_1 + 2x_2 - 10x_3 - Ma_1$

Subject to: $x_1 + x_2 - 3x_2 + s_1 \quad\quad = 6$
$\quad -4x_1 + x_2 - 2x_2 \quad - s_2 + a_1 = 7$
$\quad\quad x_1, \; x_2, \; x_3, \; s_1, \; s_2, \; a_1 \ge 0$

The preliminary simplex tableau for the modified problem is:

$$
\begin{array}{c}
\begin{array}{ccccccc} x_1 & x_2 & x_3 & s_1 & s_2 & a_1 & P \end{array} \\
\begin{array}{c} s_1 \\ s_2 \\ \end{array}
\left[\begin{array}{ccccccc|c}
1 & 1 & -3 & 1 & 0 & 0 & 0 & 6 \\
-4 & 1 & -2 & 0 & -1 & 1 & 0 & 7 \\
-8 & -2 & 10 & 0 & 0 & M & 1 & 0
\end{array}\right]
\end{array}
$$

$(-M)R_2 + R_3 \rightarrow R_3$

$$
\sim
\left[\begin{array}{ccccccc|c}
1 & ① & -3 & 1 & 0 & 0 & 0 & 6 \\
-4 & 1 & -2 & 0 & -1 & 1 & 0 & 7 \\
4M-8 & -M-2 & 2M+10 & 0 & M & 0 & 1 & -7M
\end{array}\right]
$$

$(-1)R_1 + R_2 \rightarrow R_2$ and $(M+2)R_1 + R_3 \rightarrow R_3$

$$
\sim
\left[\begin{array}{ccccccc|c}
1 & 1 & -3 & 1 & 0 & 0 & 0 & 6 \\
-5 & 0 & ① & -1 & -1 & 1 & 0 & 1 \\
5M-6 & 0 & -M+4 & M+2 & M & 0 & 1 & -M+12
\end{array}\right]
$$

$3R_2 + R_1 \rightarrow R_1$ and $(M-4)R_2 + R_3 \rightarrow R_3$

$$
\sim
\left[\begin{array}{ccccccc|c}
-14 & 1 & 0 & -2 & -3 & 3 & 0 & 9 \\
-5 & 0 & 1 & -1 & -1 & 1 & 0 & 1 \\
14 & 0 & 0 & 6 & 4 & M-4 & 1 & 8
\end{array}\right]
$$

Thus, max $P = 8$ at $x_1 = 0$, $x_2 = 9$, and $x_3 = 1$.

32. We will maximize $P = -C = -10x_1 - 12x_2 - 28x_3$
Subject to: $3x_1 - x_2 - 4x_3 \le 10$
$\quad 4x_1 + 2x_2 + 3x_3 \ge 20$
$\quad\quad x_1, \; x_2, \; x_3 \ge 0$

We introduce slack, surplus, and artificial variables to obtain the modified problem: Maximize $P = -10x_1 - 12x_2 - 28x_3 - Ma_1$

Subject to: $3x_1 - x_2 - 4x_3 + s_1 \quad\quad = 10$
$\quad 4x_1 + 2x_2 + 3x_3 \quad - s_2 + a_1 = 20$
$\quad\quad x_1, \; x_2, \; x_3, \; s_1, \; s_2, \; a_1 \ge 0$

The preliminary simplex tableau for the modified problem is:

$$
\begin{array}{c}
\\ s_1 \\ s_2 \\ \\
\end{array}
\begin{array}{c}
\begin{array}{ccccccc} x_1 & x_2 & x_3 & s_1 & s_2 & a_1 & P \end{array} \\
\left[\begin{array}{ccccccc|c}
3 & -1 & -4 & 1 & 0 & 0 & 0 & 10 \\
4 & 2 & 3 & 0 & -1 & 1 & 0 & 20 \\ \hline
10 & 12 & 28 & 0 & 0 & M & 1 & 0
\end{array}\right]
\end{array}
$$

$(-M)R_2 + R_3 \to R_3$

$$
\sim \left[\begin{array}{ccccccc|c}
\textcircled{3} & -1 & -4 & 1 & 0 & 0 & 0 & 10 \\
4 & 2 & 3 & 0 & -1 & 1 & 0 & 20 \\ \hline
-4M + 10 & -2M + 12 & -3M + 28 & 0 & M & 0 & 1 & -20M
\end{array}\right]
$$

$\frac{1}{3}R_1 \to R_1$

$$
\sim \left[\begin{array}{ccccccc|c}
\textcircled{1} & -\frac{1}{3} & -\frac{4}{3} & \frac{1}{3} & 0 & 0 & 0 & \frac{10}{3} \\
4 & 2 & 3 & 0 & -1 & 1 & 0 & 20 \\ \hline
-4M + 10 & -2M + 12 & -3M + 28 & 0 & M & 0 & 1 & -20M
\end{array}\right]
$$

$(-4)R_1 + R_2 \to R_2$ and $(4M - 10)R_1 + R_3 \to R_3$

$$
\sim \left[\begin{array}{ccccccc|c}
1 & -\frac{1}{3} & -\frac{4}{3} & \frac{1}{3} & 0 & 0 & 0 & \frac{10}{3} \\
0 & \frac{10}{3} & \textcircled{$\frac{25}{3}$} & -\frac{4}{3} & -1 & 1 & 0 & \frac{20}{3} \\ \hline
0 & \frac{-10M+46}{3} & \frac{-25M+124}{3} & \frac{4M-10}{3} & M & 0 & 1 & \frac{-20M-100}{3}
\end{array}\right]
$$

$\frac{3}{25}R_2 \to R_2$

$$
\sim \left[\begin{array}{ccccccc|c}
1 & -\frac{1}{3} & -\frac{4}{3} & \frac{1}{3} & 0 & 0 & 0 & \frac{10}{3} \\
0 & \frac{2}{5} & \textcircled{1} & -\frac{4}{25} & -\frac{3}{25} & \frac{3}{25} & 0 & \frac{4}{5} \\ \hline
0 & \frac{-10M+46}{3} & \frac{-25M+124}{3} & \frac{4M-10}{3} & M & 0 & 1 & \frac{-20M-100}{3}
\end{array}\right]
$$

$\frac{4}{3}R_2 + R_1 \to R_1$ and $\left(\frac{25M - 124}{3}\right)R_2 + R_3 \to R_3$

$$
\sim \left[\begin{array}{ccccccc|c}
1 & \frac{1}{5} & 0 & \frac{3}{25} & -\frac{4}{25} & \frac{4}{25} & 0 & \frac{22}{5} \\
0 & \textcircled{$\frac{2}{5}$} & 1 & -\frac{4}{25} & -\frac{3}{25} & \frac{3}{25} & 0 & \frac{4}{5} \\ \hline
0 & -\frac{6}{5} & 0 & \frac{82}{25} & \frac{124}{25} & M - \frac{124}{25} & 1 & -\frac{332}{5}
\end{array}\right]
$$

$\frac{5}{2}R_2 \to R_2$

$$
\sim \left[\begin{array}{ccccccc|c}
1 & \frac{1}{5} & 0 & \frac{3}{25} & -\frac{4}{25} & \frac{4}{25} & 0 & \frac{22}{5} \\
0 & \textcircled{1} & \frac{5}{2} & -\frac{2}{5} & -\frac{3}{10} & \frac{3}{10} & 0 & 2 \\ \hline
0 & -\frac{6}{5} & 0 & \frac{82}{25} & \frac{124}{25} & M - \frac{124}{25} & 1 & -\frac{332}{5}
\end{array}\right]
$$

$\left(-\frac{1}{5}\right)R_2 + R_1 \to R_1$ and $\frac{6}{5}\ R_2 + R_3 \to R_3$

$$\sim \begin{bmatrix} 1 & 0 & -\frac{1}{2} & \frac{1}{5} & -\frac{1}{10} & \frac{1}{10} & 0 & 4 \\ 0 & 1 & \frac{5}{2} & -\frac{2}{5} & -\frac{3}{10} & \frac{3}{10} & 0 & 2 \\ 0 & 0 & 3 & \frac{14}{5} & \frac{23}{5} & M - \frac{23}{5} & 1 & -64 \end{bmatrix}$$

Thus, min $C = 64$ at $x_1 = 4$, $x_2 = 2$, and $x_3 = 0$.

34. Let x_1 = the number of 16K modules manufactured daily, and x_2 = the number of 64K modules manufactured daily.

The mathematical model is: Maximize $P = 18x_1 + 30x_2$

$$\begin{aligned} \text{Subject to: } 10x_1 + 15x_2 &\le 2{,}100 \\ 2x_1 + 4x_2 &\le 500 \\ x_1 &\ge 50 \\ x_1,\ x_2 &\ge 0 \end{aligned}$$

We introduce slack, surplus, and artificial variables to obtain the modified problem: Maximize $P = 18x_1 + 30x_2 - Ma_1$

$$\begin{aligned} \text{Subject to: } 10x_1 + 15x_2 + s_1 &= 2{,}100 \\ 2x_1 + 4x_2 + s_2 &= 500 \\ x_1 - s_3 + a_1 &= 50 \\ x_1,\ x_2,\ s_1,\ s_2,\ s_3,\ a_1 &\ge 0 \end{aligned}$$

The preliminary simplex tableau for the modified problem is:

$$\begin{array}{ccccccc} x_1 & x_2 & s_1 & s_2 & s_3 & a_1 & P \end{array}$$

$$\begin{bmatrix} 10 & 15 & 1 & 0 & 0 & 0 & 0 & 2{,}100 \\ 2 & 4 & 0 & 1 & 0 & 0 & 0 & 500 \\ 1 & 0 & 0 & 0 & -1 & 1 & 0 & 50 \\ \hline -18 & -30 & 0 & 0 & 0 & M & 1 & 0 \end{bmatrix}$$

$(-M)R_3 + R_4 \to R_4$

$$\begin{array}{c} \\ s_1 \\ s_2 \\ \sim \ \ a_1 \\ P \end{array} \begin{array}{c} x_1 \quad\quad x_2 \ \ s_1 \ s_2 \quad s_3 \quad a_1 \ P \end{array}$$

$$\sim \begin{array}{c} s_1 \\ s_2 \\ a_1 \\ P \end{array} \left[\begin{array}{ccccccc|c} 10 & 15 & 1 & 0 & 0 & 0 & 0 & 2{,}100 \\ 2 & 4 & 0 & 1 & 0 & 0 & 0 & 500 \\ ① & 0 & 0 & 0 & -1 & 1 & 0 & 50 \\ \hline -M - 18 & -30 & 0 & 0 & M & 0 & 1 & -50M \end{array} \right]$$

$(-10)R_3 + R_1 \to R_1$, $(-2)R_3 + R_2 \to R_2$, and $(M + 18)R_3 + R_4 \to R_4$

$$\sim \begin{bmatrix} 0 & 15 & 1 & 0 & 10 & -10 & 0 & 1{,}600 \\ 0 & ④ & 0 & 1 & 2 & -2 & 0 & 400 \\ 1 & 0 & 0 & 0 & -1 & 1 & 0 & 50 \\ \hline 0 & -30 & 0 & 0 & -18 & M + 18 & 1 & 900 \end{bmatrix}$$

$\frac{1}{4}R_2 \to R_2$

$$\sim \begin{bmatrix} 0 & 15 & 1 & 0 & 10 & -10 & 0 & 1,600 \\ 0 & \boxed{1} & 0 & \frac{1}{4} & \frac{1}{2} & -\frac{1}{2} & 0 & 100 \\ 1 & 0 & 0 & 0 & -1 & 1 & 0 & 50 \\ 0 & -30 & 0 & 0 & -18 & M+18 & 1 & 900 \end{bmatrix}$$

$$(-15)R_2 + R_1 \rightarrow R_1 \text{ and } 30R_2 + R_4 \rightarrow R_4$$

$$\sim \begin{bmatrix} 0 & 0 & 1 & -\frac{15}{4} & \boxed{\frac{5}{2}} & -\frac{5}{2} & 0 & 100 \\ 0 & 1 & 0 & \frac{1}{4} & \frac{1}{2} & -\frac{1}{2} & 0 & 100 \\ 1 & 0 & 0 & 0 & -1 & 1 & 0 & 50 \\ 0 & 0 & 0 & \frac{15}{2} & -3 & M+3 & 1 & 3,900 \end{bmatrix}$$

$$\frac{2}{5}R_1 \rightarrow R_1$$

$$\sim \begin{bmatrix} 0 & 0 & \frac{2}{5} & -\frac{3}{2} & \boxed{1} & -1 & 0 & 40 \\ 0 & 1 & 0 & \frac{1}{4} & \frac{1}{2} & -\frac{1}{2} & 0 & 100 \\ 1 & 0 & 0 & 0 & -1 & 1 & 0 & 50 \\ 0 & 0 & 0 & \frac{15}{2} & -3 & M+3 & 1 & 3,900 \end{bmatrix}$$

$$\left(-\frac{1}{2}\right)R_1 + R_2 \rightarrow R_2, \ R_1 + R_3 \rightarrow R_3 \text{ and } 3R_1 + R_4 \rightarrow R_4$$

$$
\sim \begin{array}{c} \\ s_3 \\ x_2 \\ x_1 \\ \\ \end{array}
\begin{bmatrix}
x_1 & x_2 & s_1 & s_2 & s_3 & a_1 & P & \\
0 & 0 & \frac{2}{5} & -\frac{3}{2} & 1 & -1 & 0 & 40 \\
0 & 1 & -\frac{1}{5} & 1 & 0 & 0 & 0 & 80 \\
1 & 0 & \frac{2}{5} & -\frac{3}{2} & 0 & 0 & 0 & 90 \\
\hline
0 & 0 & \frac{6}{5} & 3 & 0 & M & 1 & 4,020
\end{bmatrix}
$$

The maximum profit is $4,020 when 90 16K modules and 80 64K modules are manufactured each day.

36. Let x_1 = the number of ads placed in the *Sentinel*,
    x_2 = the number of ads placed in the *Journal*,
and x_3 = the number of ads placed in the *Tribune*.
The mathematical model is: Minimize $C = 200x_1 + 200x_2 + 100x_3$

$$\text{Subject to:} \quad \begin{aligned} x_1 + x_2 + x_3 &\le 10 \\ 2,000x_1 + 500x_2 + 1,500x_3 &\ge 16,000 \\ x_3 &\le 4 \\ x_1, \ x_2, \ x_3 &\ge 0 \end{aligned}$$

Divide the second constraint inequality by 100 to simplify the calculations, and introduce slack, surplus, and artificial variables to obtain the equivalent form:

Maximize $P = -C = -200x_1 - 200x_2 - 100x_3 - Ma_1$

$$\text{Subject to:} \quad \begin{aligned} x_1 + x_2 + x_3 + s_1 \qquad\qquad\qquad\quad &= 10 \\ x_3 \qquad + s_2 \qquad\qquad &= 4 \\ 20x_1 + 5x_2 + 15x_3 \qquad\quad - s_3 + a_1 &= 160 \\ x_1, \ x_2, \ x_3, \ s_1, \ s_2, \ s_3, \ a_1 &\ge 0 \end{aligned}$$

The simplex tableau for the modified problem is:

$$
\begin{array}{cccccccc}
x_1 & x_2 & x_3 & s_1 & s_2 & s_3 & a_1 & P
\end{array}
$$

$$
\left[\begin{array}{ccccccc|c}
1 & 1 & 1 & 1 & 0 & 0 & 0 & 0 & 10 \\
0 & 0 & 1 & 0 & 1 & 0 & 0 & 0 & 4 \\
20 & 5 & 15 & 0 & 0 & -1 & 1 & 0 & 160 \\
\hline
200 & 200 & 100 & 0 & 0 & 0 & M & 1 & 0
\end{array}\right]
$$

$(-M)R_3 + R_4 \to R_4$

$$
\sim \left[\begin{array}{ccccccc|c}
1 & 1 & 1 & 1 & 0 & 0 & 0 & 0 & 10 \\
0 & 0 & 1 & 0 & 1 & 0 & 0 & 0 & 4 \\
\circled{20} & 5 & 15 & 0 & 0 & -1 & 1 & 0 & 160 \\
\hline
-20M+200 & -5M+200 & -15M+100 & 0 & 0 & M & 0 & 1 & -160M
\end{array}\right]
$$

$\dfrac{1}{20}R_3 \to R_3$

$$
\sim \left[\begin{array}{ccccccc|c}
1 & 1 & 1 & 1 & 0 & 0 & 0 & 0 & 10 \\
0 & 0 & \circled{1} & 0 & 1 & 0 & 0 & 0 & 4 \\
1 & \frac{1}{4} & \frac{3}{4} & 0 & 0 & -\frac{1}{20} & \frac{1}{20} & 0 & 8 \\
\hline
-20M+200 & -5M+200 & -15M+100 & 0 & 0 & M & 0 & 1 & -160M
\end{array}\right]
$$

$(-1)R_3 + R_1 \to R_1$ and $(20M - 200)R_3 + R_4 \to R_4$

$$
\sim \left[\begin{array}{ccccccc|c}
1 & \frac{3}{4} & \frac{1}{4} & 1 & 0 & \frac{1}{20} & -\frac{1}{20} & 0 & 2 \\
0 & 0 & \circled{1} & 0 & 1 & 0 & 0 & 0 & 4 \\
1 & \frac{1}{4} & \frac{3}{4} & 0 & 0 & -\frac{1}{20} & \frac{1}{20} & 0 & 8 \\
\hline
0 & 150 & -50 & 0 & 0 & 10 & M-10 & 1 & -1,600
\end{array}\right]
$$

$\left(-\dfrac{1}{4}\right)R_2 + R_1 \to R_1,\ \left(-\dfrac{3}{4}\right)R_2 + R_3 \to R_3,$ and $50R_2 + R_4 \to R_4$

$$
\sim \left[\begin{array}{ccccccc|c}
0 & \frac{3}{4} & 0 & 1 & -\frac{1}{4} & \frac{1}{20} & -\frac{1}{20} & 0 & 1 \\
0 & 0 & 1 & 0 & 1 & 0 & 0 & 0 & 4 \\
1 & \frac{1}{4} & 0 & 0 & -\frac{3}{4} & -\frac{1}{20} & \frac{1}{20} & 0 & 5 \\
\hline
0 & 150 & 0 & 0 & 50 & 10 & M-10 & 1 & -1,400
\end{array}\right]
$$

Thus, min $C = \$1,400$ at 5 ads in the *Sentinel*, 0 in the *Journal*, and 4 in the *Tribune*.

38. Let $x_1 =$ the number of bottles of brand A,
$\quad\quad x_2 =$ the number of bottles of brand B,
and $x_3 =$ the number of bottles of brand C.

The mathematical model is: Minimize $C = 0.6x_1 + 0.4x_2 + 1.5x_3$
$$
\begin{aligned}
\text{Subject to: } & 10x_1 + 10x_2 + 20x_3 \geq 100 \\
& 2x_1 + 3x_2 + 4x_3 \leq 24 \\
& x_1,\ x_2,\ x_3 \geq 0
\end{aligned}
$$

Divide the first inequality by 10, and introduce slack, surplus, and artificial variables to obtain the equivalent form:

Maximize $P = -10C = -6x_1 - 4x_2 - 15x_3 - Ma_1$
$$
\begin{aligned}
\text{Subject to: } & x_1 + x_2 + 2x_3 - s_1 \quad\quad\quad + a_1 = 10 \\
& 2x_1 + 3x_2 + 4x_3 \quad\quad + s_2 \quad\quad = 24 \\
& x_1,\ x_2,\ x_3,\ s_1,\ s_2,\ a_1 \geq 0
\end{aligned}
$$

The simplex tableau for the modified problem is:

$$
\begin{array}{ccccccc}
x_1 & x_2 & x_3 & s_1 & a_1 & s_2 & P \\
\end{array}
$$

$$
\left[
\begin{array}{ccccccc|c}
1 & 1 & 2 & -1 & 1 & 0 & 0 & 10 \\
2 & 3 & 4 & 0 & 0 & 1 & 0 & 24 \\
\hline
6 & 4 & 15 & 0 & M & 0 & 1 & 0
\end{array}
\right]
$$

$(-M)R_1 + R_3 \to R_3$

$$
\begin{array}{cccccccc}
 & x_1 & x_2 & x_3 & s_1 & a_1 & s_2 & P \\
\end{array}
$$

$$
\sim
\begin{array}{c}
a_1 \\
s_2 \\
\\
\end{array}
\left[
\begin{array}{ccccccc|c}
1 & 1 & ② & -1 & 1 & 0 & 0 & 10 \\
2 & 3 & 4 & 0 & 0 & 1 & 0 & 24 \\
\hline
-M+6 & -M+4 & -2M+15 & M & 0 & 0 & 1 & -10M
\end{array}
\right]
$$

$\frac{1}{2}R_1 \to R_1$

$$
\sim
\left[
\begin{array}{ccccccc|c}
\frac{1}{2} & \frac{1}{2} & ① & -\frac{1}{2} & \frac{1}{2} & 0 & 0 & 5 \\
2 & 3 & 4 & 0 & 0 & 1 & 0 & 24 \\
\hline
-M+6 & -M+4 & -2M+15 & M & 0 & 0 & 1 & -10M
\end{array}
\right]
$$

$(-4)R_1 + R_2 \to R_2$ and $(2M - 15)R_1 + R_3 \to R_3$

$$
\sim
\left[
\begin{array}{ccccccc|c}
\frac{1}{2} & \frac{1}{2} & 1 & -\frac{1}{2} & \frac{1}{2} & 0 & 0 & 5 \\
0 & ① & 0 & 2 & -2 & 1 & 0 & 4 \\
\hline
-1.5 & -3.5 & 0 & 7.5 & M-7.5 & 0 & 1 & -75
\end{array}
\right]
$$

$\left(-\frac{1}{2}\right)R_2 + R_1 \to R_1$ and $3.5R_2 + R_3 \to R_3$

$$
\sim
\left[
\begin{array}{ccccccc|c}
⓵\!\!/_2 & 0 & 1 & -\frac{3}{2} & \frac{3}{2} & -\frac{1}{2} & 0 & 3 \\
0 & 1 & 0 & 2 & -2 & 1 & 1 & 4 \\
\hline
-1.5 & 0 & 0 & 14.5 & M-14.5 & 3.5 & 1 & -61
\end{array}
\right]
$$

$2R_1 \to R_1$

$$
\sim
\left[
\begin{array}{ccccccc|c}
① & 0 & 2 & -3 & 3 & -1 & 0 & 6 \\
0 & 1 & 0 & 2 & -2 & 1 & 0 & 4 \\
\hline
-1.5 & 0 & 0 & 14.5 & M-14.5 & 3.5 & 1 & -61
\end{array}
\right]
$$

$1.5R_1 + R_3 \to R_3$

$$
\sim
\left[
\begin{array}{ccccccc|c}
1 & 0 & 2 & -3 & 3 & -1 & 0 & 6 \\
0 & 1 & 0 & 2 & -2 & 1 & 0 & 4 \\
\hline
0 & 0 & 3 & 10 & M-10 & 2 & 1 & -52
\end{array}
\right]
$$

Thus, min $C = \$5.20$ at 6 bottles of brand A, 4 bottles of brand B, and 0 bottles of brand C.

40. Let x_1 = the number of cubic yards of mix A,
x_2 = the number of cubic yards of mix B,
and x_3 = the number of cubic yards of mix C.

The mathematical model is: Maximize $P = 12x_1 + 16x_2 + 8x_3$
Subject to: $12x_1 + 8x_2 + 16x_3 \leq 1{,}000$
$16x_1 + 8x_2 + 16x_3 \geq 800$
$x_1, x_2, x_3 \geq 0$

We simplify the inequalities, and introduce slack, surplus, and artificial variables to obtain the modified problem:

Maximize $P = 12x_1 + 16x_2 + 8x_3 - Ma_1$

Subject to: $3x_1 + 2x_2 + 4x_3 + s_1 = 250$
$2x_1 + x_2 + 2x_3 - s_2 + a_1 = 100$
$x_1, x_2, x_3, s_1, s_2, a_1 \geq 0$

The simplex tableau for the modified problem is:

$$
\begin{array}{ccccccc}
x_1 & x_2 & x_3 & s_1 & s_2 & a_1 & P \\
\end{array}
$$

$$
\left[
\begin{array}{ccccccc|c}
3 & 2 & 4 & 1 & 0 & 0 & 0 & 250 \\
2 & 1 & 2 & 0 & -1 & 1 & 0 & 100 \\
\hline
-12 & -16 & -8 & 0 & 0 & M & 1 & 0 \\
\end{array}
\right]
$$

$(-M)R_3 + R_4 \rightarrow R_4$

$$
\begin{array}{ccccccc}
 & x_1 & x_2 & x_3 & s_1 & s_2 & a_1 & P \\
\end{array}
$$

$$
\begin{array}{c}
a_1 \\
\sim \quad s_2 \\
\\
\end{array}
\left[
\begin{array}{ccccccc|c}
3 & 2 & 4 & 1 & 0 & 0 & 0 & 250 \\
② & 1 & 2 & 0 & -1 & 1 & 0 & 100 \\
\hline
-2M-12 & -M-16 & -2M-8 & 0 & M & 0 & 1 & -100M \\
\end{array}
\right]
$$

$\dfrac{1}{2}R_2 \rightarrow R_2$

$$
\sim
\left[
\begin{array}{ccccccc|c}
3 & 2 & 4 & 1 & 0 & 0 & 0 & 250 \\
① & \frac{1}{2} & 1 & 0 & -\frac{1}{2} & \frac{1}{2} & 0 & 50 \\
\hline
-2M-12 & -M-16 & -2M-8 & 0 & M & 0 & 1 & -100M \\
\end{array}
\right]
$$

$(-3)R_2 + R_1 \rightarrow R_1$ and $(2M+12)R_2 + R_3 \rightarrow R_3$

$$
\sim
\left[
\begin{array}{ccccccc|c}
0 & \frac{1}{2} & 1 & 1 & \frac{3}{2} & -\frac{3}{2} & 0 & 100 \\
1 & ⓵\!\!\frac{1}{2} & 1 & 0 & -\frac{1}{2} & \frac{1}{2} & 0 & 50 \\
\hline
0 & -10 & 4 & 0 & -6 & M+6 & 1 & 600 \\
\end{array}
\right]
$$

$2R_2 \rightarrow R_2$

$$\sim \begin{bmatrix} 0 & \frac{1}{2} & 1 & 1 & \frac{3}{2} & -\frac{3}{2} & 0 & | & 100 \\ 1 & ① & 2 & 0 & -1 & 1 & 0 & | & 100 \\ \hline 0 & -10 & 4 & 0 & -6 & M+6 & 1 & | & 600 \end{bmatrix}$$

$$\left(-\frac{1}{2}\right)R_2 + R_1 \rightarrow R_1 \text{ and } 10R_2 + R_3 \rightarrow R_3$$

$$\sim \begin{bmatrix} -1 & 0 & 0 & 1 & ② & -2 & 0 & | & 50 \\ 2 & 1 & 2 & 0 & -1 & 1 & 0 & | & 100 \\ \hline 20 & 0 & 24 & 0 & -16 & M+16 & 1 & | & 1,600 \end{bmatrix}$$

$$\frac{1}{2}R_1 \rightarrow R_1$$

$$\sim \begin{bmatrix} -\frac{1}{2} & 0 & 0 & \frac{1}{2} & ① & -1 & 0 & | & 25 \\ 2 & 1 & 2 & 0 & -1 & 1 & 0 & | & 100 \\ \hline 20 & 0 & 24 & 0 & -16 & M+16 & 1 & | & 1,600 \end{bmatrix}$$

$$R_1 + R_2 \rightarrow R_2 \text{ and } 16R_1 + R_3 \rightarrow R_3$$

$$\sim \begin{bmatrix} -\frac{1}{2} & 0 & 0 & \frac{1}{2} & 1 & -1 & 0 & | & 25 \\ \frac{3}{2} & 1 & 2 & \frac{1}{2} & 0 & 0 & 0 & | & 125 \\ \hline 12 & 0 & 24 & 8 & 0 & M & 1 & | & 2,000 \end{bmatrix}$$

Thus, max P = 2,000 lbs. at 0 cubic yards of mix A, 125 cubic yards of mix B, and 0 cubic yards of mix C.

42. Let x_1 = the amount allocated to signature loans,
x_2 = the amount allocated to first mortgages,
x_3 = the amount allocated to second mortgages,
and x_4 = the amount allocated to automobile loans.

The mathematical model for this problem is:

Maximize $P = 0.18x_1 + 0.12x_2 + 0.14x_3 + 0.16x_4$

Subject to:
$$0.5x_2 - 0.5x_3 \geq 0$$
$$0.3x_1 - 0.7x_2 - 0.7x_3 + 0.3x_4 \leq 0$$
$$0.75x_1 - 0.25x_2 - 0.25x_3 + 0.75x_4 \leq 0$$
$$0.85x_1 - 0.15x_2 - 0.15x_3 - 0.15x_4 \leq 0$$
$$x_1 + x_2 + x_3 + x_4 \leq 3,000,000$$
$$x_1, \; x_2, \; x_3, \; x_4 \geq 0$$

44. Let x_1 = No. of lbs. of dried fruit used in regular trail mix
x_2 = No. of lbs. of dried fruit used in deluxe trail mix
x_3 = No. of lbs. of nuts used in regular trail mix
x_4 = No. of lbs. of nuts used in deluxe trail mix
x_5 = No. of lbs. of cereal used in regular trail mix
x_6 = No. of lbs. of cereal used in deluxe trail mix

Maximize $P = 0.4x_1 + 0.6x_2 + 0.4x_3 + 0.6x_4 + 0.4x_5 + 0.6x_6$

$$
\begin{aligned}
\text{Subject to} \quad x_1 + x_2 &\le 1{,}200 \\
x_3 + x_4 &\le 750 \\
x_5 + x_6 &\le 1{,}500 \\
-0.2x_1 + 0.8x_3 - 0.2x_5 &\ge 0 \\
-0.4x_1 - 0.4x_3 + 0.6x_5 &\le 0 \\
-0.3x_2 + 0.7x_4 - 0.3x_6 &\ge 0 \\
-0.25x_2 - 0.25x_4 + 0.75x_6 &\le 0 \\
x_1, \ x_2, \ x_3, \ x_4, \ x_5, \ x_6 &\ge 0
\end{aligned}
$$

46. Let x_1 = percentage of funds invested in high-tech funds
x_2 = percentage of funds invested in global funds
x_3 = percentage of funds invested in corporate bonds
x_4 = percentage of funds invested in municipal bonds
x_5 = percentage of funds invested in CDs

Minimize $C = 2.7x_1 + 1.8x_2 + 1.2x_3 + 0.5x_4$

$$
\begin{aligned}
\text{Subject to} \quad x_1 + x_2 + x_3 + x_4 + x_5 &= 1 \\
0.11x_1 + 0.10x_2 + 0.09x_3 + 0.08x_4 + 0.05x_5 &\ge 0.09 \\
x_1, \ x_2, \ x_3, \ x_4, \ x_5 &\ge 0
\end{aligned}
$$

48. Let x_1 = Number of bushels of corn in the feed mix for cows
x_2 = Number of bushels of corn in the feed mix for pigs
x_3 = Number of bushels of oats in the feed mix for cows
x_4 = Number of bushels of oats in the feed mix for pigs
x_5 = Number of bushels of soybeans in the mix for cows
x_6 = Number of bushels of soybeans in the mix for pigs

Minimize $C = 4x_1 + 4x_2 + 3.5x_3 + 3.5x_4 + 3.25x_5 + 3.25x_6$

$$
\begin{aligned}
\text{Subject to} \quad x_1 + x_2 &\le 1{,}000 \\
x_3 + x_4 &\le 500 \\
x_5 + x_6 &\le 1{,}000 \\
x_1 + x_3 + x_5 &= 1{,}000 \\
x_2 + x_4 + x_6 &= 1{,}000 \\
0.6x_1 - 0.4x_3 - 0.4x_5 &\ge 0 \\
-2x_2 + x_6 &\ge 0 \\
x_1, \ x_2, \ x_3, \ x_4, \ x_5, \ x_6 &\ge 0
\end{aligned}
$$

7 LOGIC, SETS, AND COUNTING

2. p: "11·11 = 121" q: "10·12 < 9·13"
   $p \vee q$: "11·11 = 121" or "10·12 < 9·13"; True
      T   F

4. $p \rightarrow q$: "If 11·11 = 121, then 10·12 < 9·13"; False
       T   F

6. $\neg q \rightarrow \neg p$: "If 10·12 is not less than 9·13, then 11·11
        T
     is not equal to 121"; True
      F

8. $r \wedge s$: "$2^9 + 2^8 + 2^7 > 987$" and "$9·10^2 + 8·10 + 7 = 987$"; False
        F   T

10. $\neg r$: "$2^9 + 2^8 + 2^7$ is not greater than 987"; True
    (r is False so $\neg r$ is True)

12. $s \rightarrow r$: "If $9·10^2 + 8·10 + 7 = 987$, then $2^9 + 2^8 + 2^7 > 987$"; False
         T   F

14. Conditional and is false (2 is not an odd number).

16. Conjunction and is false (9 is not a prime number).

18. Disjunction and false (15 is neither even nor is a prime number).

20. Negative and is true.

22. p: "Triangle ABC is isosceles"
    q: "The base angles of triangle ABC are congruent."
    It is given that $p \rightarrow q$.
    Converse: $q \rightarrow p$: "If the base angles of triangle ABC are congruent, then triangle ABC is isosceles."
    Contrapositive: $\neg q \rightarrow \neg p$: "If the base angles of triangle ABC are not congruent, then triangle ABC is not isosceles."

24. p: "$g(x)$ is a quadratic function"
    q: "$g(x)$ is a function that is neither increasing nor decreasing"
    It is given that $p \rightarrow q$.
    Converse: $q \rightarrow p$: "If $g(x)$ is a function that is neither increasing nor decreasing, then $g(x)$ is a quadratic function."
    Contrapositive: $\neg q \rightarrow \neg p$: "If $g(x)$ is a function that is either increasing or decreasing, then $g(x)$ is not a quadratic function."

26. p: "n is an integer that is a multiple of 6"
q: "n is an integer that is a multiple of 2 and a multiple of 3"
It is given that $p \to q$.
Converse: $q \to p$: "If n is an integer that is a multiple of 2 and a multiple of 3, then n is an integer that is a multiple of 6."
Contrapositive: $\neg q \to \neg p$: "If n is an integer that is not a multiple of 2 or not a multiple of 3, then n is an integer that is not a multiple of 6."

28.

p	q	$\neg q$	$p \vee \neg q$
T	T	F	T
T	F	T	T
F	T	F	F
F	F	T	T

Contingency

30.

p	q	$\neg q$	$p \to \neg q$
T	T	F	F
T	F	T	T
F	T	F	T
F	F	T	T

Contingency

32.

p	q	$p \wedge q$	$q \vee (p \wedge q)$
T	T	T	T
T	F	F	F
F	T	F	T
F	F	F	F

Contingency

34.

p	q	$p \to q$	$p \wedge (p \to q)$
T	T	T	T
T	F	F	F
F	T	T	F
F	F	T	F

Contingency

36.

p	q	$p \vee q$	$p \to (p \vee q)$
T	T	T	T
T	F	T	T
F	T	T	T
F	F	F	T

Tautology

38.

p	q	$p \to q$	$\neg q$	$(p \to q) \to \neg q$
T	T	T	F	F
T	F	F	T	T
F	T	T	F	F
F	F	T	T	T

Contingency

40.

p	q	$\neg p$	$p \wedge q$	$\neg p \to (p \wedge q)$
T	T	F	T	T
T	F	F	F	T
F	T	T	F	F
F	F	T	F	F

Contingency

42.

p	q	$\neg q$	$p \vee \neg q$	$q \to (p \vee \neg q)$
T	T	F	T	T
T	F	T	T	T
F	T	F	F	F
F	F	T	T	T

Contingency

44.

p	q	$\neg q$	$p \to \neg q$	$p \wedge q$	$(p \to \neg q) \wedge (p \wedge q)$
T	T	F	F	T	F
T	F	T	T	F	F
F	T	F	T	F	F
F	F	T	F	F	F

Contradiction

46. $\neg p \Rightarrow p \to q$

p	q	$\neg p$	$p \to q$
T	T	F	T
T	F	F	F
F	T	T	T
F	F	T	T

We note that whenever $\neg p$ is true (in the 3rd and 4th rows), $p \to q$ is also true.

48. $p \wedge q \Rightarrow p \to q$

p	q	$p \wedge q$	$p \to q$
T	T	T	T
T	F	F	F
F	T	F	T
F	F	F	T

We note that whenever $p \wedge q$ is true (in the 1st row only), $p \to q$ is also true.

50.

p	q	$\neg p$	$(p \wedge \neg p)$	q
T	T	F	F	T
T	F	F	F	F
F	T	T	F	T
F	F	T	F	F

We note that $(p \wedge \neg p)$ is nowhere true in this case.

52.

p	q	$\neg p$	$\neg p \wedge q$	$q \to (\neg p \wedge q)$	$p \wedge q$	$\neg(p \wedge q)$
T	T	F	F	F	T	F
T	F	F	F	T	F	T
F	T	T	T	T	F	T
F	F	T	F	T	F	T

54.

p	q	$p \to q$	$p \wedge (p \to q)$	$p \wedge q$
T	T	T	T	T
T	F	F	F	F
F	T	T	F	F
F	F	T	F	F

56.

p	q	$p \wedge q$	$p \to (p \wedge q)$	$p \to q$
T	T	T	T	T
T	F	F	F	F
F	T	F	T	T
F	F	F	T	T

58.
$$\neg p \to q = \neg(\neg p) \vee q \qquad \text{By (4)}$$
$$= p \vee q \qquad \text{By (1)}$$

60.
$$\neg(\neg p \to \neg q) = \neg(q \to p) \qquad \text{By (7)}$$
$$= \neg(\neg q \vee p) \qquad \text{By (4)}$$
$$= \neg(\neg q) \wedge \neg p \qquad \text{By (5)}$$
$$= q \wedge \neg p \qquad \text{By (1)}$$

62. No. The conditional proposition and its contrapositive have identical Truth Table.

64. Yes. If p is a contingency, then its truth table has at least one entry which is T and at least one entry which is F. Therefore, $\neg p$ will also have at least one entry which is F and at least one entry which is T. Thus, $\neg p$ will also be contingency.

EXERCISE 7-2

2. T; In a set the order of listing elements is not important; set equality definition.

4. T; Subset definition.

6. F; 1000 is not an element of {1, 10, 100}.

8. T; Subset definition.

10. T; {1} is an element of {1, {1}}. It is also a subset of {1, {1}}.

12. F; Set equality definition; these sets have nothing in common, let alone being equal.

14. {0, 6}; 0 and 6 are the only common elements.

16. {0, 3, 6, 12, 18}; elements in either or both sets.

18. {1, 2, 3, 8, 9, 10}; elements in either or both sets.

20. ∅; no common elements.

22. $\{x \mid x + 7 = 0\}$
$x + 7 = 0$ is true for $x = -7$. Hence, $\{x \mid x + 7 = 0\} = \{-7\}$.

24. $\{x \mid x^2 = 100\}$
$x^2 = 100$ is true for $x = -10$ and 10. Hence, $\{x \mid x^2 = 100\} = \{-10, 10\}$.

26. $\{x \mid x$ is a month starting with $M\}$ = {March, May}

28. U = {7, 8, 9, 10, 11} and A = {7, 11}. Then A' = {8, 9, 10}.

30. From the Venn diagram, U has 100 elements.

32. B' has 75 elements.

34. $A \cap B$ has 5 elements.

36. $A \cap B'$ has 35 elements.

38. $(A \cup B)'$ has 40 elements.

40. U' has 0 elements.

42. (A) $\{x \mid x \in R$ and $x \in T\}$.
    $= R \cap T$ ("and" translated
        as $\cap$, intersection)
    $= \{1, 3, 4\} \cap \{2, 4, 6\}$
    $= \{4\}$

(B) $R \cap T = \{4\}$

44. $Q \cup R = \{2, 4, 6\} \cup \{3, 4, 5, 6\}$
    $= \{2, 3, 4, 5, 6\}$
    $P \cap (Q \cup R)$
    $= \{1, 2, 3, 4\} \cap \{2, 3, 4, 5, 6\}$
    $= \{2, 3, 4\}$

46. $T' = \{n \in N \mid n \geq 1{,}000\}$ which is infinite.

48. $H \cap T = \{n \in N \mid 100 < n < 1{,}000\}$ which is finite.

50. $H \cup T = N$ which is infinite.

52. $P' = \{n \in N \mid n$ is not prime$\}$ which is infinite.

54. $(E \cup P)' = \{n \in N \mid n$ is odd but not prime$\}$ which is infinite.

56. E and P are disjoint since both contain number 2, which is even and prime.

58. E and E' are disjoint since by definition of E', they cannot have common elements.

60. False. Here is an example. Let A = {1, 2}, B = {1, 2, 3}. Then $A \subset B$, but $A \cup B$ = {1, 2, 3} $\neq A$ = {1, 2}.

62. True. $A \cap B = A$ can be represented by the Venn diagram. From the Venn diagram, we see that $A \subset B$.

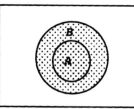

64. True. If A = ∅, then the set of all elements belonging to A and to any other set B will have no elements, i.e. $A \cap B$ = ∅.

66. True. Since $A \cup A' = B \cup B'$, if $A \subset B$, then B' must be a subset of A', i.e. $B' \subset A'$.

68. True. Let A be any set. Then A contains all the elements (none) of the empty set $\varnothing$. Therefore, $\varnothing \subset A$.

70. Let $A = \{a_1, a_2, \ldots, a_n\}$, and let $B \subset A$. We like to find out how many subsets B exist.
For a_1, we have $a_1 \in B$ or $a_1 \notin B$;
for a_2, we have $a_2 \in B$ or $a_2 \notin B$;
$\vdots$
for a_n, we have $a_n \in B$ or $a_n \notin B$.
Therefore, to count the number of subsets of A is the same as performing n operations each of which can be performed in 2 ways. Thus, all n operations, one after the other, can be performed in 2^n ways.

72. No. Let $A = \{\varnothing\}$ and $B = \{\varnothing, \{\varnothing\}\}$. A has only one element, namely $\varnothing$, whereas B has two elements $\varnothing$ and $\{\varnothing\}$. Since $\varnothing \neq \{\varnothing\}$, A and B do not have exactly the same elements and therefore cannot be equal.

74. The Venn diagram that corresponds to the given information is shown at the right. We can see that $N \cap M$ has 300 students.

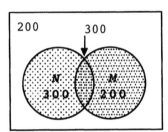

76. $(N \cap M)'$ has 700 students [because $N \cap M$ has 300 students and $(N \cap M)'$ has 1000 - 300 = 700].

78. $N' \cap M'$ has 300 students.

80. The number of commuters who listen to both news and music = number of commuters in the set $N \cap M$, which is 300.

82. The number of commuters who do not listen to both news and music = number of commuters in set $(N \cap M)'$, which is 700.

84. The number of commuters who listen to news but not music = number of commuters in the set $N \cap M'$, which is 300.

86. All subsets of $\{P, V_1, V_2, V_3\}$ that represent exactly 3 votes are $\{P, V_1\}$, $\{P, V_2\}$, $\{P, V_3\}$, $\{V_1, V_2, V_3\}$.

88. From the given Venn diagram $A \cap B = \{AB^-, AB^+\}$

90. From the given Venn diagram: $A \cup B = \{A^-, A^+, AB^-, AB^+, B^-, B^+\}$

92. From the given Venn diagram:

$(A \cup B \cup Rh)' = \{O^-\}$

94. From the given Venn diagram:

$Rh' \cap A = \{A^-, AB^-\}$

96. If a is outside the clique C, then there is at least one person b in C such that either a does not relate to b or b does not relate to a.

EXERCISE 7-3

2. $n(B) = 40 + 95 = 135$

4. $n(A') = 95 + 90 = 185$

6. $n(A \cap B) = 40$

8. $n(A \cap B') = 75$

10. $n(A' \cap B') = n((A \cup B)') = 90$

12. $n((A \cup B)') = n(A' \cap B') = 90$

14. (A) Tree Diagram

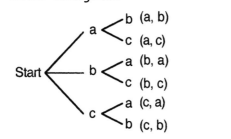

Thus, there are 4 ways.

(B) Multiplication Principle

O_1: 1st letter

N_1: 3 words

O_2: 2nd letter

N_2: 2 words

Thus, there are
$N_1 \cdot N_2 = 3 \cdot 2 = 6$ words.

16. (A) Tree Diagram

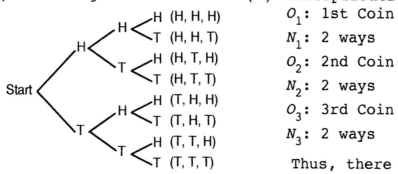

8 ways

(B) Multiplication Principle

O_1: 1st Coin

N_1: 2 ways

O_2: 2nd Coin

N_2: 2 ways

O_3: 3rd Coin

N_3: 2 ways

Thus, there are
$N_1 \cdot N_2 \cdot N_3 = 2 \cdot 2 \cdot 2 = 8$ ways

18. (A) Multiplication Principle

O_1: Selecting a history course

N_1: 2 ways

O_2: Selecting a science course

N_2: 3 ways

O_3: Selecting a mathematics course

N_3: 2 ways

O_4: Selecting a philosophy course

N_4: 2 ways

O_5: Selecting an English course

N_5: 1 way

Thus, there are $N_1 \cdot N_2 \cdot N_3 \cdot N_4 \cdot N_5 = 2 \cdot 3 \cdot 2 \cdot 2 \cdot 1 = 24$ ways

(B) Addition Principle

$N_1 + N_2 + N_3 + N_4 + N_5 = 10$ ways

20. Let A = set of "expensive" colleges,
$\quad$ B = set of "far from home" colleges.
$\quad$ Then $n(A) = 6$, $n(B) = 7$, $n(A \cap B) = 2$

(A) $n(A' \cap B') = n(U) - n(A \cup B) = n(U) - [n(A) + n(B) - n(A \cap B)]$
$$= 14 - [6 + 7 - 2] = 3$$

(B) O_1: Selecting a college for the first two years
$\quad$ N_1: $n(A' \cap B') = 3$ ways
$\quad$ O_2: Selecting a college after the first two years
$\quad$ N_2: $n(A' \cap B) = n(B) - n(A \cap B) = 7 - 2 = 5$ ways
Multiplication Principle is now used to obtain $N_1 \cdot N_2 = 15$ ways.

22. $A = (A \cap B') \cup (A \cap B)$
$\quad$ $n(A) = n(A \cap B') + n(A \cap B)$
$\quad$ Thus, $n(A \cap B') = n(A) - n(A \cap B) = 45 - 15 = 30$
$\qquad$ $B = (A' \cap B) \cup (A \cap B)$
$\quad$ $n(B) = n(A' \cap B) + n(A \cap B)$
$\quad$ Thus, $n(A' \cap B) = n(B) - n(A \cap B) = 35 - 15 = 20$
$\quad$ $n(A' \cap B') = n(U) - n(A \cup B)$
$$= 100 - (30 + 15 + 20) = 100 - 65 = 35$$

24. $n(A \cup B) = n(A) + n(B) - n(A \cap B)$
$\qquad$ $120 = 70 + 90 - n(A \cap B)$
$\quad$ Thus, $n(A \cap B) = 40$
$\quad$ $n(A' \cap B') = n(U) - n(A \cup B) = 200 - 120 = 80$
$\quad$ $n(A \cap B') = n(A) - n(A \cap B) = 70 - 40 = 30$
$\quad$ $n(A' \cap B) = n(B) - n(A \cap B) = 90 - 40 = 50$

26. $n(A \cap B') = n(B') - n(A' \cap B') = n(B') - [n(A') + n(B') - n(A' \cup B')]$
$$= n(A' \cup B') - n(A') = 95 - 35 = 60$$
$\quad$ $n(A \cap B) = n(A) - n(A \cap B') \quad = n(U) - n(A') - n(A \cap B')$
$$= 120 - 35 - 60 = 25$$
$\quad$ $n(A' \cap B) = n(B) - n(A \cap B) \quad = n(U) - n(B') - n(A \cap B)$
$$= 120 - 75 - 25 = 20$$
$\quad$ $n(A' \cap B') = n(A') + n(B') - n(A' \cup B') = 35 + 75 - 95 = 15$

28. $n(A \cap B) = 35$, $n(A' \cap B) = n(A) - n(A \cap B) = 55 - 35 = 20$
$\quad$ $n(A' \cap B) = n(B) - n(A \cap B) = 65 - 35 = 30$
$\quad$ $n(A \cup B) = n(A) + n(B) - n(A \cap B) = 55 + 65 - 35 = 85$
$\quad$ $n(A' \cap B') = n((A \cup B)') = n(U) - n(A \cup B) = 100 - 85 = 15$
$\quad$ Therefore,

	A	A'	Totals
B	35	30	65
B'	20	15	35
Totals	55	45	100

30. $n(A \cup B) = n(A) + n(B) - n(A \cap B)$
$\qquad$ $110 = 80 + 70 - n(A \cap B)$
$\quad$ Thus, $n(A \cap B) = 150 - 110 = 40$
$\quad$ $n(A' \cap B) = n(B) - n(A \cap B) = 70 - 40 = 30$
$\quad$ $n(A \cap B') = n(A) - n(A \cap B) = 80 - 40 = 40$
$\quad$ $n(A' \cap B') = n(U) - n(A \cup B) = 200 - 110 = 90$

Therefore,

	A	A'	Totals
B	40	30	70
B'	40	90	130
Totals	80	120	200

32. $n(A' \cap B) = n(A') - n(A' \cap B') = 81 - 63 = 18$
$n(A \cap B') = n(B') - n(A' \cap B') = 90 - 63 = 27$
$n(B) = n(U) - n(B') = 180 - 90 = 90$
$n(A \cap B) = n(B) - n(A' \cap B) = 90 - 18 = 72$

Thus,

	A	A'	Totals
B	72	18	90
B'	27	63	90
Totals	99	81	180

34. (A) False. $A \cap B$ is a subset of A so $n(A \cap B) \leq n(A)$. In problem 28, $n(A) = 55$, $n(B) = 65$, $n(A \cap B) = 35$, and it is clear that $55 + 65 \neq 35$.

(B) True. In general, $n(A \cup B) = n(A) + n(B) - n(A \cap B)$. If $n(A \cup B) = n(A) + n(B)$, then $n(A \cap B) = 0$ and hence A and B are disjoint (no common element).

36. Using the Multiplication Principle:

O_1: Choose bread O_3: Choose vegetable
N_1: 3 kinds N_3: 2 kinds

O_2: Choose meat
N_2: 5 kinds

Thus, there are

$N_1 \cdot N_2 \cdot N_3 = 3 \cdot 5 \cdot 2 = 30$ possible sandwiches.

38. (A) Number of five-letter code words, no letter repeated.

O_1: Selecting the first letter O_4: Selecting the fourth letter
N_1: 7 ways N_4: 4 ways

O_2: Selecting the second letter O_5: Selecting the fifth letter
N_2: 6 ways N_5: 3 ways

O_3: Selecting the third letter
N_3: 5 ways

Thus, there are

$N_1 \cdot N_2 \cdot N_3 \cdot N_4 \cdot N_5 = 7 \cdot 6 \cdot 5 \cdot 4 \cdot 3 = 2,520$
possible code words.

(B) Number of five-letter code words, allowing repetition.

O_1: Selecting the first letter O_4: Selecting the fourth letter

N_1: 7 ways N_4: 7 ways

O_2: Selecting the second letter O_5: Selecting the fifth letter

N_2: 7 ways N_5: 7 ways

O_3: Selecting the third letter

N_3: 7 ways

Thus, there are

$$N_1 \cdot N_2 \cdot N_3 \cdot N_4 \cdot N_5 = 7 \cdot 7 \cdot 7 \cdot 7 \cdot 7 = 7^5 = 16,807$$

possible code words.

(C) Number of five-letter code words, adjacent letters different.

O_1: Selecting the first letter O_4: Selecting the fourth letter

N_1: 7 ways N_4: 6 ways

O_2: Selecting the second letter O_5: Selecting the fifth letter

N_2: 6 ways N_5: 6 ways

O_3: Selecting the third letter

N_3: 6 ways

Thus, there are

$$N_1 \cdot N_2 \cdot N_3 \cdot N_4 \cdot N_5 = 7 \cdot 6 \cdot 6 \cdot 6 \cdot 6 = 7 \cdot 6^4 = 9,072$$

possible code words.

40. (A) Number of three-digit combinations, no digit repeated.

O_1: Selecting the first digit O_3: Selecting the third digit

N_1: 10 ways N_3: 8 ways

O_2: Selecting the second digit

N_2: 9 ways

Thus, there are

$$N_1 \cdot N_2 \cdot N_3 = 10 \cdot 9 \cdot 8 = 720$$

possible combinations

(B) Number of three-digit combinations, allowing repetition.

O_1: Selecting the first digit O_3: Selecting the third digit

N_1: 10 ways N_3: 10 ways

O_2: Selecting the second digit

N_2: 10 ways

Thus, there are

$$N_1 \cdot N_2 \cdot N_3 = 10 \cdot 10 \cdot 10 = 10^3 = 1,000$$

possible combinations

(C) Number of three-digit combinations, if successive digits must be different.

O_1: Selecting the first digit O_3: Selecting the third digit

N_1: 10 ways N_3: 9 ways

O_2: Selecting the second digit

N_2: 9 ways

Thus, there are

$N_1 \cdot N_2 \cdot N_3 = 10 \cdot 9 \cdot 9 = 10 \cdot 9^2 = 810$ possible combinations

42. (A) 5-digit ZIP code numbers.

O_1: Selecting the first letter O_4: Selecting the fourth digit

N_1: 10 ways N_4: 10 ways

O_2: Selecting the second letter O_5: Selecting the fifth digit

N_2: 10 ways N_5: 10 ways

O_3: Selecting the third letter

N_3: 10 ways

Thus, there are

$N_1 \cdot N_2 \cdot N_3 \cdot N_4 \cdot N_5 = 10 \cdot 10 \cdot 10 \cdot 10 \cdot 10 = 100,000$

possible 5-digit ZIP code numbers.

(B) No repeated digits are allowed.
In this case, $N_1 = 10$, $N_2 = 9$, $N_3 = 8$, $N_4 = 7$, and $N_5 = 6$.
Thus, there are $N_1 \cdot N_2 \cdot N_3 \cdot N_4 \cdot N_5 = 10 \cdot 9 \cdot 8 \cdot 7 \cdot 6 = 30,240$ possible
5-digit ZIP code numbers with no repetitions.

44. In general $n(A \cup B \cup C) = n(A) + n(B) + n(C) - n(A \cap B) - n(B \cap C) - n(A \cap C) + n(A \cap B \cap C)$.
If $C \supseteq A \cap B$, then $n(A \cap B) = n(A \cap B \cap C)$ and hence $n(A \cup B \cup C) = n(A) + n(B) + n(C) - n(B \cap C) - n(A \cap C)$. Obviously, this includes the special case $A \cap B = \varnothing$.

46. If A and B are to be disjoint then they cannot have common elements and hence y must be 0.

48. If $A \cup B = U$, then $(A \cup B)' = \varnothing$ (empty set) and hence w must be 0.

50. Let P = the number of students who play piano, and
G = the number of students who play guitar.
Then $n(P) = 13$, $n(G) = 16$, $n(P \cap G) = 5$ and $n(U) = 30$.
Note that
$n(P \cup G) = n(P) + n(G) - n(P \cap G) = 13 + 16 - 5 = 29 - 5 = 24$
$n(P' \cap G') = n(U) - n(P \cup G) = 30 - 24 = 6$.

52. Let O = the number of players who played offense last year, and
D = the number of players who played defense last year.
Then $n(O) = 16$, $n(D) = 17$, $n(O' \cap D') = 12$ and $n(U) = 40$.
$n(O \cup D) = n(U) - n(O' \cap D') = 40 - 12 = 28$
$n(O \cup D) = n(O) + n(D) - n(O \cap D)$
$\qquad 28 = 16 + 17 - n(O \cap D)$
Thus, $n(O \cap D) = 33 - 28 = 5$, i.e. 5 players from last year played both offense and defense.

54. O_1: Selecting from plant A $\qquad$ O_2: Selecting from plant B

N_1: 6 ways $\qquad\qquad\qquad\qquad$ N_2: 8 ways

Thus, there are $N_1 \cdot N_2 = 6 \cdot 8 = 48$ possible ways to select a vice-president from each plant. If selection is made without regard to plant, then for the first VP, there are 14 ways ($6 + 8 = 14$) and for the second VP, there are 13 ways. Thus, $14 \cdot 13 = 182$ ways.

56.

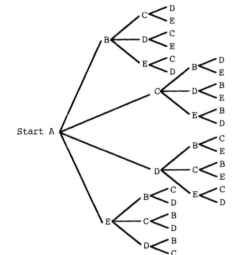

$N_1 = 4$

$N_2 = 3$

$N_3 = 2$

Thus, the number of possible ways is
$N_1 \cdot N_2 \cdot N_3 = 4 \cdot 3 \cdot 2 = 24$

58. Let P = the number of small businesses that own photocopiers, and
F = the number of small businesses that own fax machines.
Then $N(P) = 250$, $n(F) = 420$, $N(P \cap F) = 180$, and $n(U) = 800$.
(A) $n(P \cup F) = n(P) + n(F) - n(P \cap F) = 250 + 420 - 180 = 490$
i.e. there are 490 small businesses that own either a copy machine, fax machine, or both.
(B) $n(P' \cap F') = n(U) - n(P \cup F) = 800 - 490 = 310$
(C) $n(P' \cap F) = n(F) - n(P \cap F) = 420 - 180 = 240$

60. Let F = the number of customers who use call forwarding, and
W = the number of customers who use call waiting.
Then $n(F) = 3,770$, $n(W) = 3,250$, $n(F' \cap W') = 4,530$
$\qquad n(U) = 10,000$.
First, $n(F \cup W) = n(U) - n(F' \cap W') = 10,000 - 4,530 = 5,470$
Now, $\quad n(F \cup W) = n(F) + n(W) - n(F \cap W)$
$\qquad\qquad 5,470 = 3,770 + 3,250 - n(F \cap W)$
Thus, $n(F \cap W) = 7,020 - 5,470 = 1,550$, i.e. 1,550 customers use both call forwarding and call waiting.

62. (A) 367

(B) $118 + 102 = 220$

(C) Let A_1 = number of workers age 20-24,
   A_2 = number of females below minimum wage
   Then $n(A_1) = 644$, $n(A_2) = 993$, $n(A_1 \cap A_2) = 202$.
   Thus, $n(A_1 \cup A_2) = 644 + 993 - 202 = 1,435$.

(D) Males at minimum wage = 734
   Females at minimum wage = 1,056
   Thus, workers at minimum wage = $734 + 1,056 = 1,790$.

64. (A) Tree Diagram

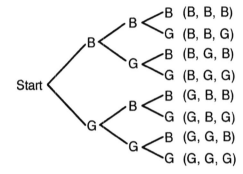

(B) Multiplication Principle
   O_1: first child
   N_1: 2 ways
   O_2: second child
   N_2: 2 ways
   O_3: third child
   N_3: 2 ways
   Thus, there are
   $N_1 \cdot N_2 \cdot N_3 = 2 \cdot 2 \cdot 2 = 8$ ways.

66. Let A = number of people who voted for him in his first election; and
   B = number of people who voted for him in his second election.
   Then $n(A) = 12,457$, $n(B) = 15,322$ and $n(A \cap B) = 9,345$.

   Now, $n(A \cup B) = n(A) + n(B) - n(A \cap B)$
   $$= 12,457 + 15,322 - 9,345 = 18,434$$

EXERCISE 7-4

2. $9! = 9 \cdot 8 \cdot 7 \cdot \ldots \cdot 2 \cdot 1 = 362,880$

4. $\dfrac{18!}{15!} = \dfrac{18 \cdot 17 \cdot 16 \cdot (15!)}{15!} = 18 \cdot 17 \cdot 16 = 4,896$

6. $\dfrac{1000!}{(1000-2)!} = \dfrac{(1000) \cdot (999) \cdot (998!)}{998!} = (1000) \cdot (999) = 999,000$

8. $\dfrac{13!}{6!\,7!} = \dfrac{(13 \cdot 12 \cdot 11 \cdot 10 \cdot 9 \cdot 8) \cdot (7!)}{(6 \cdot 5 \cdot 4 \cdot 3 \cdot 2 \cdot 1)(7!)} = 1,716$

10. $\dfrac{20!}{8!\,(20-8)!} = \dfrac{(20 \cdot 19 \cdot 18 \cdot \ldots \cdot 13) \cdot (12!)}{(8 \cdot 7 \cdot 6 \cdot \ldots \cdot 1) \cdot (12!)} = 125,970$

12. $C_{8,4} = \dfrac{8!}{4!\,(8-4)!} = \dfrac{8!}{4!\,4!} = \dfrac{40,320}{(24) \cdot (24)} = 70$ (see Problem 1)

14. $P_{8,4} = \dfrac{8!}{(8-4)!} = \dfrac{8!}{4!} = \dfrac{40,320}{24} = 1,680$

or $P_{8,4} = 4! \, C_{8,4} = (24) \cdot (70) = 1,680$ (see Problem 12)

16. $C_{52,48} = \dfrac{52!}{48!(52-48)!} = \dfrac{52 \cdot 51 \cdot 50 \cdot 49 \cdot (48!)}{48!(4!)}$

$\qquad = \dfrac{52 \cdot 51 \cdot 50 \cdot 49}{24} = 270,725$

18. $\dfrac{C_{13,3}}{C_{52,3}} = \dfrac{\frac{13!}{3!\,10!}}{\frac{52!}{3!\,49!}} = \dfrac{\frac{13 \cdot 12 \cdot 11}{6}}{\frac{52 \cdot 51 \cdot 50}{6}} = \dfrac{13 \cdot 12 \cdot 11}{52 \cdot 51 \cdot 50} = 0.012941$

20. $\dfrac{P_{365,23}}{365^{23}} = 0.492703$ (Using TI-83 calculator)

22. $\dfrac{n!}{2!\,(n-2)!} = \dfrac{n(n-1)\,((n-2)!)}{2!\,(n-2)!} = \dfrac{n(n-1)}{2}$

24. $\dfrac{(n+2)!}{(n-1)!} = \dfrac{(n+2)(n+1)n((n-1)!)}{(n-1)!} = (n+2)(n+1)n$

26. Combination: the order of selection is not important.

28. Permutation: The order of selection of books--for his father, mother, younger sister, and older brother.

30. Neither.

32. The number of finishes (1st, 2nd, 3rd, 4th, 5th) of the 50 people is the number of permutations of 50 objects 5 at a time. This is:

$P_{50,5} = \dfrac{50!}{(50-5)!} = \dfrac{50!}{45!} = \dfrac{50 \cdot 49 \cdot 48 \cdot 47 \cdot 46 \cdot 45!}{45!}$

$\qquad\qquad = 50 \cdot 49 \cdot 48 \cdot 47 \cdot 46 = 2.5425 \times 10^{8}$

34. (A) Permutation: $P_{9,3} = \dfrac{9!}{(9-3)!} = \dfrac{9!}{6!} = \dfrac{9 \cdot 8 \cdot 7 \cdot 6!}{6!} = 504$

(B) Combination: $C_{9,3} = \dfrac{9!}{3!(9-3)!} = \dfrac{9!}{3!\,6!} = 84$

$\left(\text{or } C_{9,3} = \dfrac{P_{9,3}}{3!} = \dfrac{504}{6} = 84 \right)$

36. The factorial function $x!$ grows much faster than exponential function 2^{x}, which in turn grows much faster than the square function x^2. (Check these 3 functions for $x = 1, 2, \dots, 8$ and see the growth.)

38. There are 12 face cards in a standard 52-card deck: 4 jacks, 4 queens, and 4 kings.

(A) 5-card hands only face cards: $C_{12,5} = \dfrac{12!}{5!\,(12 - 5)!}$

(B) 5-card hands only face cards, but no kings:

$$C_{8,5} = \dfrac{8!}{5!\,(8 - 5)!} = 56$$

40. There are 13 clubs and 13 hearts in a standard 52-card deck. We must count the number of ways that we can choose 5 cards from the deck so that 2 of them are clubs and 3 of them hearts. We need to choose the two clubs from the 13 clubs in $C_{13,2}$ ways; and choose the three hearts from the 13 hearts in $C_{13,3}$ ways. Thus, both selections can be done in

$C_{13,2} \times C_{13,3}$ ways, i.e. $\dfrac{13!}{2!\,(13 - 2)!} \times \dfrac{13!}{3!\,(13 - 3)!} = 22{,}308.$

42. O_1: Selecting a delegate and an alternate from the 1st department
N_1: $P_{12,2}$

O_2: Selecting a delegate and an alternate from the 2nd department
N_2: $P_{15,2}$

O_3: Selecting a delegate and an alternate from the 3rd department
N_3: $P_{18,2}$

Thus, there are $N_1 \cdot N_2 \cdot N_3 = P_{12,2} \cdot P_{15,2} \cdot P_{18,2}$

$$= \dfrac{12!}{2!\,(12 - 2)!} \cdot \dfrac{15!}{2!\,(15 - 2)!} \cdot \dfrac{18!}{2!\,(18 - 2)!}$$

$$= 12 \cdot 11 \cdot 15 \cdot 14 \cdot 18 \cdot 17 = 8{,}482{,}320 \text{ ways}$$

44. For each row, the second column entry is the third column entry times the factorial of the first column entry.

46. Observe that
$n! = n(n - 1)(n - 2) \ldots \times 3 \times 2$
If $n > 3$, then $n \geq 2^2$ and each of the remaining $(n - 2)$ factors is ≥ 2. Therefore
$n(n - 1)(n - 2) \ldots \times 3 \times 2 \geq 2^2 \cdot \underbrace{2 \cdot 2 \cdot \ldots \cdot 2}_{n - 2 \text{ times}} = 2^2 \cdot 2^{n-2} \cdot 2^n$

48. It is false. Take $n = 3$ and $r = 2$. Then

$$C_{n,r} = C_{3,2} = \dfrac{3!}{2!\,(3 - 2)!} = \dfrac{6}{2} = 3 \text{ and}$$

$C_{n,r+1} = C_{3,3} = \dfrac{3!}{3!\,(3 - 3)!} = \dfrac{6}{6} = 1$
Clearly $C_{3,2}$ is not less than $C_{3,3}$.

50. It is false. Take $n = 3$, $r = 2$. Then

$$P_{n,r} = P_{3,2} = \frac{3!}{(3-2)!} = \frac{6}{1} = 6$$

$$P_{n,n-r} = P_{3,1} = \frac{3!}{(3-1)!} = \frac{6}{2} = 3$$

52. (A) A chord joins two distinct points. Thus, the total number of chords is given by:

$$C_{5,2} = \frac{5!}{2!(5-2)!} = \frac{5!}{2!\,3!} = \frac{5 \cdot 4 \cdot 3!}{2 \cdot 1 \cdot 3!} = \frac{5 \cdot 4}{2 \cdot 1} = 10$$

(B) Each triangle requires three distinct points. Thus, there are

$$C_{5,3} = \frac{5!}{3!(5-3)!} = \frac{5!}{3!\,2!} = 10 \text{ triangles.}$$

54. The number of seating arrangements on each side of the table is $P_{5,5} = 5! = 120$. Thus, the number of seating arrangements for the delegates from both countries is $2 \cdot P_{5,5} \cdot P_{5,5} = 28{,}800$; $P_{5,5}$ for delegates from each country and the factor 2 is required because the delegates from one country have 2 choices on either side of the table.

56. (A) Combination: $C_{9,4} = \frac{9!}{4!(9-4)!} = \frac{9!}{4!\,5!} = 126$

(B) Both Jim and Mary must be on the committee. Thus, we need to choose 2 from the remaining 7 people,

i.e. $C_{7,2} = \frac{7!}{2!(7-2)!} = \frac{7!}{2!\,5!} = 21$

(C) Either Jim or Mary (but not both) must be on the committee.

The number of ways that Mary (but not Jim) will be on the committee is the number of combinations of 7 (= 9 - 2, Mary and Jim) objects 3 at a time: $C_{7,3}$.

The number of ways that Jim (but not Mary) will be on the committee is $C_{7,3}$.

Thus, the number of ways we can choose a 4-person committee so that either Mary of Jim (but not both) will be on the committee is

$$2 \cdot C_{7,3} = 2 \cdot \frac{7!}{3!(7-3)!} = 2 \cdot \frac{7!}{3!\,4!} = 70$$

58. For many calculators $k = 168$, but for yours it may be different.

60. $C_{17,8} = C_{17,9} = 24{,}310$

62. (A) Combination: $C_{30,4} = \dfrac{30!}{4!\,(30-4)!} = \dfrac{30!}{4!\,26!} = 27,405$

(B) No defective calculators chosen: We need to choose the 4 calculators from the 30 − 6 = 24 non-defective ones. The number of selections is $C_{24,4} = \dfrac{24!}{4!\,(24-4)!} = \dfrac{24!}{4!\,20!} = 10,626$

64. (A) There are 14 + 8 + 6 = 28 employees combined. The number of ways that 12 employees out of 28 can be laid off is the number of combinations of 28 objects 12 at a time,

$$C_{28,12} = \dfrac{28!}{12!\,(28-12)!} = \dfrac{28!}{12!\,16!} = 30,421,755$$

(B) O_1: Lay off 5 from the central office

N_1: $C_{14,5}$

O_2: Lay off 4 from the north office

N_2: $C_{8,4}$

O_3: Lay off 3 from the south office

N_3: $C_{6,3}$

Thus, there are

$$C_{14,5} \cdot C_{8,4} \cdot C_{6,3} = \dfrac{14!}{5!\,(14-5)!} \cdot \dfrac{8!}{4!\,(8-4)!} \cdot \dfrac{6!}{3!\,(6-3)!}$$
$$= 2,802,800 \text{ ways}$$

66. (A) O_1: Selecting 3 from A

N_1: $C_{15,3}$

O_2: Selecting 1 from B

N_2: $C_{20,1}$

Thus, there are $C_{15,3} \cdot C_{20,1} = \dfrac{15!}{3!\,(15-3)!} \cdot \dfrac{20!}{1!\,(20-1)!} = 9,100$ ways.

(B) O_1: Selecting 2 from A

N_1: $C_{15,2}$

O_2: Selecting 2 from B

N_2: $C_{20,2}$

Thus, the number of selections is: $C_{15,2} \cdot C_{20,2} = 19,950$

(C) All from A: $C_{15,4} = 1,365$

(D) 4 people regardless of department.

There are 15 + 20 = 35 and we need to select 4 out of 35. The number of selections is: $C_{35,4} = 52,360$

(E) At least 3 from department A:
This means the number of ways that exactly 3 people can be chosen from A and 1 from B (case (A) above) PLUS the number of ways that 4 people can be chosen from A (case (C) above). Thus, the number of selections is: $9,100 + 1,365 = 10,465$.

68. Combination: $C_{8,5} = \dfrac{8!}{5!(8-5)!} = 56$

70. Permutation: $P_{6,6} = 6! = 720$

8 PROBABILITY

2. $P(E) = 0$ means that E cannot happen.

4. There are 3 red sides and 2 white sides, so the probability of the event that the top side is red or white is $\dfrac{3 + 2}{6} = \dfrac{5}{6}$ (since the outcomes are equally likely).

6. There are 4 non-white sides, so the probability of the event that the top side is not white is $\dfrac{4}{6} = \dfrac{2}{3}$ (since the outcomes are equally likely).

8. P (the top side is white) $= \dfrac{2}{6} = \dfrac{1}{3}$, since all sides have the same chances and 2 out of 6 are white.

10. P (the top side is green) $= 0$, since this event will never occur, there are no green sides.

12. There are 13 diamonds in a standard deck of 52 cards, so the probability of drawing a diamond is $\dfrac{13}{52} = \dfrac{1}{4}$ (since the outcomes are equally likely).

14. There are 4 aces and 4 kings in a standard deck of 52 cards, so the probability of drawing an ace or king is $\dfrac{8}{52}$ (since the outcomes are equally likely).

16. There is only 1 queen of hearts, so the probability of drawing the queen of hearts is $\dfrac{1}{52}$ (since the outcomes are equally likely).

18. P (a red face card) $= \dfrac{6}{52} = \dfrac{3}{26}$, since all cards have the same chances and 6 out of 52 cards are red face cards; Jack, Queen, and King of Diamonds and Hearts.

22. Let $G =$ girl and $B =$ boy. Then
$S = \{(G, G), (G, B), (B, G), (B, B)\}$
where (G, G) means both children are girls, (G, B) means the first child is a girl, the second is a boy, and so on. The event E corresponding to having two girls is $E = \{(G, G)\}$. Since the simple events (outcomes) are equally likely,

$$P(E) = \frac{n(E)}{n(S)} = \frac{1}{4}.$$

24. From Problem 23(C), $P(J) = 0.26$, $P(G) = 0.14$, $P(P) = 0.30$, $P(S) = 0.30$.
P(a random customer will not choose brand S) $= 1 - P(S) = 1 - 0.30$
$= 0.70$

26. Using probabilities given in problem 23(C), P(a random customer will not choose brand J or brand P) $= 1 - P(J) - P(P) = 1 - 0.26 - 0.30 = 1 - 0.56 = 0.44$

28. $S = \{(G, G, G), (G, G, B), (G, B, G), (G, B, B), (B, G, G), (B, G, B), (B, B, G), (B, B, B)\}$

E: 2 boys and 1 girl in any order
$E = \{(G, B, B), (B, G, B), (B, B, G)\}$
Since the outcomes are equally likely and $n(S) = 8$, $n(E) = 3$,
$P(E) = \dfrac{3}{8}$.

30. The number of five-digit sequences with no digit repeated is $P_{10,5}$.
Since the possible opening combinations are equally likely, the probability of a person guessing the right combination is:

$$\frac{1}{P_{10,5}} = \frac{1}{10 \cdot 9 \cdot 8 \cdot 7 \cdot 6} \approx 0.000\ 033$$

32. Let $S = $ the set of five-card hands. Then $n(S) = C_{52,5}$.
Let $A = $ "five hearts." Then $n(A) = C_{13,5}$.
Since individual hands are equally likely to occur:

$$P(A) = \frac{n(A)}{n(S)} = \frac{C_{13,5}}{C_{52,5}} = \frac{\frac{13!}{5!\ 8!}}{\frac{52!}{5!\ 47!}} \approx 0.000\ 50$$

34. $S = $ set of five-card hands; $n(S) = C_{52,5}$.
$B = $ "five non-face cards"; $n(B) = C_{40,5}$.
Since the individual hands are equally likely to occur:

$$P(B) = \frac{n(B)}{n(S)} = \frac{C_{40,5}}{C_{52,5}} = \frac{\frac{40!}{5!\ 35!}}{\frac{52!}{5!\ 47!}} \approx 0.25$$

36. Let A and B be the two candidates running neck-and-neck and C the third candidate who is receiving half the support of either A or B according to the polls. An appropriate sample space would be $S = \{A, B, C\}$. A reasonable and acceptable assignment of probabilities to the outcomes in S (based on the polls) would be $P(A) = \dfrac{2}{5}$, $P(B) = \dfrac{2}{5}$, and $P(C) = \dfrac{1}{5}$.

38. $n(S) = P_{6,6} = 6! = 720$

Let A = all the people will get their own coats back.

Then $n(A) = 1$ and $P(A) = \dfrac{n(A)}{n(S)} = \dfrac{1}{720} \approx 0.00139$

40. Using the sample space shown in Figure 2 (page 393), we have

$n(S) = 36$, $n(A) = 3$, where event A = "Sum being 10":

$$P(A) = \dfrac{n(A)}{n(S)} = \dfrac{3}{36} = \dfrac{1}{12}.$$

42. Let B = "Sum being 8". Then $n(B) = 5$. Thus, $P(B) = \dfrac{n(B)}{n(S)} = \dfrac{5}{36}.$

44. Let C = "Sum is greater than 8".
$= \{(3, 6), (4, 5), (5, 4), (6, 3), (4, 6), (5, 5), (6, 4),$
$(5, 6), (6, 5), (6, 6)\}$

Then $n(C) = 10$ and $P(C) = \dfrac{10}{36} = \dfrac{5}{18}.$

46. Let D = "Sum is not 2, 4, or 6", and let E = "Sum is 2, 4, or 6".
Then $P(D) = 1 - P(E)$.
Observe that $E = \{(1, 1), (1, 3), (2, 2), (3, 1), (1, 5), (2, 4),$
$(3, 3), (4, 2), (5, 1)\}$,
and hence $P(E) = \dfrac{n(E)}{n(S)} = \dfrac{9}{36} = \dfrac{1}{4}.$
Therefore, $P(D) = 1 - \dfrac{1}{4} = \dfrac{3}{4}.$

48. Let F = "Sum is 13". F is empty since the maximum value of the sum is 12. Thus, $P(F) = 0$.

50. Let G = "Sum is divisible by 4". Then the possible values for the sum will be 4, 8, 12.
Thus, $G = \{(1, 3), (2, 2), (3, 1), (2, 6), (3, 5), (4, 4), (5, 3),$
$(6, 2), (6, 6)\}$,
and hence $P(G) = \dfrac{n(G)}{n(S)} = \dfrac{9}{36} = \dfrac{1}{4}.$

52. Let H = "Sum is 2, 3, or 12."
Then $P(H) = P(\text{Sum } 2) + P(\text{Sum } 3) + P(\text{Sum } 12) = \dfrac{1}{36} + \dfrac{2}{36} + \dfrac{1}{36} = \dfrac{4}{36} = \dfrac{1}{9}.$

54. Let I = "Sum is divisible by 2 and 3." Then it must be divisible by $2 \times 3 = 6$. The possible values are: 6 and 12.
$P(I) = P(\text{Sum } 6) + P(\text{Sum } 12) = \dfrac{5}{36} + \dfrac{1}{36} = \dfrac{6}{36} = \dfrac{1}{6}.$

For Problems 56—60, the sample space S is given by:

$$S = \{(H, H, H), (H, H, T), (H, T, H), (H, T, T)\}$$

The outcomes are equally likely and n(S) = 4.

56. Let A = "2 heads". Then $n(A) = 2$ and $P(A) = \dfrac{2}{4} = \dfrac{1}{2}$.

58. Let B = "0 heads". Then $n(B) = 0$ and $P(B) = 0$.

60. Let C = "more than 1 tail". Then $n(C) = 1$ and $P(C) = \dfrac{1}{4}$.

62. $S = \{H, T\}$ and the coin is fair, so we can make the equally likely assumption; $P(H) = P(T) = \dfrac{1}{2}$.

64. $S = \{0, 1, 2\}$. For this experiment there are four outcomes, HH, HT, TH, TT, which correspond to 2, 1, 1, 0 (number of heads) respectively. As you can see, 1 corresponds to two outcomes whereas 0 and 2 each correspond to one outcome. So, in general we do not make the assumption of equally likely case. For example, if the coins are fair, then $P(0) = P(2) = \dfrac{1}{4}$, but $P(1) = \dfrac{2}{4} = \dfrac{1}{2}$.

66. $S = \{R, O, Y\}$ and the seven sectors are of equal areas. Thus, $P(R) = \dfrac{3}{7}$, $P(0) = P(Y) = \dfrac{2}{7}$ and we cannot make equally likely assumptions.

68. (A) Yes, but the probability of that happening is very small.
(B) Yes, because we would expect, on the average, 1 double six in 36 rolls. The empirical probability we assign based on the given experiment is $\dfrac{11}{36}$.

For Problems 70—76, the sample space S is given by:

$$S = \begin{Bmatrix} (1,1),(1,2),(1,3) \\ (2,1),(2,2),(2,3) \\ (3,1),(3,2),(3,3) \end{Bmatrix}$$

The outcomes are equally likely and n(S) = 9.

70. Let A = "Sum is 3". Then $n(A) = 2$ and $P(A) = \dfrac{2}{9}$.

72. Let B = "Sum is 5". Then $n(B) = 2$ and $P(B) = \dfrac{2}{9}$.

74. Let C = "Sum is 7". Then $n(C) = 0$ and $P(C) = 0$.

76. Let D = "An even number". Then $D(5)$ and $P(D) = \dfrac{5}{9}$.

For Problems 78–84, the sample space S is the set of all 5-card hands. Then $n(S) = C_{52,5}$. The outcomes are equally likely.

78. Let A = "5 numbered cards, (2 through 10)". Then

$$n(A) = C_{36,5}. \text{ Thus, } P(A) = \frac{C_{36,5}}{C_{52,5}} = \frac{\frac{36!}{5!\,31!}}{\frac{52!}{5!\,47!}} \approx 0.145$$

80. Let B = "Four of a kind".
O_1: Choose 2 different face values
N_1: $C_{13,2}$

O_2: Choose 4 from a face value
N_2: $C_{4,4} = 1$

O_3: Choose 1 from the other face value
N_3: $C_{4,1} = 4$

Thus, $n(B) = 2C_{13,2} \cdot C_{4,4} \cdot C_{4,1}$ and $P(B) = \dfrac{2C_{13,2} \cdot C_{4,4} \cdot C_{4,1}}{C_{52,5}} \approx 0.00024$.

(Note: the factor 2 is there because once you choose two different face values, say 3 and 9, then you can choose four 3 and one 9 or four 9 and one 3.)

82. Let C = "2, 3, 4, 5, and 6, all in the same suit".
Then $n(C) = 4$ since there are only 4 suits.
Thus, $P(C) = \dfrac{4}{C_{52,5}} \approx 0.000\ 0015$

84. Let D = "2 kings and 3 aces".
The number of ways we can choose 2 kings is $C_{4,2}$;
The number of ways we can choose 3 aces is $C_{4,3}$.

Therefore, $n(D) = C_{4,2} \cdot C_{4,3}$ and $P(D) = \dfrac{C_{4,2} \cdot C_{4,3}}{C_{52,5}} \approx 0.000\ 009$.

86. (A) Answer depends on the results of simulation.

(B) In this case, $n(S) = 4$ and probability of each outcome is $\dfrac{1}{4} = 0.25$.

88. (A) Select 400 random integers from the integers 1 through 12.

(B) Answer depends on the results of simulation.

(C) $n(S) = 12$, so $P(8) = \dfrac{1}{12} \approx 0.83$.

90. (A) The sample space S is the set of all possible permutations of the 6 brands taken 3 at a time, and $n(S) = P_{6,3}$. Thus, the probability of selecting 3 brands and identifying them correctly, with no answer repeated, is: $\dfrac{1}{P_{6,3}} \approx 0.0083$

(B) In this case $n(S) = 6 \cdot 6 \cdot 6 = 6^3$ and the probability of the event in question is $\dfrac{1}{n(S)} = \dfrac{1}{6^3} \approx 0.0046$.

92. (A) Let A = "3 from A and 1 from B". Then

$n(A) = C_{15,3} \cdot C_{20,1}$ and $n(S) = C_{35,4}$. Thus $P(A) = \dfrac{C_{15,3} \cdot C_{20,1}}{C_{35,4}} \approx 0.174$

(B) Let B = "2 from A and 2 from B". Then

$n(B) = C_{15,2} \cdot C_{20,2}$. Thus $P(B) = \dfrac{C_{15,2} \cdot C_{20,2}}{C_{35,4}} \approx 0.381$

(C) Let C = "All from A". Then

$n(A) = C_{15,4}$ and $P(A) = \dfrac{C_{15,4}}{C_{35,4}} \approx 0.026$

(D) Let D = "At least 3 from A", then
$$P(D) = P(\text{Exactly 3 from } A) + P(4 \text{ from } A)$$
$$= P(A) + P(C) \text{ (from parts (A) and (C) above)}$$
$$\approx 0.174 + 0.026 \approx 0.200$$

94. Let A = "5 particular centers chosen", then $n(A) = 1$ and $n(S) = C_{8,5}$.

Thus, $P(A) = \dfrac{1}{C_{8,5}} \approx 0.018$.

EXERCISE 8-2

2. $P(A \cup B) = \dfrac{n(A \cup B)}{100} = \dfrac{n(A) + n(B) - n(A \cap B)}{100} = \dfrac{60 + 45 - 15}{100} = .90$

4. $P(A \cap B') = \dfrac{n(A \cap B')}{100} = \dfrac{45}{100} = .45$

6. $P((A \cap B)') = 1 - P(A \cap B) = 1 - \dfrac{n(A \cap B)}{100} = 1 - \dfrac{15}{100} = 1 - .15 = .85$

8. $P(F) = \dfrac{12}{52} = \dfrac{3}{13}$ since there are 4 suits and each has 3 faces.

10. $P(D') = \dfrac{39}{52} = \dfrac{3}{4}$ since there are 13 diamonds and 39 others (hearts, clubs, spades).

12. $P(D' \cap F) = \dfrac{9}{52}$ since there are 9 faces which are not diamonds.

14. $P(D' \cup F) = P(D') + P(F) - P(D' \cap F)$

From Exercises 8, 10, and 12, we have:

$$P(F) = \frac{3}{13}, \quad P(D') = \frac{3}{4}, \quad P(D' \cap F) = \frac{9}{52},$$

so

$$P(D' \cup F) = \frac{3}{4} + \frac{3}{13} - \frac{9}{52}$$

$$= \frac{39}{52} + \frac{12}{52} - \frac{9}{52} = \frac{39 + 12 - 9}{52} = \frac{42}{52} = \frac{21}{26}$$

16. $P(D' \cap F') = \frac{30}{52} = \frac{15}{26}$ since there are 39 non-diamond cards of which only 9 are face cards. So, there are 30 non-diamond and non-face cards.

18. $P(D' \cup F') = P(D') + P(F') - P(D' \cap F')$.

From Exercises 8, 10, and 16, we have:

$$P(F') = 1 - P(F) = 1 - \frac{3}{13} = \frac{10}{13}, \quad P(D') = \frac{3}{4} \quad \text{and}$$

$$P(D' \cap F') = \frac{15}{26}.$$

Thus,

$$P(D' \cup F') = \frac{3}{4} + \frac{10}{13} - \frac{15}{26}$$

$$= \frac{39}{52} + \frac{40}{52} - \frac{30}{52} = \frac{39 + 40 - 30}{52} = \frac{49}{52}$$

20. Let E be the event that the number drawn is divisible by 4. Then $E = \{4, 8, 12, 16, 20, 24\}$ and $P(E) = \frac{6}{25}$.

Let F be the event that the number drawn is divisible by 7. Then $F = \{7, 14, 21\}$ and $P(F) = \frac{3}{25}$.

Since E and F are mutually exclusive, from (1) we obtain $P(E \cup F) = \frac{6}{25} + \frac{3}{25} = \frac{9}{25} = .36$.

22. Let A be the event that the number drawn is odd. Then $A = \{1, 3, 5, 7, 9, 11, 13, 15, 17, 19, 21, 23, 25\}$ and $P(A) = \frac{13}{25}$.

Let B be the event that the number drawn is greater than 15. Then $B = \{16, 17, 18, 19, 20, 21, 22, 23, 24, 25\}$ and $P(B) = \frac{10}{25}$.

Note that $A \cap B = \{17, 19, 21, 23, 25\}$ and $P(A \cap B) = \frac{5}{25}$.

Thus by (2), $P(A \cup B) = \frac{13}{25} + \frac{10}{25} - \frac{5}{25} = \frac{18}{25} = .72$.

24. Let C be the event that the number drawn is less than 12. Then $P(C) = \dfrac{11}{25}$. Let D be the event that the number drawn is greater than 13, then $P(D) = \dfrac{12}{25}$. Note that C and D are mutually exclusive so by (1) $P(C \cup D) = P(C) + P(D) = \dfrac{23}{25} = .92$.

26. Let A be the even that an automobile tire fails in less than 50,000 miles. Then A' will be the event that the tire does not fail in 50,000 miles. Thus, $P(A') = 1 - P(A) = 1 - .03 = .97$.

28. $P(\text{sum of 9 or 10}) = P(\text{sum of 9}) + P(\text{sum of 10})$
$$= \frac{4}{36} + \frac{3}{36} = \frac{7}{36}$$

30. $P(\underbrace{\text{the number on the first die is a 1}}_{A} \ \text{or} \ \underbrace{\text{the number on the second die is less than 3}}_{B})$

$= P(A) + P(B) - P(A \cap B)$

$= \dfrac{6}{36} + \dfrac{12}{36} - \dfrac{2}{36} = \dfrac{16}{36} = \dfrac{4}{9}$

32. (A) $P(E) = \dfrac{3}{5}$,

$\quad P(E') = 1 - P(E) = \dfrac{2}{5}$

$\quad$ Odds for $E = \dfrac{P(E)}{P(E')}$

$\qquad = \dfrac{3/5}{2/5}$

$\qquad = \dfrac{3}{2}$ (3 to 2)

$\quad$ Odds against $E = \dfrac{P(E')}{P(E)}$

$\qquad = \dfrac{2/5}{3/5}$

$\qquad = \dfrac{2}{3}$ (2 to 3)

(B) $P(E) = \dfrac{1}{7}$, $P(E') = 1 - \dfrac{1}{7} = \dfrac{6}{7}$

$\quad$ Odds for $E = \dfrac{P(E)}{P(E')}$

$\qquad = \dfrac{1/7}{6/7} = \dfrac{1}{6}$ (1 to 6)

$\quad$ Odds against $E = \dfrac{P(E')}{P(E)}$

$\qquad = \dfrac{6}{1}$ (6 to 1)

(C) $P(E) = 0.6$, $P(E') = 1 - 0.6 = 0.4$

$\quad$ Odds for $E = \dfrac{0.6}{0.4} = \dfrac{3}{2}$ (3 to 2)

$\quad$ Odds against $E = \dfrac{0.4}{0.6} = \dfrac{2}{3}$ (2 to 3)

(D) $P(E) = 0.35$, $P(E') = 1 - 0.35 = 0.65$

$\quad$ Odds for $E = \dfrac{0.35}{0.65} = \dfrac{7}{13}$ (7 to 13)

$\quad$ Odds against $E = \dfrac{0.65}{0.35} = \dfrac{13}{7}$ (13 to 7)

34. (A) Odds for $E = \dfrac{5}{9}$, $P(E) = \dfrac{5}{5+9} = \dfrac{5}{14}$

(B) Odds for $E = \dfrac{4}{3}$, $P(E) = \dfrac{4}{4+3} = \dfrac{4}{7}$

(C) Odds for $E = \dfrac{3}{7}$, $P(E) = \dfrac{3}{3+7} = 0.3$

(D) Odds for $E = \dfrac{23}{77}$, $P(E) = \dfrac{23}{23+77} = 0.23$

36. Odds for $E = \dfrac{P(E)}{P(E')} = \dfrac{a}{b}$ and

Odds against $E = \dfrac{P(E')}{P(E)} = \dfrac{b}{a}$ or $b : a$

So, the statement is true.

38. False. The theoretical probability of heads on one flip of a fair coin is $\dfrac{1}{2}$. If we flip this coin n times and let n_H be the number of times heads show up, the empirical probability of heads will be $\dfrac{n_H}{n}$ which may not be $\dfrac{1}{2}$.

40. False. Flip a fair coin twice and let E be the event that both flips result in heads and F be the event that both result in tails. Then
$S = \{HH, HT, TH, TT\}$
$A = \{HH\}$
$B = \{TT\}$
A and B are mutually exclusive but not complementary since clearly $A \cup B \neq S$.

42. Let E = "a number divisible by 3 in a single roll of a die".
$\qquad = \{3, 6\}$
Thus, (assuming that the die is fair)
$\quad P(E) = \dfrac{2}{6} = \dfrac{1}{3}$.
The odds in favor of $E = \dfrac{P(E)}{P(E')} = \dfrac{1/3}{2/3} = \dfrac{1}{2}$ (1 to 2), 1 : 2

44. Let E = "1 head when a single coin is tossed twice"
$\qquad = \{HT, TH\}$.
Thus, (assuming that the coin is fair or balanced)
$\quad P(E) = \dfrac{2}{4} = \dfrac{1}{2}$.
The odds in favor of $E = \dfrac{P(E)}{P(E')} = \dfrac{1/2}{1/2} = \dfrac{1}{1}$ (1 to 1), 1 : 1

46. Let E = "2 heads when a single coin is tossed twice".

Then E = {HH} and $P(E) = \dfrac{1}{4}$, $P(E') = \dfrac{3}{4}$.

Odds against $E = \dfrac{P(E')}{P(E)} = \dfrac{3/4}{1/4} = \dfrac{3}{1}$ (3 to 1), 3:1

48. Let E = "an odd number or a number divisible by 3 in a single roll of a die".

Then E = {1, 3, 5, 6} and $P(E) = \dfrac{4}{6} = \dfrac{2}{3}$, $P(E') = \dfrac{1}{3}$.

Odds against $E = \dfrac{P(E')}{P(E)} = \dfrac{1/3}{2/3} = \dfrac{1}{2}$ (1 to 2), 1:2

50. (A) Let E = "a sum of 10 in a single roll of two fair dice".

Then E = {(4, 6), (5, 5), (6, 4)}, $P(E) = \dfrac{3}{36} = \dfrac{1}{12}$

and $P(E') = \dfrac{11}{12}$.

Odds for $E = \dfrac{P(E)}{P(E')} = \dfrac{1/12}{11/12} = \dfrac{1}{11}$ (1 to 11), 1:11

(B) The house should pay $11 for the game to be fair.

52. (A) Let A = "the sum is a prime number or is exactly divisible by 4".

Then $P(A)$ = P(sum 2) + P(sum 3) + P(sum 5) + P(sum 7)
$\qquad\qquad$ + P(sum 11) + P(sum 4) + P(sum 8) + P(sum 12)

$\qquad = \dfrac{10 + 30 + 70 + 150 + 80 + 50 + 170 + 70}{1000} = \dfrac{630}{1000} = 0.63$

The odds for $A = \dfrac{P(A)}{P(A')} = \dfrac{0.63}{0.37} = \dfrac{63}{37}$ (63 to 37), 63:37

(B) Let B = "the sum is an odd number or is exactly divisible by 3".

Then $P(B)$ = P(sum 3) + P(sum 5) + P(sum 7) + P(sum 9)
$\qquad\qquad$ + P(sum 11) + P(sum 6) + P(sum 12)

$\qquad = \dfrac{650}{1000} = \dfrac{65}{100} = 0.65$

OR $P(B)$ = P(sum odd) + P(sum divisible by 3)
$\qquad\qquad$ - P("sum odd" $\cap$ "sum divisible by 3")

$\qquad = \dfrac{30 + 70 + 150 + 140 + 80}{1000} + \dfrac{30 + 110 + 140 + 70}{1000} - \dfrac{30 + 140}{1000}$

$\qquad = \dfrac{470}{1000} + \dfrac{350}{1000} - \dfrac{170}{1000} = \dfrac{650}{1000} = 0.65$

The odds for $B = \dfrac{P(B)}{P(B')} = \dfrac{0.65}{0.35} = \dfrac{65}{35} = \dfrac{13}{7}$ (13 to 7), 13:7

54. Let A = "a king or a heart is drawn". Then

$P(A) = P(\text{a king}) + P(\text{a heart}) - P(\text{a king of hearts})$

$$= \frac{4}{52} + \frac{13}{52} - \frac{1}{52} = \frac{16}{52} = \frac{4}{13}$$

Odds for $A = \dfrac{P(A)}{P(A')} = \dfrac{4/13}{9/13} = \dfrac{4}{9}$ (4 to 9), 4:9

56. Let B = "a heart or a number less than 7".

Then $P(B) = P(\text{a heart}) + P(\text{a number less than 7})$

$- P(\text{"a heart"} \cap \text{"a number less than 7"})$

Thus, $P(B) = \dfrac{13}{52} + \dfrac{24}{52} - \dfrac{6}{52} = \dfrac{31}{52}$, $P(B') = 1 - \dfrac{31}{52} = \dfrac{21}{52}$

Odds for $B = \dfrac{P(B)}{P(B')} = \dfrac{31/52}{21/52} = \dfrac{31}{21}$ (31 to 21), 31:21

58. Let A = "at least 1 black card in a 7-card hand dealt from a standard 52-card deck".

Then A' = "0 black cards in a 7-card hand dealt from a standard 52-card deck".

$n(A') = C_{26,7}$ since there are 26 black cards.

$n(S) = C_{52,7}$

Thus, $P(A') = \dfrac{C_{26,7}}{C_{52,7}}$ and hence $P(A) = 1 - \dfrac{C_{26,7}}{C_{52,7}} = 1 - 0.005 = 0.995$

60. Let A = "the selected number is divisible by 6"

B = "the selected number is divisible by 9".

Then $P(A \cup B) = P(A) + P(B) - P(A \cap B)$

A number divisible by 6 will be $6k$ for $k = 1, 2, \ldots, 100$, therefore $n(A) = 100$.

A number divisible by 9 will be $9k'$ for $k' = 1, 2, \ldots, 66$, therefore $n(B) = 66$.

A number divisible by 6 and by 9 is divisible by 18 and will be $18k$ for $k = 1, 2, \ldots, 33$.

Thus, $P(A \cup B) = \dfrac{100}{600} + \dfrac{66}{600} - \dfrac{33}{600} = \dfrac{133}{600} \approx 0.2217$.

62. In general, $P(A \cup B \cup C) = P(A) + P(B) + P(C) - P(A \cap B) - P(B \cap C)$
$- P(A \cap C) + P(A \cap B \cap C)$.

If the 3 events are pairwise mutually exclusive, then
$P(A \cap B) = P(B \cap C) = P(C \cap A) = P(A \cap B \cap C) = \varnothing$
and hence $P(A \cup B \cup C) = P(A) + P(B) + P(C)$.

66. $n(S) = \underbrace{100 \times 100 \ldots \times 100}_{n \text{ times}} = 100^n$, because each person is free to choose any of the numbers between 1 and 100.

Let A = "at least two people choose the same number".

Then A' = "all n people choose different numbers".

Note that $n(A') = P_{100,n} = \dfrac{100!}{(100 - n)!}$ and hence $P(A') = \dfrac{100!}{(100 - n)!\,100^n}$.

Thus, $P(A) = 1 - P(A') = 1 - \dfrac{100!}{(100 - n)!\,100^n}$.

---

70. (A) The command selects 50 random integers from 2 through 12. Unlike the sum of a pair of dice, a 2 is just as likely as a 7.

(B) Selecting a ball at random from a box containing 11 balls numbered 2 through 12, repeated 50 times.

(C) Answer depends on the results of simulation.

(D) $\dfrac{1}{11} + \dfrac{1}{11} = \dfrac{2}{11} \approx 0.182$

72. (A) Let A = "the selected student owns a car", and
B = "the selected student owns a stereo".

Then $P(A) = \dfrac{450}{1000} = 0.45$, $P(B) = \dfrac{750}{1000} = 0.75$

and $P(A \cap B) = \dfrac{350}{1000} = 0.35$

Now, P(the student does not own a car)
$= P(A') = 1 - P(A) = 1 - 0.45 = 0.55$

(B) P(the student owns a car but not a stereo)
$= P(A \cap B') = P(A) - P(A \cap B) = 0.45 - 0.35 = 0.10$.

74. (A) Let A = "the driver has an accident"
B = "the driver drives more than 15,000 miles per year".
Then $P(A) = 0.3$, $P(B) = 0.5$, and $P(A \cap B) = 0.15$.
Thus, $P(A \cup B) = P(A) + P(B) - P(A \cap B) = 0.3 + 0.5 - 0.15 = 0.65$

(B) $P(A \cap B') = P(A) - P(A \cap B) = 0.3 - 0.15 = 0.15$

76. Let A = "at least one union employee is selected".
Then A' = "no union employee is selected".

Therefore, $n(A') = C_{12,4}$, $n(S) = C_{20,4}$, and $P(A') = \dfrac{C_{12,4}}{C_{20,4}}$.

Thus, $P(A) = 1 - P(A') = 1 - \dfrac{C_{12,4}}{C_{20,4}} \approx 0.90$.

78. Let A = "1 or more defective found in a sample of 10"
then A' = "no defective found in a sample of 10".
$$n(A') = C_{33,10}, \ n(S) = C_{40,10}, \ P(A') = \frac{C_{33,10}}{C_{40,10}}$$
and $P(A) = 1 - \dfrac{C_{33,10}}{C_{40,10}} = 0.89.$

80. (A) Let A = "the selected animal is a chimpanzee",
$\quad\quad\quad B$ = "the selected animal is a dog",
$\quad\quad\quad C$ = "the selected animal is a male",
$\quad$ and D = "the selected animal is other than a female monkey".
Then $P(A) = \dfrac{10}{30} = \dfrac{1}{3}, \ P(B) = \dfrac{10}{30} = \dfrac{1}{3}, \ P(C) = \dfrac{11}{30}, \ $ and $P(D) = \dfrac{23}{30}.$

$$P(A \cup B) = P(A) + P(B) = \frac{1}{3} + \frac{1}{3} = \frac{2}{3} \approx 0.67$$

(B) $P(A \cup C) = P(A) + P(C) - P(A \cap C)$
$$= \frac{1}{3} + \frac{11}{30} - \frac{6}{30} = \frac{15}{30} = \frac{1}{2} = 0.5$$

(C) $P(D) = \dfrac{23}{30} \approx 0.$

82. Let A = "the resident is a Democrat",
$\quad\quad B$ = "prefers candidate B",
and C = "has no preference".
Then $P(A) = \dfrac{500}{1000} = 0.5, \ P(B) = \dfrac{530}{1000} = 0.53,$

$\quad\quad P(C) = \dfrac{85}{1000} = 0.085, \ P(A \cap B) = \dfrac{250}{1000} = 0.25,$

$\quad P(C \cap D) = \dfrac{50}{1000} = 0.05.$

(A) $P(A \cup B) = P(A) + P(B) - P(A \cap B)$
$$= 0.5 + 0.53 - 0.25 = 0.78$$
The odds for this event
$$= \frac{0.78}{1 - 0.78} = \frac{0.78}{0.22} = \frac{78}{22} = \frac{39}{11} \quad (39 \text{ to } 11), \ 39{:}11.$$

(B) $P(D' \cap C) = P(C) - P(D \cap C) = 0.085 - 0.05 = 0.035$

The odds against this event $= \dfrac{1 - 0.035}{0.035} = \dfrac{965}{35} = \dfrac{193}{7}$ (193 to 7),

$\quad 193{:}7.$

2. $P(E) = .80$
See the given table.

4. $P(C \cap E) = .14$
See the given table.

6. $P(C|E) = \dfrac{P(C \cap E)}{P(E)} = \dfrac{.14}{.80} = .175$

8. $P(E|C) = \dfrac{P(E \cap C)}{P(C)} = \dfrac{.14}{.20} = .7$

10. $P(E|A) = \dfrac{P(E \cap A)}{P(A)} = \dfrac{0.40}{0.50} = 0.80$

12. $P(B|B) = \dfrac{P(B \cap B)}{P(B)} = \dfrac{P(B)}{P(B)} = \dfrac{.3}{.3} = 1$

14. $P(A) = 0.50$, $P(E) = 0.80$, $P(A \cap E) = 0.40$.
Since $P(A \cap E) = 0.40 = P(A)P(E) = (0.50)(0.80) = 0.40$, the events A and E are independent OR from problem 10, $P(A|E) = 0.50$ which is equal to $P(A) = 0.5$, so A and E are independent.

16. Dependent. Observe that:
$P(E) = 0.80$, $P(B) = 0.30$ and $P(E \cap B) = 0.26$
and
$P(E \cap B) = 0.26 \neq P(E)P(B) = (0.80)(0.30) = 0.24$

18. $P(C) = 0.20$, $P(C|E) \approx 0.18$ (from problem 6).
Since $P(C) \neq P(C|E)$, the events C and E are dependent.

20. Dependent. Observe that the event D and E are complementary events and hence they are mutually exclusive. That means if one occurs, the other cannot occur, so they are dependent events.

22. (A) Since the rolls are independent, probability of getting a 6 on the fifth roll is $\dfrac{1}{6}$ regardless of what happened on the first four rolls.

(B) $n(S) = 6 \cdot 6 \cdot 6 \cdot 6 \cdot 6 = 6^5$ and if A = "same number turns up each time", then $n(A) = 6$ (either 1, 2, 3, 4, 5, 6) and
$P(A) = \dfrac{6}{6^5} = \dfrac{1}{6^4} \approx 0.000772$.

24. Let E = "pointer lands on an odd number",
and F = "pointer lands on a prime number".
Then $P(E) = 0.3 + 0.2 + 0.1 = 0.6$ $(E = \{1, 3, 5\})$
$\qquad P(F) = 0.1 + 0.2 + 0.1 = 0.4$ $(F = \{2, 3, 5\})$
$\quad P(E \cap F) = 0.2 + 0.1 = 0.3$ $(E \cap F = \{3, 5\})$

(A) $P(F|E) = \dfrac{P(F \cap E)}{P(E)} = \dfrac{0.3}{0.6} = \dfrac{1}{2}.$

(B) Since $P(F|E) = \dfrac{1}{2} \neq P(F) = 0.4$, these two events are not independent.

OR Since $P(E \cap F) = 0.3 \neq P(E)P(F) = (0.6)(0.4) = 0.24$,
the events E and F are not independent.

26. (A) $P(N \cap R) = P(N) \cdot P(R|N) = (0.7)(0.2) = 0.14.$

(B) $P(S) = P(M \cap S) + P(N \cap S) = P(M) \cdot P(S|M) + P(N) \cdot P(S|N)$
$\qquad\qquad\qquad\qquad\qquad = (0.3)(0.6) + (0.7)(0.8)$
$\qquad\qquad\qquad\qquad\qquad = 0.18 + 0.56 = 0.74$

28. $E_1 = \{HH, HT\}$, $E_3 = \{HT, TT\}$, $E_4 = \{HH, TH\}$, $E_1 \cap E_3 = \{HT\}$,
$E_3 \cap E_4 = \varnothing$.

(A) E_1 and E_3 are independent (and not mutually exclusive) since

$$P(E_1 \cap E_3) = \frac{1}{4} = P(E_1) \cdot P(E_3) = \left(\frac{2}{4}\right)\left(\frac{2}{4}\right) = \frac{1}{4}.$$

(B) E_3 and E_4 are mutually exclusive (and dependent) since they have
no common elements.

30. Let A = "at least 5 on the first throw",
and B = "at least 5 on the second throw".
Since the throws are independent , the events A and B are

independent. Thus, $P(A \cap B) = P(A)P(B) = \left(\dfrac{2}{6}\right)\left(\dfrac{2}{6}\right) = \dfrac{1}{9}.$

$P(A \cup B) = P(A) + P(B) - P(A \cap B)$
$\qquad\qquad = \dfrac{2}{6} + \dfrac{2}{6} - \dfrac{1}{9} = \dfrac{1}{3} + \dfrac{1}{3} - \dfrac{1}{9} = \dfrac{5}{9}$

32. Let A = "the first selected card is red",
and B = "the second selected card is red".
Then we are interested in computing $P(A \cap B)$.

$P(A \cap B) = P(A) \cdot P(B|A)$

(A) Without replacement: $P(A) = \dfrac{26}{52} = \dfrac{1}{2}$ since there are 26 red cards

in a deck. After the selection of a red card, the deck will have 51
cards left of which 25 are red. So probability of choosing a
second   red card given that the first selected card was red is

$P(B|A) = \dfrac{25}{51}.$ Therefore

$$P(A \cap B) = \left(\frac{1}{2}\right)\left(\frac{25}{51}\right) = \frac{25}{102} \approx 0.245$$

(B) With replacement: In this case $P(A) = P(A) = \dfrac{26}{52}$ and $P(B|A) = \dfrac{26}{52}$

and hence $P(A \cap B) = \left(\dfrac{26}{52}\right)^2 = \dfrac{1}{4} = 0.25$.

34. We note that $n(M) = 13$, $n(N) = 20$ (since the even cards are 2, 4, 6, 8, 10 and there are 4 of each), $n(M \cap N) = 5$ (since there are only 5 even diamond cards).

(A) $P(N|M) = \dfrac{P(N \cap M)}{P(M)} = \dfrac{\frac{5}{52}}{\frac{13}{52}} = \dfrac{5}{13}$.

(B) $P(N) = \dfrac{20}{52} = \dfrac{5}{13}$. Since $P(N|M) = P(N)$, the events M and N are independent.

OR Since $P(M \cap N) = \dfrac{5}{52} = P(M)P(N) = \dfrac{13}{52} \times \dfrac{20}{52} \times \dfrac{5}{52}$ these events are independent.

36. (A) 2 coins are tossed.
Note that $S = \{HH, HT, TH, TT\}$, $A = \{HH\}$, $B = \{HH, TT\}$ and $P(A) = \dfrac{1}{4}$, $P(B) = \dfrac{2}{4} = \dfrac{1}{2}$.

$A \cap B = \{HH\}$ and hence $P(A \cap B) = \dfrac{1}{4}$.

A and B are independent since $P(A \cap B) = \dfrac{1}{4} \neq P(A)\ P(B) = \dfrac{1}{4} \times \dfrac{1}{2} = \dfrac{1}{8}$

(B) 3 coins are tossed.
In this case, $S = \{HHH, HHT, HTH, HTT, THH, THT, TTH, TTT\}$
$A = \{HHH, HHT, HTH, THH\}$, $B = \{HHH, TTT\}$
$A \cap B = \{HHH\}$
Thus, $P(A) = \dfrac{4}{8} = \dfrac{1}{2}$, $P(B) = \dfrac{2}{8} = \dfrac{1}{4}$, and $P(A \cap B) = \dfrac{1}{8}$.
The events A and B are independent since
$P(A \cap B) = \dfrac{1}{8} = P(A)P(B) = \left(\dfrac{1}{2}\right)\left(\dfrac{1}{4}\right) = \dfrac{1}{8}$.

38. (A)

$P(R_2) = P(R_1 \cap R_2) + P(W_1 \cap R_2)$
$= P(R_1)P(R_2|R_1) + P(W_1)P(R_2|W_1)$
$= \left(\dfrac{2}{7}\right)\left(\dfrac{2}{7}\right) + \left(\dfrac{5}{7}\right)\left(\dfrac{2}{7}\right) = \dfrac{2}{7}$

(B)

$$P(R_2) = \left(\frac{2}{7}\right)\left(\frac{1}{6}\right) + \left(\frac{5}{7}\right)\left(\frac{2}{6}\right) = \frac{2}{7}$$

which is the same as in (A).

(Are you surprised to get the same answer?)

40. (A) From problem 38 part (A) we have:

P(both balls have the same color) $= P(R_1 \cap R_2) + P(W_1 \cap W_2)$

$$= P(R_1)P(R_2|R_1) + P(W_1)P(W_2|W_1)$$

$$= \left(\frac{2}{7}\right)\left(\frac{2}{7}\right) + \left(\frac{5}{7}\right)\left(\frac{5}{7}\right) = \frac{4}{49} + \frac{25}{49} = \frac{29}{49}$$

(B) From problem 38 part (B) we have:

P(both balls have the same color) $= P(R_1 \cap R_2) + P(W_1 \cap W_2)$

$$= P(R_1)P(R_2|R_1) + P(W_1)P(W_2|W_1)$$

$$= \left(\frac{2}{7}\right)\left(\frac{1}{6}\right) + \left(\frac{5}{7}\right)\left(\frac{4}{6}\right) = \frac{2}{42} + \frac{20}{42} = \frac{22}{42} = \frac{11}{21}$$

42. False. Let $P(A) = 0.4$, $P(B) = 0.3$ and $P(A \cap B) = 0.12$. Then clearly A and B are independent since $P(A \cap B) = P(A)P(B)$.

However, $P(A|B) = \dfrac{P(A \cap B)}{P(B)} = \dfrac{P(A)P(B)}{P(B)} = P(A) = 0.4$

and $P(B|A) = \dfrac{P(A \cap B)}{P(A)} = \dfrac{P(A)P(B)}{P(A)} = P(B) = 0.3$

and thus, $P(A|B) \neq P(B|A)$.

44. False. Consider the sample space
$S = \{HH, HT, TH, TT\}$ and the events $A = \{HH, HT, TH\}$, $B = \{TH, HT\}$.
Then $P(A \cap B) = P(B)$ and $P(A|B) = \dfrac{P(A \cap B)}{P(B)} = \dfrac{P(B)}{P(B)} = 1$ which is not less than or equal to $P(B)$ since $B \neq S$.

48. True. Observe that:

$$P(W_1 \cap R_2) = P(W_1)P(R_2|W_1) = \left(\frac{n}{n+m}\right)\left(\frac{m}{n+m-1}\right) = \frac{nm}{(n+m)(n+m-1)};$$

$$P(R_1 \cap W_2) = P(R_1)P(W_2|R_1) = \left(\frac{m}{n+m}\right)\left(\frac{n}{n+m-1}\right) = \frac{nm}{(n+m)(n+m-1)}.$$

So, $P(W_1 \cap R_2) = P(R_1 \cap W_2)$.

50.

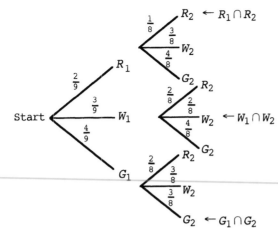

$P(\text{both balls are the same color})$

$= P(R_1 \cap W_2) + P(W_1 \cap W_2) + P(G_1 \cap G_2)$

$= P(R_1)P(R_2|R_1) + P(W_1)P(W_2|W_1)$
$\qquad\qquad + P(G_1)P(G_2|G_1)$

$= \left(\dfrac{2}{9}\right)\left(\dfrac{1}{8}\right) + \left(\dfrac{3}{9}\right)\left(\dfrac{2}{8}\right) + \left(\dfrac{4}{9}\right)\left(\dfrac{3}{8}\right) = \dfrac{5}{12}$

52. (A) $P(\text{Ann wins the match}) = P(W_1 \cap W_2) + P(W_1 \cap L_2 \cap W_3) + P(L_1 \cap W_2 \cap W_3)$,
where W_i is the event that Ann wins the ith set and L_i is the
event that Ann loses the ith set. Thus, $P(\text{Ann wins the match}) =$
$P(W_1)P(W_2) + P(W_1)P(L_2)P(W_3) + P(L_1)P(W_2)P(W_3) =$
$\left(\dfrac{2}{3}\right)\left(\dfrac{2}{3}\right) + \left(\dfrac{2}{3}\right)\left(\dfrac{1}{3}\right)\left(\dfrac{2}{3}\right) + \left(\dfrac{1}{3}\right)\left(\dfrac{2}{3}\right)\left(\dfrac{2}{3}\right) = \dfrac{20}{27}$

(B) $P(\text{3 sets are played}) = P(\text{Ann wins in 3 sets}) + P(\text{Barbara wins in 3 sets})$.
$P(\text{Ann wins in 3 sets}) = P(W_1 \cap L_2 \cap W_3) + P(L_1 \cap W_2 \cap W_3)$
$= P(W_1)P(L_2)P(W_3) + P(L_1)P(W_2)P(W_3)$
$= \left(\dfrac{2}{3}\right)\left(\dfrac{1}{3}\right)\left(\dfrac{2}{3}\right) + \left(\dfrac{1}{3}\right)\left(\dfrac{2}{3}\right)\left(\dfrac{2}{3}\right) = \dfrac{8}{27}$

$P(\text{Barbara wins in 3 sets}) = \left(\dfrac{1}{3}\right)\left(\dfrac{2}{3}\right)\left(\dfrac{1}{3}\right) + \left(\dfrac{2}{3}\right)\left(\dfrac{1}{3}\right)\left(\dfrac{1}{3}\right) = \dfrac{4}{27}$

Thus, $P(\text{sets are played}) = \dfrac{8}{27} + \dfrac{4}{27} = \dfrac{12}{27} = \dfrac{4}{9}$

(C) $P(\text{Ann wins the match}) + P(\text{Barbara wins the match})$
$= P(W_1 \cap W_2) + P(W_1 \cap L_2 \cap W_3) + P(W_1{}^* \cap W_2{}^*)$
$\qquad\qquad\qquad + P(W_1{}^* \cap L_2{}^* \cap W_3{}^*)$,
where $W_i{}^*$, $L_i{}^*$ refer to Barbara's winning and losing events
per set.
$= \left(\dfrac{2}{3}\right)\left(\dfrac{2}{3}\right) + \left(\dfrac{2}{3}\right)\left(\dfrac{1}{3}\right)\left(\dfrac{2}{3}\right) + \left(\dfrac{1}{3}\right)\left(\dfrac{1}{3}\right) + \left(\dfrac{1}{3}\right)\left(\dfrac{2}{3}\right)\left(\dfrac{1}{3}\right)$
$= \dfrac{12 + 4 + 3 + 2}{27} = \dfrac{21}{27} = \dfrac{7}{9}$

54. Suppose that $P(A|B) = P(A)$. Then $P(A \cap B) = P(B)P(A|B) = P(B)P(A)$,
and hence A and B are independent. Now suppose that $P(B|A) = P(B)$.
Then
$P(A \cap B) = P(A)P(B|A) = P(A)P(B)$, and hence A and B are independent.

56. $P(A|B) + P(A'|B) = \dfrac{P(A \cap B)}{P(B)} + \dfrac{P(A' \cap B)}{P(B)}$

$$= \dfrac{P(A \cap B) + P(A' \cap B)}{P(B)} = \dfrac{P(B)}{P(B)} = 1$$

58. If $P(B) \neq 0$ and if $B \subseteq A$, then $P(B \cap A) = P(B)$. From the formula:

$P(A|B) = \dfrac{P(A \cap B)}{P(B)} = \dfrac{P(B)}{P(B)} = 1.$

60. Let A = "car is produced at plant A"
     B = "car has defective emission control devices".
Then $P(A) = 0.37$, $P(B|A) = 0.05$.
$P(A \cap B) = P(A)P(B|A) = (0.37)(0.05) = 0.0185.$

62.

(A) P(passing on the first or second try)
   $= P(P_1) + P(F_1 \cap P_2) = 0.40 + P(F_1)P(P_2|F_1)$
   $= 0.40 + (0.60)(0.60) = 0.40 + 0.36 = 0.76$

(B) $P(F_1 \cap F_2 \cap P_3) = (0.60)(0.40)(0.20)$
                             $= 0.048$

(C) $P(F_1 \cap F_2 \cap F_3) = (0.60)(0.40)(0.80)$
                             $= 0.192$

64. (A)

	F	F'	Totals
C	0.002	0.024	0.026
C'	0.518	0.456	0.974
Total	0.520	0.480	1.000

(B) $P(F|C) = \dfrac{P(F \cap C)}{P(C)} = \dfrac{0.002}{0.026} = \dfrac{1}{13} \approx 0.077$

(C) $P(C|F') = \dfrac{P(C \cap F')}{P(F')} = \dfrac{0.024}{0.480} = 0.05$

(D) No. $P(C|F') \neq P(C)$ (E) No. $P(F|C) \neq P(F)$

66. Let D = "the selected person is a member of the Democratic party",
and V = "the selected person voted in the last election".
Then $P(D) = 0.55$ and $P(V|D) = 0.60$.
P(the selected person is a member of the Democratic party **and** voted
in the last election) $= P(D \cap V) = P(D)P(V|D) = (0.55)(0.60) = 0.33.$

2. $P(N \cap B) = P(N)P(B|N) = (0.4)(0.7) = 0.28$

4. $P(B) = P(M \cap B) + P(N \cap B) = P(M)P(B|M) + P(N)P(B|N)$
$$= (0.6)(0.2) + (0.4)(0.7) = 0.4$$

6. $P(N|B) = \dfrac{P(N \cap B)}{P(N \cap B) + P(M \cap B)} = \dfrac{P(N)P(B|N)}{P(B)} = \dfrac{(0.4)(0.7)}{0.4} = \dfrac{0.28}{0.4} = 0.7$

8. Referring to the Venn diagram:

$$P(U_2|R) = \frac{P(U_2 \cap R)}{P(R)} = \frac{\frac{35}{100}}{\frac{60}{100}} = \frac{35}{60} = \frac{7}{12} \approx 0.58$$

Using Bayes' formula:

$$P(U_2|R) = \frac{P(U_2 \cap R)}{P(U_1 \cap R) + P(U_2 \cap R)} = \frac{P(U_2)P(R|U_2)}{P(U_1)P(R|U_1) + P(U_2)P(R|U_2)}$$

$$= \frac{\left(\frac{60}{100}\right)\left(\frac{35}{60}\right)}{\left(\frac{40}{100}\right)\left(\frac{25}{40}\right) + \left(\frac{60}{100}\right)\left(\frac{35}{60}\right)} = \frac{0.35}{0.60} = \frac{35}{60} = \frac{7}{12} \approx 0.58$$

10. Referring to the Venn diagram:

$$P(U_2|R') = \frac{P(U_2 \cap R')}{P(R')} = \frac{\frac{25}{100}}{\frac{40}{100}} = \frac{25}{40} = 0.625$$

Using Bayes' formula:

$$P(U_2|R') = \frac{P(U_2)P(R|U_2)}{P(U_1)P(R|U_1) + P(U_2)P(R|U_2)}$$

$$= \frac{\left(\frac{60}{100}\right)\left(\frac{25}{60}\right)}{\left(\frac{40}{100}\right)\left(\frac{15}{40}\right) + \left(\frac{60}{100}\right)\left(\frac{25}{60}\right)} = \frac{0.25}{0.15 + 0.25} = \frac{0.25}{0.40} = 0.625$$

12. Referring to tree diagram:

$$P(V|C') = \frac{P(V \cap C')}{P(C')} = \frac{P(V \cap C')}{P(U \cap C') + P(V \cap C') + P(W \cap C')}$$

$$= \frac{P(V)P(C'|V)}{P(U)P(C'|U) + P(V)P(C'|V) + P(W)P(C'|W)}$$

$$= \frac{(0.5)(0.8)}{(0.2)(0.6) + (0.5)(0.8) + (0.3)(0.4)} = 0.63$$

14. $P(U|C') = \dfrac{(0.2)(0.6)}{(0.2)(0.6) + (0.5)(0.8) + (0.3)(0.4)} = 0.19$

16. $P(W|C') = \dfrac{(0.3)(0.4)}{(0.2)(0.6) + (0.5)(0.8) + (0.3)(0.4)} = 0.19$

18. From the Venn diagram:

$$P(U_2|R') = \frac{P(U_2 \cap R')}{P(R')} = \frac{\frac{20}{100}}{\frac{60}{100}} = \frac{1}{3} \approx 0.33$$

Using Bayes' formula:

$$P(U_2|R') = \frac{P(U_2)P(R' \mid U_2)}{P(U_1)P(R' \mid U_1) + P(U_2)P(R' \mid U_2) + P(U_3)P(R' \mid U_3)}$$

$$P(U_2|R') = \frac{\left(\frac{35}{100}\right)\left(\frac{20}{35}\right)}{\left(\frac{15}{100}\right)\left(\frac{10}{15}\right) + \left(\frac{35}{100}\right)\left(\frac{20}{35}\right) + \left(\frac{50}{100}\right)\left(\frac{30}{50}\right)} = \frac{0.20}{0.10 + 0.20 + 0.30}$$

$$= \frac{0.20}{0.60} = \frac{1}{3} \approx 0.33$$

20. From Venn diagram:

$$P(U_1|R') = \frac{P(U_1 \cap R')}{P(R')} = \frac{\frac{10}{100}}{\frac{60}{100}} = \frac{10}{60} = \frac{1}{6} \approx 0.17$$

Using Bayes' formula:

$$P(U_1|R') = \frac{P(U_1)P(R' \mid U_1)}{P(U_1)P(R' \mid U_1) + P(U_2)P(R' \mid U_2) + P(U_3)P(R' \mid U_3)}$$

$$= \frac{0.10}{0.10 + 0.20 + 0.30} = \frac{0.10}{0.60} = \frac{1}{6} \approx 0.17$$

22. From Venn diagram:

$$P(U_3|R') = \frac{P(U_3 \cap R')}{P(R')} = \frac{\frac{30}{100}}{\frac{60}{100}} = \frac{30}{60} = \frac{1}{2} = 0.50$$

Using Bayes' formula:

$$P(U_3|R') = \frac{P(U_3)P(R' \mid U_3)}{P(U_1)P(R' \mid U_1) + P(U_2)P(R' \mid U_2) + P(U_3)P(R' \mid U_3)}$$

$$= \frac{0.30}{0.10 + 0.20 + 0.30} = \frac{0.30}{0.60} = \frac{30}{60} = \frac{1}{2} = 0.50$$

24. From the first tree we have

$$P(D) = P(A \cap D) + P(B \cap D) + P(C \cap D)$$
$$= P(A)P(D|A) + P(B)P(D|B) + P(C)P(D|C)$$
$$= \left(\frac{1}{3}\right)\left(\frac{1}{8}\right) + \left(\frac{1}{3}\right)\left(\frac{3}{8}\right) + \left(\frac{1}{3}\right)\left(\frac{1}{4}\right)$$
$$= \frac{1}{3}\left(\frac{1}{8} + \frac{3}{8} + \frac{2}{8}\right) = \frac{1}{3}\left(\frac{6}{8}\right) = \frac{1}{4}$$

Thus, $P(D') = 1 - P(D) = 1 - \dfrac{1}{4} = \dfrac{3}{4}$

$$P(A|D) = \frac{P(A \cap D)}{P(D)} = \frac{P(A)P(D|A)}{P(D)} = \frac{\left(\frac{1}{3}\right)\left(\frac{1}{8}\right)}{\frac{1}{4}} = \frac{1}{6}$$

$$P(B|D) = \frac{P(B \cap D)}{P(D)} = \frac{P(B)P(D|B)}{P(D)} = \frac{\left(\frac{1}{3}\right)\left(\frac{3}{8}\right)}{\frac{1}{4}} = \frac{1}{2}$$

$$P(C|D) = \frac{P(C \cap D)}{P(D)} = \frac{P(C)P(D|C)}{P(D)} = \frac{\left(\frac{1}{3}\right)\left(\frac{1}{4}\right)}{\frac{1}{4}} = \frac{1}{3}$$

$$P(A|D') = \frac{P(A \cap D')}{P(D')} = \frac{P(A)P(D'|A)}{P(D')} = \frac{\left(\frac{1}{3}\right)\left(\frac{7}{8}\right)}{\frac{3}{4}} = \frac{7}{18}$$

$$P(B|D') = \frac{P(B \cap D')}{P(D')} = \frac{P(B)P(D'|B)}{P(D')} = \frac{\left(\frac{1}{3}\right)\left(\frac{5}{8}\right)}{\frac{3}{4}} = \frac{5}{18}$$

$$P(C|D') = \frac{P(C \cap D')}{P(D')} = \frac{P(C)P(D'|C)}{P(D')} = \frac{\left(\frac{1}{3}\right)\left(\frac{3}{4}\right)}{\frac{3}{4}} = \frac{1}{3}$$

Therefore, we
have:

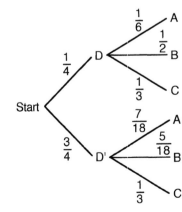

The following tree diagram is to be used for Problems 26 and 28.

26. $P(U_2|W) = \dfrac{P(U_2)P(W\mid U_2)}{P(U_1)P(W\mid U_1) + P(U_2)P(W\mid U_2)}$

$= \dfrac{(0.5)(0.6)}{(0.5)(0.2) + (0.5)(0.6)} = \dfrac{0.30}{0.10 + 0.30} = \dfrac{3}{4} = 0.75$

28. $P(U_1|R) = \dfrac{P(U_1)P(R\mid U_1)}{P(U_1)P(R\mid U_1) + P(U_2)P(R\mid U_2)}$

$= \dfrac{(0.5)(0.8)}{(0.5)(0.8) + (0.5)(0.4)} = \dfrac{0.40}{0.60} = \dfrac{2}{3} \approx 0.67$

30. $P(R_1|R_2) = \dfrac{P(R_1)P(R_2\mid R_1)}{P(R_1)P(R_2\mid R_1) + P(W_1)P(R_2\mid W_1)}$

$= \dfrac{\left(\dfrac{4}{9}\right)\left(\dfrac{3}{8}\right)}{\left(\dfrac{4}{9}\right)\left(\dfrac{3}{8}\right) + \left(\dfrac{5}{9}\right)\left(\dfrac{4}{8}\right)} = \dfrac{\left(\dfrac{4}{9}\right)\left(\dfrac{3}{8}\right)}{\dfrac{4}{9}\left(\dfrac{3}{8} + \dfrac{5}{8}\right)} = \dfrac{\left(\dfrac{4}{9}\right)\left(\dfrac{3}{8}\right)}{\dfrac{4}{9}(1)} = \dfrac{3}{8}$

32. $P(U_{W_1}|U_{W_2}) = \dfrac{P(U_{W_1})P(U_{W_2}\mid U_{W_1})}{P(U_{W_1} \cap U_{W_2}) + P(U_{R_1} \cap U_{W_2})}$

$= \dfrac{P(U_{W_1})P(U_{W_2}\mid U_{W_1})}{P(U_{W_1})P(U_{W_2}\mid U_{W_1}) + P(U_{R_1})P(U_{W_2}\mid U_{R_1})}$

$= \dfrac{\left(\dfrac{3}{10}\right)\left(\dfrac{6}{10}\right)}{\left(\dfrac{3}{10}\right)\left(\dfrac{6}{10}\right) + \left(\dfrac{7}{10}\right)\left(\dfrac{5}{10}\right)} \approx 0.34$

The tree diagram follows:

where U_{R_1} is red from urn 1,

U_{R_2} is red from urn 2,

U_{W_1} is white from urn 1,

and U_{W_2} is white from urn 2.

34. Suppose $c = d = e = f$, then

$P(M) = be + ac = bc + ac = (b + a)c = c$

$P(N) = ad + bf = ac + bc = (b + a)c = c$

$P(M \cap N) = 0$, since M and N are mutually exclusive. Thus,

$P(M \cap N) = 0 \neq P(M)P(N) = c^2$, i.e. M and N are dependent.

36. (A) False:

Example: Suppose an urn contains 2 blue balls and 3 while balls:

$P(B_1 | W_2) = \dfrac{P(B_1)P(W_2 | B_1)}{P(W_2)}$

$= \dfrac{\left(\dfrac{2}{5}\right)\left(\dfrac{3}{5}\right)}{\left(\dfrac{2}{5}\right)\left(\dfrac{3}{5}\right) + \left(\dfrac{3}{5}\right)\left(\dfrac{3}{5}\right)} = \dfrac{6}{15} = \dfrac{2}{5}$

$P(W_2 | B_1) = \dfrac{3}{5} \neq \dfrac{2}{5}$

(B) False:

Example: We use the same urn as in (A):

$P(B_1 | W_2) = \dfrac{\left(\dfrac{2}{5}\right)\left(\dfrac{3}{4}\right)}{\left(\dfrac{2}{5}\right)\left(\dfrac{3}{4}\right) + \left(\dfrac{3}{5}\right)\left(\dfrac{2}{4}\right)} = \dfrac{\left(\dfrac{2}{5}\right)\left(\dfrac{3}{4}\right)}{\dfrac{3}{5}\left(\dfrac{2}{4} + \dfrac{2}{4}\right)} = \dfrac{1}{2}$

$P(W_2 | B_1) = \dfrac{3}{4} \neq \dfrac{1}{2}$

38. Let E_1 = "the first ball chosen has number 4 on it",
E_2 = "the first ball chosen has a number less than 4 on it",
and E_3 = "the first ball chosen has a number greater than 4 on it".
Let A = "the second ball has number 4 on it".
Then we are interested in computing $P(E_2 | A)$.

$P(E_2 | A) = \dfrac{P(E_2)P(A | E_2)}{P(E_1)P(A | E_1) + P(E_2)P(A | E_2) + P(E_3)P(A | E_3)}$

$= \dfrac{\left(\dfrac{3}{10}\right)\left(\dfrac{1}{9}\right)}{\left(\dfrac{1}{10}\right)(0) + \left(\dfrac{3}{10}\right)\left(\dfrac{1}{9}\right) + \left(\dfrac{6}{10}\right)\left(\dfrac{1}{9}\right)} = \dfrac{1}{3}$

For the second part, let
F_1 = "the first ball chosen has number 4 on it",
F_2 = "the first ball chosen has an even number different from 4 on it",
and F_3 = "the first ball chosen has an odd number on it".

We are interested in computing $P(F_2|A)$ where A is defined above.

$$P(F_2|A) = \frac{P(F_2)P(A\mid F_2)}{P(F_1)P(A\mid F_1) + P(F_2)P(A\mid F_2) + P(F_3)P(A\mid F_3)}$$

$$P(F_2|A) = \frac{\left(\frac{4}{10}\right)\left(\frac{1}{9}\right)}{\left(\frac{1}{10}\right)(0) + \left(\frac{4}{10}\right)\left(\frac{1}{9}\right) + \left(\frac{5}{10}\right)\left(\frac{1}{9}\right)} = \frac{4}{9}$$

40. $P(\text{choosing a club}\mid 2 \text{ out of } 3 \text{ cards are clubs}) = \dfrac{2}{3}$

42. If the chosen card is a club, then we need to compute probability of choosing 2 cards from 51 cards so that only one of the two cards is a club. This probability is:

$$\frac{C_{12,1} \cdot C_{39,1}}{C_{51,2}} = \frac{12 \times 39}{\dfrac{51 \times 50}{2}} = 0.367$$

44. If the chosen card is not a club, then we need to compute probability of choosing 2 cards, none of which is a club. This probability is:

$$\frac{C_{38,2}}{C_{51,2}} = \frac{\dfrac{38 \times 37}{2}}{\dfrac{51 \times 50}{2}} = 0.551$$

Note that 52 − (one non club) − (13 clubs) = 38
of which 2 have to be chosen.

46. $P(U_1|E) = \dfrac{P(U_1 \cap E)}{P(U_1 \cap E) + P(U_2 \cap E)}$

$$= \frac{\dfrac{n(U_1 \cap E)}{n(S)}}{\dfrac{n(U_1 \cap E)}{n(S)} + \dfrac{n(U_2 \cap E)}{n(s)}} = \frac{n(U_1 \cap E)}{n(U_1 \cap E) + n(U_2 \cap E)}$$

48. Consider the following tree diagram:

Let A = "the person hired has work experience".
We must find $P(S|A)$.

$$P(S|A) = \frac{P(S)P(A\mid S)}{P(S)P(A\mid S) + P(NS)P(AN\mid S)}$$

$$= \frac{(0.75)(0.80)}{(0.75)(0.80) + (0.25)(0.40)} \approx 0.86$$

Now we want to compute $P(S \mid A')$.

$$P(S \mid A') = \frac{P(S)P(A' \mid S)}{P(S)P(A' \mid S) + P(NS)P(A' \mid NS)}$$

$$= \frac{(0.75)(0.20)}{(0.75)(0.20) + (0.25)(0.60)} = 0.50$$

50. Consider the following tree diagram:

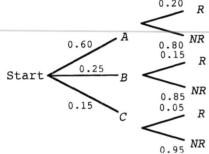

where R = "a computer is returned for service during warranty period".

Want to compute:

$$P(A \mid R) = \frac{P(A)P(R \mid A)}{P(A)P(R \mid A) + P(B)P(R \mid B) + P(C)P(R \mid C)}$$

$$= \frac{(0.60)(0.20)}{(0.60)(0.20) + (0.25)(0.15) + (0.15)(0.05)} = 0.73;$$

$$P(B \mid R) = \frac{(0.25)(0.15)}{P(R)} = 0.23; \quad P(C \mid R) = \frac{(0.15)(0.05)}{P(R)} = 0.05$$

52. Consider the following tree diagram:

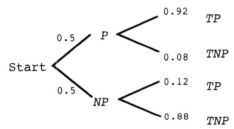

where TP means test shows pregnancy and TNP test does not show pregnancy.

$$P(TP) = P(P)P(TP \mid P) + P(NP)P(TP \mid NP)$$
$$= (0.5)(0.92) + (0.5)(0.12) = 0.52$$

Now, the question is $P(P \mid TP) = \dfrac{P(P)P(TP \mid P)}{P(TP)} = \dfrac{(0.5)(0.92)}{0.52} \approx 0.88$

Finally, we need to compute $P(NP \mid TNP)$.

$$P(NP \mid TNP) = \frac{P(NP)P(TNP \mid NP)}{P(NP)P(TNP \mid NP) + P(P)P(TNP \mid P)}$$

$$= \frac{(0.5)(0.88)}{(0.5)(0.88) + (0.5)(0.08)} \approx 0.92$$

54. Consider the following tree diagram:

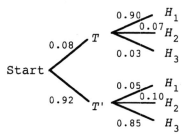

where T means the subject has tuberculosis and T' means the subject does not have tuberculosis. H_1 means the test shows the subject has tuberculosis; H_2 means the test is inconclusive; H_3 means the test indicates no tuberculosis.

We are asked to compute $P(T \mid H_1)$.

$$P(T \mid H_1) = \frac{P(T)P(H_1 \mid T)}{P(T)P(H_1 \mid T) + P(T')P(H_1 \mid T')}$$

$$= \frac{(0.08)(0.90)}{(0.08)(0.90) + (0.92)(0.05)} \approx 0.61$$

Finally,

$$P(T' \mid H_2) = \frac{P(T')P(H_2 \mid T')}{P(T')P(H_2 \mid T') + P(T)P(H_2 \mid T)}$$

$$P(T' \mid H_2) = \frac{(0.92)(0.10)}{(0.92)(0.10) + (0.08)(0.07)} \approx 0.94$$

56. Consider the following tree diagram:

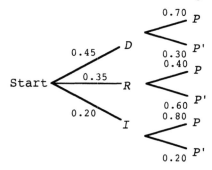

where P means voted in favor of a park and recreation land proposal. The question is $P(R \mid P) = ?$, $P(I \mid P) = ?$, $P(D \mid P) = ?$

$$P(R \mid P) = \frac{P(R)P(P \mid R)}{P(D)P(P \mid D) + P(R)P(P \mid R) + P(I)P(P \mid I)}$$

$$= \frac{(0.35)(0.40)}{(0.45)(0.70) + (0.35)(0.40) + (0.20)(0.80)} \approx 0.23;$$

$$P(I \mid P) = \frac{P(I)P(P \mid I)}{P(P)} = \frac{(0.20)(0.80)}{P(P)} \approx 0.26;$$

$$P(D \mid P) = \frac{P(D)P(P \mid D)}{P(P)} = \frac{(0.45)(0.70)}{P(P)} \approx 0.51$$

EXERCISE 8-5

2. Expected value of X:

$$E(X) = (-2)(0.1) + (-1)(0.2) + (0)(0.4) + (1)(0.2) + (2)(0.1) = 0$$

4. A family with two children may have 0, 1, or 2 boys.

$$P(0 \text{ boys}) = P(GG) = \left(\frac{1}{2}\right)\left(\frac{1}{2}\right) = \frac{1}{4}$$

$$P(1 \text{ boy}) = P(BG) + P(GB) = \frac{1}{4} + \frac{1}{4} = \frac{1}{2}$$

$$P(2 \text{ boys}) = P(BB) = \frac{1}{4}$$

Thus, the probability distribution is given by:

x_i	0	1	2
p_i	$\frac{1}{4}$	$\frac{1}{2}$	$\frac{1}{4}$

$$E(X) = 0 \cdot \frac{1}{4} + 1 \cdot \frac{1}{2} + 2 \cdot \frac{1}{4} = 1.$$

6. Assign a payoff of $1 to the event of observing a head and -$1 to the event of observing a tail. Thus, the probability distribution for X is:

x_i	-1	1
p_i	0.45	0.55

Hence, $E(X) = (-1)(0.45) + (1)(0.55) = 0.10$ or 10¢.
The game is not fair since $E(X) \neq 0$.

8. The table shows a payoff or probability distribution for the game.

Net gain x_i	-2.50	-1.50	-0.50	0.50	1.50	2.50
p_i	$\frac{1}{6}$	$\frac{1}{6}$	$\frac{1}{6}$	$\frac{1}{6}$	$\frac{1}{6}$	$\frac{1}{6}$

$$E(X) = (-2.50)\left(\frac{1}{6}\right) + (-1.50)\left(\frac{1}{6}\right) + (-0.50)\left(\frac{1}{6}\right) + (0.50)\left(\frac{1}{6}\right) + (1.50)\left(\frac{1}{6}\right)$$
$$+ (2.50)\left(\frac{1}{6}\right) = 0.$$

The game is fair.

10. The probability distribution is:

Number of Heads	Gain, x_i	Probability, p_i
0	2	$\frac{1}{4}$
1	$-x$	$\frac{1}{2}$
2	2	$\frac{1}{4}$

The expected value is:

$$E(X) = 2 \cdot \frac{1}{4} + (-x) \cdot \frac{1}{2} + 2 \cdot \frac{1}{4} = 0$$

or $\frac{x}{2} = 1$, $x = 2$. So if you lose $2 if a head and a tail turn up, then the game will be fair.

12. $P(\text{at least one } 5) = 1 - P(\text{no 5 in 3 rolls}) = 1 - \left(\dfrac{5}{6}\right)^3$

So, your net gain is $-\$10$ with a probability of $1 - \left(\dfrac{5}{6}\right)^3$ and is $\$7$

with a probability of $\left(\dfrac{5}{6}\right)^3$.

Thus, $E(X) = (-10)\left[1 - \left(\dfrac{5}{6}\right)^3\right] + (7)\left(\dfrac{5}{6}\right)^3 \approx -\$0.16$.

14. Let $x =$ amount you should win if a number not divisible by 3 turns up. Payoff table or probability distribution for this game is:

Net gain x_i	-12	x
p_i	$\dfrac{2}{6}$	$\dfrac{4}{6}$

$P(\text{die shows a number divisible by 3})$

$= P(3) + P(6) = \dfrac{1}{6} + \dfrac{1}{6} = \dfrac{2}{6}$

Game is fair if $E(X) = 0$, i.e. $(-12)\left(\dfrac{2}{6}\right) + x\left(\dfrac{4}{6}\right) = 0$ or $x = \$6$.

16. Probability distribution for this game is:

Number of Heads	Gain, x_i	Probability, p_i
0	3	$\dfrac{1}{8}$
1	x	$\dfrac{3}{8}$
2	-2	$\dfrac{3}{8}$
3	-3	$\dfrac{1}{8}$

This game is fair if $E(X) = (3)\left(\dfrac{1}{8}\right) + x\left(\dfrac{3}{8}\right) + (-2)\left(\dfrac{3}{8}\right) + (-3)\left(\dfrac{1}{8}\right) = 0$

or $3 + 3x - 6 - 3 = 0$ or $3x = 6$, $x = \$2$.

18. Assign a payoff of $-\$4$ to the event of drawing a non-diamond card and $\$10$ to the event of drawing a diamond card. Thus, the probability distribution for x, your net gain, is:

x_i	-\$4	\$10
p_i	$\dfrac{39}{52}$	$\dfrac{13}{52}$

Hence, $E(X) = (-4)\left(\dfrac{39}{52}\right) + 10\left(\dfrac{13}{52}\right) = -\dfrac{26}{52} = -\$0.50$.

20. Assign a payoff of -$4 to the event that the hand contains no diamonds and $10 to the event that the hand contains at least one diamond. Thus, the probability distribution for x, your net gain, is:

x_i	-$4	$10
p_i	$\dfrac{C_{39,5}}{C_{52,5}}$	$1 - \dfrac{C_{39,5}}{C_{52,5}}$

Hence, $E(X) = (-4)\left(\dfrac{C_{39,5}}{C_{52,5}}\right) + 10\left(1 - \dfrac{C_{39,5}}{C_{52,5}}\right) = 10 - 14\left(\dfrac{C_{39,5}}{C_{52,5}}\right)$

$$= 10 - 14\frac{\frac{39!}{5!\,34!}}{\frac{52!}{5!\,47!}} = 10 - 14 \cdot \frac{39 \cdot 38 \cdot 37 \cdot 36 \cdot 35}{52 \cdot 51 \cdot 50 \cdot 49 \cdot 48}$$

$$= 10 - 14(.2215) = 10 - 3.10 = 6.90$$

22. A_1: $E(X) = (500)(0.2) + (1,200)(0.4) + (1,200)(0.3) + (1,200)(0.1)$

$\qquad = 100 + 960 = \$1,060$

A_2: $E(X) = (400)(0.2) + (1,100)(0.4) + (1,800)(0.3) + (1,800)(0.1)$

$\qquad = 80 + 440 + 720 = \$1,240$

A_3: $E(X) = (300)(0.2) + (1,000)(0.4) + (1,700)(0.3) + (2,400)(0.1)$

$\qquad = 60 + 400 + 510 + 240 = \$1,210$

A_2 will produce the largest expected value, which is $1,240.

24. The payoff table or probability distribution for the net gain X is:

payoff table

x_i	$1	-$1
p_i	$\dfrac{18}{38}$	$\dfrac{20}{38}$

$E(X) = (1)\left(\dfrac{18}{38}\right) + (-1)\left(\dfrac{20}{38}\right) = -\dfrac{2}{38} = -\dfrac{1}{19} = -\$0.05$

26. Let p = probability of winning. Then

$-0.50 = E(X) = (18)(p) + (-2)(1 - p)$.

We solve this equation for p:

$20p - 2 = 0.50$

$\qquad 20p = 1.5$

$\qquad\quad p = \dfrac{1.5}{20} = 0.075$

28. Let X = net gain, then the probability distribution of x is:

Net gain x_i	-2	98	498	998
p_i	$\dfrac{9984}{10,000}$	$\dfrac{10}{10,000}$	$\dfrac{4}{10,000}$	$\dfrac{2}{10,000}$

$E(X) = (-2)(0.9984) + (98)(0.001) + (498)(0.0004) + (998)(0.0002)$
$= -\$1.50$

30. (A) Total number of outcomes = $n(S) = C_{8,2}$

$$= \frac{8!}{2!(8-2)!} = \frac{8!}{2!6!} = \frac{8 \times 7 \times 6!}{2 \times 6!} = 28$$

$P(\text{zero defective}) = P(0) = \dfrac{C_{5,2}}{C_{8,2}} = \dfrac{\frac{5!}{2!\,3!}}{28} = \dfrac{10}{28} = \dfrac{5}{14}$

$P(\text{one defective}) = P(1) = \dfrac{C_{5,1} \cdot C_{3,1}}{C_{8,2}} = \dfrac{5 \cdot 3}{28} = \dfrac{15}{28}$

$P(\text{two defectives}) = P(2) = \dfrac{C_{3,2}}{C_{8,2}} = \dfrac{3}{28}$

Probability distribution of X, the number of defectives in the sample is:

x_i	0	1	2
p_i	$\dfrac{5}{14}$	$\dfrac{15}{28}$	$\dfrac{3}{28}$

(B) $E(X) = (0)\left(\dfrac{5}{14}\right) + (1)\left(\dfrac{15}{28}\right) + (2)\left(\dfrac{3}{28}\right)$

$= \dfrac{15}{28} + \dfrac{6}{28} = \dfrac{21}{28} = \dfrac{3}{4} = 0.75$

32. (A) The total number of outcomes $n(s) = C_{1000,10}$

$P(0 \text{ winning ticket}) = P(0) = \dfrac{C_{997,10}}{C_{1000,10}} \approx 0.970$

$P(1 \text{ winning ticket}) = P(1) = \dfrac{C_{3,1} \cdot C_{997,9}}{C_{1000,10}} \approx 0.0295$

$P(2 \text{ winning tickets}) = P(2) = \dfrac{C_{3,2} \cdot C_{997,8}}{C_{1000,10}} \approx 0.000\ 268$

$P(3 \text{ winning tickets}) = P(3) = \dfrac{C_{3,3} \cdot C_{997,7}}{C_{1000,10}} \approx 0.000\ 000\ 722$

The payoff table is as follows:

x_i	-$10	$190	$390	$590
p_i	0.970	0.0295	0.000 268	0.000 000 722

(B) $E(X) = (-10)(0.970) + (190)(0.0295) + (390)(0.000\ 268)$
$$+ (590)(0.000\ 000\ 722) \approx -\$4$$

34. The simulated gain or loss depends on the results of the simulation; the expected loss is $21.05.

36. Consider the following table:

Number of Kings	0	1	2	3
Winning	w	100	200	300
Probability	$\dfrac{C_{48,3}}{C_{52,3}}$	$\dfrac{C_{4,1} \cdot C_{48,2}}{C_{52,3}}$	$\dfrac{C_{4,2} \cdot C_{48,1}}{C_{52,3}}$	$\dfrac{C_{4,3}}{C_{52,3}}$
	0.7826	0.2042	0.0130	0.0002

In order for the game to be fair we need to have expected winning = 0; i.e.
$$w(0.7826) = 100(0.2042) + 200(0.0130) + 300(0.0002)$$
$$w = \frac{23.08}{0.7826} = \$29.49$$

38. The payoff table is as follows:

x_i	-$4,850	$150
p_i	0.01	0.99

$$E(X) = (-4,850)(0.01) + (150)(0.99) = \$100.$$

40. The payoff table for site A is as follows:

x_i	30 million	-3 million
p_i	0.2	0.8

Hence, $E(X) = (30)(0.2) + (-3)(0.8) = \$3.6$ million

The payoff table for site B is as follows:

x_i	70 million	-4 million
p_i	0.11	0.89

Hence, $E(X) = (70)(0.11) + (-4)(0.89) = \$4.14$ million.

The company should choose site B with $E(X) = \$4.14$ million.

42. The payoff table is:

Number of W genes present x_i	p_i
0	0.25
1	0.50
2	0.25

$E(\text{number of } W \text{ genes}) = (0)(0.25) + (1)(0.50) + (2)(0.25) = 1$

EXERCISE 9-1

---

2. $S_1 = S_0 P = [0 \quad 1]\begin{bmatrix} .8 & .2 \\ .4 & .6 \end{bmatrix} = \overset{\overset{A \quad B}{}}{[.4 \quad .6]}$

$\overset{A \quad B}{[.4 \quad .6]}$, the probability of being in state A after one trial is .4 and the probability of being in state B after one trial is .6.

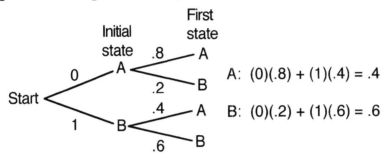

4. $S_1 = S_0 P = [.3 \quad .7]\begin{bmatrix} .8 & .2 \\ .4 & .6 \end{bmatrix} = \overset{\overset{A \quad B}{}}{[.52 \quad .48]}$

$\overset{A \quad B}{[.52 \quad .48]}$, the probability of being in state A after one trial is .52 and the probability of being in state B after one trial is .48.

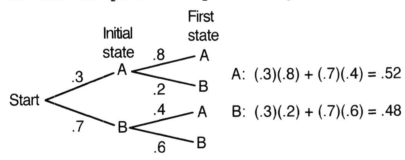

6. $S_2 = S_1 P = [.4 \quad .6]\begin{bmatrix} .8 & .2 \\ .4 & .6 \end{bmatrix} = \overset{\overset{A \quad B}{}}{[.56 \quad .44]}$

$\overset{A \quad B}{[.56 \quad .44]}$, the probability of being in state A after two trials is .56 and the probability of being in state B after two trials is .44.

8. $S_2 = S_1 P = [.52 \quad .48]\begin{bmatrix} .8 & .2 \\ .4 & .6 \end{bmatrix} = \overset{\overset{A \quad B}{}}{[.608 \quad .392]}$

$\overset{A \quad B}{[.608 \quad .392]}$, the probability of being in state A after two trials is .608 and the probability of being in state B after two trials is .392.

10. $\begin{bmatrix} .9 & .1 \\ .4 & .8 \end{bmatrix}$

This matrix cannot be a transition matrix of a Markov chain since the sum of the probabilities in the second row in not 1 (it is 1.2).

12. $\begin{bmatrix} 0 & 1 \\ 1 & 0 \end{bmatrix}$

This matrix can be a transition matrix of a Markov chain.

14. $\begin{bmatrix} .2 & .8 \\ .5 & .5 \\ .9 & .1 \end{bmatrix}$

This matrix cannot be a transition matrix of a Markov chain since it is not a square matrix.

16. $\begin{bmatrix} .3 & .3 & .4 \\ .7 & .2 & .2 \\ .1 & .8 & .1 \end{bmatrix}$

This matrix cannot be a transition matrix of a Markov chain since the sum of the probabilities in the second row is not 1 (it is 1.1).

18.

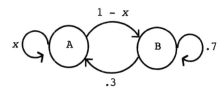

$$\begin{array}{c c} & \begin{array}{c c} A & B \end{array} \\ \begin{array}{c} A \\ B \end{array} & \begin{bmatrix} .1 & .9 \\ .8 & .2 \end{bmatrix} \end{array}$$

20. No. Choose any x, $0 \le x \le 1$, then

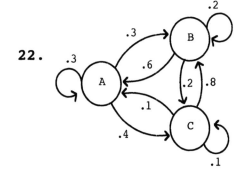

is an acceptable transition diagram, and

$$\begin{array}{c c} & \begin{array}{c c} A & B \end{array} \\ \begin{array}{c} A \\ B \end{array} & \begin{bmatrix} x & 1-x \\ .3 & .7 \end{bmatrix} \end{array}$$ is the corresponding transition matrix.

22.

$$\begin{array}{c c} & \begin{array}{c c c} A & B & C \end{array} \\ \begin{array}{c} A \\ B \\ C \end{array} & \begin{bmatrix} .3 & .3 & .4 \\ .6 & .2 & .2 \\ .1 & .8 & .1 \end{bmatrix} \end{array}$$

24. $a + 0 + .9 = 1$ implies $a = .1$
    $.2 + .3 + b = 1$ implies $b = .5$
    $.6 + c + 0 = 1$ implies $c = .4$

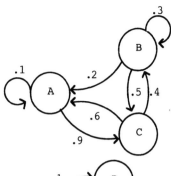

26. $0 + 1 + a = 1$ implies $a = 0$
    $0 + 0 + b = 1$ implies $b = 1$
    $c + .5 + 0 = 1$ implies $c = .5$

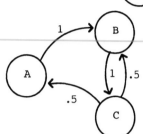

28. No. $a + .8 + .1 = 1$ implies $a = .1$
    $.3 + b + .4 = 1$ implies $b = .3$
    $.6 + .5 + c = 1$ implies $c = -.1$, which is not acceptable.

30.

$$
\begin{array}{c c}
 & \begin{array}{c c} A & B \end{array} \\
\begin{array}{c} A \\ B \end{array} &
\begin{bmatrix} .6 & .4 \\ .8 & .2 \end{bmatrix}
\end{array}
$$

32.

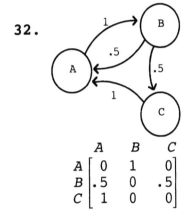

$$
\begin{array}{c c c c}
 & A & B & C \\
\begin{array}{c} A \\ B \\ C \end{array} &
\begin{bmatrix} 0 & 1 & 0 \\ .5 & 0 & .5 \\ 1 & 0 & 0 \end{bmatrix}
\end{array}
$$

34. Using P^2, the probability of going from state B to state C in two trials is the $(2,3)$ position: $.38$.

36. Using P^3 the probability of going from state B to state B in three trials is the $(2,2)$ position: $.336$.

38. $S_2 = S_0 P^2 = \begin{bmatrix} 0 & 1 & 0 \end{bmatrix} \begin{bmatrix} .43 & .35 & .22 \\ .25 & .37 & .38 \\ .17 & .27 & .56 \end{bmatrix} = \begin{array}{ccc} A & B & C \\ [.25 & .37 & .38] \end{array}$

These are the probabilities of going from state B to states A, B, and C in two trials.

40. $S_3 = S_0 P^3 = \begin{bmatrix} 1 & 0 & 0 \end{bmatrix} \begin{bmatrix} .35 & .348 & .302 \\ .262 & .336 & .402 \\ .212 & .298 & .49 \end{bmatrix} = \begin{bmatrix} .35 \\ .348 \\ .302 \end{bmatrix} \begin{array}{c} A \\ B \\ C \end{array}$

These are the probabilities of going from state A to states A, B, and C in three trials.

42. $n = 11$

44. $P = \begin{bmatrix} .8 & .2 \\ .3 & .7 \end{bmatrix}$, $P^2 = \begin{bmatrix} .8 & .2 \\ .3 & .7 \end{bmatrix}\begin{bmatrix} .8 & .2 \\ .3 & .7 \end{bmatrix} = \begin{bmatrix} .7 & .3 \\ .45 & .55 \end{bmatrix}$

$$P^4 = P^2 \cdot P^2 = \begin{bmatrix} .7 & .3 \\ .45 & .55 \end{bmatrix}\begin{bmatrix} .7 & .3 \\ .45 & .55 \end{bmatrix} = \begin{matrix} A \\ B \end{matrix}\begin{bmatrix} .625 & .375 \\ .5625 & .4375 \end{bmatrix} \begin{matrix} A \qquad\quad B \end{matrix}$$

$$S_4 = S_0 P^4 = \begin{bmatrix} .4 & .6 \end{bmatrix}\begin{bmatrix} .625 & .375 \\ .5625 & .4375 \end{bmatrix} = \begin{bmatrix} .5875 & .4125 \end{bmatrix} \quad \begin{matrix} A \qquad\quad B \end{matrix}$$

46. $P = \begin{bmatrix} 0 & 1 & 0 \\ .8 & 0 & .2 \\ 1 & 0 & 0 \end{bmatrix}$, $P^2 = \begin{bmatrix} 0 & 1 & 0 \\ .8 & 0 & .2 \\ 1 & 0 & 0 \end{bmatrix}\begin{bmatrix} 0 & 1 & 0 \\ .8 & 0 & .2 \\ 1 & 0 & 0 \end{bmatrix} = \begin{bmatrix} .8 & 0 & .2 \\ .2 & .8 & 0 \\ 0 & 1 & 0 \end{bmatrix}$,

$$P^4 = P^2 \cdot P^2 = \begin{bmatrix} .8 & 0 & .2 \\ .2 & .8 & 0 \\ 0 & 1 & 0 \end{bmatrix}\begin{bmatrix} .8 & 0 & .2 \\ .2 & .8 & 0 \\ 0 & 1 & 0 \end{bmatrix} = \begin{matrix} A \\ B \\ C \end{matrix}\begin{bmatrix} .64 & .2 & .16 \\ .32 & .64 & .04 \\ .2 & .8 & 0 \end{bmatrix} \begin{matrix} A \quad B \quad C \end{matrix}$$

$$S_4 = S_0 P^4 = \begin{bmatrix} .4 & .2 & .4 \end{bmatrix}\begin{bmatrix} .64 & .2 & .16 \\ .32 & .64 & .04 \\ .2 & .8 & 0 \end{bmatrix} = \begin{bmatrix} .4 & .528 & .072 \end{bmatrix} \quad \begin{matrix} A \quad B \quad C \end{matrix}$$

48. $S_k = S_0 P^k = \begin{bmatrix} 0 & 1 \end{bmatrix}P^k$; the entries in S_k are the entries in the second row of P^k.

50. (A) $P^2 = \begin{bmatrix} .5 & .3 & .1 & .1 \\ 0 & 1 & 0 & 0 \\ 0 & 0 & 1 & 0 \\ .1 & .2 & .3 & .4 \end{bmatrix}\begin{bmatrix} .5 & .3 & .1 & .1 \\ 0 & 1 & 0 & 0 \\ 0 & 0 & 1 & 0 \\ .1 & .2 & .3 & .4 \end{bmatrix}$

$$= \begin{bmatrix} .26 & .47 & .18 & .09 \\ 0 & 1 & 0 & 0 \\ 0 & 0 & 1 & 0 \\ .09 & .31 & .43 & .17 \end{bmatrix},$$

$$P^4 = P^2 \cdot P^2 = \begin{bmatrix} .26 & .47 & .18 & .09 \\ 0 & 1 & 0 & 0 \\ 0 & 0 & 1 & 0 \\ .09 & .31 & .43 & .17 \end{bmatrix}\begin{bmatrix} .26 & .47 & .18 & .09 \\ 0 & 1 & 0 & 0 \\ 0 & 0 & 1 & 0 \\ .09 & .31 & .43 & .17 \end{bmatrix}$$

$$= \begin{matrix} A \\ B \\ C \\ D \end{matrix}\begin{bmatrix} .0757 & .6201 & .2655 & .0387 \\ 0 & 1 & 0 & 0 \\ 0 & 0 & 1 & 0 \\ .0387 & .405 & .5193 & .037 \end{bmatrix} \quad \begin{matrix} A \qquad B \qquad C \qquad D \end{matrix}$$

(B) The probability of going from state A to state D in 4 trials is the element in the (1,4) position: .0387.

(C) The element in the (3,2) position: 0

(D) The element in the (2,1) position: 0

52. If $P = \begin{bmatrix} a & 1-a \\ 1-b & b \end{bmatrix}$ is a probability matrix,

then $0 \le a \le 1$, $0 \le b \le 1$.

$$SP = [c \quad 1-c] \begin{bmatrix} a & 1-a \\ 1-b & b \end{bmatrix}$$

$$= [ac + (1-b)(1-c) \quad c(1-a) + b(1-c)]$$

Now,

$ac + (1-b)(1-c) \ge 0$, $c(1-a) + b(1-c) \ge 0$ since $0 \le c \le 1$ also.

Furthermore,

$ac + (1-b)(1-c) + c(1-a) + b(1-c)$

$\quad = ac + 1 - c - b + bc + c - ac + b - bc = 1$.

Thus, SP is a probability matrix.

54. $P = \begin{bmatrix} .9 & .1 \\ .4 & .6 \end{bmatrix}$

(A) Let $S_0 = [0 \quad 1]$. Then $S_2 = S_0 P^2 = [.6 \quad .4]$

$$S_4 = S_0 P^4 = [.75 \quad .25]$$

$$S_8 = S_0 P^8 = [.796875 \quad .203125]$$

S_k is approaching $[.8 \quad .2]$.

(B) Let $S_0 = [1 \quad 0]$. Then $S_2 = S_0 P^2 = [.85 \quad .15]$

$$S_4 = S_0 P^4 = [.8125 \quad .1875]$$

$$S_8 = S_0 P^8 = [.80078125 \quad .19921875]$$

S_k is approaching $[.8 \quad .2]$.

(C) Let $S_0 = [.5 \quad .5]$. Then $S_2 = S_0 P^2 = [.725 \quad .275]$

$$S_4 = S_0 P^4 = [.78125 \quad .21875]$$

$$S_8 = S_0 P^8 = [.798828125 \quad .201171875]$$

S_k is approaching $[.8 \quad .2]$.

(D) $[.8 \quad .2] \begin{bmatrix} .9 & .1 \\ .4 & .6 \end{bmatrix} = [.8 \quad .2]$

(E) The state matrices appear to approach the same matrix, $S = [.8 \quad .2]$, regardless of the values in the initial state matrix.

56. $P^2 = \begin{bmatrix} .85 & .15 \\ .6 & .4 \end{bmatrix}$, $P^4 = \begin{bmatrix} .8125 & .1875 \\ .75 & .25 \end{bmatrix}$,

$$P^8 = \begin{bmatrix} .80078125 & .19921875 \\ .796875 & .203125 \end{bmatrix}, \dots$$

The matrices P^k are approaching $Q = \begin{bmatrix} .8 & .2 \\ .8 & .2 \end{bmatrix}$; the rows of Q are the

same as the matrix $S = [.8 \quad .2]$ in Problem 54.

58. Let R = denote "rain" and R' "not rain".

(A)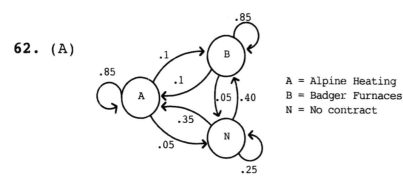

R = Rain
R' = No rain

(B) $\begin{array}{c} \\ R \\ R' \end{array} \begin{array}{cc} R & R' \\ \begin{bmatrix} .6 & .4 \\ .1 & .9 \end{bmatrix} \end{array}$

(C) Rain on Saturday: $P^2 = \begin{array}{c} \\ R \\ R' \end{array} \begin{array}{cc} R & R' \\ \begin{bmatrix} .4 & .6 \\ .15 & .85 \end{bmatrix} \end{array}$

The probability that it will rain on Saturday is .4.

Rain on Sunday: $P^3 = \begin{array}{c} \\ R \\ R' \end{array} \begin{array}{cc} R & R' \\ \begin{bmatrix} .3 & .7 \\ .175 & .825 \end{bmatrix} \end{array}$

The probability that it will rain on Sunday is .3.

60. (A) [diagram: L and K states with .8 self-loop on L, .2 L→K, .3 K→L, .7 self-loop on K] , $\begin{array}{c} \\ L \\ K \end{array} \begin{array}{cc} L & K \\ \begin{bmatrix} .8 & .2 \\ .3 & .7 \end{bmatrix} \end{array}$

$S = [.5 \quad .5]$, $S_1 = SP = [.5 \quad .5]\begin{bmatrix} .8 & .2 \\ .3 & .7 \end{bmatrix} = \begin{array}{cc} L & K \\ [.55 \quad .45] \end{array}$

55% or 55 cars LaGuardia, and 45% or 45 cars Kennedy.

(B) $S_2 = SP^2 = SP \cdot P = [.55 \quad .45]\begin{bmatrix} .8 & .2 \\ .3 & .7 \end{bmatrix} = \begin{array}{cc} L & K \\ [.575 \quad .425] \end{array}$

57.5% or 57.5 LaGuardia, and 42.5% or 42.5 Kennedy.

62. (A) [diagram: states A, B, N with transition probabilities]

A = Alpine Heating
B = Badger Furnaces
N = No contract

(B) $P = \begin{array}{c} \\ A \\ B \\ N \end{array} \begin{array}{ccc} A & B & N \\ \begin{bmatrix} .85 & .1 & .05 \\ .1 & .85 & .05 \\ .35 & .4 & .25 \end{bmatrix} \end{array}$

(C) $S = \begin{array}{ccc} A & B & N \\ [.25 & .3 & .45] \end{array}$

After one year: $SP = \begin{array}{ccc} A & B & N \\ [.4 & .46 & .14] \end{array}$

40% will have service contracts with Alpine next year.

After two years: $SP^2 = \begin{array}{ccc} A & B & N \\ [.435 & .487 & .78] \end{array}$

43.5% will have service contracts with Alpine the year after next.

(D) From part (C), we get 46% and 48.7% respectively.

64. (A)

A = Apprentice
P = Professional
T = Terminated

(B) $P = \begin{matrix} & A & P & T \\ A & \\ P & \\ T & \end{matrix} \begin{bmatrix} .7 & .1 & .2 \\ 0 & 1 & 0 \\ 0 & 0 & 1 \end{bmatrix}$

(C) $S = [.7 \quad .1 \quad .2]$

$$\qquad\qquad\qquad A \qquad P \qquad T$$

within 2 years: $SP = [.49 \quad .17 \quad .34]$

The probability that an apprentice is promoted to professional welder within 2 years is .17.

$$\qquad\qquad\qquad A \qquad\quad P \qquad\quad T$$

Within 4 years: $SP^3 = [.2401 \quad .2533 \quad .5066]$

The probability that an apprentice is promoted to professional welder within 4 years is .2533.

66. (A) $P = \begin{matrix} & LOP & HOP \\ LOP & \\ HOP & \end{matrix} \begin{bmatrix} .7 & .3 \\ .1 & .9 \end{bmatrix}$

(B) $S = \begin{matrix} LOP & HOP \\ [.4 & .6] \end{matrix}$

After last open enrollment period:

$$\qquad\qquad LOP \qquad HOP$$
$$SP = [.34 \qquad .66]$$

34% in LOP and 66% in HOP

(C) After the next open enrollment period: $SP^2 = \begin{matrix} LOP & HOP \\ [.304 & .696] \end{matrix}$

30.4% in LOP and 69.6% in HOP.

68. (A) $P = \begin{matrix} & H & R \\ H & \\ R & \end{matrix} \begin{bmatrix} .979 & .021 \\ .234 & .766 \end{bmatrix}$ $\begin{matrix} H = \text{Homeowner} \\ R = \text{Renter} \end{matrix}$

(B) $S = \begin{matrix} H & R \\ [.584 & .416] \end{matrix}$

2000: $SP = [.584 \quad .416]\begin{bmatrix} .979 & .021 \\ .234 & .766 \end{bmatrix} = \begin{matrix} H & R \\ [.66908 & .33092] \end{matrix}$

66.908% were homeowners and 33.092% were renters in 2000.

$$\qquad\qquad\qquad H \qquad\quad R$$

(C) 2010: $SP^2 = [.73246 \quad .26754]$

73.246% will be homeowners and 26.754% will be renters in 2010.

EXERCISE 9-2

2. $\begin{bmatrix} .3 & .7 \\ .2 & .6 \end{bmatrix}$

This matrix cannot be the transition matrix of a (regular) Markov chain since the sum of the probabilities in the second row is not 1 (it is .8).

4. $P = \begin{bmatrix} .5 & .5 \\ .8 & .2 \end{bmatrix}$

This matrix P can be the transition matrix of a regular Markov chain since all of the entries in P are positive.

6. $P = \begin{bmatrix} .4 & .6 \\ 1 & 0 \end{bmatrix}$

P can be a transition matrix of a regular Markov chain since $P^2 = \begin{bmatrix} .76 & .24 \\ .4 & .6 \end{bmatrix}$ has only positive entries.

8. $\begin{bmatrix} .3 & .7 \\ .2 & .6 \end{bmatrix}$

This matrix cannot be a transition matrix of a (regular) Markov chain since the sum of the probabilities in the second row is not 1 (it is .8).

10. $\begin{bmatrix} .2 & .5 & .3 \\ .6 & .3 & .1 \end{bmatrix}$

This matrix cannot be a transition matrix of a (regular) Markov chain since it is not a square matrix.

12. $P = \begin{bmatrix} .2 & 0 & .8 \\ 0 & 0 & 1 \\ .7 & 0 & .3 \end{bmatrix}$

This cannot be a transition matrix of a regular Markov chain since

$$P^2 = \begin{bmatrix} .6 & 0 & .4 \\ .7 & 0 & .3 \\ .35 & 0 & .65 \end{bmatrix}$$

and therefore no power of P will have all positive entries, since the second column of P^2 has all zeros.

14. $P = \begin{bmatrix} 0 & 0 & 1 \\ .9 & 0 & .1 \\ 0 & 1 & 0 \end{bmatrix}$

This matrix can be a transition matrix of a regular Markov chain

since $P^5 = \begin{bmatrix} .09 & .9 & .01 \\ .009 & .18 & .811 \\ .81 & .01 & .18 \end{bmatrix}$ has all positive entries.

16. Let $S = [s_1 \quad s_2]$, and solve the system:

$$[s_1 \quad s_2]\begin{bmatrix} .8 & .2 \\ .3 & .7 \end{bmatrix} = [s_1 \quad s_2], \ s_1 + s_2 = 1$$

which is equivalent to

$$\begin{array}{ll} .8s_1 + .3s_2 = s_1 & -.2s_1 + .3s_2 = 0 \\ .2s_1 + .7s_2 = s_2 \quad \text{or} & .2s_1 - .3s_2 = 0 \\ s_1 + s_2 = 1 & s_1 + s_2 = 1 \end{array}$$

The solution is: $s_1 = .6, \ s_2 = .4$

Stationary matrix: $S = [.6 \quad .4]$; limiting matrix: $\bar{P} = \begin{bmatrix} .6 & .4 \\ .6 & .4 \end{bmatrix}$.

18. Let $S = [s_1 \quad s_2]$, and solve the system:

$$[s_1 \quad s_2]\begin{bmatrix} .9 & .1 \\ .7 & .3 \end{bmatrix} = [s_1 \quad s_2], \quad s_1 + s_2 = 1$$

which is equivalent to

$$\begin{aligned}
.9s_1 + .7s_2 &= s_1 & -.1s_1 + .7s_2 &= 0 \\
.1s_1 + .3s_2 &= s_2 \quad \text{or} & .1s_1 - .7s_2 &= 0 \\
s_1 + s_2 &= 1 & s_1 + s_2 &= 1
\end{aligned}$$

The solution is: $s_1 = .875$, $s_2 = .125$.

Stationary matrix: $S = [.875 \quad .125]$; limiting matrix: $\bar{P} = \begin{bmatrix} .875 & .125 \\ .875 & .125 \end{bmatrix}$.

20. Let $S = [s_1 \quad s_2 \quad s_3]$, and solve the system:

$$[s_1 \quad s_2 \quad s_3]\begin{bmatrix} .4 & .1 & .5 \\ .2 & .8 & 0 \\ 0 & .5 & .5 \end{bmatrix} = [s_1 \quad s_2 \quad s_3], \quad s_1 + s_2 + s_3 = 1$$

which is equivalent to

$$\begin{aligned}
.4s_1 + .2s_2 &= s_1 & -.6s_1 + .2s_2 &= 0 \\
.1s_1 + .8s_2 + .5s_3 &= s_2 \quad \text{or} & .1s_1 - .2s_2 + .5s_3 &= 0 \\
.5s_1 + .5s_3 &= s_3 & .5s_1 - .5s_3 &= 0 \\
s_1 + s_2 + s_3 &= 1 & s_1 + s_2 + s_3 &= 1
\end{aligned}$$

From the first and third equations, we have $s_2 = 3s_1$, and $s_3 = s_1$.

Substituting these values into the fourth equation, we get:

$$s_1 + 3s_1 + s_1 = 1 \quad \text{or} \quad s_1 = \frac{1}{5}$$

Therefore, $s_2 = \frac{3}{5}$, $s_3 = \frac{1}{5}$.

Stationary matrix: $S = \begin{bmatrix} \frac{1}{5} & \frac{3}{5} & \frac{1}{5} \end{bmatrix} = [.2 \quad .6 \quad .2]$;

limiting matrix: $\bar{P} = \begin{bmatrix} .2 & .6 & .2 \\ .2 & .6 & .2 \\ .2 & .6 & .2 \end{bmatrix}$.

22. Let $S = [s_1 \quad s_2 \quad s_3]$, and solve the system:

$$[s_1 \quad s_2 \quad s_3]\begin{bmatrix} .2 & .8 & 0 \\ .6 & .1 & .3 \\ 0 & .9 & .1 \end{bmatrix} = [s_1 \quad s_2 \quad s_3], \quad s_1 + s_2 + s_3 = 1$$

which is equivalent to

$$\begin{aligned}
.2s_1 + .6s_2 &= s_1 & -.8s_1 + .6s_2 &= 0 \\
.8s_1 + .1s_2 + .9s_3 &= s_2 \quad \text{or} & .8s_1 - .9s_2 + .9s_3 &= 0 \\
.3s_2 + .1s_3 &= s_3 & .3s_2 - .9s_3 &= 0 \\
s_1 + s_2 + s_3 &= 1 & s_1 + s_2 + s_3 &= 1
\end{aligned}$$

From the first and third equations, we have $s_1 = \frac{3}{4}s_2$, and $s_3 = \frac{1}{3}s_2$.

Substituting these values into the fourth equation, we get:

$$\frac{3}{4}s_2 + s_2 + \frac{1}{3}s_2 = 1 \quad \text{or} \quad s_2 = \frac{12}{25} = .48 \text{ and}$$

$$s_1 = \frac{3}{4}(.48) = .36, \quad s_3 = \frac{1}{3}s_2 = \frac{1}{3}(.48) = .16$$

Stationary matrix: $S = [.36 \quad .48 \quad .16]$;

limiting matrix: $\overline{P} = \begin{bmatrix} .36 & .48 & .16 \\ .36 & .48 & .16 \\ .36 & .48 & .16 \end{bmatrix}$.

24. (A) False:

Example: Let $S = [1 \quad 1]$, $P = \begin{bmatrix} .5 & .5 \\ .5 & .5 \end{bmatrix}$.

Then $SP = S$, but $S = [1 \quad 1]$
is not a stationary matrix: $s_1 + s_2 = 2$.

(B) False:

Example: Let $S = [.5 \quad .5]$, $P = \begin{bmatrix} 1 & 0 \\ 0 & 1 \end{bmatrix}$.

Then $SP = S$, but P is not regular since $P^k = \begin{bmatrix} 1 & 0 \\ 0 & 1 \end{bmatrix}$ for any k.

26. $P = \begin{bmatrix} .68 & .32 \\ .19 & .81 \end{bmatrix}$, $P^2 = \begin{bmatrix} .5232 & .4768 \\ .2831 & .7169 \end{bmatrix}$, $P^4 = \begin{bmatrix} .40872032 & .59127968 \\ .35107231 & .64892769 \end{bmatrix}$,

$P^8 = \begin{bmatrix} .3746342231 & .6253657769 \\ .37131093 & .62868907 \end{bmatrix}$, $P^{16} = \begin{bmatrix} .3725559494 & .6274440506 \\ .3725449051 & .6274550949 \end{bmatrix}$

Therefore, $S = [.3725 \quad .6275]$.

28. $P = \begin{bmatrix} .2 & .2 & .6 \\ .5 & 0 & .5 \\ .5 & 0 & .5 \end{bmatrix}$, $P^2 = \begin{bmatrix} .44 & .04 & .52 \\ .35 & .1 & .55 \\ .35 & .1 & .55 \end{bmatrix}$, $P^4 = \begin{bmatrix} .3896 & .0736 & .5368 \\ .3815 & .079 & .5395 \\ .3815 & .079 & .5395 \end{bmatrix}$,

$P^8 = \begin{bmatrix} .3847 & .0769 & .5384 \\ .3846 & .0769 & .5385 \\ .3846 & .0769 & .5385 \end{bmatrix}$, $P^{16} = \begin{bmatrix} .3846 & .0769 & .5385 \\ .3846 & .0769 & .5385 \\ .3846 & .0769 & .5385 \end{bmatrix}$

Therefore, $S = [.3846 \quad .0769 \quad .5385]$.

30. (A)

(B) $P = \begin{array}{c} \\ \text{Red} \\ \text{Blue} \end{array} \begin{array}{c} \text{Red} \quad \text{Blue} \\ \begin{bmatrix} .625 & .375 \\ .25 & .75 \end{bmatrix} \end{array}$

(C) Let $S = [s_1 \quad s_2]$ and solve the system:

$$[s_1 \quad s_2]\begin{bmatrix} .625 & .375 \\ .25 & .75 \end{bmatrix} = [s_1 \quad s_2], \quad s_1 + s_2 = 1,$$

which is equivalent to

$$\begin{array}{ll} .625s_1 + .25s_2 = s_1 & -.375s_1 + .25s_2 = 0 \\ .375s_1 + .75s_2 = s_2 \quad \text{or} & .375s_1 - .25s_2 = 0 \\ s_1 + s_2 = 1 & s_1 + s_2 = 1 \end{array}$$

The solution is: $s_1 = .4$, $s_2 = .6$.

Thus, the stationary matrix is $S = [.4 \quad .6]$. In the long run, the red urn will be selected 40% of the time and the blue urn 60% of the time.

32. (A) $S_1 = [.2 \quad .3 \quad .5] \begin{bmatrix} 0 & 1 & 0 \\ 0 & 0 & 1 \\ 1 & 0 & 0 \end{bmatrix} = [.5 \quad .2 \quad .3]$

$S_2 = S_1 P = [.5 \quad .2 \quad .3] \begin{bmatrix} 0 & 1 & 0 \\ 0 & 0 & 1 \\ 1 & 0 & 0 \end{bmatrix} = [.3 \quad .5 \quad .2]$

$S_3 = S_2 P = [.3 \quad .5 \quad .2] \begin{bmatrix} 0 & 1 & 0 \\ 0 & 0 & 1 \\ 1 & 0 & 0 \end{bmatrix} = [.2 \quad .3 \quad .5]$

$S_4 = [.5 \quad .2 \quad .3]$; $S_5 = [.3 \quad .5 \quad .2]$; $S_6 = [.2 \quad .3 \quad .5]$ and so on.

The state matrices cycle between [.2 .3 .5], [.5 .2 .3], and [.3 .5 .2], hence they do not approach any one matrix.

(B) $S_1 = \begin{bmatrix} \frac{1}{3} & \frac{1}{3} & \frac{1}{3} \end{bmatrix} \begin{bmatrix} 0 & 1 & 0 \\ 0 & 0 & 1 \\ 1 & 0 & 0 \end{bmatrix} = \begin{bmatrix} \frac{1}{3} & \frac{1}{3} & \frac{1}{3} \end{bmatrix}$

$S_2 = S_1 P = \begin{bmatrix} \frac{1}{3} & \frac{1}{3} & \frac{1}{3} \end{bmatrix}$ and so on.

The state matrices are all equal to S_0, hence S_0 is a stationary matrix.

(C) $P = \begin{bmatrix} 0 & 1 & 0 \\ 0 & 0 & 1 \\ 1 & 0 & 0 \end{bmatrix}$, $P^2 = \begin{bmatrix} 0 & 0 & 1 \\ 1 & 0 & 0 \\ 0 & 1 & 0 \end{bmatrix}$, $P^3 = \begin{bmatrix} 1 & 0 & 0 \\ 0 & 1 & 0 \\ 0 & 0 & 1 \end{bmatrix}$, $P^4 = \begin{bmatrix} 0 & 1 & 0 \\ 0 & 0 & 1 \\ 1 & 0 & 0 \end{bmatrix}$,

and so on. The powers of P cycle between P, the 3 × 3 identity I, and a third matrix, hence they do not approach a limiting matrix.

(D) Parts *B* and *C* of Theorem 1 are not valid for this matrix. Since P is not regular, this is not a contradiction.

34. (A) $RP = [.4 \quad 0 \quad .6] \begin{bmatrix} .7 & 0 & .3 \\ 0 & 1 & 1 \\ .2 & 0 & .8 \end{bmatrix} = [.4 \quad 0 \quad .6]$

Therefore, R is a stationary matrix for P.

$SP = [0 \quad 1 \quad 0] \begin{bmatrix} .7 & 0 & .3 \\ 0 & 1 & 1 \\ .2 & 0 & .8 \end{bmatrix} = [0 \quad 1 \quad 0]$.

Therefore, S is a stationary matrix for P.
The powers of P have at least one 0 entry and hence P is not regular. As a result, P may have more than one stationary matrix.

(B) Following the hint, let
$T = a[.4 \quad 0 \quad .6] + (1 - a)[0 \quad 1 \quad 0], \quad 0 < a < 1$
$= [.4a \quad 1 - a \quad .6a]$

Now, $TP = [.4a \quad 1 - a \quad .6a] \begin{bmatrix} .7 & 0 & .3 \\ 0 & 1 & 1 \\ .2 & 0 & .8 \end{bmatrix} = [.4a \quad 1 - a \quad .6a] = T$.

Thus, [.4a 1 - a .6a] is a stationary matrix for P for every a with $0 < a < 1$. Note that if $a = 1$, then $T = R$, and if $a = 0$, $T = S$. If we let $a = .5$, then $T = [.2 \quad .5 \quad .3]$ is a stationary matrix.

(C) P has infinitely many stationary matrices.

36. $\overline{P} = \begin{bmatrix} .4 & 0 & .6 \\ 0 & 1 & 0 \\ .4 & 0 & .6 \end{bmatrix}$

Each row of $\overline{P}$ is a stationary matrix for P.

38. (A) For P^2, $m_2 = .32$; for P^3, $m_3 = .423$; for P^4, $m_4 = .435$; for P^5, $m_5 = .468$.

(B) Each entry of the third column of P^{k+1} is the product of a row of P and the third column of P^k, and each entry of the latter is $\geq m_k$. So the product is $\geq m_k$.

40. The transition matrix is:

$$P = \begin{array}{c} H \\ N \end{array}\begin{array}{c} \overset{H \quad\quad N}{\begin{bmatrix} .86 & .14 \\ .26 & .74 \end{bmatrix}} \end{array} \begin{array}{l} H = \text{home trackage} \\ N = \text{national pool} \end{array}$$

Calculating powers of P, we have

$$P^2 = \begin{bmatrix} .776 & .224 \\ .416 & .584 \end{bmatrix}, \quad P^4 \approx \begin{bmatrix} .69536 & .30464 \\ .56576 & .43424 \end{bmatrix}$$

$$P^8 \approx \begin{bmatrix} .655878656 & .344121344 \\ .639082496 & .360917504 \end{bmatrix}, \quad P^{16} \approx \begin{bmatrix} .6500987388 & .3499012612 \\ .6498166279 & .3501833721 \end{bmatrix}$$

In the long run, 65% of the company's tank cars will be on its home trackage.

42. (A) $S_0 = [.654 \quad .346]$

$$S_1 = S_0 P = [.654 \quad .346]\begin{bmatrix} .95 & .05 \\ .15 & .85 \end{bmatrix} = [.673 \quad .327]$$

$$S_2 = S_1 P = [.673 \quad .327]\begin{bmatrix} .95 & .05 \\ .15 & .85 \end{bmatrix} = [.689 \quad .311]$$

(B)

Year	Data (%)	Model (%)
1996	65.4	65.4
2000	67.4	67.3
2004	69.0	68.9

(C) $S_n = S_0 P^n$ approaches $[0.750 \quad 0.250]$, so in the long run, 75% of households will own their own home.

44. The transition matrix for this problem is:

$$\begin{array}{c} \text{APS} \\ \text{GX} \\ \text{WWP} \end{array}\begin{array}{c} \overset{\text{APS} \quad \text{GX} \quad \text{WWP}}{\begin{bmatrix} .70 & .10 & .20 \\ .15 & .75 & .10 \\ .05 & .05 & .90 \end{bmatrix}} \end{array}$$

To find the steady-state matrix, we solve the system

$$[s_1 \quad s_2 \quad s_3]\begin{bmatrix} .7 & .1 & .2 \\ .15 & .75 & .1 \\ .05 & .05 & .9 \end{bmatrix} = [s_1 \quad s_2 \quad s_3], \quad s_1 + s_2 + s_3 = 1$$

which is equivalent to the system of equations

$$.7s_1 + .15s_2 + .05s_3 = s_1 \qquad -.3s_1 + .15s_2 + .05s_3 = 0$$
$$.1s_1 + .75s_2 + .05s_3 = s_2 \quad \text{or} \quad .1s_1 - .25s_2 + .05s_3 = 0$$
$$.2s_1 + .1s_2 + .9s_3 = s_3 \qquad .2s_1 + .1s_2 - .1s_3 = 0$$
$$s_1 + s_2 + s_3 = 1 \qquad s_1 + s_2 + s_3 = 1$$

The solution of this system is $s_1 = .2$, $s_2 = .2$, $s_3 = .6$.
Thus, the expected market share of each company is:
   APS: 20%; GX: 20%; and WWP: 60%.

46. The transition matrix for this problem is:

	Poor	Satisfactory	Preferred
Poor	.6	.4	0
Satisfactory	.2	.6	.2
Preferred	0	.4	.6

To find the steady-state matrix, we solve the system

$$[\, s_1 \quad s_2 \quad s_3 \,]\begin{bmatrix} .6 & .4 & 0 \\ .2 & .6 & .2 \\ 0 & .4 & .6 \end{bmatrix} = [\, s_1 \quad s_2 \quad s_3 \,], \; s_1 + s_2 + s_3 = 1$$

which is equivalent to the system of equations:

$$.6s_1 + .2s_2 \qquad = s_1$$
$$.4s_1 + .6s_2 + .4s_3 = s_2$$
$$.4s_2 + .6s_3 = s_3$$
$$s_1 + s_2 + s_3 = 1$$

The solution of this system is $s_1 = .25$, $s_2 = .5$, and $s_3 = .25$.

Thus, the expected percentage in each category is:
   poor - 25%; satisfactory - 50%; and preferred - 25%.

48. The transition matrix is:

$$P = \begin{bmatrix} .3 & .2 & .2 & .3 \\ .2 & .2 & .2 & .4 \\ .2 & .2 & .4 & .2 \\ .1 & .2 & .3 & .4 \end{bmatrix}$$

$$S_0P = [.3 \quad .3 \quad .4 \quad 0]P = [.23 \quad .2 \quad .28 \quad .29] = S_1$$
$$S_1P = [.20 \quad .2 \quad .29 \quad .32]$$
$$S_2P = [.19 \quad .2 \quad .29 \quad .32]$$
$$S_3P = [.19 \quad .2 \quad .29 \quad .32]$$

Thus, $S = [.19 \quad .2 \quad .29 \quad .32]$ is the steady-state matrix. The expected total market share for standard Acme and brand Y is $.29 + .32 = .61$ or 61%.
Acme should market brand Y.

50. (A) $P = \begin{array}{c} \text{Type } A \\ \text{Type } B \end{array} \begin{array}{cc} \text{Type } A & \text{Type } B \\ \begin{bmatrix} .9999 & .0001 \\ .000001 & .999999 \end{bmatrix} \end{array}$

(B) To find the stationary solution, we solve the system

$[s_1 \quad s_2] \begin{bmatrix} .9999 & .0001 \\ .000001 & .999999 \end{bmatrix} = [s_1 \quad s_2], \ s_1 + s_2 = 1,$

which is equivalent to:

$.9999 s_1 + .000001 s_2 = s_1$

$.0001 s_1 + .999999 s_2 = s_2$

$s_1 + \qquad s_2 = 1$

The solution of this system is $s_1 = \dfrac{1}{101} \approx .01; \ s_2 = \dfrac{100}{101} \approx .99.$

52. (A) $[.1 \quad .9]$

(B) To find the stationary solution, we solve the system

$[s_1 \quad s_2] \begin{bmatrix} .9 & .1 \\ .1 & .9 \end{bmatrix} = [s_1 \quad s_2], \ s_1 + s_2 = 1,$

which is equivalent to

$.9 s_1 + .1 s_2 = s_1$

$.1 s_1 + .9 s_2 = s_2$

$s_1 + \quad s_2 = 1$

The solution of this system is $s_1 = .5, \ s_2 = .5.$

Thus, the stationary matrix is $S = [.5 \quad .5]$, so the probability that Senator Hanks will cast a yes vote is .5 and a no vote is also .5.

(C) The transition matrix in this case is

$P = \begin{bmatrix} 1 - p & p \\ p & 1 - p \end{bmatrix}$

From

$[s_1 \quad s_2] \begin{bmatrix} 1 - p & p \\ p & 1 - p \end{bmatrix} = [s_1 \quad s_2], \ s_1 + s_2 = 1,$ we get

$(1 - p)s_1 + ps_2 = s_1 \qquad s_1 - ps_1 + ps_2 = s_1 \qquad s_1 = s_2$

$ps_1 + (1 - p)s_2 = s_2 \quad \text{or} \quad ps_1 + s_2 - ps_2 = s_2 \quad \text{or} \quad s_1 = s_2$

$s_1 + s_2 = 1 \qquad\qquad s_1 + s_2 = 1 \qquad\qquad s_1 + s_2 = 1$

and hence $s_1 = s_2 = .5$ which is the same as in (B).

54. (A) $S_1 = S_0 P = [0.241 \quad 0.759] \begin{bmatrix} 0.61 & 0.39 \\ 0.09 & 0.91 \end{bmatrix} \approx [0.215 \quad 0.785];$

$S_2 = S_1 P = [0.215 \quad 0.785] \begin{bmatrix} 0.61 & 0.39 \\ 0.09 & 0.91 \end{bmatrix} \approx [0.202 \quad 0.798];$

$S_3 = S_2 P = [0.202 \quad 0.798] \begin{bmatrix} 0.61 & 0.39 \\ 0.09 & 0.91 \end{bmatrix} \approx [0.195 \quad 0.805].$

Year	Data (%)	Model (%)
1970	24.1	24.1
1980	21.7	21.5
1990	20.4	20.2
2000	19.0	19.5

(C) $P^2 \approx \begin{bmatrix} .4072 & .5928 \\ .1368 & .8632 \end{bmatrix}$, $P^4 \approx \begin{bmatrix} .24690688 & .75309312 \\ .17379072 & .82620928 \end{bmatrix}$,

$P^8 \approx \begin{bmatrix} .1918436029 & .8081563971 \\ .186497301 & .8135023699 \end{bmatrix}$, $P^{16} \approx \begin{bmatrix} .1875232208 & .8124767792 \\ .1874946414 & .8125053586 \end{bmatrix}$

In the long run, 18.75% of the population will live in the northeast region.

EXERCISE 9-3

2. State C is an absorbing state.

4. States A and C are absorbing states.

6. No absorbing states.

8. No absorbing states; not an absorbing chain.

10. C and D are absorbing states; the diagram represents an absorbing Markov chain since it is possible to go from either states A or B to states C and D in a finite number of steps.

12. $P = \begin{bmatrix} 1 & 0 \\ 0 & 1 \end{bmatrix}$

This can be a transition matrix of an absorbing Markov chain since it has entries 1 on the diagonal and 0 off the diagonal.

14. $P = \begin{array}{c} \\ A \\ B \end{array}\begin{array}{cc} A & B \\ \begin{bmatrix} .6 & .4 \\ 1 & 0 \end{bmatrix} \end{array}$

The probability of going from state B to state B is 0 so P does not have any absorbing state, so it cannot be a transition matrix of an absorbing Markov chain.

16. $P = \begin{array}{c} \\ A \\ B \\ C \end{array}\begin{array}{ccc} A & B & C \\ \begin{bmatrix} 0 & 1 & 0 \\ 0 & 0 & 1 \\ 1 & 0 & 0 \end{bmatrix} \end{array}$

This matrix does not have any observing state and hence cannot be a transition matrix of an absorbing Markov chain.

18. $P = \begin{array}{c} \\ A \\ B \\ C \end{array}\begin{array}{ccc} A & B & C \\ \begin{bmatrix} .5 & .5 & 0 \\ .4 & .3 & .3 \\ 0 & 0 & 1 \end{bmatrix} \end{array}$

Note that state C is the only absorbing state. The second condition in the definition of an absorbing Markov chain is satisfied if we can show that it is possible to go from the nonabsorbing states A and B to the absorbing state C in a finite number of steps. Please see the diagram on the previous page showing that it is possible to go from State B to the absorbing state C in one step and from state A to the absorbing state C in two steps. Thus, P is the transition matrix for an absorbing Markov chain.

20. $P = \begin{array}{c} \\ A \\ B \\ C \end{array} \begin{array}{c} \begin{matrix} A & B & C \end{matrix} \\ \begin{bmatrix} 1 & 0 & 0 \\ 0 & 0 & 1 \\ 0 & .7 & .3 \end{bmatrix} \end{array}$

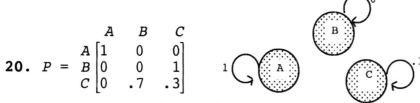

It is clear that A is the only absorbing state. However, there are no finite steps to go from B or C to A. Thus, P cannot be a transition matrix of an absorbing Markov chain.

22. The transition diagram is represented by the matrix:

$$\begin{array}{c} \\ B \\ C \\ A \end{array} \begin{array}{c} \begin{matrix} B & C & A \end{matrix} \\ \begin{bmatrix} 1 & 0 & 0 \\ 0 & 1 & 0 \\ .1 & .7 & .2 \end{bmatrix} \end{array}$$

24. The transition diagram is represented by the matrix

$$\begin{array}{c} \\ B \\ A \\ C \\ D \end{array} \begin{array}{c} \begin{matrix} B & A & C & D \end{matrix} \\ \begin{bmatrix} 1 & 0 & 0 & 0 \\ .4 & .6 & 0 & 0 \\ .7 & 0 & 0 & .3 \\ 0 & 0 & 1 & 0 \end{bmatrix} \end{array}$$

26. A standard form for

$$P = \begin{array}{c} \\ A \\ B \\ C \end{array} \begin{array}{c} \begin{matrix} A & B & C \end{matrix} \\ \begin{bmatrix} 0 & 0 & 1 \\ 0 & 1 & 0 \\ .7 & .2 & .1 \end{bmatrix} \end{array}$$

is:

$$\begin{array}{c} \\ B \\ A \\ C \end{array} \begin{array}{c} \begin{matrix} B & A & C \end{matrix} \\ \begin{bmatrix} 1 & 0 & 0 \\ 0 & 0 & 1 \\ .2 & .7 & .1 \end{bmatrix} \end{array}$$

28. A standard form for

$$P = \begin{array}{c} \\ A \\ B \\ C \\ D \end{array} \begin{array}{c} \begin{matrix} A & B & C & D \end{matrix} \\ \begin{bmatrix} 0 & .3 & .3 & .4 \\ 0 & 1 & 0 & 0 \\ 0 & 0 & 1 & 0 \\ .8 & .1 & .1 & 0 \end{bmatrix} \end{array}$$

is:

$$\begin{array}{c} \\ B \\ C \\ A \\ D \end{array} \begin{array}{c} \begin{matrix} B & C & A & D \end{matrix} \\ \begin{bmatrix} 1 & 0 & 0 & 0 \\ 0 & 1 & 0 & 0 \\ .3 & .3 & 0 & .4 \\ .1 & .1 & .8 & 0 \end{bmatrix} \end{array}$$

30. For

$$P = \begin{array}{c} \\ A \\ B \\ C \end{array} \begin{array}{c} \begin{matrix} A & B & C \end{matrix} \\ \begin{bmatrix} 1 & 0 & 0 \\ 0 & 1 & 0 \\ .3 & .2 & .5 \end{bmatrix} \end{array}$$

we have $R = [.3 \quad .2]$ and $Q = [.5]$.

The limiting matrix $\bar{P}$ has the form $\bar{P} = \left[\begin{array}{cc|c} 1 & 0 & 0 \\ 0 & 1 & 0 \\ \hline FR & & 0 \end{array}\right]$

where $F = (I - Q)^{-1} = ([1] - [.5])^{-1} = [.5]^{-1} = 2$
and $FR = 2[.3 \quad .2] = [.6 \quad .4]$.

Thus,

$$\bar{P} = \begin{array}{c} A \\ B \\ C \end{array} \begin{array}{ccc} A & B & C \\ \begin{bmatrix} 1 & 0 & 0 \\ 0 & 1 & 0 \\ .6 & .4 & 0 \end{bmatrix} \end{array}$$

Let $P(i \text{ to } j)$ denote the probability of going from state i to state j. Then $P(C \text{ to } A) = .6$, $P(C \text{ to } B) = .4$
Since $F = [2]$, it will take an average of 2 trials to go from C to either A or B.

---

32. For

$$P = \begin{array}{c} A \\ B \\ C \end{array} \begin{array}{ccc} A & B & C \\ \begin{bmatrix} 1 & 0 & 0 \\ .1 & .6 & .3 \\ .2 & .2 & .6 \end{bmatrix} \end{array}$$

we have $R = \begin{bmatrix} .1 \\ .2 \end{bmatrix}$ and $Q = \begin{bmatrix} .6 & .3 \\ .2 & .6 \end{bmatrix}$

The limiting matrix $\bar{P}$ has the form

$$\bar{P} = \left[\begin{array}{c|c} 1 & 0 \quad 0 \\ \hline FR & 0 \end{array} \right] \text{ where } F = (I - Q)^{-1} = \left(\begin{bmatrix} 1 & 0 \\ 0 & 1 \end{bmatrix} - \begin{bmatrix} .6 & .3 \\ .2 & .6 \end{bmatrix} \right)^{-1}$$

$$= \left(\begin{bmatrix} .4 & -.3 \\ -.2 & .4 \end{bmatrix} \right)^{-1} = \left(\begin{bmatrix} \frac{2}{5} & -\frac{3}{10} \\ -\frac{1}{5} & \frac{2}{5} \end{bmatrix} \right)^{-1}$$

We use row operations to find the inverse:

$$\begin{bmatrix} \frac{2}{5} & -\frac{3}{10} & 1 & 0 \\ -\frac{1}{5} & \frac{2}{5} & 0 & 1 \end{bmatrix} \sim \begin{bmatrix} 1 & -\frac{3}{4} & \frac{5}{2} & 0 \\ -\frac{1}{5} & \frac{2}{5} & 0 & 1 \end{bmatrix} \sim \begin{bmatrix} 1 & -\frac{3}{4} & \frac{5}{2} & 0 \\ 0 & \frac{1}{4} & \frac{1}{2} & 1 \end{bmatrix} \sim \begin{bmatrix} 1 & -\frac{3}{4} & \frac{5}{2} & 0 \\ 0 & 1 & 2 & 4 \end{bmatrix}$$

$$\left(\frac{5}{2} \right) R_1 \rightarrow R_1 \qquad \left(\frac{1}{5} \right) R_1 + R_2 \rightarrow R_2 \qquad 4R_2 \rightarrow R_2 \qquad \left(\frac{3}{4} \right) R_2 + R_1 \rightarrow R_2$$

$$\sim \begin{bmatrix} 1 & 0 & 4 & 3 \\ 0 & 1 & 2 & 4 \end{bmatrix}$$

Thus, $F = \begin{bmatrix} 4 & 3 \\ 2 & 4 \end{bmatrix}$ and $FR = \begin{bmatrix} 4 & 3 \\ 2 & 4 \end{bmatrix} \begin{bmatrix} .1 \\ .2 \end{bmatrix} = \begin{bmatrix} 1 \\ 1 \end{bmatrix}$

Now

$$\bar{P} = \begin{array}{c} A \\ B \\ C \end{array} \begin{array}{ccc} A & B & C \\ \begin{bmatrix} 1 & 0 & 0 \\ 1 & 0 & 0 \\ 1 & 0 & 0 \end{bmatrix} \end{array}$$

$P(B \text{ to } A) = 1$, $P(C \text{ to } A) = 1$

It will take an average of 7 trials to go from B to A; it will take an average of 6 trials to go from C to A.

34. For

$$P = \begin{array}{c} \\ A \\ B \\ C \\ D \end{array} \begin{array}{cccc} A & B & C & D \\ \left[\begin{array}{cccc} 1 & 0 & 0 & 0 \\ 0 & 1 & 0 & 0 \\ .1 & .1 & .7 & .1 \\ .3 & .1 & .4 & .2 \end{array}\right] \end{array}$$

we have $R = \begin{bmatrix} .1 & .1 \\ .3 & .1 \end{bmatrix}$ and $Q = \begin{bmatrix} .7 & .1 \\ .4 & .2 \end{bmatrix}$

The limiting matrix $\overline{P}$ has the form

$$\overline{P} = \left[\begin{array}{c|cc} I & 0 & 0 \\ & 0 & 0 \\ \hline FR & 0 & \end{array}\right]$$

where $F = (I - Q)^{-1} = \left(\begin{bmatrix} 1 & 0 \\ 0 & 1 \end{bmatrix} - \begin{bmatrix} .7 & .1 \\ .4 & .2 \end{bmatrix}\right)^{-1}$

$$= \left(\begin{bmatrix} .3 & -.1 \\ -.4 & .8 \end{bmatrix}\right)^{-1} = \begin{bmatrix} \frac{3}{10} & -\frac{1}{10} \\ -\frac{2}{5} & \frac{4}{5} \end{bmatrix}^{-1}$$

We use row operations to find the inverse:

$$\begin{bmatrix} \frac{3}{10} & -\frac{1}{10} & 1 & 0 \\ -\frac{2}{5} & \frac{4}{5} & 0 & 1 \end{bmatrix} \sim \begin{bmatrix} 1 & -\frac{1}{3} & \frac{10}{3} & 0 \\ -\frac{2}{5} & \frac{4}{5} & 0 & 1 \end{bmatrix} \sim \begin{bmatrix} 1 & -\frac{1}{3} & \frac{10}{3} & 0 \\ 0 & \frac{2}{3} & \frac{4}{3} & 1 \end{bmatrix} \sim \begin{bmatrix} 1 & -\frac{1}{3} & \frac{10}{3} & 0 \\ 0 & 1 & 2 & \frac{3}{2} \end{bmatrix}$$

$$\left(\frac{10}{3}\right)R_1 \to R_1 \qquad \left(\frac{2}{5}\right)R_1 + R_2 \to R_2 \qquad \left(\frac{3}{2}\right)R_2 \to R_2 \qquad \left(\frac{1}{3}\right)R_2 + R_1 \to R_1$$

$$\sim \begin{bmatrix} 1 & 0 & 4 & \frac{1}{2} \\ 0 & 1 & 2 & \frac{3}{2} \end{bmatrix}$$

Thus, $F = \begin{bmatrix} 4 & \frac{1}{2} \\ 2 & \frac{3}{2} \end{bmatrix}$ and $FR = \begin{bmatrix} 4 & \frac{1}{2} \\ 2 & \frac{3}{2} \end{bmatrix}\begin{bmatrix} .1 & .1 \\ .3 & .1 \end{bmatrix} = \begin{bmatrix} .55 & .45 \\ .65 & .35 \end{bmatrix}$

and

$$\overline{P} = \begin{array}{c} \\ A \\ B \\ C \\ D \end{array} \begin{array}{cccc} A & B & C & D \\ \left[\begin{array}{cccc} 1 & 0 & 0 & 0 \\ 0 & 1 & 0 & 0 \\ .55 & .45 & 0 & 0 \\ .65 & .35 & 0 & 0 \end{array}\right] \end{array}$$

$P(C \text{ to } A) = .55$, $P(C \text{ to } B) = .45$,
$P(D \text{ to } A) = .65$, $P(D \text{ to } B) = .35$

It will take an average of 4.5 trials to go from C to either A or B;
it will take an average of 3.5 trials to go from D to either A or B.

36. (A) $S_0\overline{P} = \begin{bmatrix} 0 & 0 & 1 \end{bmatrix}\begin{bmatrix} 1 & 0 & 0 \\ 0 & 1 & 0 \\ .6 & .4 & 0 \end{bmatrix} = \begin{bmatrix} .6 & .4 & 0 \end{bmatrix}$

(B) $S_0\overline{P} = \begin{bmatrix} .2 & .5 & .3 \end{bmatrix}\begin{bmatrix} 1 & 0 & 0 \\ 0 & 1 & 0 \\ .6 & .4 & 0 \end{bmatrix} = \begin{bmatrix} .38 & .62 & 0 \end{bmatrix}$

38. (A) $S_0\overline{P} = \begin{bmatrix} 0 & 0 & 1 \end{bmatrix} \begin{bmatrix} 1 & 0 & 0 \\ 1 & 0 & 0 \\ 1 & 0 & 0 \end{bmatrix} = \begin{bmatrix} 1 & 0 & 0 \end{bmatrix}$

(B) $S_0\overline{P} = \begin{bmatrix} .2 & .5 & .3 \end{bmatrix} \begin{bmatrix} 1 & 0 & 0 \\ 1 & 0 & 0 \\ 1 & 0 & 0 \end{bmatrix} = \begin{bmatrix} 1 & 0 & 0 \end{bmatrix}$

40. (A) $S_0\overline{P} = \begin{bmatrix} 0 & 0 & 0 & 1 \end{bmatrix} \begin{bmatrix} 1 & 0 & 0 & 0 \\ 0 & 1 & 0 & 0 \\ .55 & .45 & 0 & 0 \\ .65 & .35 & 0 & 0 \end{bmatrix} = \begin{bmatrix} .65 & .35 & 0 & 0 \end{bmatrix}$

(B) $S_0\overline{P} = \begin{bmatrix} 0 & 0 & 1 & 0 \end{bmatrix} \begin{bmatrix} 1 & 0 & 0 & 0 \\ 0 & 1 & 0 & 0 \\ .55 & .45 & 0 & 0 \\ .65 & .35 & 0 & 0 \end{bmatrix} = \begin{bmatrix} .55 & .45 & 0 & 0 \end{bmatrix}$

(C) $S_0\overline{P} = \begin{bmatrix} 0 & 0 & .4 & .6 \end{bmatrix} \begin{bmatrix} 1 & 0 & 0 & 0 \\ 0 & 1 & 0 & 0 \\ .55 & .45 & 0 & 0 \\ .65 & .35 & 0 & 0 \end{bmatrix} = \begin{bmatrix} .61 & .39 & 0 & 0 \end{bmatrix}$

(D) $S_0\overline{P} = \begin{bmatrix} .1 & .2 & .3 & .4 \end{bmatrix} \begin{bmatrix} 1 & 0 & 0 & 0 \\ 0 & 1 & 0 & 0 \\ .55 & .45 & 0 & 0 \\ .65 & .35 & 0 & 0 \end{bmatrix} = \begin{bmatrix} .525 & .475 & 0 & 0 \end{bmatrix}$

42. (A) False. Consider the
transition matrix:

$$P = \begin{array}{c} \\ A \\ B \\ C \end{array} \begin{array}{ccc} A & B & C \\ \begin{bmatrix} .1 & .6 & .3 \\ 0 & 1 & 0 \\ .5 & 0 & .5 \end{bmatrix} \end{array}$$

(B) True: Let $P = \begin{array}{c} \\ A \\ B \\ C \end{array} \begin{array}{ccc} A & B & C \\ \begin{bmatrix} 1 & 0 & 0 \\ 0 & 1 & 0 \\ .1 & .5 & .4 \end{bmatrix} \end{array}$

Then $S = \begin{bmatrix} x & 1 - x & 0 \end{bmatrix}$ for any x, $0 \le x \le 1$, is a stationary matrix for P.

44. By Theorem 2, P has a limiting matrix:

$$P^4 \approx \begin{bmatrix} 1 & 0 & 0 & 0 \\ 0 & 1 & 0 & 0 \\ .21 & .3804 & .2056 & .204 \\ .0852 & .505 & .204 & .2056 \end{bmatrix}, \quad P^8 \approx \begin{bmatrix} 1 & 0 & 0 & 0 \\ 0 & 1 & 0 & 0 \\ .2701 & .5617 & .0839 & .0839 \\ .1456 & .6867 & .0839 & .0839 \end{bmatrix}$$

$$P^{16} \approx \begin{bmatrix} 1 & 0 & 0 & 0 \\ 0 & 1 & 0 & 0 \\ .3055 & .6664 & .0141 & .0141 \\ .1805 & .7914 & .0141 & .0141 \end{bmatrix}; \quad P^{32} \approx \begin{bmatrix} 1 & 0 & 0 & 0 \\ 0 & 1 & 0 & 0 \\ .3123 & .6870 & 0 & 0 \\ .1873 & .8119 & 0 & 0 \end{bmatrix}, \cdots,$$

$$\overline{P} = \begin{array}{c} \\ A \\ B \\ C \\ D \end{array} \begin{array}{cccc} A & B & C & D \\ \begin{bmatrix} 1 & 0 & 0 & 0 \\ 0 & 1 & 0 & 0 \\ .3125 & .6875 & 0 & 0 \\ .1875 & .8125 & 0 & 0 \end{bmatrix} \end{array}$$

46. By Theorem 2, P has a limiting matrix:

$$P^4 \approx \begin{bmatrix} 1 & 0 & 0 & 0 & 0 \\ 0 & 1 & 0 & 0 & 0 \\ .53 & .196 & .0185 & .1575 & .098 \\ .028 & .6784 & .018 & .1612 & .1144 \\ .0785 & .518 & .0196 & .2002 & .1837 \end{bmatrix},$$

$$P^8 \approx \begin{bmatrix} 1 & 0 & 0 & 0 & 0 \\ 0 & 1 & 0 & 0 & 0 \\ .5519 & .3572 & .0051 & .0479 & .0378 \\ .0510 & .8505 & .0055 & .0517 & .0412 \\ .1089 & .7528 & .0076 & .0721 & .0586 \end{bmatrix},$$

$$P^{16} \approx \begin{bmatrix} 1 & 0 & 0 & 0 & 0 \\ 0 & 1 & 0 & 0 & 0 \\ .5613 & .4283 & 0 & 0 & 0 \\ .0612 & .9275 & 0 & 0 & 0 \\ .1232 & .8610 & 0 & 0 & 0 \end{bmatrix}, \qquad P^{32} \approx \begin{bmatrix} 1 & 0 & 0 & 0 & 0 \\ 0 & 1 & 0 & 0 & 0 \\ .5625 & .4374 & 0 & 0 & 0 \\ .0625 & .9374 & 0 & 0 & 0 \\ .1250 & .8748 & 0 & 0 & 0 \end{bmatrix}, \ \dots$$

$$\bar{P} = \begin{array}{c} \\ A \\ B \\ C \\ D \\ E \end{array} \begin{array}{c} \begin{array}{ccccc} A & B & C & D & E \end{array} \\ \begin{bmatrix} 1 & 0 & 0 & 0 & 0 \\ 0 & 1 & 0 & 0 & 0 \\ .5625 & .4375 & 0 & 0 & 0 \\ .0625 & .9375 & 0 & 0 & 0 \\ .125 & .875 & 0 & 0 & 0 \end{bmatrix} \end{array}$$

48. *Step 1.* Transition diagram:

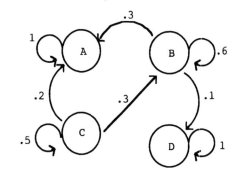

Standard form:

$$M = \begin{array}{c} \\ A \\ D \\ B \\ C \end{array} \begin{array}{c} \begin{array}{cccc} A & D & B & C \end{array} \\ \begin{bmatrix} 1 & 0 & 0 & 0 \\ 0 & 1 & 0 & 0 \\ .3 & .1 & .6 & 0 \\ .2 & 0 & .3 & .5 \end{bmatrix} \end{array}$$

Step 2. Limiting matrix:

For M, we have $R = \begin{bmatrix} .3 & .1 \\ .2 & 0 \end{bmatrix}$ and $Q = \begin{bmatrix} .6 & 0 \\ .3 & .5 \end{bmatrix}$

The limiting matrix $\bar{M}$ has the form:

$$\bar{M} = \left[\begin{array}{c|c} I & 0 \\ \hline FR & 0 \end{array} \right]$$

where $F = (I - Q)^{-1} = \left(\begin{bmatrix} 1 & 0 \\ 0 & 1 \end{bmatrix} - \begin{bmatrix} .6 & 0 \\ .3 & .5 \end{bmatrix}\right)^{-1}$

$$= \left(\begin{bmatrix} .4 & 0 \\ -.3 & .5 \end{bmatrix}\right)^{-1} = \begin{bmatrix} \frac{2}{5} & 0 \\ -\frac{3}{10} & \frac{1}{2} \end{bmatrix}^{-1}$$

We use row operations to find the inverse:

$$\begin{bmatrix} \frac{2}{5} & 0 & 1 & 0 \\ -\frac{3}{10} & \frac{1}{2} & 0 & 1 \end{bmatrix} \sim \begin{bmatrix} 1 & 0 & \frac{5}{2} & 0 \\ -\frac{3}{10} & \frac{1}{2} & 0 & 1 \end{bmatrix} \sim \begin{bmatrix} 1 & 0 & \frac{5}{2} & 0 \\ 0 & \frac{1}{2} & \frac{3}{4} & 1 \end{bmatrix}$$

$$\left(\frac{5}{2}\right)R_1 \rightarrow R_1 \qquad \left(\frac{3}{10}\right)R_1 + R_2 \rightarrow R_2 \qquad 2R_2 \rightarrow R_2$$

$$\sim \begin{bmatrix} 1 & 0 & \frac{5}{2} & 0 \\ 0 & 1 & \frac{3}{2} & 2 \end{bmatrix}$$

Thus, $F = \begin{bmatrix} \frac{5}{2} & 0 \\ \frac{3}{2} & 2 \end{bmatrix}$ and $FR = \begin{bmatrix} \frac{5}{2} & 0 \\ \frac{3}{2} & 2 \end{bmatrix}\begin{bmatrix} .3 & .1 \\ .2 & 0 \end{bmatrix} = \begin{bmatrix} .75 & .25 \\ .85 & .15 \end{bmatrix}$

Therefore, $\overline{M} = \begin{array}{c} A \\ D \\ B \\ C \end{array}\begin{bmatrix} 1 & 0 & 0 & 0 \\ 0 & 1 & 0 & 0 \\ .75 & .25 & 0 & 0 \\ .85 & .15 & 0 & 0 \end{bmatrix}$

with columns labeled $\begin{array}{cccc} A & D & B & C \end{array}$

Step 3. Transition diagram for $\overline{M}$:

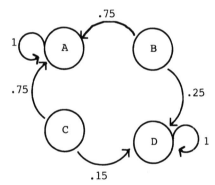

Limiting matrix for P:

$$\overline{P} = \begin{array}{c} A \\ B \\ C \\ D \end{array}\begin{bmatrix} 1 & 0 & 0 & 0 \\ .75 & 0 & 0 & .25 \\ .85 & 0 & 0 & .15 \\ 0 & 0 & 0 & 1 \end{bmatrix}$$

with columns labeled $\begin{array}{cccc} A & B & C & D \end{array}$

50. $P^4 \approx \begin{bmatrix} 1 & 0 & 0 & 0 \\ .6528 & .1296 & 0 & .2176 \\ .6459 & .2013 & .0625 & .0903 \\ 0 & 0 & 0 & 1 \end{bmatrix}$, $P^8 \approx \begin{bmatrix} 1 & 0 & 0 & 0 \\ .7374 & .0168 & 0 & .2458 \\ .8177 & .0387 & .0039 & .1397 \\ 0 & 0 & 0 & 1 \end{bmatrix}$

$P^{32} \approx \begin{bmatrix} 1 & 0 & 0 & 0 \\ .75 & 0 & 0 & .25 \\ .85 & 0 & 0 & .15 \\ 0 & 0 & 0 & 0 \end{bmatrix}$

52. Let $S = [x \quad 1 - x \quad 0 \quad 0]$, $0 \le x \le 1$. Then

$$SP = [x \quad 1 - x \quad 0 \quad 0] \begin{bmatrix} 1 & 0 & 0 & 0 \\ 0 & 1 & 0 & 0 \\ .1 & .2 & .3 & .4 \\ .6 & .2 & .1 & .1 \end{bmatrix} = [x \quad 1 - x \quad 0 \quad 0]$$

Thus, S is a stationary matrix for P.

A stationary matrix for an absorbing Markov chain with two absorbing states and two nonabsorbing states will have one of the forms
$$[x \quad 1 - x \quad 0 \quad 0], \quad [x \quad 0 \quad 1 - x \quad 0], \quad [x \quad 0 \quad 0 \quad 1 - x],$$
$$[0 \quad x \quad 1 - x \quad 0], \quad [0 \quad x \quad 0 \quad 1 - x], \quad [0 \quad 0 \quad x \quad 1 - x]$$

54. (A) $T_{k+1} = I + Q + Q^2 + \dots + Q^{k+1}$

$\qquad = I + (I + Q + Q^2 + \dots + Q^k)Q = I + T_k Q$

$\qquad = T_k Q + I$

(B) For large k, all the entries of T_k are close to the corresponding entries of $(I - Q)^{-1}$.

56. A transition matrix for this problem is:

$$\begin{array}{cc} & \begin{matrix} F & B & M & T \end{matrix} \\ P = \begin{matrix} F \\ B \\ M \\ T \end{matrix} & \begin{bmatrix} 1 & 0 & 0 & 0 \\ .3 & .6 & 0 & .1 \\ 0 & .3 & .5 & .2 \\ 0 & 0 & 0 & 1 \end{bmatrix} \end{array} \begin{matrix} F = \text{Fully qualified mechanic} \\ B = \text{Brake repair trainee} \\ M = \text{Muffler repair trainee} \\ T = \text{Terminated} \end{matrix}$$

A standard form for this matrix is:

$$\begin{array}{cc} & \begin{matrix} F & T & B & M \end{matrix} \\ M = \begin{matrix} F \\ T \\ B \\ M \end{matrix} & \begin{bmatrix} 1 & 0 & 0 & 0 \\ 0 & 1 & 0 & 0 \\ .3 & .1 & .6 & 0 \\ 0 & .2 & .3 & .5 \end{bmatrix} \end{array}$$

For this matrix, we have:

$$R = \begin{bmatrix} .3 & .1 \\ 0 & .2 \end{bmatrix} \quad \text{and} \quad Q = \begin{bmatrix} .6 & 0 \\ .3 & .5 \end{bmatrix}$$

The limiting matrix for M has the form:

$$\overline{M} = \left[\begin{array}{c|c} I & 0 \\ \hline FR & 0 \end{array} \right]$$

where $F = (I - Q)^{-1} = \left(\begin{bmatrix} 1 & 0 \\ 0 & 1 \end{bmatrix} - \begin{bmatrix} .6 & 0 \\ .3 & .5 \end{bmatrix} \right)^{-1}$

$$= \left(\begin{bmatrix} .4 & 0 \\ -.3 & .5 \end{bmatrix} \right)^{-1} = \begin{bmatrix} \frac{2}{5} & 0 \\ -\frac{3}{10} & \frac{1}{2} \end{bmatrix}^{-1}$$

This inverse was computed in Problem 48 to be

$$F = \begin{bmatrix} \frac{5}{2} & 0 \\ \frac{3}{2} & 2 \end{bmatrix}$$

Thus, $FR = \begin{bmatrix} \frac{5}{2} & 0 \\ \frac{3}{2} & 2 \end{bmatrix} \begin{bmatrix} .3 & .1 \\ 0 & .2 \end{bmatrix} = \begin{bmatrix} .75 & .25 \\ .45 & .55 \end{bmatrix}$

Therefore,

$$\overline{M} = \begin{array}{c} F \\ T \\ B \\ M \end{array} \begin{array}{cccc} F & T & B & M \\ \begin{bmatrix} 1 & 0 & 0 & 0 \\ 0 & 1 & 0 & 0 \\ .75 & .25 & 0 & 0 \\ .45 & .55 & 0 & 0 \end{bmatrix} \end{array}$$

(A) In the long run, 45% of the muffler repair trainees will become fully qualified mechanics.

(B) In the long run, 25% of the brake repair trainees will be terminated.

(C) The average number of quarters a muffler repair trainee will remain in the training program before being either terminated or promoted to fully qualified mechanic is 3.5 quarters.

58. A transition matrix in standard form for this problem is:

$$P = \begin{array}{c} A \\ B \\ C \\ N \end{array} \begin{array}{cccc} A & B & C & N \\ \begin{bmatrix} 1 & 0 & 0 & 0 \\ 0 & 1 & 0 & 0 \\ 0 & 0 & 1 & 0 \\ .04 & .14 & .07 & .75 \end{bmatrix} \end{array}$$

For this matrix, we have $R = [.04 \quad .14 \quad .07]$ and $Q = [.75]$.

The limiting matrix for P has the form:

$$\overline{P} = \left[\begin{array}{c|c} I & 0 \\ \hline FR & 0 \end{array} \right]$$

where $F = (I - Q)^{-1} = ([1] - [.75])^{-1} = [.25]^{-1} = 4$

Now, $FR = [4][.04 \quad .14 \quad .07] = [.16 \quad .56 \quad .28]$

and

$$\overline{P} = \begin{array}{c} A \\ B \\ C \\ N \end{array} \begin{array}{cccc} A & B & C & N \\ \begin{bmatrix} 1 & 0 & 0 & 0 \\ 0 & 1 & 0 & 0 \\ 0 & 0 & 1 & 0 \\ .16 & .56 & .28 & 0 \end{bmatrix} \end{array}$$

(A) In the long run, 16% of the employees will elect to join plan A; 56% plan B; 28% plan C.

(B) On the average, it takes 4 years for an employee to decide to join a plan.

60. Let I denote ICU, C denote CCW, D denote "died", and R denote "released". A transition matrix in standard form for this problem is:

$$P = \begin{array}{c} \\ D \\ R \\ I \\ C \end{array}\overset{\begin{array}{cccc} D & R & I & C \end{array}}{\left[\begin{array}{cccc} 1 & 0 & 0 & 0 \\ 0 & 1 & 0 & 0 \\ .02 & 0 & .38 & .6 \\ .01 & .19 & .05 & .75 \end{array}\right]}$$

For this matrix, we have

$$R = \begin{bmatrix} .02 & 0 \\ .01 & .19 \end{bmatrix} \quad \text{and} \quad Q = \begin{bmatrix} .38 & .6 \\ .05 & .75 \end{bmatrix}$$

The limiting matrix for P has the form:

$$\bar{P} = \left[\begin{array}{c|c} I & 0 \\ \hline FR & 0 \end{array}\right]$$

where $F = (I - Q)^{-1} = \left(\begin{bmatrix} 1 & 0 \\ 0 & 1 \end{bmatrix} - \begin{bmatrix} .38 & .6 \\ .05 & .75 \end{bmatrix}\right)^{-1}$

$$= \left(\begin{bmatrix} .62 & -.6 \\ -.05 & .25 \end{bmatrix}\right)^{-1} = \begin{bmatrix} 2 & 4.8 \\ .4 & 4.96 \end{bmatrix}$$

Now, $FR = \begin{bmatrix} 2 & 4.8 \\ .4 & 4.96 \end{bmatrix}\begin{bmatrix} .02 & 0 \\ .01 & .19 \end{bmatrix} = \begin{bmatrix} .088 & .912 \\ .0576 & .9424 \end{bmatrix}$

and

$$\bar{P} = \begin{array}{c} \\ D \\ R \\ I \\ C \end{array}\overset{\begin{array}{cccc} D & R & I & C \end{array}}{\left[\begin{array}{cccc} 1 & 0 & 0 & 0 \\ 0 & 1 & 0 & 0 \\ .088 & .912 & 0 & 0 \\ .0576 & .9424 & 0 & 0 \end{array}\right]}$$

(A) In the long run, 94.24% of the patients in the CCW are released from the hospital.

(B) In the long run, 8.8% of the patients in the ICU die without being released from the hospital.

(C) The average number of days a patient in the CCW will stay in the hospital is $.4 + 4.96 = 5.36$ days.

62. A transition matrix in standard form for this problem is:

$$P = \begin{array}{c} \\ L \\ R \\ F \\ B \end{array}\overset{\begin{array}{cccc} L & R & F & B \end{array}}{\left[\begin{array}{cccc} 1 & 0 & 0 & 0 \\ 0 & 1 & 0 & 0 \\ \frac{1}{4} & \frac{1}{4} & 0 & \frac{1}{2} \\ \frac{1}{2} & 0 & \frac{1}{2} & 0 \end{array}\right]}$$

For this matrix we have:

$$R = \begin{bmatrix} \frac{1}{4} & \frac{1}{4} \\ \frac{1}{2} & 0 \end{bmatrix} \quad \text{and} \quad Q = \begin{bmatrix} 0 & \frac{1}{2} \\ \frac{1}{2} & 0 \end{bmatrix}$$

The limiting matrix for P has the form:

$$\bar{P} = \left[\begin{array}{c|c} I & 0 \\ \hline FR & 0 \end{array}\right]$$

where $F = (I - Q)^{-1} = \left(\begin{bmatrix} 1 & 0 \\ 0 & 1 \end{bmatrix} - \begin{bmatrix} 0 & \frac{1}{2} \\ \frac{1}{2} & 0 \end{bmatrix}\right)^{-1} = \begin{bmatrix} 1 & -\frac{1}{2} \\ -\frac{1}{2} & 1 \end{bmatrix}^{-1} = \begin{bmatrix} \frac{4}{3} & \frac{2}{3} \\ \frac{2}{3} & \frac{4}{3} \end{bmatrix}$

Thus, $FR = \begin{bmatrix} \frac{4}{3} & \frac{2}{3} \\ \frac{2}{3} & \frac{4}{3} \end{bmatrix}\begin{bmatrix} \frac{1}{4} & \frac{1}{4} \\ \frac{1}{2} & 0 \end{bmatrix} = \begin{bmatrix} \frac{2}{3} & \frac{1}{3} \\ \frac{5}{6} & \frac{1}{6} \end{bmatrix}.$

Now,

$$\bar{P} = \begin{array}{c} \\ L \\ R \\ F \\ B \end{array}\begin{array}{cccc} L & R & F & B \end{array}\begin{bmatrix} 1 & 0 & 0 & 0 \\ 0 & 1 & 0 & 0 \\ \frac{2}{3} & \frac{1}{3} & 0 & 0 \\ \frac{5}{6} & \frac{1}{6} & 0 & 0 \end{bmatrix}$$

(A) The long run probability that a rat placed in room B ends up in room R is $\frac{1}{6}$.

(B) The average number of exits a rat placed in room B will choose until it finds food is $\frac{2}{3} + \frac{4}{3} = 2$.

EXERCISE 10-1

2. $\begin{bmatrix} \boxed{5} & \textcircled{-3} \\ \textcircled{-1} & \boxed{2} \end{bmatrix}$; there is no saddle value and hence the matrix game is not strictly determined.

4. $\begin{bmatrix} \boxed{\textcircled{-2}} & 3 & \boxed{\textcircled{-2}} \\ \boxed{\textcircled{-2}} & \boxed{5} & \boxed{\textcircled{-2}} \end{bmatrix}$; there are 4 saddle values and hence the matrix game is strictly determined.

6. $\begin{bmatrix} -1 & 1 & \textcircled{-3} \\ \boxed{2} & \boxed{7} & \boxed{\textcircled{1}} \\ 0 & 4 & \textcircled{-1} \end{bmatrix}$; there is a saddle value and hence the matrix game is strictly determined.

8. $\begin{bmatrix} \textcircled{-1} & 5 & 3 \\ 4 & -2 & \textcircled{-4} \\ \boxed{\textcircled{6}} & \boxed{8} & \boxed{7} \end{bmatrix}$ Circles mark the minimum value in each row, and squares mark the maximum value in each column. So, 6 is a saddle value and therefore the game is strictly determined.

10. $\begin{bmatrix} 1 & \textcircled{0} \\ \boxed{5} & \boxed{\textcircled{2}} \end{bmatrix}$; the value of the game is not 0, so the game is not fair.

12. $\begin{bmatrix} \boxed{2} & \boxed{4} & \boxed{\textcircled{0}} \\ 1 & -1 & \textcircled{-3} \end{bmatrix}$; the value of the game is 0, so the game is fair.

14. $\begin{bmatrix} \textcircled{0} & \textcircled{0} & 2 \\ \textcircled{0} & \textcircled{0} & 1 \\ \boxed{2} & \boxed{\textcircled{1}} & \boxed{3} \end{bmatrix}$ So, 1 is a saddle value which is not 0 and hence the game is not fair.

16. $\begin{bmatrix} \boxed{\textcircled{-2}} & 3 \\ \textcircled{-3} & \boxed{6} \end{bmatrix}$ (A) The -2 in row 1.
(B) *R* plays row 1, and *C* plays column 1.
(C) Value of the game is -2.

18. $\begin{bmatrix} \boxed{2} & \boxed{\textcircled{0}} \\ 0 & \textcircled{-4} \end{bmatrix}$ (A) The 0 in row 1.
(B) *R* plays row 1, and *C* plays column 2.

20. $\begin{bmatrix} \boxed{3} & \textcircled{-2} \\ \textcircled{-5} & \boxed{1} \end{bmatrix}$ The game is not strictly determined.

22. $\begin{bmatrix} ④ & ④ \\ ⊝2 & ④ \end{bmatrix}$

The game is strictly determined.

(A) 4 (1,1 position and 1,2 position).

(B) R plays row 1, C plays either column 1 or column 2.

(C) The value of the game is 4.

24. $\begin{bmatrix} ① & ⓪ & 3 & ① \\ ⊝5 & -2 & ④ & -3 \end{bmatrix}$

The game is strictly determined.

(A) 0 (1,2 position).

(B) R plays row 1 and C plays column 2.

(C) The value of the game is 0.

26. $\begin{bmatrix} 1 & ⊝3 & 5 \\ ⊝2 & ① & ⑥ \\ ③ & ⊝4 & 0 \end{bmatrix}$

The game is not strictly determined.

28. $\begin{bmatrix} 1 & ⊝2 & 0 & 3 \\ ⊝5 & 0 & -1 & ⑧ \\ ④ & ① & ① & 2 \end{bmatrix}$

The game is strictly determined.

(A) 1 (3,2 position and 3,3 position).

(B) R plays row 3, C plays column 2 or column 3.

(C) The value of the game is 1.

30. $\begin{bmatrix} ⊝1 & 9 & ⊝1 & ⊝1 \\ -2 & 4 & ⊝3 & -2 \\ ⊝1 & 5 & ⊝1 & ⊝1 \\ -3 & 0 & -2 & ⊝4 \end{bmatrix}$

The game is strictly determined.

(A) −1 (1,1; 1,3; 1,4; 3,1; 3,3; 3,4 positions)

(B) R plays either row 1 or row 3, C plays either column 1 or column 3 or column 4.

(C) The value of the game is −1.

32. Player C, because the value of the game is negative.

34. False; A counterexample is $\begin{bmatrix} ⓪ & ⓪ \\ ⓪ & ① \end{bmatrix}$.

36. True.

38. False. Consider the matrix $\begin{bmatrix} ⊝1 & ⊝1 & 2 \\ ⓪ & ⓪ & 1 \\ ① & 0 & ③ \end{bmatrix}$.

The saddle value is 0 so it is a fair game, but there are no zeros in the first row and third column.

40. The game will be strictly determined no matter what the choice of values in the other row.

42.

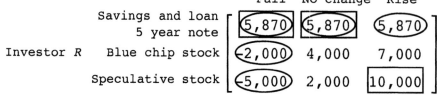

	Fall	No change	Rise
Savings and loan 5 year note	5,870	5,870	5,870
Blue chip stock	−2,000	4,000	7,000
Speculative stock	−5,000	2,000	10,000

The saddle value is $5,870 (1,1; 1,2 positions).

Optimal strategies: *R* plays row 1, *C* plays either column 1 or column 2.

44.

Store *C*

	E	F	G
E	0	1	−1
F	−1	0	−1
G	1	1	0

Store *R*

The saddle value is 0 (3,3 position).

Optimal strategies: *R* plays row 3, *C* plays column 3.

EXERCISE 10-2

2. $\begin{bmatrix} 1 & 3 \\ -2 & 0 \end{bmatrix}$ Row 2 is recessive since row 1 is a dominant row ($1 \geq -2$ and $3 \geq 0$).
Column 2 is recessive since column 1 is a dominant column ($1 \leq 3$ and $-2 \leq 0$).

4. $\begin{bmatrix} 2 & -4 & 3 \\ 1 & 2 & -5 \end{bmatrix}$ None. There is no dominant row and no dominant column.

6. $\begin{bmatrix} 2 & -5 \\ 0 & 4 \\ -1 & 3 \end{bmatrix}$ Row 3 is recessive since row 2 is a dominant row ($0 \geq -1$ and $4 \geq 3$). There is no recessive column.

8. $\begin{bmatrix} 2 & 2 & 3 \\ 4 & -1 & -1 \\ 3 & 0 & 1 \end{bmatrix}$ Column 1 and column 3 are recessive since column 2 is a dominant column ($2 \leq 2$, $-1 \leq 4$, $0 \leq 3$; $2 \leq 3$, $-1 \leq -1$, $0 \leq 1$). There are no recessive rows.

10. $\begin{bmatrix} 2 & 0 & 0 \\ 0 & 1 & 0 \\ 0 & 0 & 3 \end{bmatrix}$ None. There are no dominant rows and no dominant columns.

12. $\begin{bmatrix} 2 & -3 \\ -1 & 2 \end{bmatrix}$ The game is not strictly determined.

The optimal strategy for *R* is
$$P^* = \begin{bmatrix} \frac{d-c}{D} & \frac{a-b}{D} \end{bmatrix} = \begin{bmatrix} \frac{2-(-1)}{8} & \frac{2-(-3)}{8} \end{bmatrix} = \begin{bmatrix} \frac{3}{8} & \frac{5}{8} \end{bmatrix}$$
[<u>Note</u>: $D = (a + d) - (b + c) = (2 + 2) - (-3 - 1) = 8$.]

The optimal strategy for C is

$$Q^* = \begin{bmatrix} \dfrac{d-b}{D} \\ \dfrac{a-c}{D} \end{bmatrix} = \begin{bmatrix} \dfrac{2-(-3)}{8} \\ \dfrac{2-(-1)}{8} \end{bmatrix} = \begin{bmatrix} \dfrac{5}{8} \\ \dfrac{3}{8} \end{bmatrix}$$

The value of the game, v, is: $\dfrac{ad - bc}{D} = \dfrac{(2)(-2) - (-3)(-1)}{8} = \dfrac{1}{8}$.

14. $\begin{bmatrix} \boxed{2} & \enclose{circle}{-1} \\ \enclose{circle}{-2} & \boxed{1} \end{bmatrix}$ The game is not strictly determined.

The optimal strategy for R is

$$P^* = \begin{bmatrix} \dfrac{1-(-2)}{6} & \dfrac{2-(-1)}{6} \end{bmatrix} = \begin{bmatrix} \dfrac{1}{2} & \dfrac{1}{2} \end{bmatrix}$$

The optimal strategy for C is

$$Q^* = \begin{bmatrix} \dfrac{1-(-1)}{6} \\ \dfrac{2-(-2)}{6} \end{bmatrix} = \begin{bmatrix} \dfrac{1}{3} \\ \dfrac{2}{3} \end{bmatrix}$$

The value of the game, v, is: $\dfrac{(2)(1) - (-1)(-2)}{6} = \dfrac{0}{6} = 0$.

16. $\begin{bmatrix} \enclose{circle}{-1} & \boxed{3} \\ \boxed{2} & \enclose{circle}{-6} \end{bmatrix}$ The game is not strictly determined.

$$P^* = \begin{bmatrix} \dfrac{-6-2}{-12} & \dfrac{-1-3}{-12} \end{bmatrix} = \begin{bmatrix} \dfrac{2}{3} & \dfrac{1}{3} \end{bmatrix} \qquad Q^* = \begin{bmatrix} \dfrac{-6-3}{-12} \\ \dfrac{-1-2}{-12} \end{bmatrix} = \begin{bmatrix} \dfrac{3}{4} \\ \dfrac{1}{4} \end{bmatrix}$$

The value of the game, v, is: $\dfrac{(-1)(-6) - (3)(2)}{-12} = 0$.

18. $\begin{bmatrix} \boxed{3} & \boxed{\enclose{circle}{0}} \\ 1 & \enclose{circle}{-4} \end{bmatrix}$ The game is strictly determined.

$$P^* = \begin{bmatrix} 1 & 0 \end{bmatrix} \qquad Q^* = \begin{bmatrix} 0 \\ 1 \end{bmatrix}$$

The value of the game, v = saddle value = 0.

20. We can eliminate the recessive rows $\begin{bmatrix} 3 & -6 \end{bmatrix}$ and $\begin{bmatrix} -3 & 0 \end{bmatrix}$ to obtain

$\begin{bmatrix} \boxed{4} & \enclose{circle}{-6} \\ \enclose{circle}{-2} & \boxed{3} \end{bmatrix}$. The game is not strictly determined.

$$P^* = \begin{bmatrix} 0 & \dfrac{3-(-2)}{15} & \dfrac{4-(-6)}{15} & 0 \end{bmatrix} = \begin{bmatrix} 0 & \dfrac{1}{3} & \dfrac{2}{3} & 0 \end{bmatrix}$$

$$Q^* = \begin{bmatrix} \dfrac{3-(-6)}{15} \\ \dfrac{4-(-2)}{15} \end{bmatrix} = \begin{bmatrix} \dfrac{3}{5} \\ \dfrac{2}{5} \end{bmatrix}$$

The value of the game $v = \dfrac{(4)(3) - (-6)(-2)}{15} = 0$.

22. Eliminate the recessive columns and rows to obtain

$$\begin{bmatrix} \text{-1} & 2 \\ 2 & \text{-4} \end{bmatrix}$$ The game is not determined.

$$P^* = \begin{bmatrix} \frac{-4-2}{-9} & \frac{-1-2}{-9} & 0 \end{bmatrix} = \begin{bmatrix} \frac{2}{3} & \frac{1}{3} & 0 \end{bmatrix}$$

$$Q^* = \begin{bmatrix} \frac{-4-2}{-9} \\ \frac{-1-2}{-9} \\ 0 \end{bmatrix} = \begin{bmatrix} \frac{2}{3} \\ \frac{1}{3} \\ 0 \end{bmatrix}$$

The value of the game $v = \dfrac{(-1)(-4) - (2)(2)}{-9} = 0$.

24. $$\begin{bmatrix} -1 & 1 & \text{-5} \\ 2 & 2 & 3 \\ 0 & \text{-2} & 4 \end{bmatrix}$$ The game is strictly determined.

$$P^* = \begin{bmatrix} 0 & 1 & 0 \end{bmatrix}, \quad Q^* = \begin{bmatrix} 0 \\ 1 \\ 0 \end{bmatrix}, \quad \text{and } v = \text{saddle value} = 2.$$

26. (A) False: If optimal strategy for C is pure, then either $d - b = 0$ or $a - c = 0$. In either case, the game will be strictly determined.

(B) True: Take for example $\begin{bmatrix} 2 & 5 \\ 5 & 2 \end{bmatrix}$. The game is not strictly determined

and $P^* = \begin{bmatrix} \frac{1}{2} & \frac{1}{2} \end{bmatrix}$, $Q^* = \begin{bmatrix} \frac{1}{2} \\ \frac{1}{2} \end{bmatrix}$.

28. False; see exercise 8 of this section for a counterexample.

30. False. Take $\begin{bmatrix} 2 & 1 & 3 \\ 0 & 1 & -1 \end{bmatrix}$.

32. (A) $P = \begin{bmatrix} \frac{1}{4} & \frac{1}{4} & \frac{1}{4} & \frac{1}{4} \end{bmatrix}$, $Q = \begin{bmatrix} \frac{1}{3} \\ \frac{1}{3} \\ \frac{1}{3} \end{bmatrix}$

$$PMQ = \begin{bmatrix} \frac{1}{4} & \frac{1}{4} & \frac{1}{4} & \frac{1}{4} \end{bmatrix} \begin{bmatrix} 1 & 0 & 6 \\ 2 & 2 & 1 \\ 4 & 4 & 7 \\ 1 & 2 & 6 \end{bmatrix} \begin{bmatrix} \frac{1}{3} \\ \frac{1}{3} \\ \frac{1}{3} \end{bmatrix} = \begin{bmatrix} 2 & 2 & 5 \end{bmatrix} \begin{bmatrix} \frac{1}{3} \\ \frac{1}{3} \\ \frac{1}{3} \end{bmatrix} = 3.$$

Since you paid $4 before each game, then your expected value of the game is 3 - 4 = -$1.

(B) The smallest of the column maximums is 4 in column 1 or 2. Thus, she should play column 1, i.e., $Q = \begin{bmatrix} 1 \\ 0 \\ 0 \end{bmatrix}$ or column 2, i.e. $Q = \begin{bmatrix} 0 \\ 1 \\ 0 \end{bmatrix}$.

In either case $PMQ = 2$ and your expected value of the game is 2 - 4 = -$2.

(C) Since the largest of the row minimums is 4 in row 3, you should play row 3, i.e. $P = [0\ \ 0\ \ 1\ \ 0]$. She should play either column 1 or column 2. In either case, $PMQ = 4$ and your expected value of the game will be $4 - 4 = \$0$.

34. By (2), $P^*MQ \geq v$ for all Q; in particular for $Q = Q^*$, we have $P^*MQ^* \geq v$.
By (3), $PMQ^* \leq v$ for all P; in particular for $P = P^*$, we have $P^*MQ^* \leq v$.
Thus, $P^*MQ^* = v$.

36. Let $\begin{bmatrix} a & b \\ c & d \end{bmatrix}$ have b as a saddle value, then $a \geq b$ and $b \geq d$.

Now, if $a \geq c$, then row 2 is recessive; if $c > a$, then $c > d$ (since $c > a \geq b \geq d$) and column 1 is recessive.

38. Assign the values of a and $D \neq 0$ arbitrarily, say $D = 10$ and $a = 0$. Then solve for b, c, and d in Theorem 4, obtaining

$$\begin{cases} \frac{d-c}{D} = \frac{d-c}{10} = 0.6 \ , \\ \frac{a-b}{D} = \frac{0-b}{10} = 0.4 \ , \end{cases} \quad \begin{cases} \frac{d-b}{D} = \frac{d-b}{10} = 0.8 \\ \frac{a-c}{D} = \frac{-c}{10} = 0.2 \end{cases}$$

$b = -4$, $c = -2$, and $d = 4$. Thus, $M = \begin{bmatrix} 0 & -4 \\ -2 & 4 \end{bmatrix}$.

40. $E(P,\ Q) = ap_1q_1 + bp_1q_2 + cp_2q_1 + dp_2q_2$ (4)

(A) For $p_2 = 1 - p_1$ and $q_2 = 1 - q_1$ we have:

$E(P,\ Q) = ap_1q_1 + bp_1(1 - q_1) + c(1 - p_1)q_1 + d(1 - p_1)(1 - q_1)$

$= ap_1q_1 + bp_1 - bp_1q_1 + cq_1 - cp_1q_1$
$\qquad\qquad\qquad\qquad + d - d(p_1 + q_1) + dp_1q_1$

$= [aq_1 - bq_1 - cq_1 + dq_1 + (b - d)]p_1 + (c - d)q_1 + d$

$= \{[a - b - c + d]q_1 - (d - b)\}p_1 + (c - d)q_1 + d$

$= \{[(a + d) - (b + c)]q_1 - (d - b)\}p_1 + (c - d)q_1 + d$

$= [Dq_1 - (d - b)]p_1 + (c - d)q_1 + d,$

where $D = (a + d) - (b + c)$.

(B) In this case

$$E(P,\ Q) = (c - d)q_1 + d = \frac{(c - d)(d - b)}{D} + d = \frac{(c - d)(d - b) + dD}{D}$$

$$= \frac{cd - cb - d^2 + bd + ad + d^2 - bd - cd}{D} = \frac{ad - bc}{D} = v.$$

42. Given

	Nature films	Talk shows	Sports events	Movies
Travel	0	2	-1	0
News	1	0	-1	-2
Sitcoms	2	3	-1	1
Soaps	1	-2	0	0

Eliminating the recessive rows $[0\ \ 2\ \ -1\ \ 0]$ and $[1\ \ 0\ \ -1\ \ -2]$ and recessive column $\begin{bmatrix} 0 \\ 1 \\ 2 \\ 1 \end{bmatrix}$, we obtain $\begin{bmatrix} 3 & -1 & 1 \\ -2 & 0 & 1 \end{bmatrix}$. Now eliminating

recessive column 3 we have the 2 × 2 matrix $\begin{bmatrix} \boxed{3} & \boxed{-1} \\ \boxed{-2} & \boxed{0} \end{bmatrix}$
The game is not strictly determined.

(A) The optimal strategies for R and C are:

$$P^* = \begin{bmatrix} \frac{0-(-2)}{6} & \frac{3-(-1)}{6} \end{bmatrix} = \begin{bmatrix} \frac{1}{3} & \frac{2}{3} \end{bmatrix} \text{ and } Q^* = \begin{bmatrix} \frac{0-(-1)}{6} \\ \frac{3-(-2)}{6} \end{bmatrix} = \begin{bmatrix} \frac{1}{6} \\ \frac{5}{6} \end{bmatrix} \text{ respectively.}$$

In terms of the original problem:

$$P^* = \begin{bmatrix} 0 & 0 & \frac{1}{3} & \frac{2}{3} \end{bmatrix} \text{ and } Q^* = \begin{bmatrix} 0 \\ \frac{1}{5} \\ \frac{5}{6} \\ 0 \end{bmatrix}$$

The game value is $v = \dfrac{(3)(0) - (-1)(-2)}{6} = = -\dfrac{1}{3}.$

(B) $P = \begin{bmatrix} 1 & 0 & 0 & 0 \end{bmatrix}$ and $Q = \begin{bmatrix} 0 \\ \frac{1}{5} \\ \frac{5}{6} \\ 0 \end{bmatrix}$

$$PMQ = \begin{bmatrix} 1 & 0 & 0 & 0 \end{bmatrix} \begin{bmatrix} 0 & 2 & -1 & 0 \\ 1 & 0 & -1 & -2 \\ 2 & 3 & -1 & 1 \\ 1 & -2 & 0 & 0 \end{bmatrix} \begin{bmatrix} 0 \\ \frac{1}{5} \\ \frac{5}{6} \\ 0 \end{bmatrix}$$

$$= \begin{bmatrix} 0 & 2 & -1 & 0 \end{bmatrix} \begin{bmatrix} 0 \\ \frac{1}{5} \\ \frac{5}{6} \\ 0 \end{bmatrix} = -\frac{3}{6} = -\frac{1}{2}$$

(C) $P = \begin{bmatrix} 0 & 0 & \frac{1}{3} & \frac{2}{3} \end{bmatrix}$ and $Q = \begin{bmatrix} 0 \\ 0 \\ 0 \\ 1 \end{bmatrix}$

$$PMQ = \begin{bmatrix} 0 & 0 & \frac{1}{3} & \frac{2}{3} \end{bmatrix} \begin{bmatrix} 0 & 2 & -1 & 0 \\ 1 & 0 & -1 & -2 \\ 2 & 3 & -1 & 1 \\ 1 & -2 & 0 & 0 \end{bmatrix} \begin{bmatrix} 0 \\ 0 \\ 0 \\ 1 \end{bmatrix} = \begin{bmatrix} 0 & 0 & \frac{1}{3} & \frac{2}{3} \end{bmatrix} \begin{bmatrix} 0 \\ -2 \\ 1 \\ 0 \end{bmatrix} = \frac{1}{3}$$

(D) $P = [0 \quad 0 \quad 1 \quad 0]$ and $Q = \begin{bmatrix} 0 \\ 0 \\ 1 \\ 0 \end{bmatrix}$

$$PMQ = [0 \quad 0 \quad 1 \quad 0]\begin{bmatrix} 0 & 2 & -1 & 0 \\ 1 & 0 & -1 & -2 \\ 2 & 3 & -1 & 1 \\ 1 & -2 & 0 & 0 \end{bmatrix}\begin{bmatrix} 0 \\ 0 \\ 1 \\ 0 \end{bmatrix} = [0 \quad 0 \quad 1 \quad 0]\begin{bmatrix} -1 \\ -1 \\ -1 \\ 0 \end{bmatrix} = -1$$

44. Given

		Weather (fate)		
		Wet	Normal	Dry
Corporate farm	Wheat	-2	8	2
	Rice	7	3	-3

Eliminating the recessive column $\begin{bmatrix} 8 \\ 3 \end{bmatrix}$, we obtain the 2 × 2 matrix

$\begin{bmatrix} ⊟2 & ⬚2 \\ ⬚7 & ⊟3 \end{bmatrix}$ The game is not strictly determined.

(A) The optimal strategies for the company and the weather are:

$$P^* = \left[\frac{-3-7}{-14} \quad \frac{-2-2}{-14}\right] = \left[\frac{5}{7} \quad \frac{2}{7}\right] \text{ and } Q^* = \begin{bmatrix} \frac{-3-2}{-14} \\ \frac{-2-7}{-14} \end{bmatrix} = \begin{bmatrix} \frac{5}{14} \\ \frac{9}{14} \end{bmatrix} \text{ respectively.}$$

In terms of the original problem:

$$P^* = \left[\frac{5}{7} \quad \frac{2}{7}\right] \text{ and } Q^* = \begin{bmatrix} \frac{5}{14} \\ 0 \\ \frac{9}{14} \end{bmatrix}.$$

The game value is $v = \dfrac{(-2)(-3) - (2)(7)}{-14} = \dfrac{8}{14} \approx 0.57$ million.

(B) $P = \left[\frac{5}{7} \quad \frac{2}{7}\right]$ and $Q = \begin{bmatrix} 1 \\ 0 \\ 0 \end{bmatrix}$

$$PMQ = \left[\frac{5}{7} \quad \frac{2}{7}\right]\begin{bmatrix} -2 & 8 & 2 \\ 7 & 3 & -3 \end{bmatrix}\begin{bmatrix} 1 \\ 0 \\ 0 \end{bmatrix} = \left[\frac{5}{7} \quad \frac{2}{7}\right]\begin{bmatrix} -2 \\ 7 \end{bmatrix} = -\frac{10}{7} + \frac{14}{7} = \frac{4}{7}$$
$$\approx 0.57 \text{ million.}$$

(C) $P = \left[\frac{5}{7} \quad \frac{2}{7}\right]$ and $Q = \begin{bmatrix} 0 \\ 1 \\ 0 \end{bmatrix}$

$$PMQ = \left[\frac{5}{7} \quad \frac{2}{7}\right]\begin{bmatrix} -2 & 8 & 2 \\ 7 & 3 & -3 \end{bmatrix}\begin{bmatrix} 0 \\ 1 \\ 0 \end{bmatrix} = \left[\frac{5}{7} \quad \frac{2}{7}\right]\begin{bmatrix} 8 \\ 3 \end{bmatrix} = \frac{40}{7} + \frac{6}{7} = \frac{46}{7}$$
$$\approx 6.57 \text{ million.}$$

(D) $P = \begin{bmatrix} \frac{5}{7} & \frac{2}{7} \end{bmatrix}$ and $Q = \begin{bmatrix} 0 \\ 0 \\ 1 \end{bmatrix}$

$$PMQ = \begin{bmatrix} \frac{5}{7} & \frac{2}{7} \end{bmatrix}\begin{bmatrix} -2 & 8 & 2 \\ 7 & 3 & -3 \end{bmatrix}\begin{bmatrix} 0 \\ 0 \\ 1 \end{bmatrix} = \begin{bmatrix} \frac{5}{7} & \frac{2}{7} \end{bmatrix}\begin{bmatrix} 2 \\ -3 \end{bmatrix} = \frac{10}{7} - \frac{6}{7} = \frac{4}{7}$$

$$\approx 0.57 \text{ million.}$$

EXERCISE 10-3

2. $\begin{bmatrix} 4 & -1 \\ -1 & 2 \end{bmatrix}$

Take $k = 2$, then we will have: $\begin{bmatrix} 6 & 1 \\ 1 & 4 \end{bmatrix}$.

4. $\begin{bmatrix} 6 & 8 \\ 5 & 1 \end{bmatrix}$

Take $k = 0$.

6. $\begin{bmatrix} -3 & -2 \\ -1 & -3 \end{bmatrix}$

Take $k = 4$, then we will have: $\begin{bmatrix} 1 & 2 \\ 3 & 1 \end{bmatrix}$.

8. Convert $\begin{bmatrix} 2 & -1 \\ -2 & 1 \end{bmatrix}$ into a positive payoff matrix by adding 3 to each payoff.

$M_1 = \begin{bmatrix} 5 & 2 \\ 1 & 4 \end{bmatrix}$

Set up the two corresponding linear programming problems:

(A) Minimize $y = x_1 + x_2$

    Subject to $5x_1 + x_2 \geq 1$

               $2x_1 + 4x_2 \geq 1$

               $x_1 \geq 0, \; x_2 \geq 0$

(B) Maximize $y = z_1 + z_2$

    Subject to $5z_1 + 2z_2 \leq 1$

               $z_1 + 4z_2 \leq 1$

               $z_1 \geq 0, \; z_2 \geq 0$

Graph the feasible region and find the corner points for each of these linear programming problems:

(A)

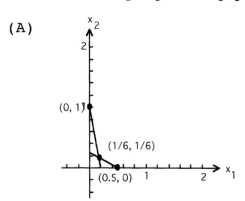

(B)

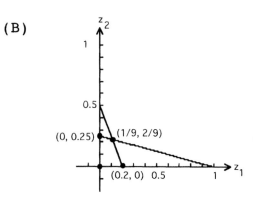

Corner points	$y = x_1 + x_2$
$(0, 1)$	$y = 0 + 1 = 1$
$\left(\frac{1}{6}, \frac{1}{6}\right)$	$y = \frac{1}{6} + \frac{1}{6} = \frac{1}{3}$ Min.
$\left(\frac{1}{2}, 0\right)$	$y = \frac{1}{2} + 0 = \frac{1}{2}$

Corner points	$y = z_1 + z_2$
$\left(0, \frac{1}{4}\right)$	$y = 0 + \frac{1}{4} = \frac{1}{4}$
$\left(\frac{1}{9}, \frac{2}{9}\right)$	$y = \frac{1}{9} + \frac{2}{9} = \frac{1}{3}$ Max.
$\left(\frac{1}{5}, 0\right)$	$y = \frac{1}{5} + 0 = \frac{1}{5}$
$(0, 0)$	$y = 0 + 0 = 0$

According to Theorems 1 and 2 in Section 5-3, the minimum value in problem (A) is $\frac{1}{3}$ at $x_1 = \frac{1}{6}$ and $x_2 = \frac{1}{6}$ and the maximum value in problem (B) is $\frac{1}{3}$ at $z_1 = \frac{1}{9}$ and $z_2 = \frac{2}{9}$.

Thus, $v_1 = \dfrac{1}{x_1 + x_2} = \dfrac{1}{z_1 + z_2} = \dfrac{1}{\frac{1}{6} + \frac{1}{6}} = \dfrac{1}{\frac{1}{9} + \frac{2}{9}} = 3$

$p_1 = v_1 x_1 = 3 \cdot \frac{1}{6} = \frac{1}{2}$ $\qquad$ $q_1 = v_1 z_1 = 3 \cdot \frac{1}{9} = \frac{1}{3}$

$p_2 = v_1 x_2 = 3 \cdot \frac{1}{6} = \frac{1}{2}$ $\qquad$ $q_2 = v_1 z_2 = 3 \cdot \frac{2}{9} = \frac{2}{3}$

The value v of the original matrix game is found by subtracting 3 from the value v_1 of M_1. Thus, $v = v_1 - 3 = 3 - 3 = 0$.

The optimal strategies and the value of the game are given by:

$$P^* = \begin{bmatrix} \frac{1}{2} & \frac{1}{2} \end{bmatrix}, \qquad Q^* = \begin{bmatrix} \frac{1}{3} \\ \frac{2}{3} \end{bmatrix}, \qquad v = 0$$

10. Convert $\begin{bmatrix} 4 & -6 \\ -2 & 3 \end{bmatrix}$ into a positive payoff matrix by adding 7 to each payoff.

$$M_1 = \begin{bmatrix} 11 & 1 \\ 5 & 10 \end{bmatrix}$$

Set up the two corresponding linear programming problems.

(A) Minimize $y = x_1 + x_2$ $\qquad$ (B) Maximize $y = z_1 + z_2$
$\quad$ Subject to $11x_1 + 5x_2 \geq 1$ $\qquad\qquad$ Subject to $11z_1 + z_2 \leq 1$
$\qquad\qquad\quad x_1 + 10x_2 \geq 1$ $\qquad\qquad\qquad\qquad 5z_1 + 10z_2 \leq 1$
$\qquad\qquad\quad x_1 \geq 0, \ x_2 \geq 0$ $\qquad\qquad\qquad\qquad z_1 \geq 0, \ z_2 \geq 0$

Graph the feasible region and find the corner points for each of these linear programming problems:

(A)

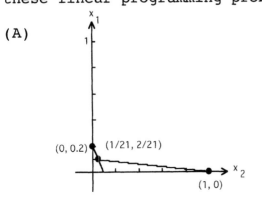

(B)

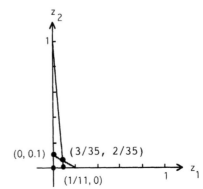

Corner points	$y = x_1 + x_2$
$\left(0, \dfrac{1}{5}\right)$	$y = 0 + \dfrac{1}{5} = \dfrac{1}{5}$
$\left(\dfrac{1}{21}, \dfrac{2}{21}\right)$	$y = \dfrac{1}{21} + \dfrac{2}{21} = \dfrac{1}{7}$ Min.
$(1, 0)$	$y = 1 + 0 = 1$

Corner points	$y = z_1 + z_2$
$\left(0, \dfrac{1}{10}\right)$	$y = 0 + \dfrac{1}{10} = \dfrac{1}{10}$
$\left(\dfrac{3}{35}, \dfrac{2}{35}\right)$	$y = \dfrac{3}{35} + \dfrac{2}{35} = \dfrac{1}{7}$ Max
$\left(\dfrac{1}{11}, 0\right)$	$y = \dfrac{1}{11} + 0 = \dfrac{1}{11}$
$(0, 0)$	$y = 0 + 0 = 0$

According to Theorems 1 and 2 in Section 5-3, the minimum value in problem (A) is $\dfrac{1}{7}$ at $x_1 = \dfrac{1}{21}$ and $x_2 = \dfrac{2}{21}$ and the maximum value in problem (B) is $\dfrac{1}{7}$ at $z_1 = \dfrac{3}{35}$ and $z_2 = \dfrac{2}{35}$.

Thus, $v_1 = \dfrac{1}{x_1 + x_2} = \dfrac{1}{z_1 + z_2} = \dfrac{1}{\dfrac{1}{21} + \dfrac{2}{21}} = 7$

$p_1 = v_1 x_1 = 7 \cdot \dfrac{1}{21} = \dfrac{1}{3}$ $\qquad$ $q_1 = v_1 z_1 = 7 \cdot \dfrac{3}{35} = \dfrac{3}{5}$

$p_2 = v_1 x_2 = 7 \cdot \dfrac{2}{21} = \dfrac{2}{3}$ $\qquad$ $q_2 = v_1 z_2 = 7 \cdot \dfrac{2}{35} = \dfrac{2}{5}$

The value v of the original matrix game is given by $v_1 - 7 = 7 - 7 = 0$. The optimal strategies and the value of the game are given by:

$$P^* = \begin{bmatrix} \dfrac{1}{3} & \dfrac{2}{3} \end{bmatrix}, \qquad Q^* = \begin{bmatrix} \dfrac{3}{5} \\ \dfrac{2}{5} \end{bmatrix}, \qquad v = 0$$

12. Convert $\begin{bmatrix} 6 & 2 \\ -1 & 1 \end{bmatrix}$ into a positive payoff matrix by adding 2 to each payoff.

$M_1 = \begin{bmatrix} 8 & 4 \\ 1 & 3 \end{bmatrix}$

Set up the two corresponding linear programming problems.

(A) Minimize $y = x_1 + x_2$
$\qquad$ Subject to $8x_1 + x_2 \geq 1$
$\qquad\qquad\qquad 4x_1 + 3x_2 \geq 1$
$\qquad\qquad\qquad x_1 \geq 0, \; x_2 \geq 0$

(B) Maximize $y = z_1 + z_2$
$\qquad$ Subject to $8z_1 + 4z_2 \leq 1$
$\qquad\qquad\qquad z_1 + 3z_2 \leq 1$
$\qquad\qquad\qquad z_1 \geq 0, \; z_2 \geq 0$

Graph the feasible region and find the corner points for each of these linear programming problems:

(A)

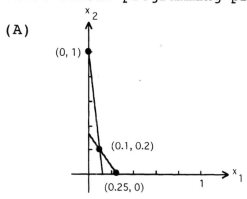

(B)

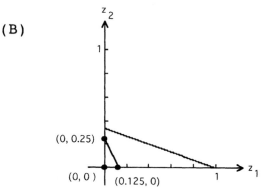

Corner points	$y = x_1 + x_2$
$(0, 1)$	$y = 0 + 1 = 1$
$\left(\dfrac{1}{10}, \dfrac{1}{5}\right)$	$y = \dfrac{1}{10} + \dfrac{1}{5} = \dfrac{3}{10}$
$\left(\dfrac{1}{4}, 0\right)$	$y = \dfrac{1}{4} + 0 = \dfrac{1}{4}$ Min.

Corner points	$y = z_1 + z_2$
$(0, 0)$	$y = 0 + 0 = 0$
$\left(0, \dfrac{1}{4}\right)$	$y = \dfrac{3}{35} + \dfrac{2}{35} = \dfrac{1}{7}$ Max.
$\left(\dfrac{1}{8}, 0\right)$	$y = \dfrac{1}{8} + 0 = \dfrac{1}{8}$

According to Theorems 1 and 2 in Section 5-3, the minimum value in problem (A) is $\dfrac{1}{4}$ at $x_1 = \dfrac{1}{4}$ and $x_2 = 0$ and the maximum value in problem (B) is $\dfrac{1}{4}$ at $z_1 = 0$ and $z_2 = \dfrac{1}{4}$.

Thus, $v_1 = \dfrac{1}{x_1 + x_2} = \dfrac{1}{z_1 + z_2} = \dfrac{1}{0 + \dfrac{1}{4}} = 4$

$p_1 = v_1 x_1 = 4\left(\dfrac{1}{4}\right) = 1$ $\qquad$ $q_1 = v_1 z_1 = 4(0) = 0$

$p_2 = v_1 x_2 = 4(0) = 0$ $\qquad$ $q_2 = v_1 z_2 = 4\left(\dfrac{1}{4}\right) = 1$

The value v of the original matrix is $v_1 - 2 = 4 - 2 = 2$.

The optimal strategies and the value of the game are given by:

$P^* = [1 \quad 0]$, $\qquad Q^* = \begin{bmatrix} 1 \\ 0 \end{bmatrix}$, $\qquad v = 2$

14. Yes. The matrix game, in problem 6, is strictly determined, so it may be solved easily by noting that $\begin{bmatrix} \boxed{6} & \boxed{2} \\ \boxed{-1} & 1 \end{bmatrix}$, 2 is a saddle value, and applying the method of Section 10-1.

16. False; for a counterexample see Exercise 8 of section 10-1, namely. $\begin{bmatrix} 0 & 0 \\ 0 & 1 \end{bmatrix}$

18. True

20. False. See Example 1 of Section 10-2.

22. In the game matrix $\begin{bmatrix} -1 & 2 & 2 \\ 2 & -4 & -2 \\ 2 & -5 & 0 \end{bmatrix}$ column 3 is recessive and can be eliminated. After that row 3 will be recessive and can be eliminated to obtain $\begin{bmatrix} -1 & 2 \\ 2 & -4 \end{bmatrix}$. Now we obtain the positive payoff matrix by adding 5 to each payoff: $M_1 = \begin{bmatrix} 4 & 7 \\ 7 & 1 \end{bmatrix}$.

The linear programming problems corresponding to M_1 are as follows:

(A) Minimize $y = x_1 + x_2$
  Subject to $4x_1 + 7x_2 \geq 1$
        $7x_1 + x_2 \geq 1$
        $x_1 \geq 0, x_2 \geq 0$

(B) Maximize $y = z_1 + z_2$
  Subject to $4z_1 + 7z_2 \leq 1$
        $7z_1 + z_2 \leq 1$
        $z_1 \geq 0, z_2 \geq 0$

Graph the feasible region and find the corner points for each of these linear programming problems:

(A)
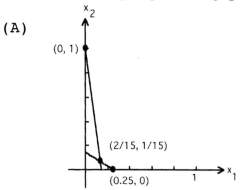

(B)
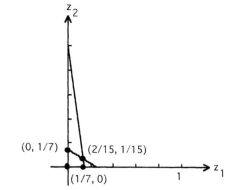

Corner points	$y = x_1 + x_2$	
$(0, 1)$	$y = 0 + 1 = 1$	
$\left(\dfrac{2}{15}, \dfrac{1}{15}\right)$	$y = \dfrac{2}{15} + \dfrac{1}{15} = \dfrac{1}{5}$	Min.
$\left(\dfrac{1}{4}, 0\right)$	$y = \dfrac{1}{4} + 0 = \dfrac{1}{4}$	

Corner points	$y = z_1 + z_2$	
$(0, 0)$	$y = 0 + 0 = 0$	
$\left(0, \dfrac{1}{7}\right)$	$y = 0 + \dfrac{1}{7} = \dfrac{1}{7}$	
$\left(\dfrac{2}{15}, \dfrac{1}{15}\right)$	$y = \dfrac{2}{15} + \dfrac{1}{15} = \dfrac{1}{5}$	Max.
$\left(\dfrac{1}{7}, 0\right)$	$y = \dfrac{1}{7} + 0 = \dfrac{1}{7}$	

According to Theorems 1 and 2 in Section 5-3, the minimum value in problem (A) is $\dfrac{1}{5}$ at $x_1 = \dfrac{2}{15}$ and $x_2 = \dfrac{1}{15}$ and the maximum value in problem (B) is $\dfrac{1}{5}$ at $z_1 = \dfrac{2}{15}$ and $z_2 = \dfrac{1}{15}$.

Thus, $v_1 = \dfrac{1}{x_1 + x_2} = \dfrac{1}{z_1 + z_2} = \dfrac{1}{\dfrac{2}{15} + \dfrac{1}{15}} = 5.$

$p_1 = v_1 x_1 = 5\left(\dfrac{2}{15}\right) = \dfrac{2}{3}$
$p_2 = v_1 x_2 = 5\left(\dfrac{1}{15}\right) = \dfrac{1}{3}$

$q_1 = v_1 z_1 = 5\left(\dfrac{2}{15}\right) = \dfrac{2}{3}$
$q_2 = v_1 z_2 = 5\left(\dfrac{1}{15}\right) = \dfrac{1}{3}$

The value v of the original matrix is given by $v = v_1 - 5 = 5 - 5 = 0$.

The optimal strategies and the value of the game are given by:

$P^* = \begin{bmatrix} \dfrac{2}{3} & \dfrac{1}{3} & 0 \end{bmatrix}, \qquad Q^* = \begin{bmatrix} \dfrac{2}{3} \\ \dfrac{1}{3} \\ 0 \end{bmatrix}, \qquad v = 0$

24. Suppose $P*$ and $Q*$ are optimal strategies for the game M with value v. If P is a strategy for R and Q is a strategy for C, then $P*MQ \geq v$ and $PMQ* \leq v$. Therefore, $P*(M + kJ)Q = P*MQ + P*kJQ \geq k + v$ and $P(M + kJ)Q* = PMQ* + PkJQ* \leq v + k$, so $P*$ and $Q*$ are also optimal strategies for the game $M + kJ$ with value $v + k$.

26. After eliminating the recessive rows $[0 \quad 2 \quad -1 \quad 0]$ and $[1 \quad 0 \quad -1 \quad -2]$,

and column $\begin{bmatrix} 0 \\ 1 \\ 2 \\ 1 \end{bmatrix}$ and subsequently column 3 we have the 2 × 2 matrix

$\begin{bmatrix} 3 & -1 \\ -2 & 0 \end{bmatrix}$. Add 3 to each element to get the positive matrix:

$M_1 = \begin{bmatrix} 6 & 2 \\ 1 & 3 \end{bmatrix}$

The linear programming problems corresponding to M_1 are as follows:

(A) Minimize $y = x_1 + x_2$
    Subject to $6x_1 + x_2 \geq 1$
                $2x_1 + 3x_2 \geq 1$
                $x_1 \geq 0, \ x_2 \geq 0$

(B) Maximize $y = z_1 + z_2$
    Subject to $6z_1 + 2z_2 \leq 1$
                $z_1 + 3z_2 \leq 1$
                $z_1 \geq 0, \ z_2 \geq 0$

Graph the feasible region and find the corner points for each of these linear programming problems:

(A)

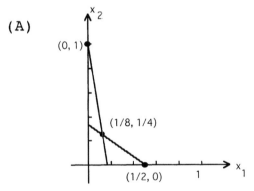

(B)

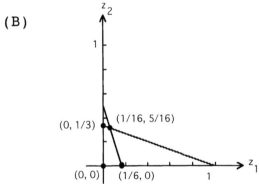

Corner points	$y = x_1 + x_2$	
$(0, 1)$	$y = 0 + 1 = 1$	
$\left(\dfrac{1}{8}, \dfrac{1}{4}\right)$	$y = \dfrac{1}{8} + \dfrac{1}{4} = \dfrac{3}{8}$	Min.
$\left(\dfrac{1}{2}, 0\right)$	$y = \dfrac{1}{2} + 0 = \dfrac{1}{2}$	

Corner points	$y = z_1 + z_2$	
$(0, 0)$	$y = 0 + 0 = 0$	
$\left(0, \dfrac{1}{3}\right)$	$y = 0 + \dfrac{1}{3} = \dfrac{1}{3}$	
$\left(\dfrac{1}{16}, \dfrac{5}{16}\right)$	$y = \dfrac{1}{16} + \dfrac{5}{16} = \dfrac{3}{8}$	Max.
$\left(\dfrac{1}{6}, 0\right)$	$y = \dfrac{1}{6} + 0 = \dfrac{1}{6}$	

According to Theorems 1 and 2 in Section 5-3, the minimum value in problem (A) is $\dfrac{3}{8}$ at $x_1 = \dfrac{1}{8}$ and $x_2 = \dfrac{1}{4}$ and the maximum value in problem (B) is $\dfrac{3}{8}$ at $z_1 = \dfrac{1}{16}$ and $z_2 = \dfrac{5}{16}$.

Thus, $v_1 = \dfrac{1}{x_1 + x_2} = \dfrac{1}{z_1 + z_2} = \dfrac{8}{3}$.

$$p_1 = v_1 x_1 = \frac{8}{3} \cdot \frac{1}{8} = \frac{1}{3} \qquad\qquad q_1 = v_1 z_1 = \frac{8}{3} \cdot \frac{1}{16} = \frac{1}{6}$$

$$p_2 = v_1 x_2 = \frac{8}{3} \cdot \frac{1}{4} = \frac{2}{3} \qquad\qquad q_2 = v_1 z_2 = \frac{8}{3} \cdot \frac{5}{16} = \frac{5}{6}$$

The value v of the original matrix is given by

$$v = v_1 - 3 = \frac{8}{3} - 3 = -\frac{1}{3}$$

and $P^* = \begin{bmatrix} 0 & 0 & \frac{1}{3} & \frac{2}{3} \end{bmatrix}$, $\qquad Q^* = \begin{bmatrix} 0 \\ \frac{1}{6} \\ \frac{5}{6} \\ 0 \end{bmatrix}$, $\qquad v = -\frac{1}{3}$

28. Eliminating the recessive column $\begin{bmatrix} 8 \\ 3 \end{bmatrix}$ we obtain the 2 × 2 matrix $\begin{bmatrix} -2 & 2 \\ 7 & -3 \end{bmatrix}$. Add 4 to each element to get the positive matrix $M_1 = \begin{bmatrix} 2 & 6 \\ 11 & 1 \end{bmatrix}$.

The linear programming problems corresponding to M_1 are as follows:

(A) Minimize $y = x_1 + x_2$ (B) Maximize $y = z_1 + z_2$
    Subject to $2x_1 + 11x_2 \geq 1$ Subject to $2z_1 + 6z_2 \leq 1$
              $6x_1 + x_2 \geq 1$ $11z_1 + z_2 \leq 1$
              $x_1 \geq 0,\ x_2 \geq 0$ $z_1 \geq 0,\ z_2 \geq 0$

Graph the feasible region and find the corner points for each of these linear programming problems:

(A)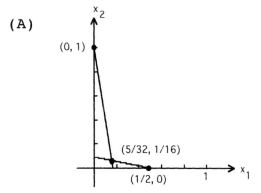

(B)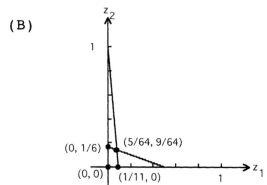

Corner points	$y = x_1 + x_2$
$(0, 1)$	$y = 0 + 1 = 1$
$\left(\dfrac{5}{32}, \dfrac{1}{16}\right)$	$y = \dfrac{5}{32} + \dfrac{1}{16} = \dfrac{7}{32}$
$\left(\dfrac{1}{2}, 0\right)$	$y = \dfrac{1}{2} + 0 = \dfrac{1}{2}$

Corner points	$y = z_1 + z_2$
$(0, 0)$	$y = 0 + 0 = 0$
$\left(0, \dfrac{1}{6}\right)$	$y = 0 + \dfrac{1}{6} = \dfrac{1}{6}$
$\left(\dfrac{5}{64}, \dfrac{9}{64}\right)$	$y = \dfrac{5}{64} + \dfrac{9}{64} = \dfrac{7}{32}$ Max.
$\left(\dfrac{1}{11}, 0\right)$	$y = \dfrac{1}{11} + 0 = \dfrac{1}{11}$

According to Theorems 1 and 2 in Section 5-3, the minimum value in problem (A) is $\dfrac{7}{32}$ at $x_1 = \dfrac{5}{32}$ and $x_2 = \dfrac{1}{16}$ and the maximum value in problem (B) is $\dfrac{7}{32}$ at $z_1 = \dfrac{5}{64}$ and $z_2 = \dfrac{9}{64}$.

Thus, $v_1 = \dfrac{1}{x_1 + x_2} = \dfrac{1}{z_1 + z_2} = \dfrac{1}{\dfrac{5}{32} + \dfrac{1}{16}} = \dfrac{32}{7}$.

$$p_1 = v_1 x_1 = \dfrac{32}{7} \cdot \dfrac{5}{3} = \dfrac{5}{7} \qquad q_1 = v_1 z_1 = \dfrac{32}{7} \cdot \dfrac{5}{64} = \dfrac{5}{14}$$

$$p_2 = v_1 x_2 = \dfrac{32}{7} \cdot \dfrac{1}{16} = \dfrac{2}{7} \qquad q_2 = v_1 z_2 = \dfrac{32}{7} \cdot \dfrac{9}{64} = \dfrac{9}{14}$$

The value v of the original matrix is given by

$$v = v_1 - 4 = \dfrac{32}{7} - 4 = \dfrac{4}{7}$$

and $P^* = \begin{bmatrix} \dfrac{5}{7} & \dfrac{2}{7} \end{bmatrix}$, $\qquad Q^* = \begin{bmatrix} \dfrac{5}{14} \\ 0 \\ \dfrac{9}{14} \end{bmatrix}$, $\qquad v = 0.57$ million.

EXERCISE 10-4

2. Convert $\begin{bmatrix} 1 & -1 \\ 2 & -2 \\ 0 & 1 \end{bmatrix}$ into a positive payoff matrix by adding 3 to each

payoff: $M_1 = \begin{bmatrix} 4 & 2 \\ 5 & 1 \\ 3 & 4 \end{bmatrix}$

The linear programming problems corresponding to M_1 are as follows:

(A) Minimize $y = x_1 + x_2 + x_3$

Subject to $4x_1 + 5x_2 + 3x_3 \geq 1$
$2x_1 + x_2 + 4x_3 \geq 1$
$x_1 \geq 0, \; x_2 \geq 0, \; x_3 \geq 0$

(B) Maximize $y = z_1 + z_2$

Subject to $4z_1 + 2z_2 \leq 1$
$5z_1 + z_2 \leq 1$
$3z_1 + 4z_2 \leq 1$
$z_1 \geq 0, \; z_2 \geq 0$

Solve (B) by using the simplex method. We introduce slack variables x_1, x_2, and x_3 to obtain:

$$
\begin{aligned}
4z_1 + 2z_2 + x_1 &= 1 \\
5z_1 + z_2 + x_2 &= 1 \\
3z_1 + 4z_2 + x_3 &= 1 \\
-z_1 - z_2 + y &= 0 \\
z_1, z_2 &\geq 0, \quad x_1, x_2, x_3 \geq 0
\end{aligned}
$$

The simplex tableau for this system is:

$$
\begin{array}{cccccc}
z_1 & z_2 & x_1 & x_2 & x_3 & y
\end{array}
$$

$$
\left[\begin{array}{cccccc|c}
4 & 2 & 1 & 0 & 0 & 0 & 1 \\
\circled{5} & 1 & 0 & 1 & 0 & 0 & 1 \\
3 & 4 & 0 & 0 & 1 & 0 & 1 \\
\hline
-1 & -1 & 0 & 0 & 0 & 1 & 0
\end{array}\right]
\begin{array}{l}
1/4 \\
1/5 \\
1/3 \\

\end{array}
$$

$$\frac{1}{5}R_2 \rightarrow R_2$$

$$
\sim
\left[\begin{array}{cccccc|c}
4 & 2 & 1 & 0 & 0 & 0 & 1 \\
\circled{1} & \frac{1}{5} & 0 & \frac{1}{5} & 0 & 0 & \frac{1}{5} \\
3 & 4 & 0 & 0 & 1 & 0 & 1 \\
\hline
-1 & -1 & 0 & 0 & 0 & 1 & 0
\end{array}\right]
\sim
\left[\begin{array}{cccccc|c}
0 & \frac{6}{5} & 1 & -\frac{4}{5} & 0 & 0 & \frac{1}{5} \\
1 & \frac{1}{5} & 0 & \frac{1}{5} & 0 & 0 & \frac{1}{5} \\
0 & \circled{\frac{17}{5}} & 0 & -\frac{3}{5} & 1 & 0 & \frac{2}{5} \\
\hline
0 & -\frac{4}{5} & 0 & \frac{1}{5} & 0 & 1 & \frac{1}{5}
\end{array}\right]
\begin{array}{l}
\frac{1}{6} \\
1 \\
\frac{2}{17} \\

\end{array}
$$

$(-4)R_2 + R_1 \rightarrow R_1, \ (-3)R_2 + R_3 \rightarrow R_3, \qquad \frac{5}{17}R_3 \rightarrow R_3$
and $R_2 + R_4 \rightarrow R_4$

$$
\sim
\left[\begin{array}{cccccc|c}
0 & \frac{6}{5} & 1 & -\frac{4}{5} & 0 & 0 & \frac{1}{5} \\
1 & \frac{1}{5} & 0 & \frac{1}{5} & 0 & 0 & \frac{1}{5} \\
0 & \circled{1} & 0 & -\frac{3}{17} & \frac{5}{17} & 0 & \frac{2}{17} \\
\hline
0 & -\frac{4}{5} & 0 & \frac{1}{5} & 0 & 1 & \frac{1}{5}
\end{array}\right]
\sim
\left[\begin{array}{cccccc|c}
0 & 0 & 1 & -\frac{2}{17} & -\frac{6}{17} & 0 & \frac{1}{17} \\
1 & 0 & 0 & \frac{4}{17} & -\frac{1}{17} & 0 & \frac{3}{17} \\
0 & 1 & 0 & -\frac{3}{17} & \frac{5}{17} & 0 & \frac{2}{17} \\
\hline
0 & 0 & 0 & \frac{1}{17} & \frac{4}{17} & 1 & \frac{5}{17}
\end{array}\right]
$$

$\left(-\frac{6}{5}\right)R_3 + R_1 \rightarrow R_1, \ \left(-\frac{1}{5}\right)R_3 + R_2 \rightarrow R_2,$

and $\dfrac{4}{5}R_3 + R_4 \rightarrow R_4$

The maximum $y = z_1 + z_2 = \dfrac{5}{17}$, occurs at $z_1 = \dfrac{3}{17}$ and $z_2 = \dfrac{2}{17}$.

Thus, $v_1 = \dfrac{1}{z_1 + z_2} = \dfrac{1}{\dfrac{3}{17} + \dfrac{2}{17}} = \dfrac{17}{5}$, and $q_1 = v_1 z_1 = \dfrac{17}{5} \cdot \dfrac{3}{17} = \dfrac{3}{5}$,

$q_2 = v_1 z_2 = \dfrac{17}{5} \cdot \dfrac{2}{17} = \dfrac{2}{5}$

The solution to minimization problem (A) can be read from the bottom row of the final simplex tableau for the dual problem above. Thus, from the row

$$
\begin{array}{ccc}
x_1 & x_2 & x_3
\end{array}
$$

$$
\left[\begin{array}{cccccc|c}
0 & 0 & 0 & \frac{1}{17} & \frac{4}{17} & 1 & \frac{5}{17}
\end{array}\right]
$$

Min $y = x_1 + x_2 + x_3 = \dfrac{5}{17}$ at $x_1 = 0$, $x_2 = \dfrac{1}{17}$, and $x_3 = \dfrac{4}{17}$.

Also,

$$p_1 = v_1 x_1 = 0$$

$$p_2 = v_1 x_2 = \frac{17}{5} \cdot \frac{1}{17} = \frac{1}{5}$$

$$p_3 = v_1 x_3 = \frac{17}{5} \cdot \frac{4}{17} = \frac{4}{5}$$

Finally,

$$P^* = \begin{bmatrix} 0 & \frac{1}{5} & \frac{4}{5} \end{bmatrix}, \qquad Q^* = \begin{bmatrix} \frac{3}{5} \\ \frac{2}{5} \end{bmatrix}, \qquad \text{and} \qquad v = \frac{17}{5} - 3 = \frac{2}{5}.$$

4. Given $M = \begin{bmatrix} 1 & 2 & 0 \\ 0 & 1 & 2 \\ 2 & 0 & 1 \end{bmatrix}$, the linear programming problems corresponding to M are as follows:

(A) Minimize $y = x_1 + x_2 + x_3$

Subject to

$$x_1 \qquad + 2x_3 \geq 1$$
$$2x_1 + x_2 \qquad \geq 1$$
$$2x_2 + x_3 \geq 1$$
$$x_1 \geq 0, \ x_2 \geq 0, \ x_3 \geq 0$$

(B) Maximize $y = z_1 + z_2 + z_3$

Subject to

$$z_1 + 2z_2 \qquad \leq 1$$
$$z_2 + 2z_3 \leq 1$$
$$2z_1 \qquad + z_3 \leq 1$$
$$z_1 \geq 0, \ z_2 \geq 0, \ z_3 \geq 0$$

We first solve (B) by using the simplex method. Introduce slack variables x_1, x_2, and x_3 to obtain:

$$z_1 + 2z_2 \qquad + x_1 \qquad \qquad = 1$$
$$z_2 + 2z_3 \qquad + x_2 \qquad = 1$$
$$2z_1 \qquad + z_3 \qquad + x_3 \qquad = 1$$
$$-z_1 - z_2 - z_3 \qquad \qquad + y = 0$$
$$z_1, \ z_2, \ z_3 \geq 0, \ x_1, \ x_2, \ x_3 \geq 0$$

The simplex tableau for this system is:

$$
\begin{array}{ccccccc}
z_1 & z_2 & z_3 & x_1 & x_2 & x_3 & y \\
\end{array}
$$

$$
\left[\begin{array}{ccccccc|c}
1 & 2 & 0 & 1 & 0 & 0 & 0 & 1 \\
0 & 1 & 2 & 0 & 1 & 0 & 0 & 1 \\
\textcircled{2} & 0 & 1 & 0 & 0 & 1 & 0 & 1 \\
-1 & -1 & -1 & 0 & 0 & 0 & 1 & 0
\end{array}\right]
\begin{array}{c} 1 \\ \\ \frac{1}{2} \\ \end{array}
$$

$$\frac{1}{2}R_3 \to R_3$$

$$
\sim \left[\begin{array}{ccccccc|c}
1 & 2 & 0 & 1 & 0 & 0 & 0 & 1 \\
0 & 1 & 2 & 0 & 1 & 0 & 0 & 1 \\
\textcircled{1} & 0 & \frac{1}{2} & 0 & 0 & \frac{1}{2} & 0 & \frac{1}{2} \\
-1 & -1 & -1 & 0 & 0 & 0 & 1 & 0
\end{array}\right]
\sim
\left[\begin{array}{ccccccc|c}
0 & \textcircled{2} & -\frac{1}{2} & 1 & 0 & -\frac{1}{2} & 0 & \frac{1}{2} \\
0 & 1 & 2 & 0 & 1 & 0 & 0 & 1 \\
1 & 0 & \frac{1}{2} & 0 & 0 & \frac{1}{2} & 0 & \frac{1}{2} \\
0 & -1 & -\frac{1}{2} & 0 & 0 & \frac{1}{2} & 1 & \frac{1}{2}
\end{array}\right]
\begin{array}{c} \frac{1}{4} \\ 1 \\ \\ \end{array}
$$

$$(-1)R_3 + R_1 \to R_1 \text{ and } R_3 + R_4 \to R_4 \qquad \frac{1}{2}R_1 \to R_1$$

$$\sim \left[\begin{array}{ccccccc|c}
0 & ① & -\frac{1}{4} & \frac{1}{2} & 0 & -\frac{1}{4} & 0 & \frac{1}{4} \\
0 & 1 & 2 & 0 & 1 & 0 & 0 & 1 \\
1 & 0 & \frac{1}{2} & 0 & 0 & \frac{1}{2} & 0 & \frac{1}{2} \\
\hline
0 & -1 & -\frac{1}{2} & 0 & 0 & \frac{1}{2} & 1 & \frac{1}{2}
\end{array}\right]\begin{array}{c}\frac{1}{4} \\ 1 \\ \\ \end{array}
\quad \sim \left[\begin{array}{ccccccc|c}
0 & 1 & -\frac{1}{4} & \frac{1}{2} & 0 & -\frac{1}{4} & 0 & \frac{1}{4} \\
0 & 0 & ⑨/④ & -\frac{1}{2} & 1 & \frac{1}{4} & 0 & \frac{3}{4} \\
1 & 0 & \frac{1}{2} & 0 & 0 & \frac{1}{2} & 0 & \frac{1}{2} \\
\hline
0 & 0 & -\frac{3}{4} & \frac{1}{2} & 0 & \frac{1}{4} & 1 & \frac{3}{4}
\end{array}\right]\begin{array}{c}\frac{1}{4} \\ \frac{1}{3} \\ 1 \\ \end{array}$$

$$(-1)R_1 + R_2 \to R_2 \text{ and } R_1 + R_4 \to R_4 \qquad\qquad \frac{4}{9}R_2 \to R_2$$

$$\sim \left[\begin{array}{ccccccc|c}
0 & 1 & -\frac{1}{4} & \frac{1}{2} & 0 & -\frac{1}{4} & 0 & \frac{1}{4} \\
0 & 0 & ① & -\frac{2}{9} & \frac{4}{9} & \frac{1}{9} & 0 & \frac{1}{3} \\
1 & 0 & \frac{1}{2} & 0 & 0 & \frac{1}{2} & 0 & \frac{1}{2} \\
\hline
0 & 0 & -\frac{3}{4} & \frac{1}{2} & 0 & \frac{1}{4} & 1 & \frac{3}{4}
\end{array}\right]$$

$$\frac{1}{4}R_2 + R_1 \to R_1, \quad \left(-\frac{1}{2}\right)R_2 + R_3 \to R_3, \quad \text{and} \quad \frac{3}{4}R_2 + R_4 \to R_4$$

$$\begin{array}{ccccccc}
z_1 & z_2 & z_3 & x_1 & x_2 & x_3 & y
\end{array}$$

$$\sim \left[\begin{array}{ccccccc|c}
0 & 1 & 0 & \frac{4}{9} & \frac{1}{9} & -\frac{2}{9} & 0 & \frac{1}{3} \\
0 & 0 & 1 & -\frac{2}{9} & \frac{4}{9} & \frac{1}{9} & 0 & \frac{1}{3} \\
1 & 0 & 0 & \frac{1}{9} & -\frac{2}{9} & \frac{4}{9} & 0 & \frac{1}{3} \\
\hline
0 & 0 & 0 & \frac{1}{3} & \frac{1}{3} & \frac{1}{3} & 1 & 1
\end{array}\right]$$

We obtain $z_1 = z_2 = z_3 = \frac{1}{3}$. Thus, $v_1 = \dfrac{1}{\frac{1}{3} + \frac{1}{3} + \frac{1}{3}} = 1$, and

$$q_1 = v_1 z_1 = 1 \cdot \frac{1}{3} = \frac{1}{3}, \quad q_2 = v_1 z_2 = 1 \cdot \frac{1}{3} = \frac{1}{3}, \quad q_3 = v_1 z_3 = 1 \cdot \frac{1}{3} = \frac{1}{3}.$$

The solution to the minimizing problem (A) can be read from the bottom row of the final simplex tableau for the dual problem above. Thus, from the row

$$\begin{array}{ccc}
x_1 & x_2 & x_3
\end{array}$$

$$\left[\begin{array}{ccccccc|c}
0 & 0 & 0 & \frac{1}{3} & \frac{1}{3} & \frac{1}{3} & 1 & 1
\end{array}\right]$$

we conclude that the solution to (A) is:

Min $y = x_1 + x_2 + x_3 = 1$ at $x_1 = x_2 = x_3 = \frac{1}{3}$

Also, $p_1 = v_1 x_1 = 1 \cdot \frac{1}{3} = \frac{1}{3}$

$$p_2 = v_1 x_2 = 1 \cdot \frac{1}{3} = \frac{1}{3}$$

$$p_3 = v_1 x_3 = 1 \cdot \frac{1}{3} = \frac{1}{3}$$

Finally,

$$P^* = \left[\begin{array}{ccc} \frac{1}{3} & \frac{1}{3} & \frac{1}{3} \end{array}\right], \qquad Q^* = \left[\begin{array}{c} \frac{1}{3} \\ \frac{1}{3} \\ \frac{1}{3} \end{array}\right], \qquad \text{and} \qquad v = v_1 - 0 = 1 - 0 = 1.$$

6. $M = \begin{bmatrix} -5 & -6 & -7 & 4 \\ -5 & 3 & 2 & 3 \\ -4 & -2 & -6 & 7 \end{bmatrix}$

Eliminate the recessive row $[-5 \quad -6 \quad -7 \quad 4]$ and the recessive columns $\begin{bmatrix} 3 \\ -2 \end{bmatrix}$ and $\begin{bmatrix} 3 \\ 7 \end{bmatrix}$ to obtain the 2×2 matrix $\begin{bmatrix} -5 & 2 \\ -4 & -6 \end{bmatrix}$. Convert this matrix to a positive payoff matrix by adding 7 to each payoff.

$M_1 = \begin{bmatrix} 2 & 9 \\ 3 & 1 \end{bmatrix}$

The linear programming problems corresponding to M_1 are:

(A) Minimize $y = x_1 + x_2$

Subject to $2x_1 + 3x_2 \geq 1$

$9x_1 + x_2 \geq 1$

$x_1 \geq 0, \ x_2 \geq 0$

(B) Maximize $y = z_1 + z_2$

Subject to $2z_1 + 9z_2 \leq 1$

$3z_1 + z_2 \leq 1$

$z_1 \geq 0, \ z_2 \geq 0$

Solve (B) by using the simplex method. We introduce slack variables $x_1, \ x_2$ to obtain:

$$2z_1 + 9z_2 + x_1 \qquad = 1$$
$$3z_1 + z_2 \qquad + x_2 = 1$$
$$z_1, \ z_2, \ x_1, \ x_2 \geq 0$$

The simplex tableau for this system is:

$\begin{array}{ccccc} z_1 & z_2 & x_1 & x_2 & y \end{array}$

$\left[\begin{array}{ccccc|c} 2 & 9 & 1 & 0 & 0 & 1 \\ ③ & 1 & 0 & 1 & 0 & 1 \\ \hline -1 & -1 & 0 & 0 & 1 & 0 \end{array}\right] \begin{array}{l} \frac{1}{2} \\ \frac{1}{3} \end{array} \sim \left[\begin{array}{ccccc|c} 2 & 9 & 1 & 0 & 0 & 1 \\ ① & \frac{1}{3} & 0 & \frac{1}{3} & 0 & \frac{1}{3} \\ \hline -1 & -1 & 0 & 0 & 1 & 0 \end{array}\right]$

$\frac{1}{3} R_2 \to R_2$ $\qquad\qquad (-2)R_2 + R_1 \to R_1 \text{ and } R_2 + R_3 \to R_3$

$\sim \left[\begin{array}{ccccc|c} 0 & ㉕\!\!/3 & 1 & -\frac{2}{3} & 0 & \frac{1}{3} \\ 1 & \frac{1}{3} & 0 & \frac{1}{3} & 0 & \frac{1}{3} \\ \hline 0 & -\frac{2}{3} & 0 & \frac{1}{3} & 1 & \frac{1}{3} \end{array}\right] \begin{array}{l} \frac{1}{25} \\ 1 \end{array} \sim \left[\begin{array}{ccccc|c} 0 & ① & \frac{3}{25} & -\frac{2}{25} & 0 & \frac{1}{25} \\ 1 & \frac{1}{3} & 0 & \frac{1}{3} & 0 & \frac{1}{3} \\ \hline 0 & -\frac{2}{3} & 0 & \frac{1}{3} & 1 & \frac{1}{3} \end{array}\right]$

$\frac{3}{25} R_1 \to R_1$ $\qquad\qquad \left(-\frac{1}{3}\right)R_1 + R_2 \to R_2 \text{ and } \frac{2}{3}R_1 + R_3 \to R_3$

$\begin{array}{ccccc} z_1 & z_2 & x_1 & x_2 & y \end{array}$

$\sim \left[\begin{array}{ccccc|c} 0 & 1 & \frac{3}{25} & -\frac{2}{25} & 0 & \frac{1}{25} \\ 1 & 0 & -\frac{1}{25} & \frac{9}{25} & 0 & \frac{8}{25} \\ \hline 0 & 0 & \frac{2}{25} & \frac{7}{25} & 1 & \frac{9}{25} \end{array}\right]$

The maximum $y = z_1 + z_2 = \dfrac{9}{25}$ occurs at $z_1 = \dfrac{8}{25}$, $z_2 = \dfrac{1}{25}$.

Thus, $v_1 = \dfrac{1}{z_1 + z_2} = \dfrac{1}{y} = \dfrac{25}{9}$ and $q_1 = v_1 z_1 = \dfrac{8}{9}$, $q_2 = v_1 z_2 = \dfrac{1}{9}$.

The solution to the minimization problem (A) can be read from the bottom row of the final simplex tableau for the dual problem (B). Thus, from the row

$$
\begin{array}{ccccc}
z_1 & z_2 & x_1 & x_2 & y \\
\end{array}
$$

$$
\begin{bmatrix} 0 & 0 & \frac{2}{25} & \frac{7}{25} & 1 \; \bigg| \; \frac{9}{25} \end{bmatrix}
$$

we find the solution to (A):

Minimum $y = x_1 + x_2 = \dfrac{9}{25}$ at $x_1 = \dfrac{2}{25}$, $x_2 = \dfrac{7}{25}$.

Also, $p_1 = v_1 x_1 = \dfrac{2}{9}$, $p_2 = v_1 x_2 = \dfrac{7}{9}$.

Finally,

$$
P^* = \begin{bmatrix} 0 & \frac{2}{9} & \frac{7}{9} \end{bmatrix}, \qquad Q^* = \begin{bmatrix} \frac{8}{9} \\ 0 \\ \frac{1}{9} \\ 0 \end{bmatrix}, \qquad \text{and} \qquad v = v_1 - 7 = \frac{25}{9} - 7 = -\frac{38}{9}.
$$

8. $M = \begin{bmatrix} 2 & -5 & -3 & -1 \\ 0 & 1 & 2 & -2 \\ -1 & 0 & 1 & 3 \\ 2 & -3 & -2 & 0 \end{bmatrix}$

Eliminate the recessive row $[2 \quad -5 \quad -3 \quad -1]$ and recessive column $\begin{bmatrix} 2 \\ 1 \\ -2 \end{bmatrix}$

to obtain $\begin{bmatrix} 0 & 1 & -2 \\ -1 & 0 & 3 \\ 2 & -3 & 0 \end{bmatrix}$. This is the matrix of problem 3. Thus,

$$
P^* = \begin{bmatrix} 0 & \frac{1}{2} & \frac{1}{3} & \frac{1}{6} \end{bmatrix}, \quad Q^* = \begin{bmatrix} \frac{1}{2} \\ \frac{1}{3} \\ 0 \\ \frac{1}{6} \end{bmatrix}, \quad v = 0.
$$

10. (A) The matrix for this game is as follows:

$$
\begin{array}{cc}
 & C \\
 & \begin{array}{ccc} 1 & 5 & 10 \end{array} \\
R \begin{array}{c} 2 \\ 5 \\ 10 \end{array} & \begin{bmatrix} -2 & -2 & 10 \\ 1 & 5 & -5 \\ -10 & -10 & 10 \end{bmatrix}
\end{array}
$$

(B) Convert this matrix into a positive payoff matrix by adding 11
to each payoff:

$$M_1 = \begin{bmatrix} 9 & 9 & 21 \\ 12 & 16 & 6 \\ 1 & 1 & 21 \end{bmatrix}$$

The linear programming problems corresponding to M_1 are as
follows:

(A) Minimize $y = x_1 + x_2 + x_3$

$$\text{Subject to } 9x_1 + 12x_2 + x_3 \geq 1$$
$$9x_1 + 16x_2 + x_3 \geq 1$$
$$21x_1 + 6x_2 + 21x_3 \geq 1$$
$$x_1, \ x_2, \ x_3 \geq 0$$

(B) Maximize $y = z_1 + z_2 + z_3$

$$\text{Subject to } 9z_1 + 9z_2 + 21z_3 \leq 1$$
$$12z_1 + 16z_2 + 6z_3 \leq 1$$
$$z_1 + z_2 + 21z_3 \leq 1$$
$$z_1, \ z_2, \ z_3 \geq 0$$

Solve (2) by using the simplex method. Introduce slack variables x_1,
x_2, and x_3 to obtain:

$$9z_1 + 9z_2 + 21z_3 + x_1 = 1$$
$$12z_1 + 16z_2 + 6z_3 + x_2 = 1$$
$$z_1 + z_2 + 21z_3 + x_3 = 1$$
$$-z_1 - z_2 - z_3 + y = 0$$
$$z_1, \ z_2, \ z_3, \ x_1, \ x_2, \ x_3 \geq 0$$

The simplex tableau for this system is given below:

$$z_1 \quad z_2 \quad z_3 \quad x_1 \ x_2 \quad x_3 \quad y$$

$$\begin{bmatrix} 9 & 9 & 21 & 1 & 0 & 0 & 0 & | & 1 \\ \boxed{12} & 16 & 6 & 0 & 1 & 0 & 0 & | & 1 \\ 1 & 1 & 21 & 0 & 0 & 1 & 0 & | & 1 \\ \hline -1 & -1 & -1 & 0 & 0 & 0 & 1 & | & 0 \end{bmatrix} \begin{matrix} \frac{1}{9} \\ \frac{1}{12} \\ 12 \\ 1 \end{matrix}$$

$$\frac{1}{12} R_2 \to R_2$$

$$\sim \begin{bmatrix} 9 & 9 & 21 & 1 & 0 & 0 & 0 & | & 1 \\ \boxed{1} & \frac{4}{3} & \frac{1}{2} & 0 & \frac{1}{12} & 0 & 0 & | & \frac{1}{12} \\ 1 & 1 & 21 & 0 & 0 & 1 & 0 & | & 1 \\ \hline -1 & -1 & -1 & 0 & 0 & 0 & 1 & | & 0 \end{bmatrix}$$

$$(-9) R_2 + R_1 \to R_1, \ (-1) R_2 + R_3 \to R_3, \ \text{and} \ R_2 + R_4 \to R_4$$

$$\sim \begin{bmatrix} 0 & -3 & \boxed{\frac{33}{2}} & 1 & -\frac{3}{4} & 0 & 0 & | & \frac{1}{4} \\ 1 & \frac{4}{3} & \frac{1}{2} & 0 & \frac{1}{12} & 0 & 0 & | & \frac{1}{12} \\ 0 & -\frac{1}{3} & \frac{41}{2} & 0 & -\frac{1}{12} & 1 & 0 & | & \frac{11}{12} \\ 0 & \frac{1}{3} & -\frac{1}{2} & 0 & \frac{1}{12} & 0 & 1 & | & \frac{1}{12} \end{bmatrix} \begin{matrix} \frac{1}{66} \\ \frac{1}{6} \\ \frac{11}{246} \end{matrix}$$

$$\frac{2}{33} R_1 \to R_1$$

$$\sim \begin{bmatrix} 0 & -\frac{2}{11} & \textcircled{1} & \frac{2}{33} & -\frac{1}{22} & 0 & 0 & \bigg| & \frac{1}{66} \\ 1 & \frac{4}{3} & \frac{1}{2} & 0 & \frac{1}{12} & 0 & 0 & \bigg| & \frac{1}{12} \\ 0 & -\frac{1}{3} & \frac{41}{2} & 0 & -\frac{1}{12} & 1 & 0 & \bigg| & \frac{11}{12} \\ \hline 0 & \frac{1}{3} & -\frac{1}{2} & 0 & \frac{1}{12} & 0 & 1 & \bigg| & \frac{1}{12} \end{bmatrix}$$

$$\left(-\frac{1}{2}\right) R_1 + R_2 \to R_2, \quad \left(-\frac{41}{2}\right) R_1 + R_3 \to R_3, \text{ and } \frac{1}{2} R_1 + R_4 \to R_4$$

$$\begin{array}{ccccccc} z_1 & z_2 & z_3 & x_1 & x_2 & x_3 & y \end{array}$$

$$\sim \begin{bmatrix} 0 & -\frac{2}{11} & 1 & \frac{2}{33} & -\frac{1}{22} & 0 & 0 & \bigg| & \frac{1}{66} \\ 1 & \frac{47}{33} & 0 & -\frac{1}{33} & \frac{7}{66} & 0 & 0 & \bigg| & \frac{5}{66} \\ 0 & \frac{10}{11} & 0 & -\frac{41}{33} & \frac{28}{33} & 1 & 0 & \bigg| & \frac{20}{33} \\ \hline 0 & \frac{8}{33} & 0 & \frac{1}{33} & \frac{2}{33} & 0 & 1 & \bigg| & \frac{1}{11} \end{bmatrix}$$

Thus, $z_1 = \frac{5}{66}$, $z_2 = 0$, $z_3 = \frac{1}{66}$,

$$v = \frac{1}{z_1 + z_2 + z_3} = \frac{1}{\frac{5}{66} + 0 + \frac{1}{66}} = \frac{1}{\frac{6}{66}} = 11, \text{ and}$$

$$q_1 = v_1 z_1 = \frac{5}{6}, \quad q_2 = v_1 z_2 = 0, \quad q_3 = v_1 z_3 = \frac{1}{6}$$

The solution to the minimization problem (1) can be read from the bottom row of the final simple tableau for the dual problem shown above. Thus, from the row

$$\begin{array}{ccc} & x_1 & x_2 & x_3 \end{array}$$

$$\begin{bmatrix} 0 & \frac{8}{33} & 0 & \frac{1}{33} & \frac{2}{33} & 0 & 1 & \bigg| & \frac{1}{11} \end{bmatrix}$$

we conclude that the solution to (1) is:

Min $y = x_1 + x_2 + x_3 = \frac{1}{33} + \frac{2}{33} + 0 = \frac{3}{33} = \frac{1}{11}$ at

$x_1 = \frac{1}{33}$, $x_2 = \frac{2}{33}$, and $x_3 = 0$.

Also,

$$p_1 = v_1 x_1 = \frac{1}{3}, \quad p_2 = v_1 x_2 = \frac{2}{3}, \quad p_3 = v_1 x_3 = 0$$

Finally,

$$P^* = \begin{bmatrix} \frac{1}{3} & \frac{2}{3} & 0 \end{bmatrix}, \quad Q^* = \begin{bmatrix} \frac{5}{6} \\ \frac{1}{3} \\ 0 \\ \frac{1}{6} \end{bmatrix}, \text{ and } v = v_1 - 11 = 11 - 11 = 0.$$

$$\begin{array}{r} \text{Economy (fate)} \\ \text{Down} \quad \text{No change} \quad \text{Up} \end{array}$$

12. (A) $\begin{array}{l} \text{Standard} \\ \text{Luxury} \end{array} \begin{bmatrix} 1 & 2 & 0 \\ 0 & 1 & 3 \end{bmatrix}$

Since the payoff matrix is not positive, we add 1 to each element to obtain the matrix:

$$M_1 = \begin{bmatrix} 2 & 3 & 1 \\ 1 & 2 & 4 \end{bmatrix}$$

The linear programming problems corresponding to M_1 are:

(A) Minimize $y = x_1 + x_2$ (B) Maximize $y = z_1 + z_2 + z_3$

Subject to $2x_1 + x_2 \geq 1$ Subject to $2z_1 + 3z_2 + z_3 \leq 1$

$\qquad\qquad 3x_1 + 2x_2 \geq 1$ $\qquad\qquad z_1 + 2z_2 + 4z_3 \leq 1$

$\qquad\qquad x_1 + 4x_2 \geq 1$ $\qquad\qquad z_1, \; z_2, \; z_3 \geq 0$

$\qquad\qquad x_1, \; x_2 \geq 0$

Solve (2) by using the simplex method. Introduce slack variables x_1 and x_2 to obtain:

$$2z_1 + 3z_2 + z_3 + x_1 \qquad\qquad = 1$$
$$z_1 + 2z_2 + 4z_3 \qquad + x_2 \qquad = 1$$
$$-z_1 - z_2 - z_3 \qquad\qquad + y = 0$$
$$z_1, \; z_2, \; z_3, \; x_1, \; x_2, \; x_3 \geq 0$$

The simplex tableau for this system is given below:

$$\begin{array}{cccccc} z_1 & z_2 & z_3 & x_1 & x_2 & y \end{array}$$

$$\begin{bmatrix} \circled{2} & 3 & 1 & 1 & 0 & 0 & | & 1 \\ 1 & 2 & 4 & 0 & 1 & 0 & | & 1 \\ -1 & -1 & -1 & 0 & 0 & 1 & | & 0 \end{bmatrix} \begin{array}{c} \frac{1}{2} \\ 1 \\ \; \end{array}$$

$$\frac{1}{2} R_1 \rightarrow R_1$$

$$\sim \begin{bmatrix} \circled{1} & \frac{3}{2} & \frac{1}{2} & \frac{1}{2} & 0 & 0 & | & \frac{1}{2} \\ 1 & 2 & 4 & 0 & 1 & 0 & | & 1 \\ -1 & -1 & -1 & 0 & 0 & 1 & | & 0 \end{bmatrix} \sim \begin{bmatrix} 1 & \frac{3}{2} & \frac{1}{2} & \frac{1}{2} & 0 & 0 & | & \frac{1}{2} \\ 0 & \frac{1}{2} & \circled{\frac{7}{2}} & -\frac{1}{2} & 1 & 0 & | & \frac{1}{2} \\ 0 & \frac{1}{2} & -\frac{1}{2} & \frac{1}{2} & 0 & 1 & | & \frac{1}{2} \end{bmatrix} \begin{array}{c} 1 \\ \frac{1}{7} \\ \; \end{array}$$

$$(-1)R_1 + R_2 \rightarrow R_2 \text{ and } R_1 + R_3 \rightarrow R_3 \qquad\qquad \frac{2}{7} R_2 \rightarrow R_2$$

$$\sim \begin{bmatrix} 1 & \frac{3}{2} & \frac{1}{2} & \frac{1}{2} & 0 & 0 & | & \frac{1}{2} \\ 0 & \frac{1}{7} & \circled{1} & -\frac{1}{7} & \frac{2}{7} & 0 & | & \frac{1}{7} \\ 0 & \frac{1}{2} & -\frac{1}{2} & \frac{1}{2} & 0 & 1 & | & \frac{1}{2} \end{bmatrix}$$

$$\left(-\frac{1}{2}\right) R_2 + R_1 \rightarrow R_1 \text{ and } \frac{1}{2} R_2 + R_3 \rightarrow R_3$$

$$\sim \begin{array}{cccccc} z_1 & z_2 & z_3 & x_1 & x_2 & y \end{array}$$

$$\sim \left[\begin{array}{cccccc|c} 1 & \frac{10}{7} & 0 & \frac{4}{7} & -\frac{1}{7} & 0 & \frac{3}{7} \\ 0 & \frac{1}{7} & 1 & -\frac{1}{7} & \frac{2}{7} & 0 & \frac{1}{7} \\ \hline 0 & \frac{4}{7} & 0 & \frac{3}{7} & \frac{1}{7} & 1 & \frac{4}{7} \end{array}\right]$$

Thus, max $y = z_1 + z_2 + z_3 = \frac{3}{7} + 0 + \frac{1}{7} = \frac{4}{7}$ occurs at $z_1 = \frac{3}{7}$, $z_2 = 0$,

and $z_3 = \frac{1}{7}$. Now, $v_1 = \frac{1}{y} = \frac{1}{4/7} = \frac{7}{4}$ and $q_1 = v_1 z_1 = \frac{3}{4}$, $q_2 = v_1 z_2 = 0$,

$q_3 = v_1 z_3 = \frac{1}{4}$. The solution to the minimization problem (1) can be read from the bottom row of the final simplex tableau for the dual problem above. Thus, from the row

$$\begin{array}{cc} x_1 & x_2 \end{array}$$

$$\left[\begin{array}{cccccc|c} 0 & \frac{4}{7} & 0 & \frac{3}{7} & \frac{1}{7} & 1 & \frac{4}{7} \end{array}\right]$$

we conclude that the solution to (1) is:

Min $y = x_1 + x_2 = \frac{3}{7} + \frac{1}{7} = \frac{4}{7}$ at

$\quad x_1 = \frac{3}{7}$ and $x_2 = \frac{1}{7}$.

Also,

$$p_1 = v_1 x_1 = \frac{3}{4}, \quad p_2 = v_1 x_2 = \frac{1}{4}.$$

Finally, the optimal strategies are

$$P* = \begin{bmatrix} \frac{3}{4} & \frac{1}{4} \end{bmatrix}, \quad Q* = \begin{bmatrix} \frac{3}{4} \\ 0 \\ \frac{1}{4} \end{bmatrix}, \text{ and } v = v_1 - 1 = \frac{7}{4} - 1 = \frac{3}{4},$$

Therefore the value of the game is $\frac{3}{4}$ million dollars.

(B) $\frac{3}{4}$ standard and $\frac{1}{4}$ luxury

(C) $PMQ = \begin{bmatrix} 0 & 1 \end{bmatrix} \begin{bmatrix} 1 & 2 & 0 \\ 0 & 1 & 3 \end{bmatrix} \begin{bmatrix} 1 \\ 0 \\ 0 \end{bmatrix} = \begin{bmatrix} 0 & 1 \end{bmatrix} \begin{bmatrix} 1 \\ 0 \end{bmatrix} = 0$

$\quad P*MQ = \begin{bmatrix} \frac{3}{4} & \frac{1}{4} \end{bmatrix} \begin{bmatrix} 1 & 2 & 0 \\ 0 & 1 & 3 \end{bmatrix} \begin{bmatrix} 0 \\ 1 \\ 0 \end{bmatrix} = \begin{bmatrix} \frac{3}{4} & \frac{1}{4} \end{bmatrix} \begin{bmatrix} 2 \\ 1 \end{bmatrix} = 1.75$

2. (A)

CLASS INTERVAL	TALLY	FREQUENCY	RELATIVE FREQUENCY
0.5-1.5			
1.5-2.5	I	1	.1
2.5-3.5			
3.5-4.5	I	1	.1
4.5-5.5			
5.5-6.5	IIII	4	.4
6.5-7.5	III	3	.3
7.5-8.5			
8.5-9.5	I	1	.1
9.5-10.5			

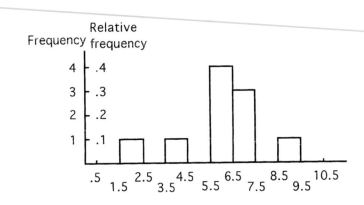

(B)

CLASS INTERVAL	TALLY	FREQUENCY	RELATIVE FREQUENCY
0.5-1.5	I	1	.1
1.5-2.5			
2.5-3.5	I	1	.1
3.5-4.5			
4.5-5.5	II	2	.2
5.5-6.5	II	2	.2
6.5-7.5	I	1	.1
7.5-8.5	II	2	.2
8.5-9.5			
9.5-10.5	I	1	.1

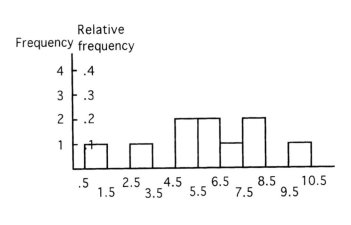

(C) The histogram of (B) is more spread out than that of (A).

4. (A) Let X min = 1.5, X max = 25.5, change X scl from 1 to 2, and multiply Y max and Y scl by 2; let X min = -0.5, X max = 26.5, change X scl from 1 to 3, and multiply Y max and Y scl by 3.

(B) The shape becomes more symmetrical and more triangular.

6.

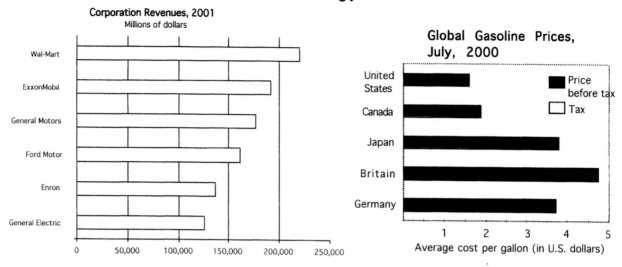

Corporation Revenues, 2001
Millions of dollars

8.

Global Gasoline Prices, July, 2000

10. Vertical bars; No, because a whole is not divided among several categories.

12.

$$100\left(\frac{1.34}{2.43}\right)\% = 55\%$$

$$100\left(\frac{.53}{2.43}\right)\% = 22\%$$

$$100\left(\frac{.10}{2.43}\right)\% = 4\%$$

$$100\left(\frac{.46}{2.43}\right)\% = 19\%$$

Costs in a gallon of gasoline in March 2006

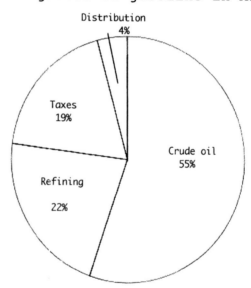

14. (A)

CLASS INTERVAL	TALLY	FREQUENCY	RELATIVE FREQUENCY
.15-.35	‖‖	3	.09
.35-.55	⊪‖ ‖	6	.19
.55-.75	⊪‖ ‖‖	8	.25
.75-.95	⊪‖ ‖	6	.19
.95-1.15	⊪‖ ‖‖	7	.22
1.15-1.35	‖‖	2	.06

(B)

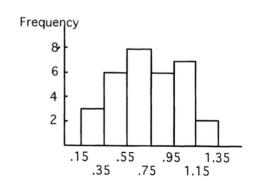

(D)

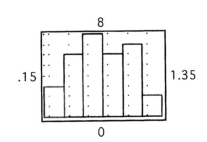

16. (A)

Interval	Frequency	Relative frequency
41.5-43.5	3	.03
43.5-45.5	7	.07
45.5-47.5	13	.13
47.5-49.5	17	.17
49.5-51.5	19	.19
51.5-53.5	17	.17
53.5-55.5	15	.15
55.5-57.5	7	.07
57.5-59.5	2	.02
	100	1.00

(B)

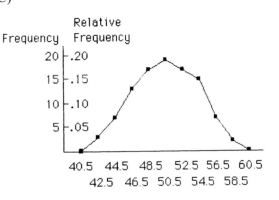

(C)

(D)

Interval	Frequency	Cumulative frequency	Relative cumulative frequency
41.5-43.5	3	3	.03
43.5-45.5	7	10	.10
45.5-47.5	13	23	.23
47.5-49.5	17	40	.40
49.5-51.5	19	59	.59
51.5-53.5	17	76	.76
53.5-55.5	15	91	.91
55.5-57.5	7	98	.98
57.5-59.5	2	100	1.00

Probability = .66 of weight being between 45.5 and 53.5

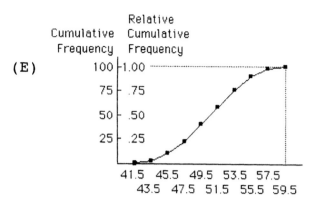

(E)

18. 47; 56; 1985-2010; none

20.

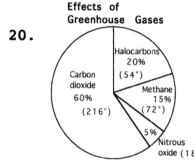

Effects of Greenhouse Gases

If θ is the central angle for the 5% portion, then the central angles for 15%, 20%, and 60% will be 3θ, 4θ, and 16θ respectively. Since sum of the angles is 360°, we have $\theta + 3\theta + 4\theta + 6\theta = 360°$ or $\theta = 18°$.

22. The double bacon cheeseburger with mayo would supply 76.5% of the calories from fat allowed for the entire day.

24. A pie graph would be less effective than the bar graph, because the number of categories (countries) is too large.

26.

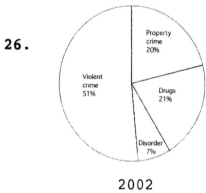

2002

EXERCISE 11-2

2. Mean = $\bar{x}$ = $\dfrac{1 + 1 + 1 + 1 + 2 + 3 + 4 + 5 + 5 + 5}{10}$ = 2.8

To find the median we need to arrange the given numbers in increasing order, which in this problem are given in that order: 1, 1, 1, 1, 2, 3, 4, 5, 5, 5,. Since the number of data is $n = 10$, an even number, the median will be the average of the two middle numbers, namely 2 and 3.

So Median $\dfrac{2 + 3}{2}$ = 2.5. Mode = 1.

4. The mean and median are not suitable for these data. The modal preference for car color is white.

6. We construct a frequency table which indicates the class intervals, the class mid-points x_i, the frequencies f_i, and the products $x_i f_i$.

Class interval	Midpoint x_i	Frequency f_i	Product $x_i f_i$
0.5–2.5	1.5	5	7.5
2.5–4.5	3.5	1	3.5
4.5–6.5	5.5	2	11.0
6.5–8.5	7.5	7	52.5
		$n = \sum_{i=1}^{4} f_i = 15$	$\sum_{i=1}^{4} x_i f_i = 74.5$

$$\text{Mean} = \frac{1}{n} \sum_{i=1}^{k} x_i f_i = \frac{1}{15}(74.5) \approx 5.0$$

8. The mean; there are no extreme values which can distract the mean.

10. (A) We would expect the mean and the median to be close to 7.
(B) The answer depends on the results of your simulation.

12. (A) Let v, w, x, y, z be the five numbers, with $v \leq w \leq x \leq y \leq z$.
Since the mode is 50, $v = w = 50$.
Since the median is 150, and the number of data is odd,
median = x, so $x = 150$. Since the mean is 200,

$$\frac{50 + 50 + 150 + y + z}{5} = 200$$

$$250 + y + z = 1{,}000$$

$$y + z = 750$$

We can now choose y and z so that $y \leq z$ and $y + z = 750$; e.g. take $y = 374$, then $z = 750 - 374 = 376$. Our five numbers are: 50, 50, 150, 374, 376.

(B) Let the five numbers be v, w, x, y, z where v and w are both equal to m_3 and $x = m_2$. Choose y and z to be different numbers, each greater than m_2, such that the mean of all 5 numbers is m_1.

14. Mean $= \frac{1}{8}(25 + 30.25 + 31.1 + 24.5 + 23 + 20 + 18 + 13.9) \approx 23.2$

Median $= \frac{(23 + 24.5)}{2} = 23.75$

Mode: There are none; There are no repetitions.

16.

Class interval	Midpoint x_i	Frequency f_i	Product $x_i f_i$
−0.5–4.5	2	5	10
4.5–9.5	7	54	378
9.5–14.5	12	25	300
14.5–19.5	17	9	153
19.5–24.5	22	4	88
24.5–29.5	27	1	27
29.5–34.5	32	2	64
		$n = \sum_{i=1}^{7} f_i = 100$	$\sum_{i=1}^{7} x_i f_i = 1{,}020$

Mean $= \bar{x} = \dfrac{1}{n} \displaystyle\sum_{i=1}^{k} x_i f_i = \dfrac{1,020}{100} = 10.2$ hours.

To find the median, we draw the histogram of the data.

Total area $= 25 + 270 + 125 + 45$
$\qquad\qquad + 20 + 5 + 10 = 500$

Let M be the median. Then
$\quad 5(5) + (M - 4.5)54 = 250$
$\qquad\quad (M - 4.5)54 = 225$
$\qquad\qquad\qquad M = \dfrac{225 + (4.5)54}{54}$
$\qquad\qquad\qquad\quad \approx 8.67$

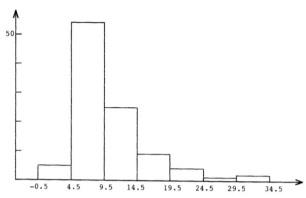

18. Mean $= \dfrac{1}{10}(72.3 + 32.9 + 29.6 + 25.9 + 17.8 + 17.2 + 15.9 + 12.0 + 10.8 + 9.2)$

$\qquad \approx \$24.4$ billion

Median $= \dfrac{(17.2 + 17.8)}{2} = \$17.5$ billion; Mode: There are none; no repetitions.

20.

Class interval	Midpoint x_i	Frequency f_i	Product $x_i f_i$
149.5-169.5	159.5	4	638
169.5-189.5	179.5	11	1974.5
189.5-209.5	199.5	15	2992.5
209.5-229.5	219.5	25	5487.5
229.5-249.5	239.5	13	3113.5
249.5-269.5	259.5	7	1816.5
269.5-289.5	279.5	3	838.5
289.5-309.5	299.5	2	599
		$n = \displaystyle\sum_{i=1}^{8} f_i = 80$	$\displaystyle\sum_{i=1}^{8} x_i f_i = 17,460$

Mean $= \bar{x} = \dfrac{1}{n} \displaystyle\sum_{i=1}^{k} x_i f_i = \dfrac{1}{80}(17,460) = 218.25$

The histogram for the data is shown at the right.

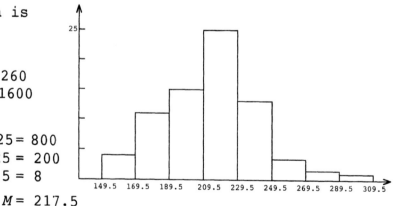

Total area
$\quad = 80 + 220 + 300 + 500 + 260$
$\qquad + 140 + 60 + 40 = 1600$

Let M be the median. Then
$80 + 220 + 300 + (M - 209.5)25 = 800$
$\qquad\qquad (M - 209.5)25 = 200$
$\qquad\qquad\quad M - 209.5 = 8$
$\qquad\qquad\qquad\quad M = 217.5$

22.

Class interval	Midpoint x_i	Frequency f_i	Product $x_i f_i$
1.95–2.15	2.05	21	43.05
2.15–2.35	2.25	19	42.75
2.35–2.55	2.45	17	41.65
2.55–2.75	2.65	14	37.10
2.75–2.95	2.85	9	25.65
2.95–3.15	3.05	6	18.30
3.15–3.35	3.25	5	16.25
3.35–3.55	3.45	4	13.80
3.55–3.75	3.65	3	10.95
3.75–3.95	3.85	2	7.70
		$n = \sum\limits_{i=1}^{10} f_i = 100$	$\sum\limits_{i=1}^{10} x_i f_i = 257.2$

$$\text{Mean} = \bar{x} = \frac{1}{n} \sum_{i=1}^{k} x_i f_i = \frac{1}{100}(257.2) = 2.572$$

The histogram for the data is:

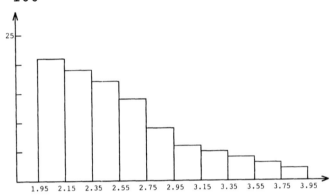

Total area $= 4.2 + 3.8 + 3.4 + 2.8 + 1.8 + 1.2 + 1$
$$+ 0.8 + 0.6 + 0.4 = 20$$

Let M be the median. Then
$$4.2 + 3.8 + (M - 2.35)17 = 10$$
$$M - 2.35 = \frac{10 - 4}{17} \approx 0.12$$
$$M \approx 2.47$$

24.

Class interval	Midpoint x_i	Frequency f_i	Product $x_i f_i$
39.5–44.5	42	2	84
44.5–49.5	47	6	282
49.5–54.5	52	12	624
54.5–59.5	57	13	741
59.5–64.5	62	7	434
64.5–69.5	67	2	134
69.5–74.5	72	1	72
		$n = \sum\limits_{i=1}^{7} f_i = 43$	$\sum\limits_{i=1}^{7} x_i f_i = 2{,}371$

$$\text{Mean} = \bar{x} = \frac{1}{n} \sum_{i=1}^{k} x_i f_i = \frac{1}{43}(2{,}371) \approx 55 \text{ years;}$$

Median class is 54.5–59.5 and hence

$$\text{Median} = 54.5 + \frac{\left(\frac{43}{2} - 20\right)}{13}(5) = 54.5 + .577 \approx 55 \text{ years.}$$

EXERCISE 11-3

2. $\bar{x} = 2.8$ (see Problem 2, Exercise 11-2)

$$s = \sqrt{\frac{\sum_{i=1}^{n}(x_i - \bar{x})^2}{n-1}}$$

$$= \sqrt{\frac{\begin{array}{l}(1 - 2.8)^2 + (1 - 2.8)^2 + (1 - 2.8)^2 + (1 - 2.8)^2 + (2 - 2.8)^2 \\ + (3 - 2.8)^2 + (4 - 2.8)^2 + (5 - 2.8)^2 + (5 - 2.8)^2 + (5 - 2.8)^2\end{array}}{10-1}}$$

$$= 1.81$$

4. (A) $\bar{x} = \frac{1}{10} \sum_{i=1}^{10} x_i = \frac{30}{10} = 3$

$$s = \sqrt{\frac{\sum_{i=1}^{10}(x_i - 3)^2}{10-1}}$$

$$= \sqrt{\frac{\begin{array}{l}(3 - 3)^2 + (5 - 3)^2 + (1 - 3)^2 + (2 - 3)^2 + (1 - 3)^2 \\ + (5 - 3)^2 + (4 - 3)^2 + (5 - 3)^2 + (1 - 3)^2 + (3 - 3)^2\end{array}}{9}}$$

$$= \sqrt{\frac{0 + 4 + 4 + 1 + 4 + 4 + 1 + 4 + 4 + 0}{9}} = \sqrt{\frac{26}{9}} \approx 1.7$$

The measurements that are in the interval $(\bar{x} - s, \bar{x} + s) =$ (1.3, 4.7) are within one standard deviation of the mean; 40% of the measurements, {3, 2, 4, 3}, are in this interval.

The measurements that are in the interval $(\bar{x} - 2s, \bar{x} + 2s) =$ (-0.4, 6.4) are within two standard deviations of the mean; 100% of the measurements are in this interval. It follows immediately that 100% of the measurements are within three standard deviations of the mean.

(B) No. For the bell-shaped histogram, approximately 68% of the measurements are within one standard deviation.

(C)

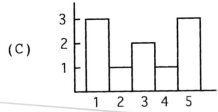

6.

Interval	Midpoint x_i	Frequency f_i	$x_i f_i$	$(x_i - \overline{x})^2$	$(x_i - \overline{x})^2 f_i$
0.5– 3.5	2	5	10	27.04	135.20
3.5– 6.5	5	1	5	4.84	4.84
6.5– 9.5	8	2	16	0.64	1.28
9.5–12.5	11	7	77	14.44	101.08
		$n = 15$	$\sum\limits_{i=1}^{4} x_i f_i = 108$		$\sum\limits_{i=1}^{4} (x_i - \overline{x})^2 f_i = 242.4$

$$\overline{x} = \frac{108}{15} \approx 7.2, \qquad s = \sqrt{\frac{242.40}{15 - 1}} \approx 4.16$$

8. (A) False: If all the measurements are the same, then there is no dispersion and hence variance is 0.

(B) True:
$$s^2 = \frac{(x_1 - \overline{x})^2 + (x_2 - \overline{x})^2}{2 - 1} = (x_1 - \overline{x})^2 + (x_2 - \overline{x})^2$$
$$= \left[x_1 - \left(\frac{x_1 + x_2}{2}\right)\right]^2 + \left[x_2 - \left(\frac{x_1 + x_2}{2}\right)\right]^2$$
$$= \left(\frac{x_1 + x_2}{2}\right)^2 + \left(\frac{x_1 + x_2}{2}\right)^2 = \frac{(x_1 - x_2)^2}{4} + \frac{(x_1 - x_2)^2}{4} = \frac{(x_1 - x_2)^2}{2}$$

10. (A) The second data set. It is more likely that the minimum is closer to 1, for example, than to 6.

(B) The answer depends on the results of your simulation.

12.

x_i	$(x_i - \overline{x})^2$
4.6	16
8.5	0.01
6.1	6.25
7.8	0.64
10.9	5.29
9.3	0.49
11.4	7.84
5.8	7.84
9.7	1.21
8.8	0.04
6.7	3.61
13.2	21.16
$\sum\limits_{i=1}^{12} x_i = 102.8$	$\sum\limits_{i=1}^{12} (x_i - \overline{x})^2 = 70.38$

$$\text{Mean} = \overline{x} = \frac{102.8}{12} \approx 8.6 \text{ min.};$$

$$s = \sqrt{\frac{\sum\limits_{i=1}^{12} (x_i - \overline{x})^2}{12 - 1}} = \sqrt{\frac{70.38}{11}}$$

$$\approx 2.5 \text{ min.}$$

14.

Interval	Midpt.	Freq.	$x_i f_i$	$(x_i - \overline{x})^2$	$(x_i - \overline{x})^2 f_i$
-0.5- 4.5	2	5	10	64	320
4.5- 9.5	7	54	378	9	486
9.5-14.5	12	25	300	4	100
14.5-19.5	17	13	221	49	637
19.5-24.5	22	0	0	144	0
24.5-29.5	27	1	27	289	289
29.5-34.5	32	2	64	484	968
		$\sum_{i=1}^{7} f_i = 100$	$\sum_{i=1}^{7} x_i f_i = 1{,}000$		$\sum_{i=1}^{12} (x_i - \overline{x})^2 f_i = 2{,}800$

$$\text{Mean} = \overline{x} = \frac{1}{n} \sum_{i=1}^{k} x_i f_i = \frac{1}{100}(1{,}000) = 10;$$

$$s = \sqrt{\frac{\sum_{i=1}^{12} (x_i - \overline{x})^2 f_i}{n - 1}} = \sqrt{\frac{2{,}800}{99}} \approx 5.3$$

16.

Interval	Midpt.	Freq.	$x_i f_i$	$(x_i - \overline{x})^2$	$(x_i - \overline{x})^2 f_i$
41.5-43.5	42.5	3	127.5	64	192
43.5-45.5	44.5	7	315.5	36	252
45.5-47.5	46.5	13	604.5	16	208
47.5-49.5	48.5	17	824.5	4	68
49.5-51.5	50.5	19	959.5	0	0
51.5-53.5	52.5	17	892.5	4	68
53.5-55.5	54.5	15	817.5	16	240
55.5-57.5	56.5	7	395.5	36	252
57.5-59.5	58.5	2	117	64	128
		$n = \sum_{i=1}^{9} f_i = 100$	$\sum_{i=1}^{9} x_i f_i = 5{,}054$		$\sum_{i=1}^{9} (x_i - \overline{x})^2 f_i = 1{,}408$

$$\text{Mean} = \overline{x} = \frac{5{,}054}{100} \approx 50.5 \text{ grams}; \quad s = \sqrt{\frac{1{,}408}{99}} \approx 3.8$$

18.

Interval	Midpt.	Freq.	$x_i f_i$	$(x_i - \overline{x})^2$	$(x_i - \overline{x})^2 f_i$
1.95-2.15	2.05	21	43.05	0.3025	6.3525
2.15-2.35	2.25	19	42.75	0.1225	2.3275
2.35-2.55	2.45	17	41.65	0.0225	0.3825
2.55-2.75	2.65	14	37.10	0.0025	0.0350
2.75-2.95	2.85	9	25.65	0.0625	0.5625
2.95-3.15	3.05	6	18.30	0.2025	1.2150
3.15-3.35	3.25	5	16.25	0.4225	2.1125
3.35-3.55	3.45	4	13.80	0.7225	2.8900
3.55-3.75	3.65	3	10.95	1.1025	3.3075
3.75-3.95	3.85	2	7.70	1.5625	3.1250
		$n = \sum_{i=1}^{10} f_i = 100$	$\sum_{i=1}^{10} x_i f_i = 257.2$		$\sum_{i=1}^{10} (x_i - \overline{x})^2 f_i = 22.31$

$$\text{Mean} = \overline{x} = \frac{257.2}{100} = 2.572 \approx 2.6; \quad s = \sqrt{\frac{22.31}{99}} \approx 0.5$$

2. $p = \dfrac{1}{2}, \; q = 1 - \dfrac{1}{2} = \dfrac{1}{2}, \; C_{5,2}\left(\dfrac{1}{2}\right)^2\left(\dfrac{1}{2}\right)^{5-2} = \dfrac{5!}{2!\,3!}\left(\dfrac{1}{32}\right) = \dfrac{5}{16} \approx .313$

4. $p = .4, \; q = 1 - .4 = .6, \; C_{6,6}(.4)^6(.6)^{6-6} = (.4)^6 \approx .004$

6. $p = \dfrac{1}{3}, \; q = 1 - \dfrac{1}{3} = \dfrac{2}{3}, \; C_{4,3}\left(\dfrac{1}{3}\right)^3\left(\dfrac{2}{3}\right)^{4-3} = \dfrac{4!}{3!\,1!} \cdot \dfrac{2}{81} \approx \dfrac{8}{81} \approx .099$

8. Let x be the number of heads obtained. Then x is binomial with parameters $n = 4$, $p = .5$. Thus, $q = .5$ and
$P(\text{Exactly one head}) = P(x = 1) = C_{4,1}(.5)^1(.5)^{4-1} = 4(.5)^4 = .25$

10. You are asked to compute
$P(\text{TTTH}) + P(\text{TTTT}) = \left(\dfrac{1}{2}\right)^4 + \left(\dfrac{1}{2}\right)^4 = \dfrac{1}{16} + \dfrac{1}{16} = \dfrac{2}{16} = \dfrac{1}{8}$

12. Referring to the solution of exercise 8, we need to compute
$P(x = 4) = C_{4,4}\left(\dfrac{1}{2}\right)^4\left(\dfrac{1}{2}\right)^{4-4} = \dfrac{1}{16}$

14. $p = \dfrac{3}{4}, \; q = 1 - p = 1 - \dfrac{3}{4} = \dfrac{1}{4}.$
Thus $\mu = np = 3 \cdot \dfrac{3}{4} = \dfrac{9}{4} = 2.25$

$\sigma = \sqrt{npq} = \sqrt{3 \cdot \dfrac{3}{4} \cdot \dfrac{1}{4}}$

$= \sqrt{\dfrac{9}{16}} = \dfrac{3}{4} = .75$

16. $p = \dfrac{1}{3}, \; q = 1 - \dfrac{1}{3} = \dfrac{2}{3}.$
Thus $\mu = np = 5 \cdot \dfrac{1}{3} = \dfrac{5}{3} = 1.667;$

$\sigma = \sqrt{npq} = \sqrt{5 \cdot \dfrac{1}{3} \cdot \dfrac{2}{3}}$

$= \sqrt{\dfrac{10}{9}} = 1.054$

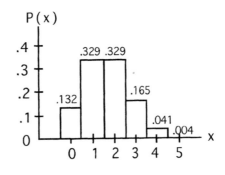

18. $p = 0$, $q = 1 - 0 = 1$.
Thus $\mu = 0$, $\sigma = 0$.

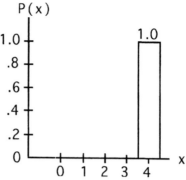

20. We can have one of the following cases: $(6,6,5)$, $(6,5,6)$, and $(5,6,6)$. Probability of each case is $\left(\frac{1}{6}\right)^3 = \frac{1}{216}$.

Thus $P(6, 5,$ and $6,$ in any order$) = 3 \cdot \frac{1}{216} = \frac{3}{216} = .014$.

22. Let x be the number of times 6 occurs. Then x is binomial with parameters $n = 3$ and $p = \frac{1}{6}$. Thus, $q = 1 - \frac{1}{6} = \frac{5}{6}$ and we need to compute

$$C_{3,1}\left(\frac{1}{6}\right)^1\left(\frac{5}{6}\right)^{3-1} = 3 \cdot \frac{1}{6} \cdot \frac{25}{36} = \frac{75}{216} = .347.$$

24. Let x be the number of times 5 occurs. Then x is binomial with parameters $n = 3$, $p = \frac{1}{6}$. Thus, $q = 1 - \frac{1}{6} = \frac{5}{6}$ and we need to compute

$$1 - P(x = 0) = 1 - C_{3,0}\left(\frac{1}{6}\right)^0\left(\frac{5}{6}\right)^{3-0} = 1 - \frac{125}{216} = .421.$$

26. Let $p =$ probability of guessing the right answer $= \frac{1}{2}$,

$q =$ probability of not guessing the right answer $= \frac{1}{2}$.

(A) $n = 10$, $x = 7$

$$P(7) = C_{10,7}\left(\frac{1}{2}\right)^7\left(\frac{1}{2}\right)^{10-7} = \frac{10!}{7!\,3!}\left(\frac{1}{2}\right)^7\left(\frac{1}{2}\right)^3 \approx 0.117$$

(B) $P(7) + P(8) + P(9) + P(10) = C_{10,7}\left(\frac{1}{2}\right)^{10} + C_{10,8}\left(\frac{1}{2}\right)^{10}$

$$+ C_{10,9}\left(\frac{1}{2}\right)^{10} + C_{10,10}\left(\frac{1}{2}\right)^{10}$$

$$\approx 0.172$$

28. Let $p =$ probability of the electorate supports the mayor $= 0.60$ and $q =$ probability of the electorate not supporting the mayor $= 0.40$. $n = 10$, $x \leq 4$

$P(0) + P(1) + P(2) + P(3) + P(4)$

$= C_{10,0}(0.6)^0(0.4)^{10} + C_{10,1}(0.6)(0.4)^9 + C_{10,2}(0.6)^2(0.4)^8$

$\quad + C_{10,3}(0.6)^3(0.4)^7 + C_{10,4}(0.6)^4(0.4)^6 \approx 0.166$

30. $P(x) = C_{6,x}(0.6)^x(0.4)^{6-x}$, $x = 0, 1, ..., 6$

x	$P(x)$
0	0.003
1	0.04
2	0.14
3	0.28
4	0.31
5	0.19
6	0.05

The histogram for this distribution is shown at the right.

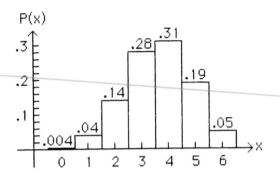

$\mu = np = 6 \times 0.6 = 3.6$

$\sigma = \sqrt{npq} = \sqrt{6 \times 0.6 \times 0.4} = 1.2$

32. $P(x) = C_{8,x}(0.7)^x(0.3)^{8-x}$, $x = 0, 1, ..., 8$

x	$P(x)$
0	0.0001
1	0.001
2	0.01
3	0.05
4	0.14
5	0.25
6	0.30
7	0.20
8	0.06

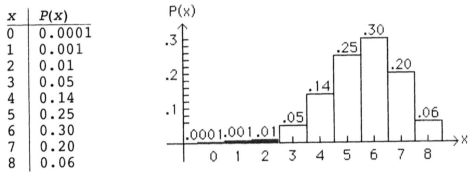

The histogram for this distribution is shown above.
$\mu = np = 8 \times 0.7 = 5.6$
$\sigma = \sqrt{npq} = \sqrt{8 \times 0.7 \times 0.6} = 1.3$

34. Given $p = 0.45$, $q = 0.55$, $n = 20$

(A) $\mu = np = 20 \times 0.45 = 9$; $\sigma = \sqrt{npq} = \sqrt{20 \times 0.45 \times 0.55} = 2.225$

(B) For within one standard deviation, we must look at $\mu - \sigma < x < \mu + \sigma$
or $9 - 2.225 < x < 9 + 2.225$ or $6.775 < x < 11.225$.
Thus, $x = 7, 8, 9, 10,$ or 11.

$P(x = 7) = C_{20,7}(0.45)^7(0.55)^{13}$

$P(x = 8) = C_{20,8}(0.45)^8(0.55)^{12}$

$P(x = 9) = C_{20,9}(0.45)^9(0.55)^{11}$

$P(x = 10) = C_{20,10}(0.45)^{10}(0.55)^{10}$

$P(x = 11) = C_{20,11}(0.45)^{11}(0.55)^9$

Therefore,

$P(7 \leq x \leq 11) = P(7) + P(8) + P(9) + P(10) + P(11) \approx 0.739$.

36. Let p = probability of getting a "head" in one trial = 0.75, and q = probability of not getting a "head" in one trial = 0.25. If x is the number of heads obtained in 5 trials, then
$$P(x) = C_{5,x}(0.75)^x(0.25)^{5-x}, \quad x = 0, 1, ..., 5.$$
P(exactly 2 heads or exactly 2 tails)

$= P$(exactly 2 heads) $+ P$(exactly 3 heads)

$= P(2) + P(3) = C_{5,2}(0.75)^2(0.25)^{5-2} + C_{5,3}(0.75)^3(0.25)^{5-3}$

$= \dfrac{5!}{2! \, 3!}(0.75)^2(0.25)^3 + \dfrac{5!}{3! \, 2!}(0.75)^3(0.25)^2 \approx 0.352$

38. Theoretical probability distribution is given by
$$P(x) = C_{3,x}\left(\frac{1}{6}\right)^x\left(\frac{5}{6}\right)^{3-x}$$

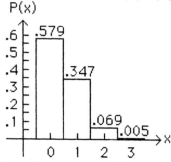

Frequency of fives turning up in 100 rolls of 3 dice

Number of fives	Theoretical frequency	Actual frequency
0	57.9	(List your
1	34.7	experimental
2	6.9	results here)
3	0.5	

40. They are mirror images in the vertical line $x = 500$: $n = 1000$, $p = 0.15$
$$P(x_1) = C_{1000,x}(0.15)^{x_1}(0.85)^{1000-x_1}, \quad x_1 = 0, 1, ..., 1,000$$
$$n = 1000, \quad p = 0.85$$
$$P(x_2) = C_{1000,x_2}(0.85)^{x_2}(0.15)^{1000-x_2}, \quad x_2 = 0, 1, ..., 1,000$$

You can see that $P(x_1 = 100) = C_{1000,100}(0.15)^{100}(0.85)^{900}$
$$P(x_2 = 900) = C_{1000,900}(0.85)^{900}(0.15)^{100}$$
since $C_{1000,100} = C_{1000,900}$, $P(x_1 = 100) = P(x_2 = 900)$.
This is true for all cases of this form.

42. Let p = probability of getting 7 or 11 in one roll of a pair of fair dice $= \dfrac{8}{36} = \dfrac{2}{9}$
$$q = 1 - p = \frac{7}{9}$$
Let x = number of 7's or 100's in ten rolls of a pair of fair dice.
Then $P(x) = C_{10,x}\left(\dfrac{2}{9}\right)^x\left(\dfrac{7}{9}\right)^{10-x}$, $x = 0, 1, ..., 10$

(A) $\mu = np = 10 \times \dfrac{2}{9} = \dfrac{20}{9} \approx 2.222$

$\sigma = \sqrt{npq} = \sqrt{10 \times \dfrac{2}{9} \times \dfrac{7}{9}} \approx 1.315$

(B) Answer depends on the results of your simulation.

44. Let p = probability of a new employee still being with the company at the end of 1 year = 0.6,

and q = probability of a new employee not being with the company at the end of 1 year = 0.4.

(A) $n = 8$, $x = 5$

$$P(5) = C_{8,5}(0.6)^5(0.4)^3 = \frac{8!}{5!\ 3!}(0.6)^5(0.4)^3 \approx 0.279$$

(B) $P(5 \text{ or more}) = P(x \geq 5) = \sum_{x=5}^{8} C_{8,x}(0.6)^x(0.4)^{8-x}$

$$= \frac{8!}{5!\ 3!}(0.6)^5(0.4)^3 + \frac{8!}{6!\ 2!}(0.6)^6(0.4)^2$$

$$+ \frac{8!}{7!\ 1!}(0.6)^7(0.4) + \frac{8!}{8!\ 0!}(0.6)^8(0.4)^0 \approx 0.594$$

46. Let p = probability of an item shipped being defective = 0.03,
and q = probability of an item shipped not being defective = 0.97.

Let x = number of defective item in a shipment of 10 items.

Then $P(x) = C_{10,x}(0.03)^x(0.97)^{10-x}$, $x = 0, 1, \ldots, 10$.

$P(\text{box will fail to satisfy the guarantee}) = P(x \geq 2) = 1 - P(x \leq 1)$

$= 1 - P(0) - P(1) = 1 - C_{10,0}(0.03)^0(0.97)^{10} - C_{10,1}(0.03)(0.97)^9 \approx$

0.035

48. p = probability of success = 0.40 and hence
q = probability of failure = $1 - 0.40 = 0.60$.

(A) $P(x) = C_{5,x}(0.4)^x(0.6)^{5-x}$, $x = 0, 1, 2, 3, 4, 5$

(B)

x	$P(x)$
0	0.078
1	0.259
2	0.346
3	0.230
4	0.077
5	0.010
	1.000

(C)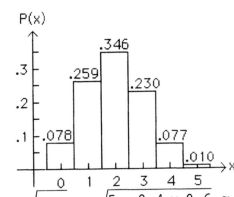

(D) $\mu = np = 5 \times 0.4 = 2$; $\sigma = \sqrt{npq} = \sqrt{5 \times 0.4 \times 0.6} \approx 1.095$

50. Let p = probability that the drug causes side effect = 0.02,
and q = probability that the drug does not cause side effect = 0.98

Let x = number of people in a sample of size $n = 10$ develop side effect.

Then $P(x) = C_{10,x}(0.02)^x(0.98)^{10-x}$, $x = 0, 1, \ldots, 10$.

$$P(3) = C_{10,3}(0.02)^3(0.98)^{10-3} = \frac{10!}{3!\ 7!}(0.02)^3(0.98)^7 \approx 0.000\ 8$$

52. Let p = probability of gene mutations under a given level of radiation
$$= 3 \times 10^{-5},$$
and $q = 1 - p = 1 - 3 \times 10^{-5}$

Let x = number of gene mutations if 10^5 genes are exposed.

Then $P(x) = C_{10^5,x}(3 \times 10^{-5})^x(1 - 3 \times 10^{-5})^{10^5-x}$, $x = 0, 1, ..., 10^5$

We are asked to compute:

$$P(x \geq 1) = 1 - P(x = 0) = 1 - P(0) = 1 - (1 - 3 \times 10^{-5})^{10^5}$$
$$= 1 - 0.04978$$
$$\approx 0.95$$

54. Let p = probability of causing side effect = 0.02,
and q = probability of not causing side effect = 0.98.

Let x = number of people developing side effect in a sample of 450 people.

Then $P(x) = C_{450,x}(0.02)^x(0.98)^{450-x}$, $x = 0, 1, ..., 450$.

$\mu = np = 450 \times 0.02 = 9$; $\sigma = \sqrt{npq} = \sqrt{450 \times 0.02 \times 0.98} \approx 2.97$

56. $p = 0.40$, $q = 0.60$, $n = 7$

$$P(x \geq 4) = \sum_{x=4}^{7} P(x) = \sum_{x=4}^{7} C_{7,x}(0.4)^x(0.6)^{7-x}$$
$$= C_{7,4}(0.4)^4(0.6)^3 + C_{7,5}(0.4)^5(0.3)^2$$
$$+ C_{7,6}(0.4)^6(0.3) + C_{7,7}(0.4)^7$$
$$\approx 0.29 \text{ (better than one chance out of four!)}$$

58. $p = 0.4$, $q = 1 - 0.4 = 0.6$, $n = 1000$.
$\mu = np = 1000 \times 0.4 = 400$
$\sigma = \sqrt{npq} = \sqrt{1000 \times 0.4 \times 0.6} \approx 15.49$

EXERCISE 11-5

2. The area under the standard normal curve from 0 to 3.30 is .4995.

4. The area under the standard normal curve from 0 to 1.08 is .3599.

6. The area under the standard normal curve from -0.92 to 0 is .3212.

8. $x = 132$, $\mu = 100$, $\sigma = 10$
$$z = \frac{132 - 100}{10} = 3.2$$
$x = 132$ is 3.2 standard deviations away from μ.

10. $x = 77$, $\mu = 100$, $\sigma = 10$
$$z = \frac{77 - 100}{10} = -2.3$$
$x = 77$ is 2.3 standard deviations away from μ.

12. $x = 83.1$, $\mu = 100$, $\sigma = 10$

$$z = \frac{83.1 - 100}{10} = -1.69$$

$x = 83.1$ is 1.69 standard deviations away from μ.

14. From Problem 8, $z = 3.2$.
From the table of areas for the
normal distribution, we have
the area corresponding to $z =$
3.2 is 0.4993.

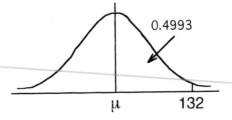

16. From Problem 10, $z = -2.3$.
From the table, the area
corresponding to $z = 2.3$ is
0.4893.

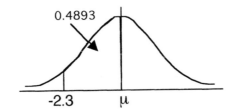

18. From Problem 12, $z = -1.69$.
From the table, the area
corresponding to $z = 1.69$ is
0.4545.

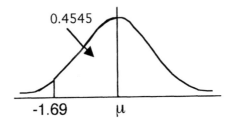

20. $\mu = 70$, $\sigma = 8$

$$z \text{ (for } x = 50) = \frac{50 - 70}{8} = -2.5$$

$$z \text{ (for } x = 90) = \frac{90 - 70}{8} = 2.5$$

Area $A_1 = 0.4938$
Area $A_2 = 0.4938$
Total area $= A = A_1 + A_2 = 0.9876$

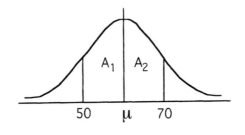

22. $\mu = 70$, $\sigma = 8$

$$z \text{ (for } x = 66) = \frac{66 - 70}{8} = -0.5$$

$$z \text{ (for } x = 78) = \frac{78 - 70}{8} = 1$$

Area $A_1 = 0.1915$
Area $A_2 = 0.3413$
Total area $= A = A_1 + A_2 = 0.5328$

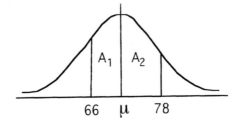

24. $\mu = 70$, $\sigma = 8$

z (for $x = 90$) $= \dfrac{90 - 70}{8} = 2.5$

Required area $= 0.5 - $ (area corresponding to $z = 2.5$)

$\quad\quad\quad\quad\quad = 0.5 - 0.4938$

$\quad\quad\quad\quad\quad = 0.0062$

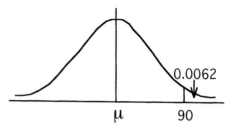

26. $\mu = 70$, $\sigma = 8$

z (for $x = 56$) $= \dfrac{56 - 70}{8} = -1.75$

Required area $= 0.5 - $ (area corresponding to $z = 1.75$)

$\quad\quad\quad\quad\quad = 0.5 - 0.4599$

$\quad\quad\quad\quad\quad = 0.0401$

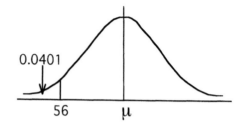

28. (A) False: There may be a large number of good students and a large number of weak students.

(B) False: It is extremely small but not zero; the graph of the normal distribution never touches the x axis.

30. With $n = 12$, $p = 0.6$, and $q = 0.4$, the mean and standard deviation of the binomial distribution are:

$\mu = np = 12 \times 0.6 = 7.2$

$\sigma = \sqrt{npq} = \sqrt{12 \times 0.6 \times 0.4} \approx 1.7$

$[\mu - 3\sigma, \mu + 3\sigma] = [2.1, 12.3]$

Since this interval is not contained in the interval $[0, 12]$, the normal distribution should *not* be used to approximate the binomial distribution.

32. With $n = 20$, $p = 0.6$, and $q = 0.4$, the mean and standard deviation of the binomial distribution are:

$\mu = np = 20 \times 0.6 = 12$

$\sigma = \sqrt{npq} = \sqrt{20 \times 0.6 \times 0.4} \approx 2.2$

$[\mu - 3\sigma, \mu + 3\sigma] = [5.4, 18.6]$

Since this interval is contained in the interval $[0, 20]$, the normal distribution *is* a suitable approximation for the binomial distribution.

34. With $n = 200$, $p = 0.03$, and $q = 0.97$, the mean and standard deviation of the binomial distribution are:

$\mu = np = 200 \times 0.03 = 6$

$\sigma = \sqrt{npq} = \sqrt{200 \times 0.03 \times 0.97} \approx 2.4$

$[\mu - 3\sigma, \mu + 3\sigma] = [-1.2, 13.2]$

Since this interval is not contained in the interval $[0, 200]$, the normal distribution should *not* be used to approximate the binomial distribution.

36. With $n = 400$, $p = 0.08$, and $q = 0.92$, the mean and standard deviation of the binomial distribution are:

$\mu = np = 400 \times 0.08 = 32$

$\sigma = \sqrt{npq} = \sqrt{400 \times 0.08 \times 0.92} \approx 5.4$

$[\mu - 3\sigma, \mu + 3\sigma] = [15.8, 48.2]$

Since this interval is contained in the interval $[0, 400]$, the normal distribution *is* a suitable approximation for the binomial distribution.

38. Solve the inequalities $np - 3\sqrt{npq} \geq 0$ and $np + 3\sqrt{npq} \leq n$ to obtain

$$\frac{9}{109} \leq p \leq \frac{100}{109}$$

In Problems 40-46, $\mu = 500(0.4) = 200$, and $\sigma = \sqrt{npq} = \sqrt{500(0.4)(0.6)} \approx$ 10.95. The intervals are adjusted as in Examples 3 and 4.

40. z (for $x = 189.5$) $= \dfrac{189.5 - 200}{10.95} = -0.96$

z (for $x = 205.5$) $= \dfrac{205.5 - 200}{10.95} = 0.50$

Thus, the probability that the number of successes will be between 190 and 205

    = area A_1 + area A_2

    = (area corresponding to $z = -0.96$) + (area corresponding to $z = 0.50$)

    = 0.3315 + 0.1915

    = 0.52

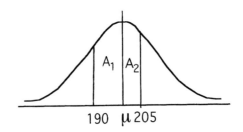

42. z (for $x = 174.5$) $= \dfrac{174.5 - 200}{10.95} = -2.33$

z (for $x = 185.5$) $= \dfrac{185.5 - 200}{10.95} = -1.32$

Thus, the probability that the number of successes will be between 175 and 185

    = area A

    = (area corresponding to $z = 2.33$) − (area corresponding to $z = 1.32$)

    = 0.4901 − 0.4066

    ≈ 0.084

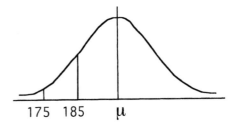

44. z (for $x = 211.5$) $= \dfrac{211.5 - 200}{10.95} = 1.05$

Thus, the probability that the number of successes will be 212 or more

    = area A

    = 0.5 − (area corresponding to $z = 1.05$)

    = 0.5 − 0.3531

    ≈ 0.15

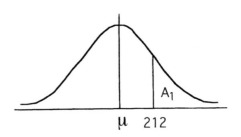

46. z (for $x = 188.5$) $= \dfrac{188.5 - 200}{10.95} = -1.05$

Thus, the probability that the number of successes will be 188 or less

= area A

= 0.5 - (area corresponding to $z = 1.05$)

= 0.5 - 0.3531

≈ 0.15

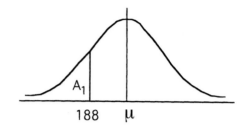

48.

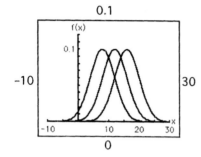

50.

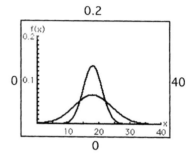

52. 250 scores are selected from a normal distribution with mean $\mu = 100$, and standard deviation $\sigma = 10$.

(A) The area under the normal curve to the right of 110:

$z = \dfrac{x - \mu}{\sigma} = \dfrac{110 - 100}{10} = 1$; Area = 0.3413   (Table 1)

$P(x > 110) = 0.5 - 0.3413 = 0.1587$

The number of scores greater than 110 will be $(250)(0.1587) \approx 40$.

(B) The answer depends on the results of your simulation.

54. $\mu = 170$, $\sigma = 10$, $x \leq 3 \times 52 = 156$ weeks

z (for $x = 156$) $= \dfrac{156 - 170}{10} = -1.4$

$P(x \leq 156)$

= Area A

= 0.5 - P (area corresponding to $z = 1.4$)

= 0.5 - 0.4192

= 0.0808 or 8.08%

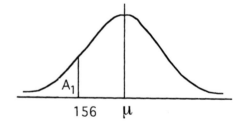

56. $\mu = 7.55$, $\sigma = 0.02$, $x < \mu - 0.05$ or $x > \mu + 0.05$

$P(x < \mu - 0.05) = P(x > \mu + 0.05)$ because of the symmetry.

Thus,

P (parts rejected) $= A_1 + A_2$

$= 2P(x > 7.60)$

z (for $x = 7.60$) $= \dfrac{7.60 - 7.55}{0.02} = 2.5$

= 0.5 - (area corresponding to $z = 2.5$)

= 0.5 - 0.4938 = 0.0062

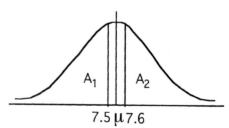

Therefore, P (parts rejected) $= 2(0.0062) = 0.0124$ or 1.24%.

58. With $n = 100$, $p = 0.6$, $q = 0.4$, the mean and standard deviation of the binomial distribution are:

$\mu = np = 100 \times 0.6 = 60$

$\sigma = \sqrt{npq} = \sqrt{100(0.6)(0.4)} \approx 4.9$

$z \text{ (for } x = 47.5) = \dfrac{47.5 - 60}{4.9} = -2.55$

The probability that 47 or fewer of membership favor the settlement

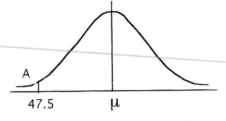

    = Area A

    = 0.5 - (area corresponding to $z = 2.55$)

    = 0.5 - 0.4946 = 0.0054

Conclusion: Either a rare event has happened or the claim of 60% is false.

60. $\mu = 38$, $\sigma = 1.5$

$z \text{ (for } x = 40) = \dfrac{40 - 38}{1.5} = 1.33$

Percentage of the crop which will be 40 inches or more

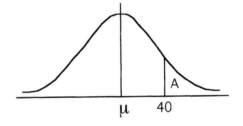

    = Area A

    = 0.5 - P (area corresponding to $z = 1.33$)

    = 0.5 - 0.4082

    = 0.0918 or 9.18%

62. $p = 0.25$, $q = 0.75$, $n = 1,000$

$\mu = np = 1000 \times 0.25 = 250$

$\sigma = \sqrt{npq} = \sqrt{1000(0.25)(0.75)} \approx 13.69$

$224.5 \leq x \leq 275.5$

$z \text{ (for } x = 224.5) = \dfrac{224.5 - 250}{13.69} = -1.86$

$z \text{ (for } x = 275.5) = \dfrac{275.5 - 250}{13.69} = 1.86$

Probability that at least 225 and not more than 275 families will have two girls

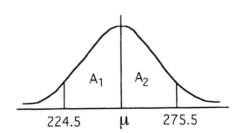

    = Area A_1 + Area A_2

    = 2 Area A_1 (because of symmetry)

    = 2 (area corresponding to $z = 1.86$)

    = 2(0.4686) = 0.9372

64. $p = 0.52$, $q = 0.48$, $n = 1,000$

$\mu = np = 1000(0.52) = 520$

$\sigma = \sqrt{npq} = \sqrt{1000(0.52)(0.48)} \approx 15.8$

$x = 470.5$ or less

z (for $x = 470.5$) $= \dfrac{470.5 - 520}{15.8} = -3.13$

Probability that 470 or fewer Harkin's
= 0.5 - (area corresponding to 3.13)
= 0.5 - 0.4991
= 0.00009.

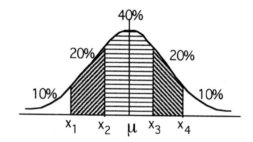

Conclusion: Either a rare event has happened or Harkins' claim is false.

66. $\mu = 50$, $\sigma = 10$

We compute x_1, x_2, x_3, and x_4 corresponding to z_1, z_2, z_3, and z_4 respectively. The area between μ and x_3 is 0.2.

Hence, from the table, $z_3 = 0.52$
(approximately). Thus, we have

$$0.52 = \frac{x_3 - 50}{10}$$

$$x_3 - 50 = 5.2$$

$$x_3 = 55.2$$

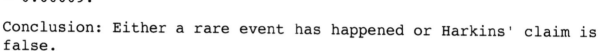

By the symmetry of the graph $x_2 = 50 - 5.2 = 44.8$

The area between μ and x_4 is 0.4, hence, from the table, $z_4 = 1.28$
(approximately). Thus, we have

$$1.28 = \frac{x_4 - 50}{10}$$

$$x_4 - 50 = 12.8$$

$$x_4 = 62.8$$

By the symmetry of the graph $x_1 = 50 - 12.8 = 37.2$.

Therefore,
Passive: 37.2 or less; Moderately passive: 37.2 - 44.8;
Average: 44.8 - 55.2; Moderately aggressive: 55.2 - 62.8;
Aggressive: 62.8 or higher

EXERCISE A-1
_____

2. $7 + x$ **4.** $(xy)z$ **5.** $9m$

8. T; Commutative property of multiplication

10. T; Distributive property   **12.** T; Multiplicative inverse property

14. F; Let $x = y = 1$, then $\dfrac{x}{3y} \div \dfrac{5y}{x} = \dfrac{1}{3} \div \dfrac{5}{1} = \dfrac{1}{3} \cdot \dfrac{1}{5} = \dfrac{1}{15}$, $\dfrac{15y^2}{x^2} = 15$.

16. T; Property of negatives

18. T; Property of additive inverse   **20.** T; Property of negatives

22. F; Let $k = 2$, $b = 1$, then $\dfrac{k}{k + b} = \dfrac{2}{3}$, $\dfrac{1}{1 + b} = \dfrac{1}{2}$.

24. T; Distributive property

26. T; Zero property

28. Yes. If neither u nor v are zero, then $uv \neq 0$.

30. (A) True
(B) False. For example, 4 is a real number, but is not irrational.
(C) True

32. $\dfrac{3}{5}$ and -1.43 are two examples of infinitely many.

34. (A) $-3 \in Z$, Q, R (B) $3.14 \in Q$, R
(C) $\pi \in R$ (D) $\dfrac{2}{3} \in Q$, R

36. (A) True. This is the commutative property of addition.
(B) False. For example, $5 - 3 \neq 3 - 5$.
(C) True. This is the commutative property of multiplication.
(D) False. For example, $9 \div 3 \neq 3 \div 9$.

38.
$$C = 0.181818\ldots$$
$$100C = 18.1818\ldots$$
$$100C - C = (18.1818\ldots) - (0.181818\ldots)$$
$$99C = 18$$
$$C = \frac{18}{99} = \frac{2}{11}$$

40. (A) $0.888888888\ldots$ (B) $0.27272727\ldots$ (C) $2.23606797\ldots$ (D)
$1.375000000\ldots$

2. The term of highest degree in $2x - 3$ is $2x$ and the degree of this term is 1.

4. $(2x - 3) + (2x^2 - x + 2) = 2x^2 + x - 1$

6. $(2x^2 - x + 2) - (2x - 3) = 2x^2 - x + 5$

8. $(2x - 3)(x^3 + 2x^2 - x + 3) = 2x^4 + x^3 - 8x^2 + 9x - 9$

10. $2(x - 1) + 3(2x - 3) - (4x - 5) = 2x - 2 + 6x - 9 - 4x + 5 = 4x - 6$

12. $2y - 3y[4 - 2(y - 1)] = 2y - 3y[4 - 2y + 2]$
$$= 2y - 3y[6 - 2y]$$
$$= 2y - 18y + 6y^2$$
$$= 6y^2 - 16y$$

14. $(m - n)(m + n) = m^2 - n^2$ (Special product)

16. $(4t - 3)(t - 2) = 4t^2 - 8t - 3t + 6 = 4t^2 - 11t + 6$

18. $(3x + 2y)(x - 3y) = 3x^2 - 9xy + 2xy - 6y^2$
$$= 3x^2 - 7xy - 6y^2$$

20. $(2m - 7)(2m + 7) = (2m)^2 - (7)^2 = 4m^2 - 49$ (Special product)

22. $-(5 - 3x)^2 = -(25 - 30x + 9x^2) = -25 + 30x - 9x^2$

24. $(3x - 2y)(3x + 2y) = (3x)^2 - (2y)^2$
$$= 9x^2 - 4y^2 \text{ (Special product)}$$

26. $(4x - y)^2 = 16x^2 - 8xy + y^2$

28. $(a + b)(a^2 - ab + b^2) = a(a^2 - ab + b^2) + b(a^2 - ab + b^2)$
$$= a^3 - a^2b + ab^2 + a^2b - ab^2 + b^3$$
$$= a^3 + b^3$$

30. $[a - (2b - c)][a + (2b - c)] = a^2 - (2b - c)^2 = a^2 - (4b^2 - 4bc + c^2)$
$$= a^2 - 4b^2 + 4bc - c^2$$

32. $2x - 3\{x + 2[x - (x + 5)] + 1\} = 2x - 3\{x + 2[x - x - 5] + 1\}$
$$= 2x - 3\{x + 2(-5) + 1\}$$
$$= 2x - 3\{x - 10 + 1\}$$
$$= 2x - 3\{x - 9\}$$
$$= 2x - 3x + 27$$
$$= -x + 27$$

34. $(3x - 2y)^2(2x + 5y) = (9x^2 - 12xy + 4y^2)(2x + 5y)$
$$= 18x^3 + 45x^2y - 24x^2y - 60xy^2 + 8xy^2 + 20y^3$$
$$= 18x^3 + 21x^2y - 52xy^2 + 20y^3$$

36. $(2x - 1)^2 - (3x + 2)(3x - 2) = (2x - 1)^2 - ((3x)^2 - (2)^2)$

$$= (4x^2 - 4x + 1) - (9x^2 - 4)$$
$$= 4x^2 - 4x + 1 - 9x^2 + 4$$
$$= -5x^2 - 4x + 5$$

38. $(x - 3)(x + 3) - (x - 3)^2 = x^2 - 9 - (x^2 - 6x + 9)$

$$= x^2 - 9 - x^2 + 6x - 9$$
$$= 6x - 18$$

40. $(3m + n)(m - 3n) - (m + 3n)(3m - n)$

$$= 3m^2 - 9mn + mn - 3n^2 - (3m^2 - mn + 9mn - 3n^2)$$
$$= 3m^2 - 9mn + mn - 3n^2 - 3m^2 + mn - 9mn + 3n^2$$
$$= -16mn$$

42. $(x - y)^3 = (x - y)(x - y)^2 = (x - y)(x^2 - 2xy + y^2)$

$$= x^3 - 2x^2y + xy^2 - x^2y + 2xy^2 - y^3$$
$$= x^3 - 3x^2y + 3xy^2 - y^3$$

44. $(2m - n)^3 = (2m - n)(2m - n)^2 = (2m - n)(4m^2 - 4mn + n^2)$

$$= 8m^3 - 8m^2n + 2mn^2 - 4m^2n + 4mn^2 - n^3$$
$$= 8m^3 - 12m^2n + 6mn^2 - n^3$$

46. $\{(3m^2 - 3m - 2) + (m^3 + m^2 + 2)\} - \{(3m^2 - 2m + 5) + (4m^2 - m)\}$

$$= \{3m^2 - 3m - 2 + m^3 + m^2 + 2\} - \{3m^2 - 2m + 5 + 4m^2 - m\}$$
$$= \{m^3 + 4m^2 - 3m\} - \{7m^2 - 3m + 5\}$$
$$= m^3 + 4m^2 - 3m - 7m^2 + 3m - 5 = m^3 - 3m^2 - 5$$

48. $[5x(3x + 1) - 5(2x - 1)^2]^2 = [15x^2 + 5x - 5(4x^2 - 4x + 1)]^2$

$$= [15x^2 + 5x - 20x^2 + 20x - 5]^2$$
$$= [-5x^2 + 25x - 5]^2$$
$$= 25x^4 + 625x^2 + 25 - 250x^3 + 50x^2 - 250x$$
$$= 25x^4 - 250x^3 + 675x^2 - 250x + 25$$

50. $-3x\{x[x - x(2 - x)] - (x + 2)(x^2 - 3)\}$

$$= -3x\{x[x - 2x + x^2] - [x^3 - 3x + 2x^2 - 6]\}$$
$$= -3x\{x[-x + x^2] - x^3 + 3x - 2x^2 + 6\}$$
$$= -3x\{-x^2 + x^3 - x^3 + 3x - 2x^2 + 6\}$$
$$= -3x\{-3x^2 + 3x + 6\} = 9x^3 - 9x^2 - 18x$$

52. m

54. Now the degree is less than or equal to m.

56. $(2 - 1)^2 \neq 2^2 - 1^2$; since
$(a - b)^2 = a^2 - 2ab + b^2$, $(a - b)^2 = a^2 - b^2$ only when
$a = b$ in which case $a^2 - 2ab + b^2 = a^2 - 2a^2 + a^2 = 0$ or
$b = 0$ in which case $a^2 - 2ab + b^2 = a^2$.

58. Let x = amount invested at 7%,
$2x$ = amount invested at 9%,
and $100,000 - 3x$ = amount invested at 11%.
$$I = 0.07x + (0.09)(2x) + 0.11(100,000 - 3x)$$
$$= 11,000 - 0.08x$$

60. Let x = number of tickets at \$9.
Then $6,000$ = number of tickets at \$15.
The total receipts R are:

$$R = 9x + 15(6,000 - x) = 90,000 - 6x$$

62. Let x = number of ounces of food M used.
Then $160 - x$ = number of ounces of food N used.
The total number of units of calcium, C, in the diet mix is given by:
$$C = 8x + 5(160 - x) = 800 + 3x$$

EXERCISE A-3

---

2. $2x^2$ is a common factor: $6x^4 - 8x^3 - 2x^2 = 2x^2(3x^2 - 4x - 1)$

4. $5xy$ is a common factor: $10x^3y + 20x^2y^2 - 15xy^3 = 5xy(2x^2 + 4xy - 3y^2)$

6. $(x + 1)$ is a common factor: $5x(x + 1) - 3(x + 1) = (x + 1)(5x - 3)$

8. $3(b - 2c)$ is a common factor:
$$12a(b - 2c) - 15b(b - 2c) \quad = 3(b - 2c)[4a - 5b]$$
$$= 3(b - 2c)(4a - 5b)$$

10. $x^2 - 3x + 2x - 6 = (x^2 - 3x) + (2x - 6)$
$$= x(x - 3) + 2(x - 3)$$
$$= (x - 3)(x + 2)$$

12. $2x^2 - x + 6x - 3 = (2x^2 - x) + (6x - 3)$
$$= x(2x - 1) + 3(2x - 1)$$
$$= (2x - 1)(x + 3)$$

14. $6x^2 + 9x - 2x - 3 = (6x^2 + 9x) + (-2x - 3)$
$$= 3x(2x + 3) - (2x + 3)$$
$$= (2x + 3)(3x - 1)$$

16. $ac + ad + bc + bd = (ac + ad) + (bc + bd)$
$$= a(c + d) + b(c + d)$$
$$= (a + b)(c + d)$$

18. $ab + 6 + 2a + 3b = (ab + 2a) + (6 + 3b)$
$$= a(b + 2) + 3(b + 2)$$
$$= (a + 3)(b + 2)$$

20. $2x^2 + 5x - 3$

$a = 2, \; b = 5, \; c = -3$

Step 1. Use the *ac*-test to test for factorability

$ac = (2)(-3) = -6$

$\underline{pq}$

(1)(-6)

$\boxed{(-1)(6)}$

(2)(-3)

(-2)(3)

Note that $-1 + 6 = 5 = b$. Thus, $2x^2 + 5x - 3$ has first-degree factors with integer coefficients.

Step 2. Split the middle term using $b = p + q$ and factor by grouping.

$5 = -1 + 6$

$$2x^2 + 5x - 3 = (2x^2 - x) + (6x - 3)$$
$$= x(2x - 1) + 3(2x - 1)$$
$$= (2x - 1)(x + 3)$$

22. $x^2 - 4xy - 12y^2$

$a = 1, \; b = -4, \; c = -12$

Step 1. Use the *ac*-test

$ac = 1(-12) = -12$

$\underline{pq}$

(1)(-12)

(-1)(12)

(-2)(6)

$\boxed{(2)(-6)}$

(-3)(4)

(3)(-4)

Note that $2 + (-6) = -4 = b$. Thus $x^2 - 4xy - 12y^2$ has first-degree factors with integer coefficients.

Step 2. Factor by grouping

$-4 = 2 + (-6)$

$$x^2 + 2xy - 6xy - 12y^2 = (x^2 + 2xy) - (6xy + 12y^2)$$
$$= x(x + 2y) - 6y(x + 2y)$$
$$= (x + 2y)(x - 6y)$$

24. $x^2 + x - 4$

$a = 1, \; b = 1, \; c = -4$

Step 1. Use the *ac*-test

$ac = (1)(1) = 1$

$\underline{pq}$

(1)(1)

(-1)(-1)

None of the factors add up to $1 = b$. Thus, this polynomial is *not factorable*.

26. $25m^2 - 16n^2 = (5m - 4n)(5m + 4n)$ (difference of squares)

28. $x^2 + 10xy + 25y^2 = (x + 5y)^2$ (perfect square)

30. $u^2 + 81$
 $a = 1, \ b = 0, \ c = 81$
 Step 1. Use the ac-test
$$ac = (1)(81) = 81$$

$$\underline{pq}$$
$$(1)(81)$$
$$(-1)(-81)$$
$$(3)(27)$$
$$(-3)(-27)$$
$$(9)(9)$$
$$(-9)(-9)$$

None of the factors add up to $0 = b$. Thus this polynomial is *not factorable*.

32. $6x^2 + 48x + 72 = 6(x^2 + 8x + 12) = 6(x + 2)(x + 6)$

34. $2y^3 - 22y^2 + 48y = 2y(y^2 - 11y + 24)$
$$= 2y(y - 3)(y - 8)$$

36. $16x^2y - 8xy + y = y(16x^2 - 8x + 1)$
$$= y(4x - 1)^2$$

38. $6s^2 + 7st - 3t^2 = (3s - t)(2s + 3t)$

40. $x^3y - 9xy^3 = xy(x^2 - 9y^2) = xy(x - 3y)(x + 3y)$

42. $3m^3 - 6m^2 + 15m = 3m(m^2 - 2m + 5)$ [Note: $m^2 - 2m + 5$ is *not factorable*.]

44. $5x^3 + 40y^3 = 5(x^3 + 8y^3)$
$$= 5[x^3 + (2y)^3]$$
$$= 5(x + 2y)(x^2 - 2xy + y^2)$$ (sum of cubes)

46. $8a^3 - 1 = (2a)^3 - (1)^3$
$$= (2a - 1)(4a^2 + 2a + 1)$$ (difference of cubes)

48. $(a - b)^2 - 4(c - d)^2 = [(a - b) - 2(c - d)][(a - b) + 2(c - d)]$

50. $3x^2 - 2xy - 4y^2$ is *not factorable*

52. $4(A + B)^2 - 5(A + B) - 6$
 Let $x = A + B$, then $4x^2 - 5x - 6$ can be written as
 $4x^2 - 5x - 6 = (2x + 3)(x - 2)$. Now, replace x with $A + B$ to obtain:
 $4(A + B)^2 - 5(A + B) - 6 = [2(A + B) + 3][(A + B) - 2]$

54. $m^4 - n^4 = (m^2 - n^2)(m^2 + n^2)$

$\qquad = (m - n)(m + n)(m^2 + n^2)$ [Note: $m^2 + n^2$ is not factorable.]

56. $15x^2$ and $(3x - 1)^3$ are common factors:

$\quad 15x^2(3x - 1)^4 + 60x^3(3x - 1)^3 = 15x^2(3x - 1)^3[(3x - 1) + 4x]$

$\qquad\qquad\qquad\qquad\qquad\qquad = 15x^2(3x - 1)^3[3x - 1 + 4x]$

$\qquad\qquad\qquad\qquad\qquad\qquad = 15x^2(3x - 1)^3(7x - 1)$

58. False. Here is a counterexample. Consider $u^4 - v^2$, $m = 4$, $n = 2$, $m \neq n$, but $u^4 - v^2 = (u^2 - v)(u^2 + v)$.

60. True. $u^{2k+1} + v^{2k+1} = (u + v)(u^{2k} - u^{2k-1}v + u^{2k-2}v^2 - \dots + v^{2k})$. For example, if $k = 2$, then as you know $u^3 + v^3 = (u + v)(u^2 - uv + v^2)$.

EXERCISE A-4

2. $\left(\dfrac{d^5}{3a} \div \dfrac{d^2}{6a^2}\right) \cdot \dfrac{a}{4d^3} = \left(\dfrac{d^5}{3a} \cdot \dfrac{6a^2}{d^2}\right) \cdot \dfrac{a}{4d^3} = (2ad^3) \cdot \dfrac{a}{4d^3} = \dfrac{a^2}{2}$

4. $\dfrac{2y}{18} - \dfrac{-1}{28} - \dfrac{y}{42}$

$= \dfrac{28y}{252} - \dfrac{-9}{252} - \dfrac{6y}{252}$

$\qquad = \dfrac{28y + 9 - 6y}{252} = \dfrac{22y + 9}{252}$

We find the LCD of 18, 28, 42:

$18 = 2 \cdot 3^2$, $28 = 2^2 \cdot 7$, $42 = 2 \cdot 3 \cdot 7$.

Thus, LCD $= 2^2 \cdot 3^2 \cdot 7 = 252$.

6. $\dfrac{3x + 8}{4x^2} - \dfrac{2x - 1}{x^3} - \dfrac{5}{8x}$

$= \dfrac{2x(3x + 8)}{8x^3} - \dfrac{8(2x - 1)}{8x^3} - \dfrac{5x^2}{8x^3}$

$= \dfrac{6x^2 + 16x - 16x + 8 - 5x^2}{8x^3} = \dfrac{x^2 + 8}{8x^3}$

Find the LCD of $4x^2$, x^3, $8x$:

$4x^2 = 2^2 x^2$, $x^3 = x^3$,

$8x = 2^3 \cdot x$.

Thus, LCD $= 8x^3$.

8. $\dfrac{2x^2 + 7x + 3}{4x^2 - 1} \div (x + 3)$

$= \dfrac{(2x^2 + 7x + 3)}{(4x^2 - 1)(x + 3)} = \dfrac{(2x + 1)(x + 3)}{(2x - 1)(2x + 1)(x + 3)} = \dfrac{1}{2x - 1}$

10. $\dfrac{5}{m - 2} - \dfrac{3}{2m + 1} = \dfrac{5(2m + 1) - 3(m - 2)}{(m - 2)(2m + 1)} = \dfrac{10m + 5 - 3m + 6}{(m - 2)(2m + 1)} = \dfrac{7m + 11}{(m - 2)(2m + 1)}$

12. $\dfrac{3}{x^2 - 5x + 6} - \dfrac{5}{(x - 2)^2} = \dfrac{3}{(x - 2)(x - 3)} - \dfrac{5}{(x - 2)^2}$ LCD $= (x - 2)^2(x - 3)$

$$= \dfrac{3(x - 2) - 5(x - 3)}{(x - 2)^2(x - 3)} = \dfrac{3x - 6 - 5x + 15}{(x - 2)^2(x - 3)}$$

$$= \dfrac{-2x + 9}{(x - 2)^2(x - 3)}$$

14. $m - 3 - \dfrac{m - 1}{m - 2} = \dfrac{(m - 3)(m - 2)}{m - 2} - \dfrac{m - 1}{m - 2}$ LCD $= m - 2$

$$= \dfrac{(m - 3)(m - 2) - (m - 1)}{(m - 2)}$$

$$= \dfrac{m^2 - 2m - 3m + 6 - m + 1}{m - 2} = \dfrac{m^2 - 6m + 7}{m - 2}$$

16. $\dfrac{5}{x - 3} - \dfrac{2}{3 - x} = \dfrac{5}{(x - 3)} - \dfrac{-2}{(x - 3)}$ (property of negatives)

$$= \dfrac{5 - (-2)}{x - 3} = \dfrac{7}{x - 3}$$

18. $\dfrac{m + 2}{m^2 - 2m} - \dfrac{m}{m^2 - 4} = \dfrac{m + 2}{m(m - 2)} - \dfrac{m}{(m - 2)(m + 2)}$ LCD $= m(m - 2)(m + 2)$

$$= \dfrac{(m + 2)^2}{m(m - 2)(m + 2)} - \dfrac{m^2}{m(m - 2)(m + 2)}$$

$$= \dfrac{(m + 2)^2 - m^2}{m(m - 2)(m + 2)} = \dfrac{m^2 + 4m + 4 - m^2}{m(m - 2)(m + 2)}$$

$$= \dfrac{4(m + 1)}{m(m - 2)(m + 2)}$$

20. $\dfrac{y}{y^2 - y - 2} - \dfrac{1}{y^2 + 5y - 14} - \dfrac{2}{y^2 + 8y + 7}$

$$= \dfrac{y}{(y - 2)(y + 1)} - \dfrac{1}{(y + 7)(y - 2)} - \dfrac{2}{(y + 1)(y + 7)} \qquad \text{LCD} = (y - 2)(y + 1)(y + 7)$$

$$= \dfrac{y(y + 7)}{(y - 2)(y + 1)(y + 7)} - \dfrac{(y + 1)}{(y - 2)(y + 1)(y + 7)} - \dfrac{2(y - 2)}{(y - 2)(y + 1)(y + 7)}$$

$$= \dfrac{y(y + 7) - (y + 1) - 2(y - 2)}{(y - 2)(y + 1)(y + 7)} = \dfrac{y^2 + 7y - y - 1 - 2y + 4}{(y - 2)(y + 1)(y + 7)}$$

$$= \dfrac{y^2 + 4y + 3}{(y - 2)(y + 1)(y + 7)}$$

$$= \dfrac{(y + 1)(y + 3)}{(y - 2)(y + 1)(y + 7)}$$

$$= \dfrac{y + 3}{(y - 2)(y + 7)}$$

22. $\dfrac{2}{5 - \dfrac{3}{4x + 1}} = \dfrac{2}{\dfrac{5(4x + 1) - 3}{4x + 1}} = \dfrac{2}{\dfrac{20x + 5 - 3}{4x + 1}} = \dfrac{2}{20x + 2} \cdot \dfrac{4x + 1}{1}$

$$= \dfrac{1}{10x + 1} \cdot \dfrac{4x + 1}{1} = \dfrac{4x + 1}{10x + 1}$$

24. $\dfrac{x + 7}{ax - bx} + \dfrac{y + 9}{by - ay} = \dfrac{x + 7}{x(a - b)} + \dfrac{y + 9}{-y(a - b)}$ $\text{LCD} = xy(a - b)$

$$= \dfrac{y(x + 7)}{xy(a - b)} - \dfrac{x(y + 9)}{xy(a - b)}$$

$$= \dfrac{y(x + 7) - x(y + 9)}{xy(a - b)} = \dfrac{xy + 7y - xy - 9x}{xy(a - b)} = \dfrac{7y - 9x}{xy(a - b)}$$

26. $\dfrac{1 - \dfrac{y^2}{x^2}}{1 - \dfrac{y}{x}} = \dfrac{\dfrac{x^2 - y^2}{x^2}}{\dfrac{x - y}{x}} = \dfrac{x^2 - y^2}{x^2} \cdot \dfrac{x}{x - y}$

$$= \dfrac{(x - y)(x + y)}{x^2} \cdot \dfrac{x}{x - y}$$

$$= \dfrac{x(x - y)(x + y)}{x^2(x - y)}$$

$$= \dfrac{x + y}{x}$$

28. $\dfrac{\dfrac{1}{x + h} - \dfrac{1}{x}}{h} = \dfrac{\dfrac{x}{x(x + h)} - \dfrac{x + h}{x(x + h)}}{h} = \dfrac{\dfrac{x - (x + h)}{x(x + h)}}{h}$

$$= \dfrac{\dfrac{-h}{x(x + h)}}{h} = -\dfrac{h}{x(x + h)} \cdot \dfrac{1}{h}$$

$$= -\dfrac{1}{x(x + h)}$$

30. $\dfrac{1 + \dfrac{2}{x} - \dfrac{15}{x^2}}{1 + \dfrac{4}{x} - \dfrac{5}{x^2}} = \dfrac{\dfrac{x^2}{x^2} + \dfrac{2x}{x^2} - \dfrac{15}{x^2}}{\dfrac{x^2}{x^2} + \dfrac{4x}{x^2} - \dfrac{5}{x^2}} = \dfrac{\dfrac{x^2 + 2x - 15}{x^2}}{\dfrac{x^2 + 4x - 5}{x^2}}$

$$= \dfrac{x^2 + 2x - 15}{x^2} \cdot \dfrac{x^2}{x^2 + 4x - 5}$$

$$= \dfrac{(x + 5)(x - 3)}{x^2} \cdot \dfrac{x^2}{(x + 5)(x - 1)}$$

$$= \dfrac{x^2(x + 5)(x - 3)}{x^2(x + 5)} = \dfrac{x - 3}{x - 1}$$

32. (A) $\dfrac{x^2 - 3x - 4}{x - 4} = x - 3$: Incorrect

(B) $\dfrac{x^2 - 3x - 4}{x - 4} = \dfrac{(x - 4)(x + 1)}{x - 4} = x + 1$

34. (A) $\dfrac{(x + h)^3 - x^3}{h} = 3x^2 + 3x + 1$: Incorrect

(B) $\dfrac{(x + h)^3 - x^3}{h} = \dfrac{((x + h) - x)((x + h)^2 + x(x + h) + x^2)}{h}$

$= \dfrac{(x + h - x)(x^2 + 2hx + h^2 + x^2 + xh + x^2)}{h}$

$= \dfrac{h(3x^2 + 3hx + h^2)}{h}$

$= 3x^2 + 3hx + h^2$

36. (A) $\dfrac{2}{x - 1} - \dfrac{x + 3}{x^2 - 1} = \dfrac{1}{x + 1}$: Correct

38. (A) $x + \dfrac{x - 2}{x^2 - 3x + 2} = \dfrac{2}{x - 2}$: Incorrect

(B) $x + \dfrac{x - 2}{x^2 - 3x + 2} = x + \dfrac{x - 2}{(x - 2)(x - 1)}$

$= x + \dfrac{1}{x - 1} \qquad \text{LCD} = x - 1$

$= \dfrac{x(x - 1)}{x - 1} + \dfrac{1}{x - 1}$

$= \dfrac{x(x - 1) + 1}{x - 1} = \dfrac{x^2 - x + 1}{x - 1}$

40. $\dfrac{\dfrac{1}{(x + h)^2} - \dfrac{1}{x^2}}{h} = \left[\dfrac{1}{(x + h)^2} - \dfrac{1}{x^2}\right] \div \dfrac{h}{1}$

$= \dfrac{x^2 - (x + h)^2}{x^2(x + h)^2} \cdot \dfrac{1}{h}$

$= \dfrac{x^2 - (x^2 + 2xh + h^2)}{x^2(x + h)^2 h}$

$= \dfrac{x^2 - x^2 - 2xh - h^2}{x^2(x + h)^2 h}$

$= \dfrac{-2xh - h^2}{x^2(x + h)^2 h} = \dfrac{-h(2x + h)}{x^2(x + h)^2 h}$

$= -\dfrac{2x + h}{x^2(x + h)^2}$

42. $2 - \dfrac{1}{1 - \dfrac{2}{a+2}} = 2 - \dfrac{1}{\dfrac{a+2-2}{a+2}} = 2 - \dfrac{1}{\dfrac{a}{a+2}}$

$$= 2 - \frac{1}{1} \cdot \frac{a+2}{a} = 2 - \frac{a+2}{a}$$

$$= \frac{2a - (a+2)}{a} = \frac{2a - a - 2}{a} = \frac{a-2}{a}$$

EXERCISE A-5

2. $3y^{-5} = \dfrac{3}{y^5}$

4. $\dfrac{5}{4x^{-9}} = \dfrac{5x^9}{4}$

6. $3c^{-9}c^4 = 3c^{-9+4} = 3c^{-5} = \dfrac{3}{c^5}$

8. $\dfrac{m^{-11}}{m^{-5}} = m^{-11}m^5 = m^{-11+5} = m^{-6} = \dfrac{1}{m^6}$

10. $7d^{-4}d^4 = 7d^{-4+4} = 7d^0 = 7$

12. $(5b^{-2})^2 = \left(\dfrac{5}{b^2}\right)^2 = \dfrac{25}{b^4}$

14. $(a^{-3}b^4)^{-3} = a^{(-3)(-3)}b^{4(-3)} = a^9 b^{-12} = \dfrac{a^9}{b^{12}}$

16. $5,380,000 = 5.38 \times 10^6$

18. $0.019 = 1.9 \times 10^{-2}$

20. $0.000\ 000\ 007\ 832 = 7.832 \times 10^{-9}$

22. $9 \times 10^6 = 9,000,000$

24. $2 \times 10^{-5} = 0.00002$

26. $3.044 \times 10^3 = 3,044$

28. $1.13 \times 10^{-2} = 0.0113$

30. $(2x^3 y^4)^0 = 1$

32. $\dfrac{10^{-17} \cdot 10^{-5}}{10^{-3} \cdot 10^{-14}} = \dfrac{10^{-22}}{10^{-17}} = 10^{-22} \cdot 10^{17} = 10^{-5} = \dfrac{1}{10^5}$

34. $(2m^{-3}n^2)^{-3} = \dfrac{1}{(2m^{-3}n^2)^3} = \dfrac{1}{8m^{-9}n^6} = \dfrac{m^9}{8n^6}$

36. $\left(\dfrac{2a}{3b^2}\right)^{-3} = \dfrac{1}{\left(\dfrac{2a}{3b^2}\right)^3} = \dfrac{1}{\dfrac{8a^3}{27b^6}} = \dfrac{27b^6}{8a^3}$

38. $\dfrac{9m^{-4}n^3}{12m^{-1}n^{-1}} = \dfrac{3}{4}m^{-4}n^3 mn = \dfrac{3}{4}m^{-4+1}n^{3+1} = \dfrac{3}{4}m^{-3}n^4 = \dfrac{3n^4}{4m^3}$

40. $\dfrac{5x^3 - 2}{3x^2} = \dfrac{5x^3}{3x^2} - \dfrac{2}{3x^2} = \dfrac{5}{3}x - \dfrac{2}{3}x^{-2}$

42. $\dfrac{2x^3 - 3x^2 + x}{2x^2} = \dfrac{2x^3}{2x^2} - \dfrac{3x^2}{2x^2} + \dfrac{x}{2x^2} = x - \dfrac{3}{2} + \dfrac{1}{2}x^{-1}$

44. $\dfrac{5x^4(x+3)^2 - 2x^5(x+3)}{(x+3)^4} = \dfrac{x^4(x+3)[5(x+3) - 2x]}{(x+3)^4}$

$$= \dfrac{x^4(x+3)[5x + 15 - 2x]}{(x+3)^4}$$

$$= \dfrac{x^4(x+3)(3x + 15)}{(x+3)^4}$$

$$= \dfrac{3x^4(x+3)(x+5)}{(x+3)^4}$$

$$= \dfrac{3x^4(x+5)}{(x+3)^3}$$

46. $2x(x+3)^{-1} - x^2(x+3)^{-2} = \dfrac{2x}{x+3} - \dfrac{x^2}{(x+3)^2}$

$$= \dfrac{2x(x+3) - x^2}{(x+3)^2}$$

$$= \dfrac{2x^2 + 6x - x^2}{(x+3)^2}$$

$$= \dfrac{x^2 + 6x}{(x+3)^2} = \dfrac{x(x+6)}{(x+3)^2}$$

48. $\dfrac{(60,000)(0.000003)}{(0.0004)(1,500,000)} = \dfrac{(6 \times 10^4)(3 \times 10^{-6})}{(4 \times 10^{-4})(1.5 \times 10^6)}$

$$= \dfrac{18 \times 10^{-2}}{6 \times 10^2} = 3 \times 10^{-4}; \ 0.0003$$

50. $\dfrac{(0.00000082)(230,000)}{(625,000)(0.0082)} = \dfrac{(8.2 \times 10^{-7})(2.3 \times 10^5)}{(6.25 \times 10^5)(8.2 \times 10^{-3})}$

$$= \dfrac{2.3 \times 10^{-2}}{6.25 \times 10^2} = 0.368 \times 10^{-4}$$

$$= 3.68 \times 10^{-5}; \ 0.000 \ 0368$$

52. $2^{(3^2)} = 2^9 = 512$ while $(2^3)^2 = 8^2 = 64$ which is the calculator result.

56. $\dfrac{x^{-2} - y^{-2}}{x^{-1} + y^{-1}} = \dfrac{\dfrac{1}{x^2} - \dfrac{1}{y^2}}{\dfrac{1}{x} + \dfrac{1}{y}} = \dfrac{\dfrac{y^2 - x^2}{x^2y^2}}{\dfrac{y + x}{xy}} = \dfrac{y^2 - x^2}{x^2y^2} \cdot \dfrac{xy}{y + x} = \dfrac{(y-x)(y+x)xy}{x^2y^2(y+x)}$

$$= \dfrac{y-x}{xy}$$

58. $\dfrac{xy^{-2} - yx^{-2}}{y^{-1} - x^{-1}} = [\,xy^{-2} - yx^{-2}\,] \div [\,y^{-1} - x^{-1}\,]$

$$= \left[\dfrac{x}{y^2} - \dfrac{y}{x^2}\right] \div \left[\dfrac{1}{y} - \dfrac{1}{x}\right] = \dfrac{x^3 - y^3}{x^2 y^2} \div \dfrac{x - y}{xy}$$

$$= \dfrac{(x - y)(x^2 + xy + y^2)}{x^2 y^2} \cdot \dfrac{xy}{x - y} = \dfrac{x^2 + xy + y^2}{xy}$$

60. (A) 1.0934×10^{12}

(B) $\dfrac{1.0934 \times 10^{12}}{4.158 \times 10^{11}} = \left(\dfrac{1.0934}{4.158}\right) \times 10 = 2.6296$

(C) $\dfrac{4.158 \times 10^{11}}{1.0934 \times 10^{12}} = \left(\dfrac{4.158}{1.0934}\right) \times \dfrac{1}{10} = 0.3803$

62. (A) $\dfrac{3,233,300,000,000}{248,765,170} = \dfrac{3.233 \times 10^{12}}{2.4876517 \times 10^8} = 1.2997 \times 10^4 = \$12,997$

(B) $\dfrac{264,800,000,000}{248,765,170} = \dfrac{2.648 \times 10^{11}}{2.4876517 \times 10^8} = 1.064 \times 10^3 = \$1,064$

(C) $\dfrac{264,800,000,000}{3,233,300,000,000} = \dfrac{2.648 \times 10^{11}}{3.2333 \times 10^{12}} = 0.0819 \text{ or } 8.19\%$

64. (A) $0.03 \text{ ppm} = \dfrac{0.03}{1,000,000} = \dfrac{3 \times 10^{-2}}{10^6} = 3 \times 10^{-8}$

(B) $0.000\ 000\ 03$ (C) $0.000\ 003\%$

66. $\dfrac{2.994 \times 10^8}{3.539 \times 10^6} = \left(\dfrac{2.994}{3.539}\right) \times 10^2 = 84.6$ so 84 or 85 people per square mile.

EXERCISE A-6

2. $7y^{2/5} = 7\sqrt[5]{y^2}$ **4.** $(7x^2y)^{5/7} = \sqrt[7]{(7x^2y)^5}$

6. $x^{1/2} + y^{1/2} = \sqrt{x} + \sqrt{y}$ **8.** $7m\sqrt[5]{n^2} = 7mn^{2/5}$

10. $\sqrt[7]{(8x^4y)^3} = ((8x^4y)^3)^{1/7} = (8^3 x^{12} y^3)^{1/7} = (2^9 x^{12} y^3)^{1/7}$

12. $\sqrt[3]{x^2 + y^2} = (x^2 + y^2)^{1/3}$

14. $64^{1/3} = (4^3)^{1/3} = 4$ **16.** $16^{3/4} = (16^{1/4})^3 = ((2^4)^{1/4})^3 = 2^3 = 8$

18. $(-49)^{1/2}$ is not a real number.

20. $(-64)^{2/3} = (-2^6)^{2/3} = ((-2^6)^2)^{1/3} = (2^{12})^{1/3} = 2^{12/3} = 2^4 = 16$

22. $\left(\dfrac{8}{27}\right)^{2/3} = \left(\dfrac{2^3}{3^3}\right)^{2/3} = \dfrac{2^2}{3^2} = \dfrac{4}{9}$

24. $8^{-2/3} = (8^{1/3})^{-2} = ((2^3)^{1/3})^{-2} = (2)^{-2} = \dfrac{1}{4}$

26. $y^{-3/7}y^{4/7} = y^{(-3/7)\,+\,(4/7)} = y^{1/7}$

28. $\dfrac{x^{1/4}}{x^{3/4}} = \dfrac{1}{x^{3/4}x^{-1/4}} = \dfrac{1}{x^{(3/4)-(1/4)}} = \dfrac{1}{x^{1/2}}$

30. $(4u^{-2}v^4)^{1/2} = 4^{1/2}u^{-2\times(1/2)}v^{4\times(1/2)} = 2u^{-1}v^2 = \dfrac{2v^2}{u}$

32. $\left(\dfrac{w^4}{9x^{-2}}\right)^{-1/2} = \dfrac{w^{4(-1/2)}}{(9x^{-2})^{-1/2}} = \dfrac{w^{-2}}{9^{-1/2}x} = \dfrac{3}{xw^2}$

34. $\dfrac{6a^{3/4}}{15a^{-1/3}} = \dfrac{2}{5}a^{(3/4)\,+\,(1/3)} = \dfrac{2}{5}a^{13/12}$

36. $\sqrt[3]{(7+2y)^3} = (7+2y)^{3/3} = 7+2y$

38. $\sqrt[5]{16a^4}\ \sqrt[5]{4a^2}\ \sqrt[5]{8a^3} = \sqrt[5]{(16a^4)(4a^2)(8a^3)} = \sqrt[5]{16\cdot4\cdot8\,a^9}$
$$= \sqrt[5]{(2^5a^5)\cdot16a^4} = 2a\sqrt[5]{16a^4}$$

40. $\dfrac{\sqrt{8}\sqrt{12y}}{\sqrt{6y}} = \dfrac{\sqrt{96y}}{\sqrt{6y}} = \sqrt{\dfrac{96y}{6y}} = \sqrt{16} = 4$

42. $2m^{1/3}(3m^{2/3} - m^6) = 6m^{(1/3)+(2/3)} - 2m^{(1/3)+6} = 6m - 2m^{19/3}$

44. $(a^{1/2} + 2b^{1/2})(a^{1/2} - 3b^{1/2})$
$$= a^{(1/2)+(1/2)} - 3a^{1/2}b^{1/2} + 2a^{1/2}b^{1/2} - 6b^{(1/2)+(1/2)}$$
$$= a - (ab)^{1/2} - 6b$$

46. $(2x - 3y^{1/3})(2x^{1/3} + 1) = 4x^{4/3} + 2x - 6x^{1/3}y^{1/3} - 3y^{1/3}$

48. $(x^{1/2} + 2y^{1/2})^2 = (x^{1/2})^2 + 4(x^{1/2})(y^{1/2}) + (2y^{1/2})^2 = x + 4x^{1/2}y^{1/2} + 4y$

50. $\dfrac{12\sqrt{x} - 3}{4\sqrt{x}} = \dfrac{12x^{1/2} - 3}{4x^{1/2}} = \dfrac{12x^{1/2}}{4x^{1/2}} - \dfrac{3}{4x^{1/2}} = 3 - \dfrac{3}{4}x^{-1/2}$

52. $\dfrac{3\sqrt[3]{x^2} + \sqrt{x}}{5x} = \dfrac{3x^{2/3} + x^{1/2}}{5x} = \dfrac{3x^{2/3}}{5x} + \dfrac{x^{1/2}}{5x}$
$$= \dfrac{3}{5}x^{2/3}x^{-1} + \dfrac{1}{5}x^{1/2}x^{-1}$$
$$= \dfrac{3}{5}x^{-1/3} + \dfrac{1}{5}x^{-1/2}$$

54. $\dfrac{x^2 - 4\sqrt{x}}{2\sqrt[3]{x}} = \dfrac{x^2 - 4x^{1/2}}{2x^{1/3}} = \dfrac{x^2}{2x^{1/3}} - \dfrac{4x^{1/2}}{2x^{1/3}}$

$\qquad\qquad = \dfrac{1}{2}x^2 x^{-1/3} - 2x^{1/2}x^{-1/3}$

$\qquad\qquad = \dfrac{1}{2}x^{5/3} - 2x^{1/6}$

56. $\dfrac{14x^2}{\sqrt{7x}} = \dfrac{14x^2}{\sqrt{7x}} \cdot \dfrac{\sqrt{7x}}{\sqrt{7x}} = \dfrac{14x^2\sqrt{7x}}{7x} = 2x\sqrt{7x}$

58. $\dfrac{3(x + 1)}{\sqrt{x + 4}} = \dfrac{3(x + 1)}{\sqrt{x + 4}} \cdot \dfrac{\sqrt{x + 4}}{\sqrt{x + 4}} = \dfrac{3(x + 1)\sqrt{x + 4}}{x + 4}$

60. $\dfrac{3a - 3b}{\sqrt{a} + \sqrt{b}} = \dfrac{3(a - b)}{\sqrt{a} + \sqrt{b}} \cdot \dfrac{\sqrt{a} - \sqrt{b}}{\sqrt{a} - \sqrt{b}} = \dfrac{3(a - b)(\sqrt{a} - \sqrt{b})}{(\sqrt{a})^2 - (\sqrt{b})^2}$

$\qquad\qquad = \dfrac{3(a - b)(\sqrt{a} - \sqrt{b})}{a - b} = 3(\sqrt{a} - \sqrt{b})$

62. $\dfrac{\sqrt{3mn}}{3mn} = \dfrac{\sqrt{3mn}}{3mn} \cdot \dfrac{\sqrt{3mn}}{\sqrt{3mn}} = \dfrac{3mn}{3mn\sqrt{3mn}} = \dfrac{1}{\sqrt{3mn}}$

64. $\dfrac{\sqrt{2(a + h)} - \sqrt{2a}}{h} = \dfrac{\sqrt{2(a + h)} - \sqrt{2a}}{h} \cdot \dfrac{\sqrt{2(a + h)} + \sqrt{2a}}{\sqrt{2(a + h)} + \sqrt{2a}}$

$\qquad\qquad = \dfrac{2(a + h) - 2a}{h[\sqrt{2(a + h)} + \sqrt{2a}]}$

$\qquad\qquad = \dfrac{2a + 2h - 2a}{h[\sqrt{2(a + h)} + \sqrt{2a}]}$

$\qquad\qquad = \dfrac{2}{\sqrt{2(a + h)} + \sqrt{2a}}$

66. $\dfrac{\sqrt{x} - \sqrt{y}}{\sqrt{x} + \sqrt{y}} = \dfrac{\sqrt{x} - \sqrt{y}}{\sqrt{x} + \sqrt{y}} \cdot \dfrac{\sqrt{x} + \sqrt{y}}{\sqrt{x} + \sqrt{y}} = \dfrac{x - y}{(\sqrt{x} + \sqrt{y})^2} = \dfrac{x - y}{x + 2\sqrt{xy} + y}$

68. $(x^3 + y^3)^{1/3} \overset{?}{=} x + y$

Let $x = y = 1$, then $(x^3 + y^3)^{1/3} = (1 + 1)^{1/3} = 2^{1/3}$

$1 + 1 = 2;\ 2^{1/3} \neq 2$

70. $(x + y)^{-1/2} \overset{?}{=} \dfrac{1}{(x + y)^2}$

Let $x = y = 1$, then $(x + y)^{-1/2} = (2)^{-1/2} = \dfrac{1}{\sqrt{2}}$,

$\dfrac{1}{(x + y)^2} = \dfrac{1}{(1 + 1)^2} = \dfrac{1}{4};\ \dfrac{1}{\sqrt{2}} \neq \dfrac{1}{4}$

72. True; $\sqrt{x^2} = \sqrt{|x|^2} = |x|$

74. True; $\sqrt[3]{x^3} = (x^3)^{1/3} = x^{3/3} = x$

76. False. $r = 2\sqrt{6} - 5 < 0$ and negative numbers do not have square roots.

78. True. $(1 - \sqrt{2})^3 = -.0710678119$ and $7 - 5\sqrt{2} = -.0710678119$. Therefore, $1 - \sqrt{2}$ is a cube root of $7 - 5\sqrt{2}$.

80. $2(x - 2)^{-1/2} - \dfrac{1}{2}(2x + 3)(x - 2)^{-3/2} = \dfrac{2}{(x - 2)^{1/2}} - \dfrac{2x + 3}{2(x - 2)^{3/2}}$

$$= \dfrac{4(x - 2) - (2x + 3)}{2(x - 2)^{3/2}}$$

$$= \dfrac{4x - 8 - 2x - 3}{2(x - 2)^{3/2}}$$

$$= \dfrac{2x - 11}{2(x - 2)^{3/2}}$$

82. $\dfrac{(2x - 1)^{1/2} - (x + 2)\left(\dfrac{1}{2}\right)(2x - 1)^{-1/2}(2)}{2x - 1}$

$$= \dfrac{(2x - 1)^{1/2}}{2x - 1} - \dfrac{(x + 2)(2x - 1)^{-1/2}}{2x - 1}$$

$$= \dfrac{1}{(2x - 1)^{1/2}} - \dfrac{x + 2}{(2x - 1)^{3/2}} = \dfrac{(2x - 1) - (x + 2)}{(2x - 1)^{3/2}}$$

$$= \dfrac{2x - 1 - x - 2}{(2x - 1)^{3/2}} = \dfrac{x - 3}{(2x - 1)^{3/2}}$$

84. $\dfrac{2(3x - 1)^{1/3} - (2x + 1)\left(\dfrac{1}{3}\right)(3x - 1)^{-2/3}(3)}{(3x - 1)^{2/3}}$

$$= \dfrac{2(3x - 1)^{1/3}}{(3x - 1)^{2/3}} - \dfrac{(2x + 1)(3x - 1)^{-2/3}}{(3x - 1)^{2/3}}$$

$$= \dfrac{2}{(3x - 1)^{1/3}} - \dfrac{2x + 1}{(3x - 1)^{4/3}} = \dfrac{2(3x - 1) - (2x + 1)}{(3x - 1)^{4/3}}$$

$$= \dfrac{6x - 2 - 2x - 1}{(3x - 1)^{4/3}} = \dfrac{4x - 3}{(3x - 1)^{4/3}}$$

86. $15^{5/4} = 15^{1.25} = 29.52$

88. $103^{-3/4} = \dfrac{1}{103^{3/4}} = \dfrac{1}{(103)^{0.75}} = 0.03093$

90. $2.876^{8/5} = (2.876)^{1.6} = 5.421$

92. (A) $2\sqrt[3]{2 + \sqrt{5}} = 3.236$ (B) $\sqrt{8} = 2.828$ (C) $\sqrt{3} + \sqrt{7} = 4.378$

(D) $\sqrt{3 + \sqrt{8}} + \sqrt{3 - \sqrt{8}} = 2.828$ (E) $\sqrt{10 + \sqrt{84}} = 4.378$

(F) $1 + \sqrt{5} = 3.236$

(A) and (F) have the same value:

$$\left(2\sqrt[3]{2 + \sqrt{5}}\right)^3 = 8(2 + \sqrt{5}) = 16 + 8\sqrt{5}$$

$$(1 + \sqrt{5})^3 = 1 + 3\sqrt{5} + 15 + 5\sqrt{5} = 16 + 8\sqrt{5}$$

(B) and (D) have the same value:

$$(\sqrt{8})^2 = 8$$

$$\left(\sqrt{3 + \sqrt{8}} + \sqrt{3 - \sqrt{8}}\right)^2 = 3 + \sqrt{8} + 3 - \sqrt{8} + 2\sqrt{(3 + \sqrt{8})(3 - \sqrt{8})}$$

$$= 6 + 2\sqrt{9 - 8} = 6 + 2 = 8$$

(C) and (E) have the same value:

$$(\sqrt{3} + \sqrt{7})^2 = 3 + 7 + 2\sqrt{21} = 10 + 2\sqrt{21}$$

$$\left(\sqrt{10 + \sqrt{84}}\right)^2 = 10 + \sqrt{84} = 10 + \sqrt{4 \times 21} = 10 + 2\sqrt{21}$$

EXERCISE A-7

2. $3m^2 - 21 = 0$

$\qquad 3m^2 = 21$

$\qquad m^2 = 7$

$\qquad m = \pm\sqrt{7}$

4. $(2x + 1)^2 = 16$

$\qquad 2x + 1 = \pm 4$

$\qquad 2x = \pm 4 - 1$

$\qquad x = \dfrac{\pm 4 - 1}{2}$

$\qquad x = -\dfrac{5}{2}$ and $x = \dfrac{3}{2}$

6. $3x^2 - 18x + 15 = 0$

$\qquad x^2 - 6x + 5 = 0$

$\qquad (x - 1)(x - 5) = 0$

$\qquad x - 1 = 0$ or $x - 5 = 0$

$\qquad x = 1$ or $x = 5$

8. $\qquad n^2 = 3n$

$\qquad n^2 - 3n = 0$

$\qquad n(n - 3) = 0$

$\qquad n = 0$ or $n - 3 = 0$

$\qquad n = 0$ or $n = 3$

10. $m^2 + 8m + 3 = 0$

$$m = \frac{-b \pm \sqrt{b^2 - 4ac}}{2a}, \quad a = 1, \ b = 8, \ c = 3$$

$$= \frac{-8 \pm \sqrt{64 - 12}}{2} = \frac{-8 \pm \sqrt{52}}{2} = \frac{-8 \pm 2\sqrt{13}}{2} = -4 \pm \sqrt{13}$$

12. $2x^2 - 20x - 6 = 0$

$x^2 - 10x - 3 = 0$

$x = \dfrac{-b \pm \sqrt{b^2 - 4ac}}{2a}, \quad a = 1, \ b = -10, \ c = -3$

$= \dfrac{-(-10) \pm \sqrt{100 + 12}}{2} = \dfrac{10 \pm \sqrt{112}}{2} = \dfrac{10 \pm 4\sqrt{7}}{2} = 5 \pm 2\sqrt{7}$

14. $x^2 = -\dfrac{3}{4}x$

$x^2 + \dfrac{3}{4}x = 0$

$x\left(x + \dfrac{3}{4}\right) = 0$

$x = 0 \text{ and } x = -\dfrac{3}{4}$

16. $9y^2 - 25 = 0$

$9y^2 = 25$

$y^2 = \dfrac{25}{9}$

$y = \pm\sqrt{\dfrac{25}{9}} = \pm\dfrac{5}{3}$

18. $9x^2 - 6 = 15x$

$3x^2 - 2 = 5x$

$3x^2 - 5x - 2 = 0$

$x = \dfrac{-b \pm \sqrt{b^2 - 4ac}}{2a}, \quad a = 3, \ b = -5, \ c = -2$

$= \dfrac{5 \pm \sqrt{25 + 24}}{6} = \dfrac{5 \pm \sqrt{49}}{6} = \dfrac{5 \pm 7}{6}$

$x = \dfrac{5 - 7}{6} = -\dfrac{1}{3}, \quad x = \dfrac{5 + 7}{6} = 2$

20. $m^2 = 1 - 3m$

$m^2 + 3m - 1 = 0$

$m = \dfrac{-b \pm \sqrt{b^2 - 4ac}}{2a}, \quad a = 1, \ b = 3, \ c = -1$

$= \dfrac{-3 \pm \sqrt{9 + 4}}{2} = \dfrac{-3 \pm \sqrt{13}}{2}$

22. $2x^2 = 4x - 1$

$2x^2 - 4x + 1 = 0$

$x = \dfrac{-b \pm \sqrt{b^2 - 4ac}}{2a}, \quad a = 2, \ b = -4, \ c = 1$

$x = \dfrac{4 \pm \sqrt{16 - 8}}{4} = \dfrac{4 \pm \sqrt{8}}{4} = \dfrac{4 \pm 2\sqrt{2}}{4} = \dfrac{2 \pm \sqrt{2}}{2}$

24. $x^2 - 2x = -3$

$x^2 - 2x + 3 = 0$

$x = \dfrac{-b \pm \sqrt{b^2 - 4ac}}{2a}, \quad a = 1, \ b = -2, \ c = 3$

$b^2 - 4ac = 4 - 12 = -8$

Since $b^2 - 4ac < 0$, there are no real solutions.

26. $(5x - 2)^2 = 7$

$5x - 2 = \pm\sqrt{7}$

$5x = \pm\sqrt{7} + 2$

$x = \dfrac{\pm\sqrt{7} + 2}{5}$

$x = \dfrac{2 - \sqrt{7}}{5} \ \text{ and } \ x = \dfrac{2 + \sqrt{7}}{5}$

28. $x - \dfrac{7}{x} = 0$

Since $x \neq 0$, $\dfrac{x^2 - 7}{x} = 0$ will be determined and $x^2 - 7 = 0$

implies $x = \pm\sqrt{7}$.

30. $2 + \dfrac{5}{u} = \dfrac{3}{u^2}$

Multiply both sides by $u^2 \neq 0$.

$2u^2 + 5u = 3$

$2u^2 + 5u - 3 = 0$

$u = \dfrac{-5 \pm \sqrt{25 + 24}}{4} = \dfrac{-5 \pm \sqrt{49}}{4} = \dfrac{-5 \pm 7}{4}$

$u = \dfrac{-5 - 7}{4} = -3 \ \text{ and } \ u = \dfrac{-5 + 7}{4} = \dfrac{1}{2}$

32. $x^2 - 28x - 128$

Step 1. Test for factorability

$\sqrt{b^2 - 4ac} = \sqrt{(-28)^2 - 4(1)(-128)} = 36$

Since the result is an integer, the polynomial has first-degree factors with integer coefficients.

Step 2. Use the factor theorem

$x^2 - 28x - 128 = 0$

$x = \dfrac{28 \pm 36}{2} = -4, \ 32 \quad \text{(by the quadratic formula)}$

Thus, $x^2 - 28x - 128 = [x - (-4)](x - 32) = (x + 4)(x - 32)$

34. $x^2 + 52x + 208$

Step 1. Test for factorability
$$\sqrt{b^2 - 4ac} = \sqrt{(52)^2 - 4(1)(208)} = \sqrt{1872} \approx 43.27$$
Since this is not an integer, the polynomial is not factorable.

36. $3x^2 - 32x - 140$

Step 1. Test for factorability
$$\sqrt{b^2 - 4ac} = \sqrt{(-32)^2 - 4(3)(-140)} = 52$$
Thus, the polynomial has first-degree factors with integer coefficients.

Step 2. Use the factor theorem
$$3x^2 - 32x - 140 = 0$$
$$x = \frac{32 \pm 52}{6} = -\frac{10}{3}, \ 14$$
Thus, $3x^2 - 32x - 140 = 3\left[x - \left(-\frac{10}{3}\right)\right](x - 14)$
$$= 3 \cdot \frac{(3x + 10)}{3} \cdot (x - 14)$$
$$= (3x + 10)(x - 14)$$

38. $6x^2 - 427x - 360$

Step 1. Test for factorability
$$\sqrt{b^2 - 4ac} = \sqrt{(-427)^2 - 4(6)(-360)} = 437$$
Thus, the polynomial has first-degree factors with integer coefficients.

Step 2. Use the factor theorem
$$6x^2 - 427x - 360 = 0$$
$$x = \frac{427 \pm 437}{12} = -\frac{5}{6}, \ 72$$
Thus, $6x^2 - 427x - 360 = 6\left[x - \left(-\frac{5}{6}\right)\right](x - 72) = (6x + 5)(x - 72)$

40. $x^2 + 3mx - 3n = 0$
$$x = \frac{-3m \pm \sqrt{9m^2 + 12n}}{2}$$
$$x = \frac{-3m - \sqrt{9m^2 + 12n}}{2} \quad \text{and} \quad x = \frac{-3m + \sqrt{9m^2 + 12n}}{2}$$

42. $x^2 - 2x + C = 0$
The discriminant is: $4 - 4c$

(A) If $4 - 4c > 0$, i.e., if $c < 1$, then the equation has two distinct real roots.

(B) If $4 - 4c = 0$, i.e., if $c = 1$, then the equation has one real double root.

(C) If $4 - 4c < 0$, i.e., if $c > 1$, then there are no real roots.

44. Setting the supply equation equal to the demand equation, we have

$$\frac{x}{6} + 9 = \frac{24,840}{x}$$

$$\frac{1}{6}x^2 + 9x = 24,840$$

$$x^2 + 54x - 149,040 = 0$$

$$x = \frac{-54 \pm \sqrt{(54)^2 - 4(1)(149,040)}}{2}$$

$$= \frac{-54 \pm 774}{2} = 360 \text{ units}$$

Note, we discard the negative root since a negative number of units cannot be produced or sold. Substituting $x = 360$ into either equation (we use the demand equation), we get

$$p = \frac{24,840}{1,360} = 69$$

Supply equals demand at $69 per unit.

46. $A = P(1 + r)^2 = P(1 + 2r + r^2)$
Let $P = \$1,000$, $A = \$1,210$. Then,

$$1,210 = 1,000(1 + 2r + r^2)$$

$$r^2 + 2r + 1 = \frac{1210}{1000} = 1.21$$

$$r^2 + 2r - .21 = 0$$

$$r = \frac{-2 \pm \sqrt{4 - 4(-.21)}}{2} = \frac{-2 \pm \sqrt{4 + .84}}{2}$$

$$= \frac{-2 \pm \sqrt{4.84}}{2} = \frac{-2 \pm 2.2}{2}$$

$$= 0.10 \text{ or } 10\%$$

48. $d = 0.044v^2 + 1.1v$
For $d = 550$ we have

$$0.044v^2 + 1.1v - 550 = 0$$

$$44v^2 + 1100v - 550,000 = 0$$

$$v^2 + 25v - 12,500 = 0$$

$$v = \frac{-25 \pm \sqrt{625 + 50,000}}{2} = \frac{-25 \pm 225}{2}$$

$$= \frac{200}{2}$$

$$= 100 \text{ miles per hour}$$

APPENDIX B SPECIAL TOPICS

2. $a_n = 4n - 3;$ $a_1 = 4 \cdot 1 - 3 = 1$
$a_2 = 4 \cdot 2 - 3 = 5$
$a_3 = 4 \cdot 3 - 3 = 9$
$a_4 = 4 \cdot 4 - 3 = 13$

4. $a_n = \dfrac{2n + 1}{2n};$ $a_1 = \dfrac{2 \cdot 1 + 1}{2 \cdot 1} = \dfrac{3}{2}$

$a_2 = \dfrac{2 \cdot 2 + 1}{2 \cdot 2} = \dfrac{5}{4}$

$a_3 = \dfrac{2 \cdot 3 + 1}{2 \cdot 3} = \dfrac{7}{6}$

$a_4 = \dfrac{2 \cdot 4 + 1}{2 \cdot 4} = \dfrac{9}{8}$

6. $a_n = \left(-\dfrac{1}{4}\right)^{n-1};$ $a_1 = \left(-\dfrac{1}{4}\right)^{1-1} = \left(-\dfrac{1}{4}\right)^0 = 1$

$a_2 = \left(-\dfrac{1}{4}\right)^{2-1} = \left(-\dfrac{1}{4}\right)^1 = -\dfrac{1}{4}$

$a_3 = \left(-\dfrac{1}{4}\right)^{3-1} = \left(-\dfrac{1}{4}\right)^2 = \dfrac{1}{16}$

$a_4 = \left(-\dfrac{1}{4}\right)^{4-1} = \left(-\dfrac{1}{4}\right)^3 = -\dfrac{1}{64}$

8. $a_n = 4n - 3;$ $a_{15} = 4 \cdot 15 - 3 = 57$

10. $a_n = \dfrac{2n + 1}{2n};$ $a_{200} = \dfrac{2 \cdot 200 + 1}{2 \cdot 200} = \dfrac{401}{400}$

12. $\displaystyle\sum_{k=1}^{5} k^2 = (1)^2 + (2)^2 + (3)^2 + (4)^2 + (5)^2 = 1 + 4 + 9 + 16 + 25 = 55$

14. $\displaystyle\sum_{k=0}^{4} (-2)^k = (-2)^0 + (-2)^1 + (-2)^2 + (-2)^3 + (-2)^4$
$= 1 - 2 + 4 - 8 + 16 = 11$

16. $\displaystyle\sum_{k=1}^{4} \dfrac{1}{2^k} = \dfrac{1}{2^1} + \dfrac{1}{2^2} + \dfrac{1}{2^3} + \dfrac{1}{2^4}$

$= \dfrac{1}{2} + \dfrac{1}{4} + \dfrac{1}{8} + \dfrac{1}{16} = \dfrac{8 + 4 + 2 + 1}{16} = \dfrac{15}{16}$

18. $a_1 = 7, a_2 = 9, a_3 = 9, a_4 = 2, a_5 = 4.$ Here $n = 5$ and the arithmetic mean is given by:

$\bar{a} = \dfrac{1}{5} \displaystyle\sum_{i=1}^{5} a_i = \dfrac{1}{5}(7 + 9 + 9 + 2 + 4) = \dfrac{31}{5} = 6.2$

20. $a_1 = 100$, $a_2 = 62$, $a_3 = 95$, $a_4 = 91$, $a_5 = 82$, $a_6 = 87$, $a_7 = 70$, $a_8 = 75$, $a_9 = 87$, and $a_{10} = 82$. Here $n = 10$ and the arithmetic mean is given by:

$$\bar{a} = \frac{1}{10} \sum_{i=1}^{10} a_i = \frac{1}{10}(100 + 62 + 95 + 91 + 82 + 87 + 70 + 75 + 87 + 82)$$

$$= \frac{830}{10} = 83.1$$

22. $a_n = (-1)^n(n-1)^2$;

$$a_1 = (-1)^1(1-1)^2 = 0$$
$$a_2 = (-1)^2(2-1)^2 = 1$$
$$a_3 = (-1)^3(3-1)^2 = -4$$
$$a_4 = (-1)^4(4-1)^2 = 9$$
$$a_5 = (-1)^5(5-1)^2 = -16$$

24. $a_n = \dfrac{1 - (-1)^n}{n}$;

$$a_1 = \frac{1 - (-1)^1}{1} = 2$$
$$a_2 = \frac{1 - (-1)^2}{2} = 0$$
$$a_3 = \frac{1 - (-1)^3}{3} = \frac{2}{3}$$
$$a_4 = \frac{1 - (-1)^4}{4} = 0$$
$$a_5 = \frac{1 - (-1)^5}{5} = \frac{2}{5}$$

26. $a_n = \left(-\dfrac{1}{2}\right)^{n+1}$;

$$a_1 = \left(-\frac{1}{2}\right)^{1+1} = \frac{1}{4}$$
$$a_2 = \left(-\frac{1}{2}\right)^{2+1} = -\frac{1}{8}$$
$$a_3 = \left(-\frac{1}{2}\right)^{3+1} = \frac{1}{16}$$
$$a_4 = \left(-\frac{1}{2}\right)^{4+1} = -\frac{1}{32}$$
$$a_5 = \left(-\frac{1}{2}\right)^{5+1} = \frac{1}{64}$$

28. Given 4, 5, 6, 7, … The sequence is the set of successive integers beginning with 4. Thus, $a_n = n + 3$, $n = 1, 2, …$.

30. Given -3, -6, -9, -12, … The sequence is the set of negative integers of the form $-3n$. Thus, $a_n = -3n$, $n = 1, 2, …$.

32. Given $\dfrac{1}{2}, \dfrac{2}{3}, \dfrac{3}{4}, \dfrac{4}{5}, …$ The sequence is the set of all fractions of positive integers whose denominator is 1 plus the numerator. Thus,

$$a_n = \frac{n}{n+1}, \quad n = 1, 2, … .$$

34. Given -2, 4, -8, 16, ... The sequence consists of positive integer powers of (-2). Thus,

$$a_n = (-2)^n, \quad n = 1, 2, \ldots .$$

36. Given 3, -6, 9, -12, ... The sequence consists of integer multiples of 3 with alternating sign. Thus,

$$a_n = (-1)^{n+1} 3n, \quad n = 1, 2, \ldots .$$

38. Given $\dfrac{4}{3}, \dfrac{16}{9}, \dfrac{64}{27}, \dfrac{256}{81}, \ldots$ The sequence consists of the positive integer powers of $\left(\dfrac{4}{3}\right)$. Thus,

$$a_n = \left(\frac{4}{3}\right)^n, \quad n = 1, 2, \ldots .$$

40. Given 1, $2x$, $3x^2$, $4x^3$, ... The sequence consists of non-negative integer powers of x multiplied by a number which is one more than the power. Thus, $a_n = nx^{n-1}$, $n = 1, 2, \ldots$.

42. Given x, $\dfrac{x^2}{2}, \dfrac{x^3}{3}, \dfrac{x^4}{4}, \ldots$ The sequence consists of positive integer powers of x divided by the power. Thus,

$$a_n = \frac{x^n}{n}, \quad n = 1, 2, \ldots .$$

44. $\displaystyle\sum_{k=1}^{4} \frac{(-2)^{k+1}}{2k+1} = \frac{(-2)^{1+1}}{2 \cdot 1 + 1} + \frac{(-2)^{2+1}}{2 \cdot 2 + 1} + \frac{(-2)^{3+1}}{2 \cdot 3 + 1} + \frac{(-2)^{4+1}}{2 \cdot 4 + 1}$

$$= \frac{4}{3} + \frac{-8}{5} + \frac{16}{7} + \frac{-32}{9}$$

$$= \frac{4}{3} - \frac{8}{5} + \frac{16}{7} - \frac{32}{9}$$

46. $\displaystyle\sum_{k=3}^{7} \frac{(-1)^k}{k^2 - k} = \frac{(-1)^3}{3^2 - 3} + \frac{(-1)^4}{4^2 - 4} + \frac{(-1)^5}{5^2 - 5} + \frac{(-1)^6}{6^2 - 6} + \frac{(-1)^7}{7^2 - 7}$

$$= -\frac{1}{6} + \frac{1}{12} - \frac{1}{20} + \frac{1}{30} - \frac{1}{42}$$

48. $\displaystyle\sum_{k=1}^{3} \frac{1}{k} \, x^{k+1} = \frac{1}{1} x^{1+1} + \frac{1}{2} x^{2+1} + \frac{1}{3} x^{3+1}$

$$= x^2 + \frac{x^3}{2} + \frac{x^4}{3}$$

50. $\displaystyle\sum_{k=0}^{4} \frac{(-1)^k x^{2k}}{2k+2} = \frac{(-1)^0 x^{2(0)}}{2(0)+2} + \frac{(-1)^1 x^{2(1)}}{2(1)+2} + \frac{(-1)^2 x^{2(2)}}{2(2)+2} + \frac{(-1)^3 x^{2(3)}}{2(3)+2} + \frac{(-1)^4 x^{2(4)}}{2(4)+2}$

$$= \frac{1}{2} - \frac{x^2}{4} + \frac{x^4}{6} - \frac{x^6}{8} + \frac{x^8}{10}$$

52. (A) $1^2 + 2^2 + 3^2 + 4^2 = \sum\limits_{k=1}^{4} k^2$ (B) $1^2 + 2^2 + 3^2 + 4^2 = \sum\limits_{j=0}^{3} (j + 1)^2$

54. (A) $1 - \dfrac{1}{3} + \dfrac{1}{5} - \dfrac{1}{7} + \dfrac{1}{9} = \sum\limits_{k=1}^{5} \dfrac{(-1)^{k+1}}{2k - 1}$

(B) $1 - \dfrac{1}{3} + \dfrac{1}{5} - \dfrac{1}{7} + \dfrac{1}{9} = \sum\limits_{j=0}^{4} \dfrac{(-1)^{j}}{2j + 1}$

56. $1 + \dfrac{1}{2^2} + \dfrac{1}{3^2} + \ldots + \dfrac{1}{n^2} = \sum\limits_{k=1}^{n} \dfrac{1}{k^2}$

58. $1 - 4 + 9 - \ldots + (-1)^{n+1} n^2 = \sum\limits_{k=1}^{n} (-1)^{k+1} k^2$

60. True. Let $I = \dfrac{1}{2} + \dfrac{1}{4} + \dfrac{1}{8} + \ldots + \dfrac{1}{2^n}$, then

$$I = \dfrac{1}{2} + \dfrac{1}{2}\left(\dfrac{1}{2} + \dfrac{1}{4} + \cdots + \dfrac{1}{2^{n-1}}\right) = \dfrac{1}{2} + \dfrac{1}{2}\left(I - \dfrac{1}{2^n}\right)$$

So, $I = \dfrac{1}{2} + \dfrac{1}{2}I - \dfrac{1}{2^{n+1}}$ or $\dfrac{1}{2}I = \dfrac{1}{2} - \dfrac{1}{2^{n+1}}$.

Thus, $I = 1 - \dfrac{1}{2^n} < 1$.

62. True. Observe that if n is even, then

$$1 - \dfrac{1}{2} + \dfrac{1}{3} - \dfrac{1}{4} + \ldots + \dfrac{(-1)^{n+1}}{n} = \left(1 - \dfrac{1}{2}\right) + \left(\dfrac{1}{3} - \dfrac{1}{4}\right) + \ldots + \left(\dfrac{1}{n-1} - \dfrac{1}{n}\right)$$
$$> 1 - \dfrac{1}{2} = \dfrac{1}{2};$$

if n is odd, then

$$1 - \dfrac{1}{2} + \dfrac{1}{3} - \dfrac{1}{4} + \ldots + \dfrac{(-1)^{n+1}}{n} = \left(1 - \dfrac{1}{2}\right) + \left(\dfrac{1}{3} - \dfrac{1}{4}\right) + \ldots + \left(\dfrac{1}{n-2} - \dfrac{1}{n-1}\right) + \dfrac{1}{n}$$
$$> 1 - \dfrac{1}{2} = \dfrac{1}{2}.$$

64. $a_1 = 3$ and $a_n = 2a_{n-1} - 2$
for $n \geq 2$.

$a_1 = 3$
$a_2 = 2 \cdot 3 - 2 = 4$
$a_3 = 2 \cdot 4 - 2 = 6$
$a_4 = 2 \cdot 6 - 2 = 10$
$a_5 = 2 \cdot 10 - 2 = 18$

66. $a_1 = 1$ and $a_n = -\dfrac{1}{3}a_{n-1}$
for $n \geq 2$.

$a_1 = 1$
$a_2 = -\dfrac{1}{3} \cdot 1 = -\dfrac{1}{3}$
$a_3 = -\dfrac{1}{3} \cdot \left(-\dfrac{1}{3}\right) = \dfrac{1}{9}$
$a_4 = -\dfrac{1}{3} \cdot \left(\dfrac{1}{9}\right) = -\dfrac{1}{27}$
$a_5 = -\dfrac{1}{3} \cdot \left(-\dfrac{1}{27}\right) = \dfrac{1}{81}$

68. In $a_1 = \dfrac{A}{2}$, $a_n = \dfrac{1}{2}\left(a_{n-1} + \dfrac{A}{a_{n-1}}\right)$, $n \geq 2$, let $A = 6$. Then:

$$a_1 = \frac{6}{2} = 3$$

$$a_2 = \frac{1}{2}\left(a_1 + \frac{A}{a_1}\right) = \frac{1}{2}\left(3 + \frac{6}{3}\right) = \frac{1}{2}(3 + 2) = \frac{5}{2}$$

$$a_3 = \frac{1}{2}\left(a_2 + \frac{A}{a_2}\right) = \frac{1}{2}\left(\frac{5}{2} + \frac{6}{5/2}\right) = \frac{1}{2}\left(\frac{5}{2} + \frac{12}{5}\right) = \frac{49}{20}$$

$$a_4 = \frac{1}{2}\left(a_3 + \frac{A}{a_3}\right) = \frac{1}{2}\left(\frac{49}{20} + \frac{6}{49/20}\right) = \frac{4,801}{1,960};$$

$$a_4 = \frac{4,801}{1,960} \approx 2.4494898, \quad \sqrt{6} \approx 2.4494897$$

70. $b_1 = \dfrac{\sqrt{5}}{5}\left(\dfrac{1 + \sqrt{5}}{2}\right) = \dfrac{\sqrt{5}}{5}(1.618034) \approx 0.724$

$b_2 = \dfrac{\sqrt{5}}{5}\left(\dfrac{1 + \sqrt{5}}{2}\right)^2 = b_1 \cdot \left(\dfrac{1 + \sqrt{5}}{2}\right) = 0.724 \cdot (1.618034) \approx 1.171$

$b_3 = b_2(1.618034) \approx 1.894$

$b_4 = b_3(1.618034) \approx 3.065$

$b_5 = b_4(1.618034) \approx 4.960$ The closest integer to

$b_6 = b_5(1.618034) \approx 8.025$ b_n is the nth

$b_7 = b_6(1.618034) \approx 12.985$ Fibonacci number

$b_8 = b_7(1.618034) \approx 21.010$

$b_9 = b_8(1.618034) \approx 33.994$

$b_{10} = b_9(1.618034) \approx 55.005$

EXERCISE B-2

2. (A) 5, 20, 100, …

This is neither an arithmetic sequence (20 − 5 ≠ 100 − 20) nor a geometric sequence $\left(\dfrac{20}{5} \neq \dfrac{100}{20}\right)$.

(B) −5, −5, −5, …

This is an arithmetic sequence with $d = 0$, and is a geometric sequence with $r = 1$; −5, −5 are the next two terms.

(C) 7, 6.5, 6, …

This is an arithmetic sequence with $d = -0.5$; the next two terms are: 5.5, 5.

(D) 512, 256, 128, …

This is a geometric sequence with common ratio $r = \dfrac{1}{2}$;

$(512)r = 256$, $(256)r = 128$;

The next two terms are: 64, 32.

4. $\sum\limits_{k=1}^{200} 3$. This series is both arithmetic with $d = 3$ and geometric with $r = 1$. $S_{200} = 3 \times 200 = 600$.

6. This is a geometric series with $r = -3$. Using sum formula we have

$$S_{20} = \frac{3((-3)^{20} - 1)}{-3 - 1} = -2{,}615{,}088{,}300.$$

8. Neither arithmetic nor geometric, since $a_n - a_{n-1}$ is not the same for any n and $\dfrac{a_n}{a_{n-1}}$ is not the same for any n.

10. $a_1 = -2; \; d = -3$

$a_2 = a_1 + d = -2 - 3 = -5$

$a_3 = a_2 + d = -5 - 3 = -8$

12. $a_1 = 8; \; d = -10$:

$a_{15} = a_1 + (15 - 1)d = 8 + (14)(-10) = 8 - 140 = -132$

$S_{23} = \dfrac{23}{2} [2a_1 + (23 - 1)d] = \dfrac{23}{2} [16 + 22(-10)] = -2{,}346$

14. $a_1 = 203; \; a_{30} = 261$:

$S_{30} = \dfrac{30}{2} (a_1 + a_{30})$

$\quad\;\; = \dfrac{30}{2} (203 + 261) = 6{,}960$

16. $a_1 = 32; \; r = -\dfrac{1}{2}$:

$a_2 = a_1 r = 32\left(-\dfrac{1}{2}\right) = -16$

$a_3 = a_2 r = (-16)\left(-\dfrac{1}{2}\right) = 8$

$a_4 = a_3 r = 8\left(-\dfrac{1}{2}\right) = -4$

18. $a_1 = 3; \; a_7 = 2{,}187; \; r = 3$:

$S_7 = \dfrac{ra_7 - a_1}{r - 1} = \dfrac{3(2{,}187) - 3}{3 - 1}$

$\quad\;\; = 3{,}279$

20. $a_1 = 240; \; r = 1.06$:

$a_{12} = a_1 r^{11} = 240(1.06)^{11}$

$\quad\;\;\; = 455.59$

22. $a_1 = 100; \; a_{10} = 300$:

$a_{10} = a_1 r^9$

$300 = 100 r^9$

$r^9 = 3$

$r = 3^{1/9} = 1.13$

24. $a_1 = 8{,}000; \; r = 0.4$:

$S_{10} = \dfrac{a_1(r^{10} - 1)}{r - 1} = \dfrac{8{,}000(.4^{10} - 1)}{.4 - 1} = 13{,}331.94$

$S_\infty = \dfrac{a_1}{1 - r} = \dfrac{8{,}000}{1 - .4} = 13{,}333.33$

. $S_{50} = \sum\limits_{k=1}^{50} (2k - 3)$. The sequence of terms is an arithmetic sequence. Therefore,

$S_{50} = \dfrac{50}{2} (a_1 + a_{50}) = \dfrac{50}{2} (-1 + 97) = 2{,}400$

28. $S_8 = \sum\limits_{k=1}^{8} 2^k$. The sequence of terms is a geometric sequence with common ratio $r = 2$ and $a_1 = 2^1 = 2$.

$$S_8 = \frac{2(2^8 - 1)}{2 - 1} = 510$$

30. Let $a_1 = 24$, $d = 2$. Then, using the formula $a_n = a_1 + (n - 1)d$ we can find n.

$$96 = 24 + (n - 1)2$$
$$2(n - 1) = 96 - 24 = 72$$
$$n - 1 = 36$$
$$n = 37$$

Therefore,

$$S_{37} = \frac{37}{2}[24 + 96] = 2{,}220.$$

32. (A) 16, 4, 1, $\cdots$. Since $r = \dfrac{4}{16} = \dfrac{1}{4} = \cdots = \dfrac{1}{4}$ and $|r| < 1$, the sum exists:

$$S_\infty = \frac{16}{1 - 1/4} = \frac{16}{3/4} = \frac{64}{3} \approx 21.33$$

(B) 1, -3, 9, $\cdots$

$$r = -\frac{3}{1} = \frac{9}{-3} = \cdots = -3. \text{ Since } |r| = 3 > 1, \text{ the sum does not exist.}$$

34. $g(t) = 18 - 3t$:

$g(1) = 15$, $g(2) = 12$, $g(3) = 9$, $\cdots$

This is an arithmetic progression with $a_1 = 15$, $d = -3$.

Thus, using the formula $S_n = \dfrac{n}{2}[2a_1 + (n - 1)d]$, we have:

$$S_{100} = \frac{100}{2}[2(15) + 99(-3)] = -13{,}350$$

36. $g(x) = 2^x$

$g(1) = 2$, $g(2) = 2^2$, $\cdots$, $g(10) = 2^{10}$. This is a geometric progression with $a_1 = 2$, $r = 2$. Thus, using formula $S_n = \dfrac{a_1(r^n - 1)}{r - 1}$, we have:

$$S_{10} = \frac{2(2^{10} - 1)}{2 - 1} = 2{,}046$$

38. Use $a_1 = 2$ and $d = 2$ in $S_n = \dfrac{n}{2}[2a_1 + (n - 1)d]$:

$$S_n = \frac{n}{2}[2(2) + (n - 1)2] = \frac{n}{2}(4 + 2n - 2) = \frac{n}{2}(2n + 2)$$

$$= \frac{2n(n + 1)}{2} = n(n + 1)$$

40. Yes. Let $a_1 = \dfrac{1}{2}$ and let $0 < r < 1$, then $S = \dfrac{\frac{1}{2}}{1 - r}$. For $S \geq 1000$, we

should solve the inequality $\dfrac{\frac{1}{2}}{1 - r} \geq 1000$ or $1 \geq 2{,}000 - 2{,}000r$ which

has a set of solutions for $0 < r < 1$.

42. Yes. Using the sum formula $S_n = \dfrac{n}{2}(a_1 + a_n)$ with $a_1 = 1$, $a_n = 1.1$

and $S_n = 105$, we obtain $n = 100$.

44. No. Using the sum formula for infinite geometric series $S = \dfrac{a_1}{1 - r}$.
For $a_1 = 10$, $S = 5$ we obtain, from this formula, $r = -1$. However, the

sum of infinite geometric series is given by $\dfrac{a_1}{1 - r}$ when $|r| < 1$.

Therefore such a series does not exist.

46. Consider the time line:

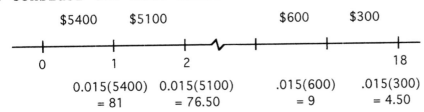

The total cost of the loan is:

$4.50 + 9 + 13.50 + \ldots + 76.50 + 81$

The terms of an arithmetic progression with $n = 18$, $a_1 = 4.50$,

and $a_{18} = 81$. Thus,

$$S_{18} = \frac{18}{2}(4.50 + 81) = \$769.50$$

48. This is a geometric progression with $a_1 = (1{,}200)(.65) = 780$ and

$r = 0.65$. Thus, $S_\infty = \dfrac{780}{1 - 0.65} = \$2{,}229.$

0.

P

$1 \qquad 2$

$(1 + r)P \qquad (1 + r)^2 P$

This is a geometric sequence with $a_1 = P$ and ratio $(1 + r)$.

Thus, $A = P(1 + r)^n$.

2. $7! = 7 \cdot 6 \cdot 5 \cdot 4 \cdot 3 \cdot 2 \cdot 1 = 5{,}040$

4. $\dfrac{20!}{19!} = \dfrac{20(19!)}{19!} = 20$

6. $\dfrac{10!}{6!} = \dfrac{10 \cdot 9 \cdot 8 \cdot 7 \cdot (6!)}{6!} = 5{,}040$

8. $\dfrac{7!}{3! \, 4!} = \dfrac{7 \cdot 6 \cdot 5 \cdot (4!)}{3 \cdot 2 \cdot 1(4!)} = 35$

10. $\dfrac{7!}{4!(7-4)!} = \dfrac{7!}{4! \, 3!} = 35$ (see Problem 8)

12. $\dfrac{52!}{50! \, 2!} = \dfrac{52 \cdot 51 \cdot (50!)}{50! \, 2 \cdot 1} = \dfrac{52 \cdot 51}{2} = 1{,}326$

14. $C_{7,3} = \dfrac{7!}{3!(7-3)!} = \dfrac{7!}{3! \, 4!} = 35$ (see Problem 8)

16. $C_{7,4} = \dfrac{7!}{4!(7-4)!} = 35$ (see Problem 10)

18. $C_{5,5} = \dfrac{5!}{5!(5-5)!} = \dfrac{5!}{5! \, 0!} = \dfrac{5!}{5!} = 1$ $(0! = 1)$

20. $C_{18,3} = \dfrac{18!}{3!(18-3)!} = \dfrac{18 \cdot 17 \cdot 16 \cdot (15!)}{3!(15!)} = \dfrac{18 \cdot 17 \cdot 16}{3 \cdot 2 \cdot 1} = 816$

22. $(m+n)^5 = C_{5,0}m^5 + C_{5,1}m^4 n + C_{5,2}m^3 n^2 + C_{5,3}m^2 n^3 + C_{5,4}mn^4 + C_{5,5}n^5$

$\qquad = m^5 + 5m^4 n + 10m^2 n^3 + 10m^3 n^2 + 5mn^4 + n^5$

24. $(u-2)^5 = C_{5,0}u^5 + C_{5,1}u^4(-2) + C_{5,2}u^3(-2)^2 + C_{5,3}u^2(-2)^3$

$\qquad\qquad\qquad + C_{5,4}u(-2)^4 + C_{5,5}(-2)^5$

$\qquad = u^5 - 10u^4 + 40u^3 - 80u^2 + 80u - 32$

. $(x-2y)^5 = C_{5,0}x^5 + C_{5,1}x^4(-2y) + C_{5,2}x^3(-2y)^2 + C_{5,3}x^2(-2y)^3$

$\qquad\qquad\qquad + C_{5,4}x(-2y)^4 + C_{5,5}(-2y)^5$

$\qquad = x^5 - 10x^4 y + 40x^3 y^2 - 80x^2 y^3 + 80xy^4 - 32y^5$

The third term in the expansion of $(x-3)^{20}$ is:

$C_{20,2}x^{18}(-3)^2 = \dfrac{20!}{2! \, 18!}x^{18}(9) = \dfrac{20 \cdot 19 \cdot (18!)9}{2 \cdot 1 \cdot (18!)}x^{18} = 1{,}710x^{18}$

he 13th term in the expansion of $(p+q)^{15}$ is:

$C_{5,12} \, p^3 q^{12} = \dfrac{15!}{12! \, 3!}p^3 q^{12} = 455p^3 q^{12}$

32. The third term in the expansion of $(2x + y)^{12}$ is:

$$C_{12,2}(2x)^{10}y^2 = \frac{12!}{2! \, 10!} 2^{10} x^{10} y^2 = 67,584 x^{10} y^2$$

34. $C_{n,r} = \dfrac{n!}{r!(n-r)!} = \dfrac{n!}{(n-r)! \, r!} = \dfrac{n!}{(n-r)![n-(n-r)]!} = C_{n,n-r}$

36. According to the Binomial Theorem:

$$(a + b)^n = \sum_{r=0}^{n} C_{n,r} \, a^r b^{n-r}.$$

Letting $a = b = 1$, we have

$$2^n = \sum_{r=0}^{n} C_{n,r} = \text{sum of the entries in each row of Pascal's triangle.}$$

38. $C_{n,r} = \dfrac{n!}{r!(n-r)!} = \dfrac{n-r+1}{r} \cdot \dfrac{n!}{(r-1)!(n-r+1)!}$

$$= \frac{n-r+1}{r} \cdot \frac{n!}{r'!(n-r')!} \quad \text{where } r' = r - 1$$

$$= \frac{n-r+1}{r} C_{n,r'} = \frac{n-r+1}{r} C_{n,r-1}$$